Contents

Additional optional units on hair relaxing treatments and techniques and hair extension services can be found online at www.hoddereducation.co.uk/HairProfessionals

Dedication

I would like to thank my husband Mark, family and friends for their continued support and encouragement during the times I spend writing my textbooks. Their enthusiasm really motivates and encourages me. I am forever grateful for their understanding and acceptance when my social life is put on hold during the months of weekends spent working on the book.

Thank you, I love and cherish you all.

Keryl x

Acknowledgements

The author and publishers would like to thank the following.

For their invaluable hairdressing expertise

Shelley Dalton
Eugene Davis
Sam Grice
Denise Johnson
Maurice Lister

For their help with the photoshoots

Hodder Education would like to thank the following for their invaluable contributions to the photoshoots for this book; Avant Garde Salons: www.avantgardesalons.co.uk; Jet Hairdressing Academy: www.j-etraining.com; Men's Hairdressing Federation: www.mhfed.com; Big Yin Salons: http://bigyinsalon.com; SO's Smooth Operators: www.sosmoothoperators.com; Elite Hair Academy: www.elitehairacademy.co.uk; Melissa Birch; Diane Mitchell and Melanie Mitchell for their technical expertise.

The photographer was Phil Jones: www.philjones-photography.co.uk and the make-up artist was Grace Gray. Thanks to all of our models and everyone else who helped out at the shoots. In the picture credits on the next page, these photos are identified as 'PJP' for reasons of space.

Thanks also to everyone who has contributed to previous City & Guilds photoshoots, on which we have drawn for this book. In particular, thanks to Maurice Lister; Adam Sloan and the Men's Hairdressing Federation; Billy Moore at Central Training Group; Melissa Birch, India Flaherty, Sarah Hawtin, Melanie Mitchell and Alison Pick at Cheynes Training; Chris Connors at Coco's; Maria Howard and Kate Meek at Enfield Training Services; Lorraine Pamenter, Donna McClelland, Liz Dickinson, Avril Hall, Sandra Griffin and Danielle Skeats at Epping Forest College; Pav Sagoo and Tracey O'Connor at Havering College; Jo Newland, Tracey Shakeshaft and Terri-Ann Neighbour at Hertford Regional College; Mandy Cresswell, Chanel Turner Rowley, Leslie Smith and Tracey Hesson at Walsall College; Hector Obeng at Hector's Global Hair with Zeal.

Level 2

Diploma for Hair Professionals

FOR APPRENTICES IN PROFESSIONAL HAIRDRESSING AND PROFESSIONAL BARBERING

Keryl Titmus

The City & Guilds textbook

Although every effort has been made to ensure that website addresses are correct at time of going to press, Hodder Education cannot be held responsible for the content of any website mentioned in this book. It is sometimes possible to find a relocated web page by typing in the address of the home page for a website in the URL window of your browser.

Hachette UK's policy is to use papers that are natural, renewable and recyclable products and made from wood grown in sustainable forests. The logging and manufacturing processes are expected to conform to the environmental regulations of the country of origin.

Orders: please contact Bookpoint Ltd, 130 Park Drive, Milton Park, Abingdon, Oxon OX14 4SE. Telephone: (44) 01235 827720. Fax: (44) 01235 400454. Email education@bookpoint.co.uk Lines are open from 9 a.m. to 5 p.m., Monday to Saturday, with a 24-hour message answering service. You can also order through our website: www.hoddereducation.co.uk

ISBN: 978 1 5104 1638 3

First published in 2017 by

Hodder Education,

An Hachette UK Company

Carmelite House

50 Victoria Embankment

London EC4Y 0DZ

www.hoddereducation.co.uk

Impression number 10 9 8 7 6 5 4 3 2 1

Year 2021 2020 2019 2018 2017

Cover photo Cover image used under licence from INNOluxe ltd. Hair by Sophia Hilton at Not Another Salon. www.innoluxe.com

Illustrations by Integra Software Services LTD

Typeset in Integra Software Services Pvt. Ltd., Pondicherry, India

Printed in Slovenia

A catalogue record for this title is available from the British Library

Picture credits

Every effort has been made to acknowledge all copyright holders as below and the publishers will, if notified, correct any errors in future editions.

pvii ©PJP; pix ©City and Guilds; p2 © Vladimir/stock.adobe.com; p3 Jibow Ezra Iridisu; p4 © Jacek Dudzinski/123RF; p5 *tr* © Gustavo Frazao/123RF, *cr* © Gustavo Frazao/123RF, *br* © Stokkete/123RF; p6 © Rafał Olechowski/123RF; p7© Cathy Yeulet/123RF; p8 *t* © Cathy Yeulet/123RF, *b* © Darrin Henry/123RF; p9 *t* © Antonio Diaz/123RFk, *b* © Stepan Gojda/123RF;p10–2 ©City & Guilds; p13 *tr* © wavebreakmedia/Shutterstock, ©City & Guilds; p15 ©City & Guilds; p16 *t* © Jennyt/Shutterstock.com, *tm* © Hartphotography/Shutterstock.com, *tb* © Wavebreakmedia/Shutterstock.com, *b* © Urbanbuzz/Shutterstock.com; p17 *t* © Mark William Richardson/Shutterstock.com, *b* © Venus Angel/Shutterstock.com; p18 ©PJP, *mr* ©Crown copyright; p20 © Iqoncept/123RF; p21 *t* © Andriy Popov/123RF, *c* © Ponsulak Kunsub/123RF, *b* ©Tyler Olson/Shutterstock.com; p22 *t* © Fabio Formaggio/123RF, *b* © Andrey Dubrovskiy/123RF; p23 *t* © Blueskyimage/123RF, *b* ©PJP; p24 *t* © Kowit Paikhamnam/123RF, *b* © Cathy Yeulet/123RF; p25© Demarcomedia/Shutterstock.com; p26 *l* Renscene Ltd, *m* City & Guilds, *r* © saloncidesolutions.co.uk; p27 *t* © aztekphoto/Shutterstock.com, *m* © Jamie Pham/Alamy Stock Photo; p28 © Wavebreak Media Ltd/123RF; p29 *l* ©PJP,*tr* © Piyapong Rotnaparai/123RF, *br*© Jim Selby/Science Photo Library; p31 *t* © Kunertus/Shutterstock.com, *c* © Sandsun/ Shutterstock.com, *b* © Ewelina Kowalska/123RF; p32 City & Guilds; p33 City & Guilds, *bl* The Academy, Enfield Training Services; p34 *tl* © Sudowoodo/123RF, *c* ©Fon_nongkran/Shutterstock.com; p35 *t* © Arcady31/123RF, *c* © Benjaporn/Shutterstock.com, *b* © akiyoko/Shutterstock.com; p36 *t* © pryzmat/Shutterstock.com, *b* © manop/Shutterstock.com; p37 *tl* ©Maxx-Studio/Shutterstock.com, *tr* © Oleksiy Mark/Shutterstock.com, *m* Ecoheads, *b* © gmstockstudio/Shutterstock.com; p38 *t* Denman International Ltd, *b* EcoTowels; p39 *t* © Kues/Shutterstock.com, *b* © Citizen of the Planet/Alamy Stock Photo; p40 *t* Wella, *b* Goldwell; p41 *t* © Fairtrade, *b* © Africa Studio/Shutterstock.com; p42 *t* © Monthon Wachirasettakul/123RF, *b* © *Venturelli Luca/Shutterstock.com;* p43 *t* © Alexandr Makarov/Shutterstock.com, *b* © Budimir Jevtic/Shutterstock.com; p45 *t* © Bowie15/123RF, *b* © lculig/123RF; p46 *t* © Dusit Panyakhom/123RF, *b* © Convisum/123RF; p47 second row left © bertys30/Fotolia, right © Samo Trebizan/Shutterstock.com, all others City & Guilds; p48 City & Guilds; p49 *t* © Marek Uliasz/123RF, *b* City & Guilds; p50 *t* © Samantha Craddock/123RF, *b* © Dmitriy Shironosov/123RF; p51 *t* © Racorn/123RF, *c* © Oscarmcwhite/123RF, *b* © Kzenon/Shutterstock.com; p52 City & Guilds; p53 *t* © Convisum/123RF, *b* © MICHAIL PANAGIOTIDIS/123RF; p54 © Asiln/123RF; p55 City & Guilds; p56 © bikeriderlondon/Shutterstock.com; p57 City & Guilds; p58 City & Guilds; p60 © *t* Karramba Production/Shutterstock.com, *b* City & Guilds; p61 © bikeriderlondon/Shutterstock.com; p62 The Chapel; p63©PJP; p64 City & Guilds; p65©PJP; p66©PJP; 67©PJP; p72© Air Images/Shutterstock.com; p73 Georgia Fielder; p74 Andrew Buckle/Big Yin Salon; p75 *t* © Andrey Kiselev/123RF, © Nikola Nikolovski/123RF, © Igor Stevanovic/123RF, *b* Rawpixel/Shutterstock.com; p76 *t* Big Yin Salon, *b* City & Guilds/Havering College; p77 © Ion Chiosea/123RF; p78 *t* © Kunertus/Shutterstock.com, *m* City & Guilds / Wallsal College, *b*© Tyler Olson/Shutterstock.com; p79 *tr* © Auremar/123RF, *br* ©PJP, *l* © *Prykhodov/123RF*; p80©PJP; p81–2 City & Guilds; p84 *tl* © Monkey Business Images/Shutterstock.com, *tr* © Domenicogelermo/123RF, *bl* © ardni/Shutterstock.com, *br* © Rob Hainer/Shutterstock.com; p85 *t* © Dmitry Bakulov/Shutterstock.com, *ml* © Iko/Shutterstock.com, *mr* © djma/Fotolia, *b* © Ampyang/Shutterstock.com, © auremar/Shutterstock.com; p86 *t* © Paul Prescott/Shutterstock.com, *mt* © Malivan_Iuliia/Shutterstock.com, *mb* © Picture Store/Shutterstock.com, *b* City & Guilds; p87*t* © Steve Gschmeissner/Science Photo Library, *tm* © Power And Syred/ Science Photo Library, *bm* City & Guilds, *b* © PHB.cz (Richard Semik)/Shutterstock.com; p88 *t* © Sparkling Moments Photography/Shutterstock.com, *all others* City & Guilds; p90 *t* © paul prescott/Shutterstock.com, *b*© Eye Of Science/Science Photo Library; p91 *t* Images courtesy of Shelley Dalton by John Innes UK, *m* Interactive Medical Media, *b* © Joti/Science Photo Library; p92 *t* © Science Photo Library, *tm and b* © Dr P. Marazzi/Science Photo Library, *bm* © Joti/Science Photo Library; p93 *t* © Nathalie Speliers Ufermann/Shutterstock.com, *tm and b* © Dr P. Marazzi/Science Photo Library, *bm* © Dr Harout Tanielian/Science Photo Library; p94 *t* © Dr P. Marazzi/Science Photo Library, *m* © Steschke / https://creativecommons.org/licenses/bysa/3.0/deed.en/ https://commons.wikimedia.org/wiki/File:Acarodermatitis_Hand.jpg, *b* ©Arthito/Shutterstock.com; p95 *t* © Dr P. Marazzi/Science Photo Library, *m* © Eye Of Science/Science Photo Library, *b* © Dr Jeremy Burgess/Science Photo Library; p96 KMS California; p99 © Steve Gschmeissner/Science Photo Library; p100 © Marisha5/123RF; p104 City & Guilds; p105 ©PJP; p106 ©Tyler Olson/Shutterstock.com; p107 Marcello Moccia: Hair by Marcello Moccia @ Room:97, make-up by Justine; p110 ©PJP; p111 ©Abi Britt; p113 *t* © Sergejs Rahunoks/123RF, *b*© Air Images/Shutterstock.com; p114 *t* EcoTowels, *b* City & Guilds; p115 *t*©PJP, *b* City & Guilds; p116 *l*© Olga Miltsova/Shutterstock.com, *r*© Dr P. Marazzi/Science Photo Library ; p118 *t* © Steve Gschmeissner/Science Photo Library, *ml* schankz/Shutterstock.com, *mr and br* Redken, *bl* © Alliance/

Shutterstock.com; p119 *t* © wavebreakmedia/Shutterstock.com, *ml* © roblan/Fotolia.com, *mr* Wella; p120 *tl*© takayuki/Shutterstock.com, *tr* Sassoon, *bl* © wavebreakmedia/Shutterstock, *br* © Hair Wizard; p121 *t*© Stacey Newman/Shutterstock.com, *m* © Dr P. Marazzi/Science Photo Library, *bl* © EYE OF SCIENCE/SCIENCE PHOTO LIBRARY, *br* Goldwell; p122 *tl* © Arthito/Shutterstock.com, *tr* Goldwell, *m* © Adam J/Shutterstock.com, *br* © Adam J/Shutterstock.com; p123 Wella; p124 *m* © Artography/Shutterstock.com, *b* © Cre8tive Images/Shutterstock.com; p125 *tl* © Science Photo Library, *bl* © Siloto/Shutterstock.com; p128 *bl* Wella, all others City & Guilds; p130 © Biker3/stock.adobe.com; p131 ©sirtravelalot/Shutterstock.com; p132 *t* Sassoon, *all others* Goldwell; p133 *t* Paul Mitchell, *b* Goldwell; p134 Wella; p135 Wella; p136 *t* © Jean-Marie Guyon/123RF, *b* © Jenny Sturm/Shutterstock.com; p137 'Pauline' © Fotoluminate LLC, 'Lenka' © Blend Images, 'Roxanne' and 'Anita' © Sheftsoff, 'Gita' © Nadino, 'Dave' © Vladimir Gjorgiev, 'Suzie' © Belinka, 'Paul' © Axel Bueckert, all Shutterstock.com; p138 *t* ©PJP, *b* © Monkey Business Images/Shutterstock.com; p139 Big Yin Salon; p141 © Tiero/123RF; p142 © Dean bertoncelj/Shutterstock.com; p143 *t* © Kasto/123RF, *b* ©PJP; p145–7 City & Guilds; p150 ©PJP; p151 Bethan Polley; p152 City & Guilds; p153 *tl* © Pavel L Photo and Video/Shutterstock.com, *tr* © Nomad_Soul/Shutterstock.com, *b* ©PJP; p154 *t and m* ©PJP, *b* © saloncidesolutions.co.uk; p155 City & Guilds; p156 *tl* © Dr Harout Tanielian/Science Photo Library, *top row* © Paul Prescott/Shutterstock.com , *second row* © Yeko Photo Studio/Shutterstock.com, *third row* © G Allen Penton/Shutterstock.com, *bottom row* © Rob Hainer/Shutterstock.com; p157 *top row* © Valua Vitaly/Shutterstock.com, *second row* © ardni/Shutterstock.com, *third row* © Sta/Shutterstock.com, *fourth row* © wavebreakmedia/Shutterstock.com, *bottom row* © Kite_rin/Shutterstock.com; p158 *t* © Michael Simons/123RF, *m* © Focus and Blur/Shutterstock.com, *b* © Ampyang/Shutterstock.com; p159 *t* © Aleksandar Todorovic/Shutterstock.com, *tm* © Franck Boston/Shutterstock.com, *others* City & Guilds; p160 *l* © PHB.cz (Richard Semik)/Shutterstock.com, *cl* ©Sparkling Moments Photography/Shutterstock.com, *cr* Menschliche doppelte Haarwirbel' by User:Mattes – Own work. (Licensed under Creative Commons Attribution-Share Alike 3.0 via Wikimedia Commons – http://commons.wikimedia.org/wiki/File:Menschliche_doppelte_Haarwirbel.JPG#mediaviewer/File:Menschliche_doppelte_Haarwirbel.JPG), *r* City & Guilds;p162 *t* © Fotolia, *tm* © Michaelheim/Shutterstock.com, *bm* © ARENA Creative/Shutterstock.com, *b* City & Guilds; p163 *t* © Ingram Publishing Limited/Ingram Image Library 500-Peopl, *tm* © iconogenic/Shutterstock.com, *bm* © Irina Bg/Shutterstock.com, *b* © Luba V Nel/Shutterstock.com; p164 *t* City & Guilds, *b* ©PJP; p165 City & Guilds; p166 *t* © Super Prin/Shutterstock.com, *m* City & Guilds, p167 *t* ©PJP, *m and br* City & Guilds, *bl* ©Nayladen/Shutterstock.com, *bml* Wella, *bmr* Wahl; p168 *t* City & Guilds, *b* ©PJP; p169 *t,m* City & Guilds, *b* ©PJP, p170 *t* ©PJP, *all others* Andrew Buckle/ Cambridge College; p171 *t* Andrew Buckle/ Cambridge College, *all others* ©PJP; p172 ©PJP;p173 *first and last row* ©PJP, *all others* City & Guilds;p175 *mr and bl* ©PJP, *all others* City & Guilds; p176 *t* City & Guilds, *b* ©PJP; p177 City & Guilds; p178 ©PJP; p179 *t* © Baltskars/Shutterstock.com, *b* ©PJP; p181 ©PJP; p182 *t* ©PJP, *all others* City & Guilds, p183–5 City & Guilds; p186–7 ©PJP; p188 *t* ©PJP, *all others* City & Guilds; p189–92 City & Guilds; p193–4 ©PJP; p198 ©PJP; p199 Evie Spensley; p201 *tl* © bikeriderlondon/Shutterstock.com, *ml and bl* ©PJP, *br* City & Guilds; p202 ©PJP; p203 © David Stuart Productions/Shutterstock.com; p204 City & Guilds; p205 © In Tune/Shutterstock.com; p206 *t* City & Guilds, *b* ©PJP; p207 *top 1*© Paul Prescott, *2*© Paffy, *3*© Monkey Business Images, *bottom 1*© Phovoir, *2*© auremar, *3*© Aleksandar Todorovic all Shutterstock.com; p208 *t* © Shutterstock, *m* © Jyliana/Shutterstock.com, © Djomas/Shutterstock.com, *b* City & Guilds; p209 *1* © Benoit Daoust/ Shutterstock.com, *2*© Vitaly Maksimchuk/Shutterstock.com, *3*© Paul Maguire/Shutterstock.com, *4*©PJP, *5*© Cameron Whitman/Shutterstock.com, *6*© Sparkling Moments Photography/Shutterstock.com; p210 *1*© Nadino/Shutterstock.com, *2*© Minerva Studio/Shutterstock.com, *3*'Menschliche doppelte Haarwirbel' by User:Mattes – Own work. (Licensed under Creative Commons Attribution-Share Alike 3.0 via Wikimedia Commons http://commons.wikimedia.org/wiki/File:Menschliche_doppelte_Haarwirbel.JPG#mediaviewer/File:Menschliche_doppelte_Haarwirbel.JPG, *4*City & Guilds, *5*© PathDoc/Shutterstock.com; p211 *1* © Andrii_K, *2* © michaeljung, *3* © Y Photo Studio, *4* © Cara-Foto, *5* © brieldesign83, *6* © David Gilder, all Shutterstock.com; p212 © *t* Wavebreakmedia/Shutterstock.com, *tm*© Ingram Publishing Limited/Ingram Image Library 500-People, *bm*©PJP, *b*© Dr P. Marazzi/Science Photo Library; p213 *t*© Alan Poulson Photography/Shutterstock.com, *m*© Karlowac/Shutterstock.com, *b*© Vladimirs Poplavskis/123RF; p214 *t*©PJP, *b*© Dr P. Marazzi/Science Photo Library; p215 ©PJP; p216 *t,m* ©PJP, *b*© Konstantynov/123RF; p217 ©PJP; p218 *tl* © Rido/123RF, *all others* City & Guilds; p219 *tl and ml* ©PJP, *all others* City & Guilds; p220 *tl* © Francesco mou/123RF, *all others* City & Guilds; p221 *tr, third and b*©PJP, *second* City & Guilds, *m* FAB Hair and Beauty; p222 *t* City & Guilds, *m*© Nayladen/Shutterstock.com, *b* Wella; p223 City & Guilds; p224 *t* City & Guilds, *all others* ©PJP; p225 *t* ©PJP, *all others* City & Guilds; p226 *ml* ©PJP, *all others* City & Guilds; p227 *t* City & Guilds, *all others* ©PJP; p228 ©PJP; p229 *tl* © Kanea/Shutterstock.com, *tr* City & Guilds, *all others* ©PJP; p230 City & Guilds; p232 *tl and mr* ©PJP, *all others* City & Guilds; p233 *t* City and Guilds/ Cambridge Regional College, *b* City & Guilds, *br* ©PJP; p234 City & Guilds; p237 *tl* © Pawel Horosiewicz/123RF, *all others* ©PJP; p238 *ml* City and Guilds, *all others* ©PJP; p239 *t* © Paul Brown/ Alamy Stock Photo, *b* © Dr P. Marazzi/Science Photo Library; p241 *ml* ©

Miceking/123RF; p242 *ml* © Maksym Darakchi/123RF, *lb* © Alvaro Cabrera Jiménez/123RF, *m* © Peter Hermes Furian/123RF, *r* © 123RF, *b* City & Guilds; p243 *t* © Prykhodov/123RF, *b* ©PJP; p244 *fourth* © American Crew, *others* © MHFed; p245 *t* © MHFed, *m* ©PJP, *b* City & Guilds; p246 *l* © Nanette Grebe/123RF, *r* Graff Etch, others MKHSA, *b* City & Guilds; p247 *t*©PJP, *b*© KKulikov/Shutterstock.com; p249 *m* © Shutterstock, *all others* ©PJP; p250–1 ©PJP; p252–4 City & Guilds; p255–6 ©PJP; p257 *t and ml* ©PJP, *all others* City & Guilds; 258–62 ©PJP; p263 *t*©PJP, *b* City & Guilds; 264–8 ©PJP; p272 HOB Salons, p273 Hannah Stoneham; p274 City & Guilds / Hertford Regional College; p275 *t*© Yeko Photo Studio/Shutterstock, *all others* ©PJP; p276 *t* © Kornienko/123RF; *tm*© Daisydaisy/123RF, *mb*© Mr. Bundit Chailaipanich/123RF, *b*© Anastasiia Averina/123RF; p277 *t* City & Guilds, © Donets/123RF, © Alona Stepaniuk/123RF, © LHLK/Shutterstock.com;p278 Valpak; p279 *tl* © Jackethead/123RF; *tr* EcoTowels, *mr* ©PJP; *br* City & Guilds; p280 ©PJP; p284 *1* Indola, *2,5 and 6* KMS California, *3 and 4* Goldwell, *7 and 8* L'Oreal; p285 *1* L'Oreal, *2*Wella, *3*© Maria Nila, *4*Wella, *5*L'Oreal; p286 *t* KMS California, *b* Wella; *p287 top four* City & Guilds, others Denman; p288 *first row* Denman, *seventh row* Wella, *all others* City & Guilds; p289 ©PJP; p290 *ml* ©Paul Prescott/ Shutterstock.com, *bl*© Eduard Derule/Shutterstock.com; p291 *top row* © Ampyang/Shutterstock.com, *second row* © Accord/Shutterstock.com; *third row* © Eugenio Marongiu/ Shutterstock.com, *fourth row* City & Guilds, *bottom row* © Lars Zahner/Shutterstock.com; p292 *t*© Anatolii Riepin/ Shutterstock.com, *b* City & Guilds; p203 *top row*© PHB.cz (Richard Semik)/Shutterstock.com, *bottom row* © Sparkling Moments Photography/Shutterstock.com, *all others* City & Guilds; p294 *top row* © G Allen Penton/Shutterstock.com, *second row* City & Guilds; *third row* © XiXinXing/ Shutterstock.com, *bottom row* © Rob Hainer/Shutterstock.com; p295 *top row* © Fotoluminate LLC/Shutterstock.com, *second row* © Lenar Musin/Shutterstock.com, *third row* © Karyna Che/Shutterstock.com, *bottom row* © Pawel Sierakowski/Shutterstock.com; p296 *t* © Kite_rin/ Shutterstock.com, *m* © Rido/Shutterstock.com, *b* ©PJP; p297 *top row* © DreamBig/Shutterstock.com, *second row* City & Guilds, *third row* © iconogenic/Shutterstock.com, *fourth row* © ArtFamily/Shutterstock.com, *fifth row* © Irina Bg/Shutterstock.com; p298 *l* © Stephen Coburn/ Shutterstock.com, *r* © Zdenka Darula/Shutterstock.com; p299–300 City & Guilds, p301 *t* image courtesy of Shelley Dalton by John Innes UK, *all others* City & Guilds; p302 *t* KMS California, *m* ©PJP, *b* © wavebreakmedia/Shutterstock.com; p303 *t* © Subbotina Anna/stock.adobe.com, *b* Hair Wizard; p304 *rows one to three* City & Guilds, *fourth and fifth row* Denman, *sixth row* L'Oreal, *seventh row* © Coprid/ Shutterstock.com, *bottom row* Wella; p305 *second row* ©Stockforlife/Shutterstock.com, *all others* City & Guilds; p306 *b* Wella, *all others* City & Guilds; p307 *t* City & Guilds, *b* L'Oreal; p308 *t* Wella, *b* City & Guilds; p310 City & Guilds; p312 *tl* © forestmavka/Shutterstock.com, *bl* City & Guilds, *br* © Carlo Dapino/Shutterstock.com; p313 *tr* © Sofia Zhuravetc/Shutterstock.com, *all others* City & Guilds; p314 ©PJP; p315 *tr* © Jackethead/123RF, *all others* City & Guilds; p316 © Sirle Kabanen/Shutterstock.com; p317 *t* © Vladimirfloyd/stock.adobe.com, © photomak/Shutterstock.com; p319 *right and bottom right* Renscene Ltd, *others* City & Guilds; p320 *b*©PJP; *tr* ©PJP, *br* L'Oreal; p322 City & Guilds; p323–330 City & Guilds; p331 *top row* City & Guilds, *bottom row* ©PJP; p332 *top row* ©PJP, *idle and bottom* City & Guilds;p333–4 City & Guilds; p335–7 ©PJP; p338–9 Great Lengths Hair Extensions; p340 Balmain; p342 ©PJP; p343 Ignas Dilys; p344 © Alexander Sorokopud/12RF; p345 © NejroN/123RF; p346 *t* ©PJP, *b* © lsantilli/123RF; p347 © Dean Drobot/123RF; p348 *first row* © Frugo/123RF, *second row* © Eduardo Lopez Coronado/123RF, *third row* © Eugenio Marongiu/123RF, *fourth row* © Avemario/123RF, *fifth row* © Branislav Ostojic/123RF; p349 *first row* © IKO/123RF, *second row* © Andrey Kiselev/123RF, *third row* © Auremar/123RF, *fourth row* © Imagesbavaria/123RF, *fifth row* © Cameron Whitman/123RF; p350 *t* © Dean Drobot/123RF, *m* © Andrey Kekyalyaynen/123RF, *b* © Dean Drobot/123RF; p351 *t* © Julief514/123RF, *m* © Cameron Whitman/123RF, *b*© Stephen Lovekin/Getty Images Entertainment/Getty Images; p352 *t and m* City & Guilds, *bl* © belinka/123RF, *br* © goodluz/123RF; p535 top left © wong yuliang/123RF, right © PathDoc/Shutterstock.com, second row © HONGQI ZHANG/123RF, third row ©Dean Drobot/123RF, bottom left © lopolo/123RF, right © Wavebreak Media Ltd/123RF; p355 *t* ©PJP; p356 *second and third row* Denman, *fifth row* L'Oreal, *all others* City & Guilds; p357 *second* row FAB Hair and Beauty, *third row* Lock, Stock and Barrel, *fourth row* FAB Hair and Beauty, *bottom row* © bioar.pl; p358 *top row* FAB Hair and Beauty, *second row* © Morgan's Pomade, *third row* FAB Hair and Beauty, *fourth row* Fudge Urban, p359 © NejroN/123RF, p360 *t* ©PJP, *m* © Svyatoslav Lypynskyy/123RF, *b* © AlenKadr/Shutterstock.com; p361 *t and m* ©PJP, *b*© Michael Simons/123RF; p362 *t* ©PJP, *b* City & Guilds / Cambridge Regional College; p363 ©PJP; p364–8 ©PJP; p369 Omolade Adeyiga, p371 *t* City & Guilds, *b* ©PJP; p372 *t*© Keith Bell/123RF, *b* City & Guilds; p373 City & Guilds; p374 ©PJP; p375 *t* © Africa Studio/ Shutterstock.com, *b* © Jim Selby/Science Photo Library; p376–8 City & Guilds; p380 *ml* © Science Photo Library, *mr* Wella, *b* © Steve Gschmeissner/Science Photo Library; p381–90 City & Guilds; p394 Goldwell; p395 *top row* Schwarzkopf, *bl* Wella, *br* City & Guilds; p397 Wella; p398 *t* Goldwell, *b* Wella; p399 Goldwell; p400 *t* L'Oreal, *b* Goldwell; p402 *top row l* City & Guilds, *m* © stockyimages/ Shutterstock.com, *r* © Jozef Polc/123RF, *bl* © Petukhov Anton/Shutterstock.com, *br* © Double Photo Studio/ Shutterstock.com; p403 Goldwell; p404 ©PJP; p405 Wella; p406 City & Guilds; p407 *first and third* City & Guilds, *all others* ©PJP; p408 *t* Wella, *m* City & Guilds, *b l* © Markus Gann/Shutterstock.com, *m* © Mark Nazh/Shutterstock.com, *r* © Julio Embun/Shutterstock.com; p410 ©PJP; p411 *b* © Pawel Sierakowski/Shutterstock.com, *all others* City & Guilds, p412 © Anastasiia Kazakova/Shutterstock.com; p413 Wella, p414 City & Guilds; p415 City & Guilds; p416 © WAYHOME studio/Shutterstock.com; p417 City & Guilds; p418 *ml* © Steve Gschmeissner/Science Photo Library, *mr* Goldwell; p420 © Skydive Erick/Shutterstock.com; p423 *m* Wella, *b* City & Guilds; p424 *t* City & Guilds / Walsall College, *b* ©PJP; p425 ©PJP; p426 *bl* © LValeriy/Shutterstock.com, *mr* © ESB Professional/Shutterstock.com; p427 City & Guilds; p428 *t* Havering College, *b* City & Guilds; p429–31 City & Guilds; p432 ©PJP; p433 *t* ©PJP, *b* City & Guilds; p434 Wella; p435 *t* Wella, *b* ©PJP; p436–8 ©PJP; p442 © Jasminko Ibrakovic/Shutterstock.com; p443 Sophie Hendy; p445 *tl* City & Guilds, *tm* © PJP, *tr* FAB Hair and Beauty, *r* City & Guilds, *table top row* © baibaz/Shutterstock.com, *b* © Dr P. Marazzi/Science Photo Library; p446 *t* © Demarcomedia/Shutterstock.com, *m* © Pavel L Photo and Video/Shutterstock.com, *b* © Sandsun/Shutterstock.com; p447 *t* © bikeriderlondon/Shutterstock.com, *b* City & Guilds; p448 *t* City & Guilds, *b* © Antonio Diaz/Shutterstock.com; p450 *r* © David Stuart Productions/Shutterstock.com, *all others* City & Guilds; p451 *t* © Monkey Business Images/Shutterstock.com, *m* © Featureflash/Shutterstock.com, *b* © Nikitin Victor/Shutterstock.com; p452 *t* © diplomedia/Shutterstock.com, *b* City & Guilds; p453 *first* © leungchopan/Shutterstock.com, *second* © Dimedrol68/Shutterstock.com, *third* © Sta/Shutterstock.com, *fourth* © Ammit Jack/Shutterstock.com; p454 *l* © Nor Gal/Shutterstock.com, *m* © Maksym Vlasenko/Shutterstock.com, *r* © Kichigin/Shutterstock.com; p455 *b* © uwimages/Fotolia, *all others* © Dr P. Marazzi/Science Photo Library; p456 *b* © Nathalie Speliers Ufermann/Shutterstock.com, *all others* © Dr P. Marazzi/Science Photo Library; p457 *t* © Dr P. Marazzi/Science Photo Library, *m* © Stephen Lovekin/Getty Images Entertainment/Getty Images, *b* © mikeledray/Shutterstock.com; p458 *t* © Caroline Eibl/Shutterstock.com, *b* © Antonio Diaz/123RF; p459 City & Guilds; p460 *t* City & Guilds, *bl* © iofoto/Shutterstock.com, *bm* © bikeriderlondon/Shutterstock.com, *br* © Anton Oparin/Shutterstock.com; p461 *tl* © Tom Grundy/123RF, *tm* © es/Michele Constantini/PhotoAlto/Alamy Stock Photo, *tr* © luminaimages/Shutterstock.com, *bl* © szefei/Shutterstock.com, *bm* © Hybrid Images/Cultura Creative (RF)/Alamy Stock Photo, *br* © Jasminko Ibrakovic/Shutterstock.com; p463 *m* © Nayladen/Shutterstock.com, *all others* City & Guilds; p464 *b* © Nednapa Sopasuntorn/Shutterstock.com, *all others* City & Guilds; p465 *t* Shave Doctor, *b* City & Guilds; p466 © PJP; p467 *t* © indira's work/Shutterstock.com, *bl* © Korionov/Shutterstock.com, *m* © Ozgur Coskun/Shutterstock.com, *br* © Lulia Iun/123RF; p468 *second* © Britanskiy/stock.adobe.com, *third* City & Guilds, *all others* © PJP; p469 *t* © Dmitry A/Shutterstock.com, *second* © PJP, *third* © Andphotography/stock.adobe.com, *b* © ALIAKSEI/stock.adobe.com; pp470–1 © PJP; pp473–6 City & Guilds; p477 Cambridge Regional College; pp478–9 City & Guilds; pp480–1 © PJP; p484 © PJP; p485 Yolanda Douglas; p486 © PJP; p487 *t* © Cyril R Salter, *b* © PJP; p488 *t* FAB Hair and Beauty, *all others* © PJP; p489 *m* City & Guilds, *all others* © PJP; p490 *t* © bikeriderlondon/Shutterstock.com, *m* © PJP, *b* © David Stuart Productions/Shutterstock.com; p493 *t* © PJP, *b* © Dr P. Marazzi/Science Photo Library; p494 *b* © Electra K. Vasileiadou/Moment/Getty Images, *all others* © PJP; p495 © Wahl UK Ltd; p496 *b* © PJP; p500 *t* © Adam J/Shutterstock.com, *second* © Kirk Peart Professional Imaging/Shutterstock.com, *third* © Vchalup/stock.adobe.com, *fourth* © M eye view/Shutterstock.com; p501 *t* © GIRAND/GJM/BSIP SA/Alamy Stock Photos, *second* © Wanchai/stock.adobe.com, *third* © schankz/Shutterstock.com, *fourth* © Dr P. Marazzi/Science Photo Library, *fifth* © Axel Bueckert/123RF; p502 *t* © Daxiao Productions/Shutterstock.com, *all others* © Dr P. Marazzi/Science Photo Library; p503 © PJP; pp508–12 © PJP; p513 *t* image courtesy of Denman; pp515–20 © PJP; p521 *b* City & Guilds; p524 © Balmain/Josh Goldsworthy – Goldsworthy's Hairdressing; p526 City & Guilds; p527 *t* Crown copyright, *bl* City & Guilds, *all others* © Wella; p528 *t* © Jim Selby/Science Photo Library, *bm* © Wella, *all others* City & Guilds; p530 *t* © Wella, *b* City & Guilds; pp531–3 City & Guilds; p536 *t* © Sam72/Shutterstock.com; p539 *r* © Wella, *all others* City & Guilds; p540 *second and bottom* © Wella, *third* Hertford Regional College/ Walsall College, *all others* City & Guilds; pp541–2 City & Guilds; p543 *bl* © Zotos Professional, *all others* © Goldwell; p544 *t* McBride Research Labs Inc., makers of Design Essentials, *b* © Goldwell; p545 *t* © Wella, *b* © Zotos Professional; p546 *b* © Blend Images/Shutterstock.com, *all others* McBride Research Labs Inc., makers of Design Essentials; p547 *first and third* City & Guilds, *all others* © Wella; p548 *t* © Group Momentum, *b* © Glenn R. Specht-grs photo/Shutterstock.com; p549 *m* © Arthur-studio10/Shutterstock.com, *b* © Africa Studio/Shutterstock.com; p550 *t* © rubchikovaa/Shutterstock.com, *b* VERSUSstudio/Shutterstock.com; p552 *m, mr* City & Guilds, *b* L'Oréal Professionnel; p553 *t* Wella, *b* City & Guilds; p554 City & Guilds; p556 *b* simonmasters /Getty Images, *all others* City & Guilds; p557 *t* © David Scharf/Science Photo Library, *second* © lukas_zb/Shutterstock.com, *third* © Anastasia/stock.adobe.com, b City & Guilds; p558 *t* © Denise Hager/Catchlight Visual Services/Alamy stock Photo, *b* © Sharon Dominick Photography/istockphoto; pp559–61 City & Guilds; p562 © Karramba Production/Shutterstock.com; pp563–6 City & Guilds; p567 *t* © Goldwell, *all others* City & Guilds; pp568–71 City & Guilds.

About the author

Over the years I have had many exciting career opportunities and have been amazed at the occupation pathways presented to me in this remarkable industry.

My mum is a hairdresser and I grew up wanting to be a hairdresser too. I loved the smells, the people and the buzz and excitement of life in the salon. I started training as an assistant hairstylist the day after I left school, over 25 years ago, and completed the youth training scheme – the equivalent of today's apprenticeship. My apprenticeship was carried out in a local salon in Leigh on Sea called 71, and when I passed my YTS, I went to further my career working at Andrew Jose salon in London. As my skills improved, I moved closer to home and began managing salons for Jerry Bell (working in Rayleigh and then Great Wakering). Before I began training learners I worked for a salon group called Hair Warehouse.

My job roles have ranged from working in a vibrant West End London salon, developing my skills as a newly qualified stylist, running my own business and developing a full clientele, gaining my teaching and assessing qualifications and passing on my industry skills and knowledge to others by training students in a college. In the last six years I have worked closely with City & Guilds as a consultant for qualification development and I am the author of several hairdressing and barbering textbooks.

I started teaching and assessing 20 years ago, and my love of hairdressing and training has gone from strength to strength. I have taught numerous learners at various levels, covering different qualifications in hairdressing and barbering. I spent 21 years working at Central Training Group and worked up to being a Senior Manager and Group Head of Curriculum, developing the curriculum across all the centres, and training and assessing the hairdressing and barbering learners.

Sharing my skills and knowledge with new learners throughout my teaching career has been a highlight. Now I'm working as the Apprenticeship Programme Manager at HOB salons and this gives me the opportunity to watch apprentices master the art of hairdressing and achieve their qualification – enabling them to start their 'career' journey. This is what training is all about, and I love it.

Keryl Titmus

Foreword

So ... you chose hairdressing. It's a really good choice if you ask me. You're going to be paid to chat to people for a start – that's pretty cool isn't it? You're going to get paid to be creative, which, let's be honest, there are a million creative courses with no jobs available, and if you're good at what you do, you'll probably never be out of work. You will get to transform people and make them smile from ear to ear, and you will probably have a few clients in your career that will be so grateful for how you made them feel that they will actually cry. You could use how awesomely flexible hairdressing is to have a family, or you could train to be a top colourist in a major city and make the money that young doctors make. You could become a teacher and inspire hundreds of young people, or you could even travel the world on a cruise ship. Yes, hairdressing is pretty awesome.

My advice would be this – take responsibility for your own education and training and always do more than expected. At EVERY opportunity, you need to be doing your friends' hair at home and watching YouTube videos. Video your tutor, watch it back at home and sit with your scissors by your side when watching TV at night. Every time the adverts come on, practise opening and closing them.

I got to where I am with a lot of hard work. I started entering competitions while I trained, then national competitions and pretty much anything I could to get recognised. I found a good salon and I did a LOT of extra hours. I got into teaching, which I did through my weekends in my spare time, and I went to every single hairdressing event there was until people started remembering me. Fast forward ten years and I now teach across ten countries and have my own salon in London with 16 staff. I've won multiple awards and I get to be creative every day. It really is living a dream.

This career has amazing opportunities, but you are the one that has to make them happen. You, and no one but you, will make your career.

Good luck!

Sophia Hilton, Director and Owner of Not Another Salon

How to use this textbook

This textbook covers all the necessary knowledge and skills outlined in the Hair Professional Apprenticeship standards, to support you in the successful completion of your Diploma.

This textbook is laid out to align with your City & Guilds Logbooks for Level 2 Diploma for Hair Professionals, both Hairdressing and Barbering. Each chapter makes reference to health and safety and explains how you can prepare yourself and your client for each service. The chapter then demonstrates the practical step by steps to carrying out each technique.

The following chapters cover everything you will need to understand to complete Route 1 – Hairdressing:

- Chapter 1: The hairdressing professional in the workplace
- Chapter 2: Consultation
- Chapter 3: Shampoo, condition and treat the scalp
- Chapter 4: Cut hair using a variety of techniques
- Chapter 6: Style and finish hair using a range of techniques
- Chapter 8: Colour and lighten hair using a range of techniques

The following chapters cover everything you will need to understand to complete Route 2 – Barbering:

- Chapter 1: The hairdressing professional in the workplace
- Chapter 2: Consultation
- Chapter 3: Shampoo, condition and treat the scalp
- Chapter 5: Cut hair using barbering techniques
- Chapter 7: Style and finish men's hair
- Chapter 9: Cut facial hair into shape
- Chapter 10: Shaving Services

At the start of each chapter, you will find information about which Hair Professional Apprenticeship standards each chapter maps to. You will also find a personal profile on a successful hairdressing or barbering apprentice. They offer you invaluable insight and advice to help you get the most from your own apprenticeship as well as useful tips to perfect your skills in the salon workplace.

Advanced Product Information Sheet

City & Guilds
A City & Guilds Group Business

Apprenticeship Logbook
Level 2 Diploma for Hair Professionals: Hairdressing

This new logbook is designed to help learners work towards their Level 2 Hairdressing qualification by showing them what they need to achieve and helping them to record their achievements and evidence.

This logbook is an essential tool, containing the forms that learners and assessors will use for the Level 2 Diploma for Hair Professionals qualification. It contains all the units that learners will need. It also includes lots of helpful pictures, hints, tips and more from top names in the industry – all designed to make the qualification simple to understand and more fun to do.

This logbook includes:

- useful glossary definitions
- a summary of unit achievement
- progress tracking sheets
- coverage of professionalism and values
- coverage of behaviours and communications
- coverage of safe working practices
- a list of the necessary health and safety legislation.

Every unit contains three main parts:

- 'What you must do' identifies different aspects of practical work that learners will do for the unit.
- 'What you must cover' signposts the range.
- 'What you must know' contains all of the knowledge areas that learners will need to show, via online or written tests, that they have achieved.

Hairdressing

Information	
Code:	TL700202
ISBN:	9780851933900
Price	£14
Size:	A4
Extent:	172pp
Published	July 2017

To order call +44 (0)844 543 0000 (select option 5 and then option 2) or email directsales@cityandguilds.com.
To view a full range of City & Guilds textbooks visit: www.cityandguilds.com.

▲ Level 2 Hairdressing logbook

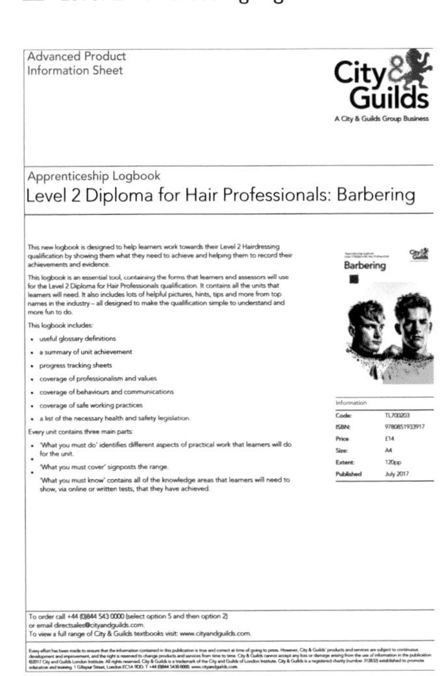

Advanced Product Information Sheet

City & Guilds
A City & Guilds Group Business

Apprenticeship Logbook
Level 2 Diploma for Hair Professionals: Barbering

This new logbook is designed to help learners work towards their Level 2 Hairdressing qualification by showing them what they need to achieve and helping them to record their achievements and evidence.

This logbook is an essential tool, containing the forms that learners and assessors will use for the Level 2 Diploma for Hair Professionals qualification. It contains all the units that learners will need. It also includes lots of helpful pictures, hints, tips and more from top names in the industry – all designed to make the qualification simple to understand and more fun to do.

This logbook includes:

- useful glossary definitions
- a summary of unit achievement
- progress tracking sheets
- coverage of professionalism and values
- coverage of behaviours and communications
- coverage of safe working practices
- a list of the necessary health and safety legislation.

Every unit contains three main parts:

- 'What you must do' identifies different aspects of practical work that learners will do for the unit.
- 'What you must cover' signposts the range.
- 'What you must know' contains all of the knowledge areas that learners will need to show, via online or written tests, that they have achieved.

Barbering

Information	
Code:	TL700203
ISBN:	9780851933917
Price	£14
Size:	A4
Extent:	120pp
Published	July 2017

To order call +44 (0)844 543 0000 (select option 5 and then option 2) or email directsales@cityandguilds.com.
To view a full range of City & Guilds textbooks visit: www.cityandguilds.com.

▲ Level 2 Barbering logbook

Throughout this textbook you will see the following features:

HANDY HINT

HANDY HINTS are particularly useful pieces of advice that can assist you in your workplace or help you remember something important.

KEY TERMS

KEY TERMS in bold in the text are explained in the margin to aid your understanding.

ACTIVITY

ACTIVITIES help to test and apply your knowledge in the salon and learn from your colleagues' experiences.

HEALTH AND SAFETY

HEALTH AND SAFETY boxes flag important points to keep yourself, colleagues and clients safe in the workplace. They also link to sections in the health and safety chapter for you to recap learning.

THE HAIR PROFESSIONAL AT WORK

THE HAIR PROFESSIONAL AT WORK boxes highlight helpful practical information to be aware of when in the workplace.

KEY TERM

IMPROVE YOUR ENGLISH items combine improving your understanding of hairdressing and barbering with practising or improving your English skills.

ACTIVITY

IMPROVE YOUR MATHS items combine improving your understanding of hairdressing and barbering with practising or improving your maths skills.

'Test your knowledge' questions are designed to identify any areas where you might need further practice.

Introduction to your qualification

You are completing one of the following City & Guilds qualifications:

- Route 1 – Level 2 Diploma for Hair Professionals – Hairdressing
- Route 2 – Level 2 Diploma for Hair Professionals – Barbering

Apprenticeships are training programmes used by employers and education providers for all structured workplace learning and development, to help up-skill the workforce. Apprenticeships combine on- and off-the-job training that gives practical and theoretical knowledge and are designed to provide you with a sustainable and progressive journey into your future career.

How to achieve your qualification

Your qualification is divided into units. Each unit covers a different area of your work. The apprenticeship structure is made up of units. In Route 1 – Hairdressing, there are mandatory units that you must complete, and optional units: you can select the optional units that best match your interests and the needs of your salon. All the Barbering units are mandatory.

To achieve your qualification you need to successfully complete an End Point Assessment (EPA).

The end-point assessment stage will provide a 'snap shot' holistic assessment of your practical skills, similar to an industry trade test. You will demonstrate that you can complete a range of services on a number of models to industry standards and within commercial timings. Your consultation skills, communication skills, safe working practices, professionalism, values and behaviours will be integrated into the end-point assessment. Your textbook will guide you through each of the services and skills needed to successfully complete this assessment.

Your EPA will test the skills, knowledge and behaviours set out in the standard through practical assessment plus oral questioning

by the Independent Assessment Examiner while you carry out a number of services.

Preparing for your end-point assessment

This section provides you with information about what you will be expected to do for your end-point assessment for both the Hair Professional standards in hairdressing and barbering. Your Hair Professional Apprenticeship includes your on-programme qualification and the end-point assessment. The achievement of this qualification, including the end-point assessment, is a mandatory requirement for the Hair Professional Apprenticeship. Guidance is given on how to prepare for your assessment so you are ready to perform to the best of your capabilities and showcase your skills as a hairdresser or barber.

The end-point assessment is the final stage of your qualification and is carried out by an Independent Assessment Examiner (IAE) from an assessment organisation (AO) on the Register of Apprentice Assessment Organisations, for example, City & Guilds.

Your IAE will observe you carrying out a practical assessment of the mandatory skills set out in the Hair Professional standards. The IAE will also ask questions while the practical assessment is taking place to assess the knowledge and behaviours aspects of the Hair Professional standards.

Your overall grade (pass or distinction) for the apprenticeship will be determined by the end-point assessment. The on-programme Diploma for Hair Professionals (Hairdressing/Barbering) will not be graded.

The qualification will be completed via three stages as described below.

On-programme stage

Hairdressing – Mandatory Units

- Unit 201 – Consultation
- Unit 202 – Shampoo, condition and treat the hair and scalp
- Unit 203 – Cut hair using a range of techniques to create a variety of looks
- Unit 204 – Style and finish hair using a range of techniques to achieve a variety of looks
- Unit 205 – Colour and lighten hair using a range of techniques

Hairdressing – Optional Units

You must choose one optional unit to complete (on programme only):

- Unit 206 – Perming hair
- Unit 207 – Hair relaxing treatments and techniques
- Unit 208 – Hair extension services

Barbering – All units are mandatory

- Unit 201 – Consultation
- Unit 202 – Shampoo, condition and treat the hair and scalp
- Unit 209 - Cutting hair using barbering techniques to create a variety of looks
- Unit 210 – Style and finish men's hair
- Unit 211 – Cut facial hair into shape
- Unit 212 – Provide shaving services

▲ The stages of your apprenticeship

Gateway stage

Before you can take your end-point assessment, you must complete all of the assessments in every mandatory unit and within your chosen optional unit – including the knowledge tests and all of the range requirements.

During this time frame you must pass Level 1 Maths and English Functional Skills and have worked towards and sat the tests for Functional Skills Level 2.

However, if you have already achieved a GCSE Grade C and above or a Grade 4 to 9 in the new GCSEs, you will not be required to complete your Functional Skills. As Maths and English are important elements in hairdressing and barbering, use the Maths and English activities in this book as an opportunity to improve your skills and knowledge.

When your on-programme assessments and your Functional Skills (if required) are completed, your employer, you and your training provider (if you have one) will decide together if you are ready for your final end-point assessment – this is your trade test.

Your end-point assessment

You will be assessed on how you carry out a consultation for *all* services completed during the assessment. You must shampoo and condition hair as part of at least *one* service of the end assessment (note that you may be required to demonstrate more).

Your skills, knowledge and behaviours will be assessed through observation of practical assessment and questioning by the Independent Assessment Examiner while you carry out the required services.

You are responsible for providing suitable models for your end-point assessment and your employer and/or training provider should support you in this where necessary.

To ensure you are ready for your end-point assessment you will need to:

- maintain and refresh your theory knowledge (to be ready for the oral questioning from the assessor)
- plan suitable models
- prepare in advance for the practical element of the assessments.

Refreshing your knowledge

- Regularly review your knowledge and understanding to check that you still remember key content from every unit, especially content covered at the start of your qualification.
- Remember the 3 Rs – Recap, Revise and Recall – and use these both in the classroom and when using online resources and activities. Find out which learning strategies work best for you – reading, hands-on practice or being taught and shown.
- Always take notes in class. Developing your note-taking skills will enable you to capture and summarise the most important aspects of the content. These notes will be invaluable when you are preparing for your unit tests and for recap during your EPA. They will also help identify any gaps in your knowledge and understanding.
- Do not just memorise facts and figures, but try to make links and deeper connections. Visualisation and concept mapping can help you to apply your knowledge and understanding in different contexts and situations.
- Remember to get enough sleep, drink plenty of water, eat well and get enough downtime in the build-up to your end-point assessment. Simple relaxation techniques can help if you are feeling stressed.

Planning your models

- Make sure you choose the right models. Check they are suitable for the assessment brief: Hairdressing – can you carry out a creative restyle on their hair? Is the hair long enough to be put up? Barbering – is your model's skin suitable for a full shaving service?
- Is your model's hair suitable for the assessment required? You must consider their hair condition, length, compatible previous services and results of hair tests.

- Are they a suitable model? Will they be reliable and not let you down on the day? Will they behave like a client and not be too friendly? Do they have sufficient time for the service? Will they have any childcare concerns if the service overruns? Could they become a difficult client?
- Ask your models to arrive at the centre 10 minutes earlier than you actually need them to arrive.

Planning in advance for the practical

- Check that your models are fully aware of the time and location of the EPA Centre.
- Make sure your equipment is clean and in good working order.
- Make a list of the tools and equipment you will need for each service – brushes, combs, drying and styling equipment, colour bowls and brushes.
- Make sure you have all the products you need. Which styling and finishing products will be most suitable? What colouring, lightening and peroxides will you need? Have you considered whether you need a toner?
- Time yourself and practise each look – on a training head if you cannot find additional practice models.
- Know where you are going and visit the location of the EPA Centre in advance of EPA day (if this is different to your place of training).
- Be on time – check public transport or nearby parking facilities.

HANDY HINT

Remember – failing to prepare is preparing to fail.

Refer back to this section once you are near to completing your EPA.

ACTIVITY

Imagine you are planning for the two services described below. List the tools, equipment and products you would need for the assessments. Barbering assessments and services:

- Quiff men's haircut and pompadour blow-dry
- Full shave service
- Partial beard and moustache

Hairdressing assessments and services:

- Block colour and weaves and slices, full head colour in between the packets
- Above shoulder restyle and round brush blow-dry
- Below shoulder dry set and hair up

HANDY HINT

Have a 'dress rehearsal' for your EPA. Carry out a mock test before your actual formal end-point assessment. Your salon manager or college tutor could be your mock assessor.

HANDY HINT

Remember the 3 Ps – Plan, Prepare and Perform.

HANDY HINT

Imagine your EPA is a trade test and job interview rolled into one. Put on a performance and always strive to do your very best.

On the day of your EPA

- Go to bed early the night before and set your alarm to allow you plenty of time in the morning to get ready.
- Have a healthy, filling breakfast.
- Look professional – shower, dress smartly but comfortably, style your hair, wear a little makeup/trim facial hair as applicable, and look like a confident stylist or barber. Remember health and safety, do not wear open toe shoes and limit the amount of jewellery you wear.
- Be fully prepared – use your checklist to confirm you have all your required tools, equipment and products.
- Leave early, check your traffic routes are clear and allow plenty of time.
- Arrive with plenty of time to prepare yourself mentally and reduce stress. It is better to arrive with time to spare than to arrive 10 minutes late.
- Perform the plan – do not deviate from the plan but be prepared to adapt the service to suit the real-life situation.
- Be confident – you have worked hard for this and prepared for this day.
- SMILE and PERFORM!

THE HAIR PROFESSIONAL AT WORK

Choose your models carefully, ensure your clients behave like clients and that you act professionally throughout. Do not be over familiar with your client – you need to demonstrate your professionalism as well as your skills.

CHAPTER 1

THE HAIRDRESSING PROFESSIONAL IN THE WORKPLACE

JIBOW EZRA IRIDISU – HAIR RESOLUTION TRAINING ACADEMY

I am training as a stylist at Hair Resolution Training Academy. I was raised in Jamaica before moving to Africa, where it is unusual for a young, black man to embark upon a career in hairdressing. If anything, this has made me more determined to pursue my passion for the industry, though it hasn't been easy. I've had to work hard get taken seriously professionally as well as supporting myself financially – at one point I even had to start a part-time cleaning job away from hairdressing.

When you take on an Apprenticeship, your success depends on how much effort you're willing to put in – you need to be prepared to challenge yourself. I am naturally very shy communicating with new clients but I've worked really hard to overcome this, to the point where I am the top retail seller in the salon and at my academy. I am constantly trying to improve upon my last cut, colour, blow-dry or twist out by asking and seeking honest feedback from my peers, tutor and employer.

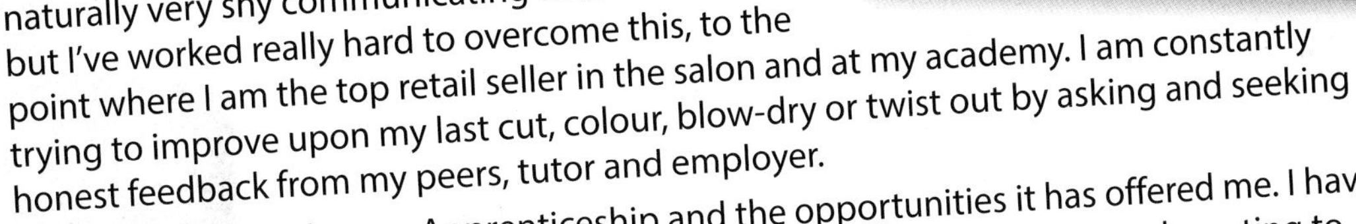

I'm very committed to my Apprenticeship and the opportunities it has offered me. I have got the most out of studying and working by remaining eager to learn and wanting to be a part of the best the hairdressing industry can offer. The best way to progress is to remain totally focused about learning and by treating each model you have and each haircut, colour or relax as another learning journey.

Job opportunities are endless with an Apprenticeship. You increase your employability gaining so much through experiential and observational learning – my tutor, Laverne, has provided great mentoring about the business behind the chair. I have had the opportunity to work with industry leaders of Afro hairdressing – to work among the greats and then replicate this back into my Apprenticeship is a fantastic inspiration.

I will now complete my Apprenticeship and have the confidence to work anywhere in the world as I've covered all aspects of hairdressing, even barbering. I have learned how to promote and sell products and services to clients to make sure it's a 360-degree service I offer. I understand how important it is to keep up to date with hairdressing all over the world through social media. Also, I work hard to develop effective working relationships with everyone I work with – good teamwork benefits everyone.

This chapter introduces the following mandatory standards outlined in both the *Hair Professional Apprenticeship Standards for Hairdressing* and *Hair Professional Apprenticeship Standards for Barbering*:

- Professionalism and values
- Behaviours and communication
- Safe working practices

These three standards are also embedded throughout the chapters and key points are flagged by 'The Hair Professional at Work' feature.

INTRODUCTION

In recent years, an average of 22,000 people started a hairdressing apprenticeship, putting hairdressing in the Top 10 most popular apprenticeships in England.

Working in the hairdressing and barbering industry is amazing and your future career opportunities are vast. In recent surveys, hairstylists/barbers have been described as 'content in their jobs', 'happy and fulfilled' and able to 'achieve job satisfaction'. Not everyone is this fortunate in their jobs.

This remarkable industry consists of hairdressers, barbers and beauty therapists and in 2016 generated almost £7 billion in turnover. Up to 270,000 people work in the industry, and there are around 40,000 businesses you could work in, but 93 per cent of these businesses employ fewer than 10 people – so competition is tight and you'll need to excel in order to compete.

After reading this chapter, you will:

- understand the health and safety practices you need to follow by law, and the safe working practices required by the industry to keep you and those around you safe
- know why professionalism and values are of paramount importance to employers and their businesses, and to your potential clients
- understand the industry's expected working behaviours and excellent communication skills required by you to work effectively and successfully within this profession.

But, before we begin, let's see if you are ready for work.

THE HAIR PROFESSIONAL AT WORK

The above statistics are from The NHF – the UK's largest trade association for hairdressing, barbering and beauty salon owners. Refer to www.nhf.org for more interesting industry statistics and facts.

ARE YOU READY FOR WORK?

If you are not yet working in a salon, but you're preparing for your apprenticeship and looking for work, you should prepare for your interview.

Preparing for an interview is as important as the interview itself and you need to promote your strengths, without drawing attention to your weaker areas.

Your potential employer's first impression of you will be your **CV** and your **covering letter** – you want to ensure he or she reads these and places you at the top of the pile for interviews, and not at the top of the waste paper bin.

SALON OWNER'S TIPS AND GUIDANCE

Mark and Jo Bidston are the salon owners of fx Hair and Colour Studio, in Leigh on Sea, Essex. Mark is the hairstylist director, while Jo manages the salon, organises the staff training and interviews prospective employees. Together they make a great team, focusing on the needs of the client and also the training needs of their team.

▲ Mark and Jo Bidston

KEY TERMS

Covering letter– a letter sent with your CV explaining the contents of the CV and why you would like to work for the company.

CV – Curriculum Vitae, a brief description of your education and previous employment history.

Both Mark and Jo work closely with local schools and hairdressing training providers/colleges. They offer work experience placements in their salon for young people just starting out in the industry, recruit Level 2 and Level 3 hairdressing and barbering apprentices and visit training providers, giving advice to learners.

Mark offers advice on:

- what you can expect from the industry/employers
- what the industry/employers expect from you.

Jo offers advice on:

- how to write a covering letter
- how to write a CV, including what not to write
- preparing for the interview and what to expect
- mock interviews and interview techniques.

Jo's covering letter and email tips

If you send your CV through the post to salons, or attach a CV to an email, you must make sure that your covering letter or email is well written. It should be brief but to the point, including only what a potential employer may want to read about you.

Follow Jo's simple tips:

- Make sure you proofread what you have written, checking for punctuation, spelling and grammar; ideally you should ask another person to read it through too. Note that it is not acceptable to use lower case 'i' instead of 'I' just because you are sending your CV via email.
- Explain the salon position you are applying for and why you would like the job
- Briefly describe why you would 'love' to work with the salon and join their team, but do not go over the top! You could drop in a factual comment about the salon, demonstrating to the employer that you know about their business or have researched their business.
- Briefly list some of your skills that show you would make a suitable candidate for the job role and employee for their business – focus on client care, communication skills, willingness to learn, professionalism, being a team player.
- Briefly state any relevant qualifications or training that could pitch you above the other applicants.
- Avoid mentioning too much personal information that is not relevant to the job role.
- Don't forget to attach your CV.

Do not rely on your computer's spell checker – ask someone else to read your CV, covering letter and email for you (ideally your college tutor), or re-read it a day or two later, when the contents are not fresh in your mind.

HANDY HINT

You may find the following websites useful for further hints and tips, apprenticeship vacancies or for CV templates:

www.nidirect.gov.uk – search CVs and covering letters

www.gov.uk/apply-apprenticeship

Jo's curriculum vitae tips

When writing your CV, the layout is extremely important. Make sure the presentation is balanced and the contents are clear, ideally on one or two pages at most. Many applicants list their experience in date order, oldest to most recent. However, most employers will want to know the applicant's most recent qualifications, training and job roles, as these are the most crucial and important for the current application.

Follow Jo's steps to successful CV writing:

1. Contact details – name, address and telephone number. Only list a professional sounding email address and you must remember to regularly check your emails. Do not use an email address if it is something like hotbabe@hotmail.com – save this email for your friends only.
2. Job roles – if you are already employed or have worked in a salon, list your most recent job first. Describe the duties you carried out, demonstrating your knowledge of the industry – especially if this highlights your capabilities and matches your skills and experience with the employer's needs. State the start and end date of each job role. If the reason for leaving this job is positive and you are looking to move on for career progression, you should write your reason for leaving. If you have been dismissed, didn't get on with the team or disliked your line-manager, it would be best to leave out these details in your CV.
3. Qualifications – start with your most recent qualifications, particularly your maths and English GCSE grades or predicted grades. Then give

details of the school/college you attended, listing your leave date. You should include any other relevant qualifications or attributes that could be relevant to the job position you are applying for, such as first aid qualifications, computer courses completed and positions of responsibility such as being head girl or boy.

4 Additional personal information – add some details about you, such as hobbies, clubs you attend/are a member of, achievements and anything else that may demonstrate your people skills or show personal dedication, commitment and trustworthiness. You should avoid listing your interests as clubbing or partying; instead state you enjoy socialising with family and friends.
5 References – finally you need to include two names and addresses for references: one should be a professional reference – from an employer/work experience provider or school/college tutor. The second reference can be an additional professional reference or a personal reference. Under no circumstances should your personal reference be your mum or another family member – they are likely to be biased and potential employers are very unlikely to take the reference seriously.

HANDY HINT

Remember, adding your age or date of birth is not mandatory, so you can choose whether or not you want to put your date of birth on your CV.

HANDY HINT

Use the initials 'CV' or spell Curriculum Vitae correctly – Jo has had one CV sent to her with the spelling of 'CV' as 'Curiclum Veetay'! This does not create a good first impression and could put a potential employer off, before they have even read your name. Presentation of your CV is also of vital importance, but avoid making it look too busy with various fonts. Do not add a variety of colours or any pictures/artwork in an attempt to stand out.

▲ On-the-job training

Interview

Once the potential employer has read all the CVs and covering letters, she will make a shortlist of the successful candidates to be interviewed. Read Jo's interview tips below when you are fortunate enough to be invited to the interview stage.

If you are unsuccessful and not chosen for an interview you may receive a rejection letter. With so many applicants for each position it is quite likely you will receive a rejection letter or possibly not hear anything back from the employer at all. Do not get disheartened about the process, but do make sure you improve your CV and covering letter in readiness for the next job you apply for.

HANDY HINT

When writing your CV, make sure you tell the truth about your skills and experience and avoid making it too long – employers are very busy people and if they are presented with a lengthy CV, they may not read it properly or will select shorter CVs that have been submitted instead.

▲ Plan your transport route, so you do not arrive late

▲ A well-presented interviewee

Jo's interview tips

Follow Jo's simple steps to preparing for that all-important interview:

- Double check the interview date and time.
- Research the company before the interview. You should aim to know everything there is to know about the salon – the services they offer, the size of the business or how long they have been trading.
- Think about why you would like to work for the company – you may be asked this question.
- Prepare a few questions to ask the interviewer, such as:
  - why the position is vacant
  - what your key responsibilities would be
  - what training opportunities you would be given
  - what is the expected time length of the training
  - what are the company's growth plans
  - how would the interviewer describe the culture and atmosphere of the salon and the team
  - once qualified, what would the financial opportunities be and what career paths would be available to you?
- Know how to get to the interview via public transport (if relevant) to ensure you arrive in good time.
- Work out what time you need to leave home, in order to arrive 10 to 15 minutes before the time of your interview.
- Tell someone where you are going and roughly when you expect to return.
- Be well presented – especially your clothes and hair.
- Turn off your mobile phone prior to walking into the salon.
- Resist the temptation to smoke a cigarette before your interview and ensure your breath is fresh.
- During the interview listen to the questions, and if you don't understand what is being asked, say so.
- Be honest with your answers and your expected exam grades.
- If you are still at school/college, let the interviewer know if you can work weekends, school holidays or evenings.
- If you are keen to work for the company – show it!
- After the interview, write down any questions that you felt you could have answered better and work on your answers.

Jo's interview questions

Below are some examples of the sort of questions that Jo asks her interviewees, and what other employers may ask you during an interview.

Beginning of the interview

Employers are aware that people get nervous when being interviewed so will usually ask some general questions to try to calm your nerves. A good interviewer will try to put you at ease with some straightforward questions, in order the get the most from you during an interview:

- How was your journey here?
- Tell me about yourself.

Questions about your past

The interviewer is trying to get to know about you – sell yourself, but be honest:

- What achievements are you most proud of?
- How IT literate are you?
- What changes would you make if you could go back in time?

Future opportunity questions

The interviewer is now trying to decide if you are suitable for their business:

- What do you know about us?
- Why have you applied for this position?
- What can you bring to this job/company?
- What are your long-term career plans and goals?

Personality questions

The employer is still trying to decide how well you will fit into the company:

- What is your attitude to authority?
- How would you deal with a difficult person?
- What do you do with your spare time?
- What motivates you?
- What would you do if you won the lottery?
- What is your definition of success?
- How well can you handle stress?

Finishing questions

Your final chance to make a good impression:

- What questions do you have for me?
- Why should we employ you?

Now go and prepare for your interview – good luck and be positive!

HANDY HINT

Ask if there is an opportunity for a trial day, where you can prove how you work in a team environment.

▲ Employer and applicant – interview in progress

▲ Think positively

HEALTH AND SAFETY LEGISLATION

As with most things in life, there are right and wrong ways of doing things. To ensure things are done correctly in the workplace, you will have to follow some rules. In your salon, your employer makes the rules and this is called your salon policy.

If the government passes a law (an **Act**), for example, the Health and Safety at Work Act, you have to know what the rules are relating to that law. These rules are called **regulations**. As you can imagine, there are many rules (regulations) covering such a large subject as health and safety.

Health and safety legislation that impacts on working practices in your hairdressing and barbering job role is described below.

KEY TERMS

Act – a government law.

Regulations – the rules of the Act.

Health and Safety at Work Act (HASAWA) 1974

The Health and Safety at Work Act1974 is the over-arching Act that covers all health and safety legislation and the responsibilities that you and your employer both have. Your employer's responsibility is to staff, clients and visitors; your responsibility is to yourself, your colleagues and your clients.

HASAWA 1974 covers everyone – employees, employers, self-employed people and visitors, including clients and representatives. This Act outlines everyone's responsibilities, including your own, and is about your health and safety in your place of work.

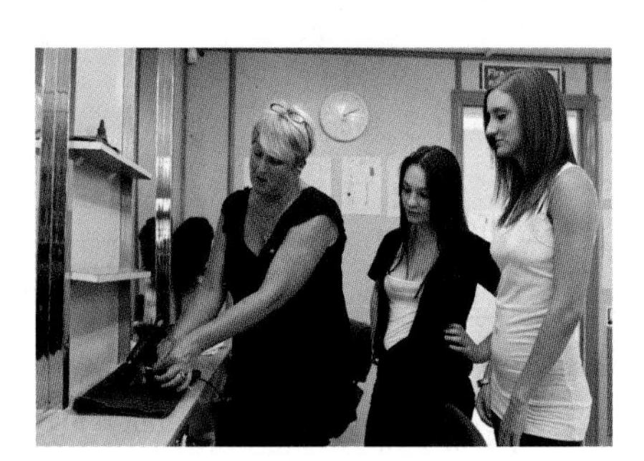

▲ Training staff to use electrical items

Your employer's responsibilities under the Act are to:

- maintain the workplace
- give staff appropriate training and supervision
- keep access and exit points clear and free from hazards at all times
- provide a suitable working environment and facilities that comply with the Act.

Your responsibilities under this Act are to:

- maintain the health and safety of yourself and others who may be affected by your actions
- co-operate and communicate with your employer about health and safety issues, so your employer can keep within the law.

ACTIVITY

With a colleague, discuss some examples of health and safety matters that you would need to refer to someone else and identify who you would refer them to (for example, a leaking pipe in the salon).

Who is the person responsible for reporting health and safety matters? YOU are!

If you see a health and safety problem, you must deal with it or report it. Everyone is responsible for putting it right.

Reporting of Injuries, Diseases and Dangerous Occurrences Regulations (RIDDOR) 2013

The Reporting of Injuries, Diseases and Dangerous Occurrences Regulations 2013 include reporting occurrences of the following to the Health and Safety Executive (HSE):

- a fracture, other than to fingers and toes
- amputation of digits or limbs (fingers/toes or arms/legs)
- death to workers and non-workers if they arise from work-related accidents
- crush injuries that lead to internal organ damage
- unconsciousness caused by a head injury or asphyxia (crushing of the wind pipe)
- injuries that require admittance to hospital for more than 24 hours or resuscitation.

The following diseases (made worse by work) are also reportable under RIDDOR:

- occupational dermatitis
- carpal tunnel syndrome
- occupational asthma.

ACTIVITY

Research other occupational diseases that need to be reported.

All of the situations listed above need to be reported to the HSE – this can be done online. To confirm what needs to be reported visit www.hse.gov.uk/riddor/reportable-incidents.htm

Your employer's responsibility under these regulations is to:

- report and record any of the above occurrences.

Your responsibilities under these regulations are to:

- prevent any work-related disease by wearing personal protective equipment (PPE) such as gloves, etc.
- report any work-related diseases to the person responsible for health and safety
- prevent any accidents or injuries by maintaining a safe and tidy working environment
- report any accidents or injuries that you sustain.

All accidents must be written in the accident book with clear details recorded. The salon's accident book must be kept in a safe place and every member of staff must know where this is.

Ensure you record the date and time of the incident, the name and address of the person involved and of any witnesses. Record the treatment given or that none was required. This must be completed in case of any legal consequences from the injury.

Since the personal details are recorded, these pages must be removed in order to follow the Data Protection Act and keep personal details confidential. Forward the page from the accident book to the person responsible for health and safety.

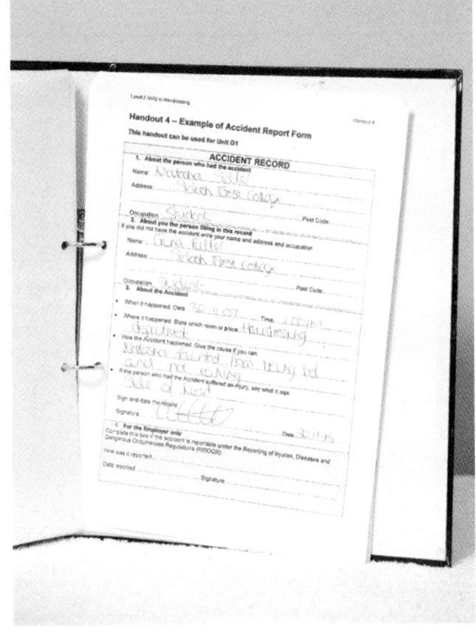

▲ A page from an accident book

Control of Substances Hazardous to Health Regulations (COSHH)

Chemicals and hazardous substances can enter the body through ingestion, absorption and inhalation, so they present a high risk to salon staff. According to the HSE website, every year thousands of workers are made ill by hazardous substances, contracting lung diseases such as asthma or cancer, or skin diseases such as dermatitis. These diseases cost many millions of pounds each year: for the industry to replace trained workers, for society in disability allowances and for individuals who may lose their jobs.

Hazardous substances must be:

- **s**tored correctly, ideally on a low shelf and in a cool, dark, dry, secure, fireproof cabinet
- **h**andled correctly, ensuring PPE (personal protective equipment) is worn when mixing chemicals
- **u**sed correctly, ensuring you and your client are protected from chemicals
- **d**isposed of correctly in an environmentally friendly and safe manner.

We refer to this as SHUD:

S Store
H Handle
U Use
D Dispose

KEY TERM

Local by-laws – local government rules.

When following SHUD you must do so following the manufacturer's instructions (MFIs), the **local by-laws** and your salon policy.

The MFIs will instruct you on how to store, handle, use and dispose of the chemicals or substances; the local by-laws will tell you how to dispose of the chemicals/substances to suit the environment and follow the local authority's guidelines on waste and refuse. Your salon policy will explain where to store and mix the chemicals and where to dispose of them in the workplace.

Your employer's responsibilities under these regulations are to:

- ensure COSHH information sheets are available for substances and chemicals in the workplace
- supply PPE
- ensure waste disposal is suitable for the environment and follows local by-laws.

Your responsibilities under these regulations are to:

- follow SHUD
- read and follow MFIs, follow local by-laws and your salon policy
- know where to find the COSHH information sheets.

▲ Always follow MFIs

▲ Chemicals being safely mixed

▲ Wear your PPE

ACTIVITY

Substances include all powders, liquids, creams or lotions in your salon – everything from washing powder to peroxide. Take a look around your salon, laundry room, staff areas and bathrooms, and identify all substances that need to be controlled under COSHH. How many can you list?

Personal Protective Equipment Regulations

These regulations were updated in 2002 and include legislation on what personal protective equipment (PPE) must be supplied and made available free of charge to employees. PPE is required to protect skin, body, lungs and clothes from chemicals or injury.

To ascertain what PPE an organisation requires, you must first look at what are the employees exposed to, how long are they exposed to it and how much are they exposed to?

Your employer's responsibilities under these regulations are to:

- provide employees with the following:
  - gloves
  - aprons
  - particle masks
  - eye protection
- check and replenish supplies of PPE when they run low
- provide training on how to use PPE (if relevant).

Your responsibilities under these regulations are to:

- wear the PPE provided
- report loss, damage or shortage of PPE supplies.

▲ Non-latex disposable gloves

HANDY HINT

Black gloves are often used by barbers when razoring on the skin so the tiny speaks of blood that can come from razor bumps are not seen by the client. Black or flesh coloured gloves are used by many stylists when colouring hair. Blue gloves are usually used in the catering business.

Electricity at Work Regulations

Use electrical appliances with caution. Electrical equipment must be handled correctly, checked and tested. Plug sockets must be safe and faulty electrical equipment must be labelled, removed and reported to the relevant person. After use, equipment must be correctly stored.

Your employer's responsibilities under these regulations are to:

- ensure that a qualified electrician completes a portable appliance test (PAT) on electrical items in the salon each year
- keep a record of these tests.

Your responsibilities under these regulations are to:

- not use electrical appliances until you have been trained
- use appliances correctly and switch them off after use
- check each item is in working order before using – check wires, switches and plugs
- report, label and remove any faulty items.

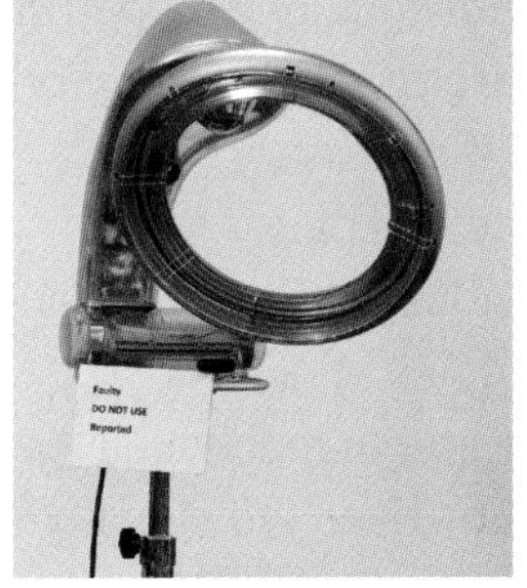

▲ Faulty dryer and climazone – report, label and remove from the salon floor

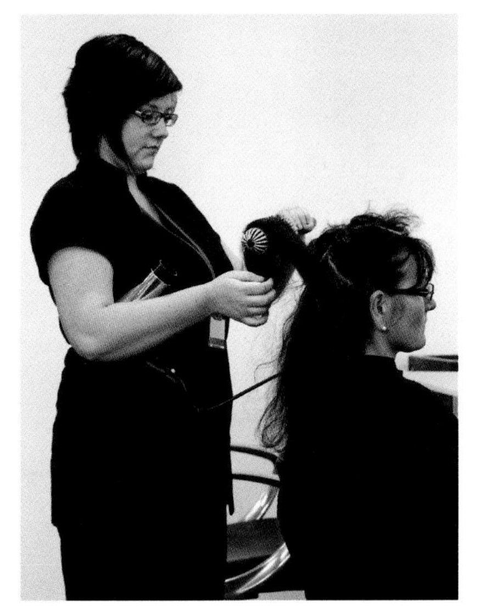

▲ Incorrect handling of a hairdryer

Environmental Protection Act

The Environmental Protection Act 1990 covers a wide range of areas relating to the control of emissions into the environment and waste management. This Act affects every business – from large factories emitting masses of fumes and excessive waste to small hairdressing salons with marginal waste and minimal emissions.

HANDY HINT

Help the environment by switching off lights when they are not in use. Saving power helps to save energy and reduces harmful greenhouse gas emissions.

ACTIVITY

You can estimate your own carbon footprint using the online calculator and entering details about your home, your travel and your appliances. The calculator estimates how many tonnes of carbon dioxide you produce each year: www.myclimate.org/

For more information on reducing your carbon footprint visit www.energysavingtrust.org.uk/resources/tools-calculators

Health and Safety (First Aid) Regulations

These regulations were updated in 2013. They apply to all workplaces in the UK, including those with fewer than five employees and self-employed staff. Their aim is to protect everyone in the workplace by ensuring risk assessments are carried out to prevent accidents and injuries at work.

Your employer's responsibilities under these regulations are to:

- take immediate action if employees are injured or taken ill at work
- consider providing a first aider
- nominate an appointed person to be responsible for first aid arrangements
- provide a well-stocked first aid container.

According to the HSE website (www.hse.gov.uk/firstaid/changes-first-aid-regulations.htm) there is no mandatory list of items to be included in a first-aid container. They recommend (as a guide only):

- a leaflet giving general guidance on first aid (for example, HSE's leaflet *Basic Advice on First Aid at Work*)
- twenty individually wrapped sterile plasters (assorted sizes) appropriate to the type of work (hypoallergenic plasters can be provided if necessary)
- two sterile eye pads
- two individually wrapped triangular bandages, preferably sterile
- six safety pins
- two large sterile individually wrapped unmedicated wound dressings
- six medium-sized individually wrapped unmedicated wound dressings
- at least two pairs of disposable gloves.

The appointed person should check the contents of the first aid container frequently and ensure it is restocked soon after use. He or she should ensure the safe disposal of items once they reach their expiry date.

Your responsibilities under these regulations are to:

- avoid taking any unnecessary risks that might put you or others in danger
- report any first aid shortages to your appointed person.

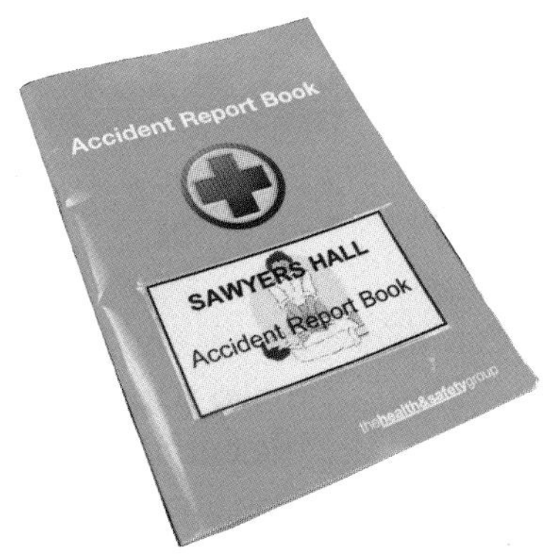

▲ First aid container and accident book

Regulatory Reform (Fire Safety) Order

The Regulatory Reform (Fire Safety) Order came about in 2005 and was put in place to ensure that appropriate steps were taken to protect human life. The order consolidates previous fire safety legislation and aligns fire safety legislation and health and safety law.

Every building, structure or open space to which the public have access (such as clients and employees) is covered by the order. The order puts the onus onto a 'responsible person' – the person accountable for the business or property; this could be the owner, occupier, employer or landlord.

The responsible person must ensure they:

- protect any persons on the premises or those who may be affected by a fire at the premises
- provide adequate safety measures to minimise risk
- carry out a risk assessment to check possible dangers and risks – this involves considering who may be at risk and how to reduce the risks, make sure there is protection available (firefighting equipment), create an emergency plan (fire evacuation procedure) and keep the risk assessment up to date.

Your responsibilities are to know:

- where the firefighting equipment is located in the salon
- which extinguishers should be used on different types of fires
- your evacuation procedure and identify your meeting point.

Firefighting equipment

The most widely used extinguishers in salons contain water or carbon dioxide (CO_2). Currently most extinguishers are red and can be identified by their coloured label. The types of extinguisher found in the hairdressing industry are shown in the table below, which explains where they should be located, how they should be used, how they work and the dangers of using them incorrectly.

ACTIVITY

Draw a simple plan of your salon. Label the fire extinguishers, exits and meeting point. Add the name of your salon's responsible person.

HANDY HINT

Along with your salon policy and government laws, you will also need to follow other rules or regulations. These are the instructions provided by the manufacturers of your equipment and products, and your local by-laws. Local by-laws are your local council regulations, rather than government regulations.

Type of extinguisher	Identified by	Used for	Location	How to use	How it works	Dangers
Water extinguisher	Red label and a thin hose	Class A fires involving wood, paper, hair and textiles	Salon Staff areas Corridors	Point the jet at the base of the flames and move across the burning area until the flames are out	Water has a great effect on cooling the fuel surfaces; with the spray nozzle covering a wide surface area using the water pressure, it cools the fire down and extinguishes the flame and heat source	Do not use on electrical fires as electrical shock may occur and the fire may spread
Foam extinguisher	Cream label and a thin hose	Class B fires involving flammable liquids except cooking oils	Salon Staff areas Corridors	Aim the jet around the side edge of the fire – do not aim the jet directly into the liquid. Allow the foam to build up across the liquid	As the extinguisher is mainly water-based with a foaming agent, the foam floats on top of the burning item and breaks the contact between the flames and the fuel's surface	Do not use on electrical fires as electrical shock may occur and the fire may spread
CO_2 extinguisher	Black label and wide nozzle	Class C fires involving electrics and flammable gases	Salon Office area	Direct the nozzle at the base of the fire and move the nozzle over the flames	CO_2 does not burn; instead it replaces the oxygen in the air. Fire needs oxygen to burn; CO_2 suffocates the fire by the removal of the oxygen.	Not good at cooling fires. The extinguisher horn gets very cold and can cause 'freeze' burns and blisters, so it must not be touched when in use
Dry powder extinguisher	Blue label and a thin hose	Class C fires involving electrics and flammable liquids	Salon	Aim the jet at the base of the flames and sweep over the flames	Dry powder helps to reduce the chemical reactions needed for the fire to continue.	Not good at penetrating into appliances, so electrical fires may re-ignite. Not very good at cooling fire down

Type of extinguisher	Identified by	Used for	Location	How to use	How it works	Dangers
Fire blanket	Blanket	Class F fires involving cooking fats. Also to be used to wrap around people if their clothes are on fire	Staff kitchen area	Wrap the person on fire in the fire blanket or cover the item on fire	Suffocating the flames by removal of oxygen while the person is wrapped or item is covered	Needs to be left to cool, to prevent re-ignition when the person is unwrapped or item uncovered and exposed to oxygen

HANDY HINT

If water or foam extinguishers were used on an electrical fire, the fire could spread and electric shocks could occur.

HANDY HINT

Do not use water-based extinguishers on oil-based fires (such as chip pan fires), as water is heavier than oil and sinks to the bottom. It can also create steam and then let out a blast of steam, causing the fire to spread. Do not use foam-based extinguishers on oil-based fires as the oil gets extremely hot and may explode.

▲ An extinguisher sign indicates where to find an extinguisher

▲ A fire assembly point sign indicates where people should assemble in case of fire

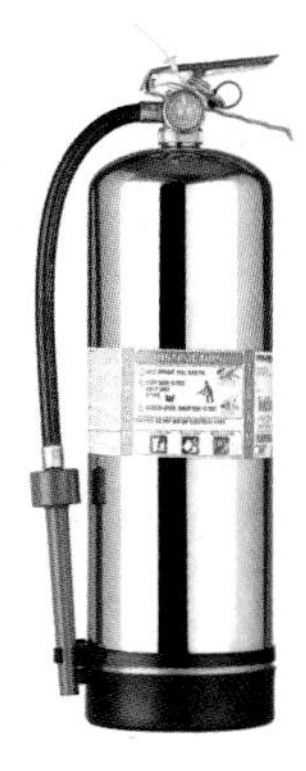

▲ Polished stainless steel fire extinguisher

If a modern appearance of your salon is important, your employer may choose to purchase stainless steel or polished alloy extinguishers. The labels are colour-coded in the same way, but the extinguishers are not red in colour like the majority of extinguishers.

Manual Handling Operations Regulations

You are sometimes required to move equipment and stock around the salon and this is called manual handling. There are correct ways to lift heavy items so you do not injure yourself.

According to the HSE, more than a third of all injuries resulting in over three days' absence from work are caused by manual handling. In recent surveys over 12.3 million working days are lost each year due to work-related **musculoskeletal disorders** that have been caused or made worse by poor manual handling.

Your employer's responsibility under these regulations is to:

- carry out risk assessments on all employees for manual lifting.

Your responsibility under these regulations is to:

- always ask yourself 'Can I lift this?'. If the answer is no, then don't! Ask for help.

KEY TERM

Musculoskeletal disorders – muscle or bone disorders.

If you are able to lift it, remember to bend your knees and keep your back straight. Lift the weight with your knees, not your back, and keep the item you are lifting close to your body.

STEP 1 – Check the area in front is clear and hazard-free. Bend your knees.

STEP 2 – Keep your back straight.

STEP 3 – Lift the weight with your legs.

▲ The HSE guide to manual handling

Management of Health and Safety at Work Regulations

The Management of Health and Safety at Work Regulations 1999 require employers to carry out risk assessments, make arrangements to implement necessary measures, appoint competent people and arrange for appropriate information and training.

A risk assessment is a checklist of what could cause harm to you and others. It helps to identify if enough precautions have been taken to prevent harm or risks in the workplace.

Advice from the Health and Safety Executive (HSE) on risk assessment is to follow these five simple steps:

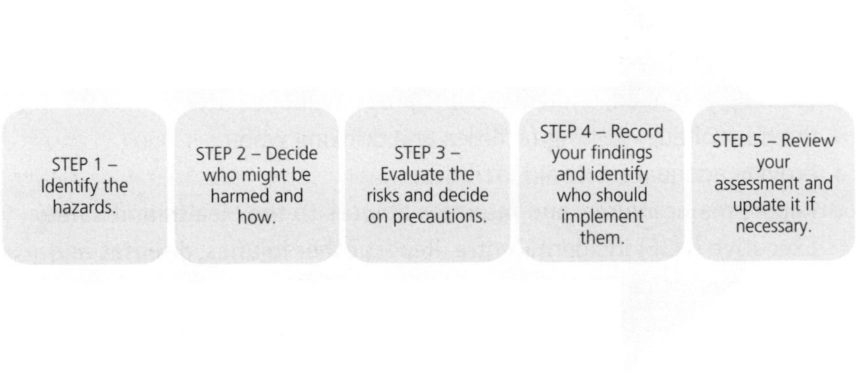

STEP 1 – Identify the hazards.

STEP 2 – Decide who might be harmed and how.

STEP 3 – Evaluate the risks and decide on precautions.

STEP 4 – Record your findings and identify who should implement them.

STEP 5 – Review your assessment and update it if necessary.

▲ Risk assessment process

Workplace (Health, Safety and Welfare) Regulations

The Workplace (Health, Safety and Welfare) Regulations 1992 covers a wide range of basic health, safety and welfare issues that apply to most workplaces. It covers the regulatory requirements on issues such as ventilation, lighting, temperature, cleanliness, room dimensions, workstations and seating, floor condition, windows, sanitary conveniences and washing facilities.

It is the employer's responsibility to take any relevant action within his or her control, or report to the building owner/landlord any of these regulations that are beyond their control.

Health and Safety (Information for Employees) Regulations

The Health and Safety (Information for Employees) Regulations 1989 was amended and updated in 2009 and requires employers to display a poster telling employees what they need to know about health and safety. Your employer is responsible for health and safety, but you must help by taking responsibility as well.

The following information is displayed on the health and safety poster and your employer should write on it the names of your health and safety representative:

All workers have a right to work in places where risks to their health and safety are properly controlled. Health and safety is about stopping you getting hurt at work or ill through work.

In line with these regulations, your employer must do the following:

- Decide what could harm you in your job and the precautions to stop it. This is part of risk assessment.
- Explain how risks will be controlled and tell you who is responsible for this.

- Consult and work with you and your health and safety representatives in protecting everyone from harm in the workplace.
- Provide you (free of charge) with the health and safety training you need to do your job.
- Provide you (free of charge) with any equipment and protective clothing you need, and ensure it is properly looked after.
- Provide toilets, washing facilities and drinking water.
- Provide adequate first aid facilities.
- Report major injuries and fatalities at work to the Health and Safety Executive (HSE) Incident Centre. Report other injuries, diseases and dangerous incidents online at www.hse.gov.uk.
- Have insurance that covers you in case you get hurt at or ill through work. Display a hard copy or electronic copy of the current insurance certificate where you can easily read it.
- Work with any other employers or contractors sharing the workplace or providing employees (such as agency workers), so that everyone's health and safety is protected.

In line with these regulations, you must do the following:

- Follow the training you have received when using any work items your employer has given you.
- Take reasonable care of your own and other people's health and safety.
- Co-operate with your employer on health and safety.
- Tell someone (your employer, supervisor or health and safety representative) if you think the work or inadequate precautions are putting anyone's health and safety at serious risk.

The above information is taken from www.hse.gov.uk/pubns/law.pdf

Visit the HSE website for more information about your rights and how to ensure you are protected by health and safety while at work: www.hse.gov.uk

▲ Employee handbook

EMPLOYEE AND CONSUMER LEGISLATION

As well as health and safety legislation there are acts or regulations to protect the **consumer** and the employee.

KEY TERMS

Consumer – shopper/customer/client.

Characteristics – qualities or features.

Equality Act

The Equality Act came into force in 2010 and combined 116 separate pieces of legislation into one Act. This Act protects the rights of individuals and provides equality for all.

There are nine protected **characteristics** in this Act:

1. Age
2. Gender
3. Sexual orientation
4. Gender reassignment
5. Pregnancy and maternity

6 Marriage
7 Disability
8 Race
9 Religion or belief.

Working time directives

The UK law states that workers are not expected to work more than 48 hours per week on average, unless they choose to. This average is calculated over a 17-week period. If you are aged 18 or over, you can choose to opt out of the 48 hours limit for a certain period of time or indefinitely. This must be voluntary and stated in writing – you can choose to cancel your 'opt-out' at any time. Employers can ask you to opt out, but if you choose not to, they must not sack you or treat you unfairly.

If you are under 18 years old, you can only work eight hours a day and 40 hours per week; these hours are not averaged out and you cannot opt out.

These regulations also include:

- working limits and exemptions/exclusions
- working at night
- health assessment for night workers
- time off
- rest breaks at work
- paid annual leave.

HANDY HINT

For more information on working hours and your legal rights, visit the government website – www.gov.uk/maximum-weekly-working-hours

ACTIVITY

Agostina gets 28 days holiday each year, including the 8 yearly Bank Holiday days.

She used three holiday days in January and nine days in April. She wants to book a fortnight's holiday this summer.

Does Agostina have enough holiday days remaining to book this? (Don't forget the Bank Holidays.)

Data Protection Act

The Data Protection Act protects the client's personal details by ensuring that:

- only authorised staff have access to client details
- details are recorded accurately and are kept up to date
- client's personal details are only for official use
- out-of-date details are destroyed securely
- the salon is registered with the Data Protection Registrar if the details are held on a computer system.

ACTIVITY

Along with the Equal Pay Act, what other main pieces of legislation have been merged into this one single Equality Act? Carry out some research and try to list eight.

▲ There are rules on the number of hours you can work

▲ Client data should be kept secure in line with the Data Protection Act

▲ Clients are protected by the Consumer Rights Act when they purchase goods or retail from the salon

HANDY HINT

The Sale of Goods Act has been replaced by the Consumer Rights Act, but goods purchased before October 2015 are still covered by this Act.

▲ Consumer Rights Day

HANDY HINT

As of 13 June 2014, the Distance Selling Act no longer applies in UK law as it has been replaced by the Consumer Contracts Regulations.

Consumer Rights Act

According to Citizens Advice, UK consumers spend £90 billion per month on goods and services. This Act gives the consumer transparent rights to help them make better choices when they buy, to save them time and money.

The Consumer Rights Act came into force in 2015, replacing the Sale of Goods Act and the Sale of Goods and Services Act. The main areas affecting salon clients relate to:

- what should happen if goods or digital content are faulty or counterfeit
- what should happen if the service received is poor
- how services should match up to what has been agreed, and what should happen when they do not, or when they are not provided with reasonable care and skill.

Citizens Advice can also refer client complaints to local Trading Standards officers who may then investigate the situation on the client's behalf.

For more information on the Consumer Rights Act go to www.legislation.gov.uk or www.citizensadvice.org.uk

Consumer Contracts (Information, Cancellation and Additional Charges) Regulations

These new regulations came into force in 2014, revoking the previous Distance Selling Regulations.

These regulations apply to anyone selling goods, services or digital content to a consumer. Some of these regulations relate to:

- the information which a seller must give to a consumer before and after making a sale
- how that information should be given
- the right for consumers to change their minds when buying at a distance or off-premises
- delivery times.

Consumer Protection legislation

This legislation is aimed at protecting the public by:

- prohibiting the manufacture and sale of unsafe goods
- making the manufacturer or seller of defective products responsible for any damage caused
- allowing local councils to seize unsafe goods and suspend the sale of any suspected unsafe goods
- prohibiting misleading price indications.

Generally speaking, this means that consumers have rights that make sure what is purchased does what it says it will. You must ensure your products and equipment are safe to sell to the client and will not put them at risk.

Cosmetic Products Regulations

The Cosmetic Product Regulations were updated in 2013 and were put in place to safeguard public health. They cover any substance that is to be placed on external human skin (including epidermis and hair system):

- to clean – such as shampoo
- to perfume
- to change appearance – such as hair colour
- to correct body odour
- to protect – such as styling products
- to keep hair or skin in good condition – such as conditioner.

So the regulations relate to everything from hair colouring products to hand cream and deodorants.

Under these regulations the following restrictions have been put in place:

- Products and substances must have been safety assessed by a qualified professional.
- Ingredients must be clearly labelled
- Warnings must be displayed such as: 'not intended for use on persons under 16 years of age', 'may contain nuts', 'do not use to dye eye-lashes'.
- Instructions on use and how to dispose of the substance and container.

The container must include:

- country of origin
- best before date
- weight and measurements
- batch number.

▲ Clients are protected against the sale of unsafe goods

HANDY HINT

The Trade Descriptions Act 1972 prevented salons from misleading their customers as to what they were spending their money on. This Act was superseded by Consumer Protection legislation.

▲ Product consultation

ACTIVITY

Look at three different substances in the salon and check to confirm the bottles or packaging meets the requirements of the Cosmetic Products Regulations.

SAFE WORKING PRACTICES

Following health and safety is vital as hairdressing and barbering involves strong chemicals and sharp tools. Working with the general public can put you at risk and the job puts stresses on your body from standing up for long hours and concentrated work with your hands. It is essential that you follow safe working practices in the salon to avoid putting yourself or others at risk.

Along with all the health and safety Acts that must be followed by law, you also need to follow your organisation's requirements.

▲ Let's save the world together

For professional use only.

Always read the safety instructions and follow the directions for use carefully.

IMPORTANT: This product is not intended for use on persons under the age of 16.

▲ Colour instructions with age restrictions

▲ If your client looks younger than 25 years old, you should check their ID before a colour service

HANDY HINT

Refer to your local council regulations for further information on disposing of waste in your area.

KEY TERM

Salon policy – your salon's rules.

Environmental working conditions

Your salon manager is responsible for maintaining the health and safety of employees and visitors. They must ensure there is adequate lighting within the salon, good ventilation (particularly when mixing and handling chemicals) and they must maintain suitable working temperatures. The salon equipment, furniture and workstations should be positioned so there is space for you and your clients to move and work safely.

If you have any problems with your environmental working conditions you have a responsibility to report these to your manager.

Current legal requirements and guidance relating to age restrictions for colouring and lightening services

There is an EU (European Union) directive (a legal requirement) that salons ensure their clients are aged 16 or over, if they are having any colour or lightening treatments. All salon staff are required to check the ID of younger clients to confirm their age before commencing with the colouring service.

Adhere to workplace, suppliers' or manufacturer's instructions for the safe use of tools, equipment, materials and products

Your salon's representative or supplier may provide you with products, tools, equipment, salon fixtures and fittings as well as general salon supplies such as foil or salon towels. When you are using the tools and equipment it is important that you read any manufacturer's instructions (MFIs) and follow the advice given by your supplier. Also follow the MFIs for advice on storing, handling, using and disposing products.

It is important to use equipment correctly and safely at all times. You must follow the manufacturer's instructions on how to use equipment as well as your **salon policy**, ensuring you are trained in how to use unfamiliar electrical appliances.

When using electrical equipment, you must follow the Electricity at Work Regulations and equipment should be PAT tested (Portable Appliance Testing) and fit for use. If you identify any faulty equipment you should report it to your manager, label it as faulty and remove it from use.

Always visually check your equipment prior to use to ensure the wires are not frayed or plugs damaged, and make sure it is cleaned and maintained regularly.

Clean and store away equipment after use, ensuring wires are not left trailing. Remember to allow heated styling equipment time to cool down before storing items away.

Following instructions properly ensures that you use equipment correctly, which not only prolongs the life of the item, but also ensures the safety of yourself and others. Following the MFIs for products, such as colouring products, should ensure that the correct result is achieved and prevent any damage to the client's hair or skin.

▲ Damaged wires are a hazard

Maintain responsibilities for health and safety throughout the service

Throughout salon services every staff member is responsible for health and safety.

If you see a potential hazard that you can deal with, such as a spillage, mop it up. If you can't deal with a problem, for example, a faulty electrical cable, then you should report it to your manager.

Take health and safety considerations into account

It is important to follow health and safety guidelines and work safely to prevent injuries, accidents and cross-infection. Always consider the impacts to you and the people around you if you take risks and do not follow heath and safety advice.

If a client has not had a skin test, then a colour service must not take place – there is the potential risk to your client of an allergic reaction and legal proceedings to you and the salon if you do not take health and safety into account. Always consider the consequences of failing to:

- carry out tests on the hair and skin – to avoid potential damage to hair and skin
- check the safety of your tools – to avoid potential damage to hair and skin
- sterilise tools, equipment and work surfaces – to prevent cross infection and infestation
- work safely – to prevent risk of injury to self and others
- report concerns – to prevent problems from escalating.

Maintain effective, hygienic and safe working methods

It is essential that salon cleanliness is maintained throughout the day. This will ensure that a professional image is projected to your clients. Always use a clean towel and gown for each client and ensure that the salon floor is kept free of hair cuttings. At the start of a service you must ensure that tools and equipment are ready for use. When you have finished, tidy wires and items away, returning styling products to the product area. After every service you must ensure that equipment is cleaned and **sterilised**, ready for the next client and to prevent **cross-contamination.**

KEY TERMS

Cross-contamination – spreading of infections or infestations.

Sterilised – free of live bacteria.

KEY TERM

Sanitised – clean and germ free.

Cleaning

Work surfaces and non-electrical equipment should be wiped clean. Always clean brushes and combs with warm soapy water before sterilising them. A hair-covered brush will not be effectively sterilised and will look unprofessional and unclean. Also remove excess hair from scissors, clippers and razors prior to sterilising.

- Tools and equipment must be disinfected, **sanitised** or sterilised in an appropriate manner using chemical disinfectants or an autoclave, or sanitised using an ultraviolet (UV) light.
- Disinfectants use chemicals on objects and surfaces to kill or destroy *most* bacteria, viruses, fungi and spores.
- Sanitising with a UV light works by ultraviolet germicidal irradiation (UVGI). This method uses short wavelength UV light to kill and destroy most microorganisms and disrupt their DNA, so they cannot multiply or reproduce and the microorganism dies.
- Sterilising uses chemicals, temperature and pressure to kill or inactivate *all* bacteria, viruses, fungi or spores

Disinfecting

Chemical solutions and wipes are often used in salons as effective ways of disinfecting tools and equipment. A common liquid disinfectant is Barbicide, but some salons may use chemical sprays and wipes or even a bleach solution. Items suitable for a liquid disinfectant are placed in the solution for about 10 minutes, then rinsed and used as normal.

▲ Barbicide

▲ Chemical sprays

▲ Chemical wipes

▲ Saloncide spray

Sanitising

When sanitising using UV lights, the equipment needs to be placed in the cabinet for a minimum of five minutes; in some cases it is then turned over for a further five minutes. This method is only effective if used with cleaned, sterile equipment and the equipment is turned properly.

Sterilising

Autoclaves are the most effective method of sterilising and are used by medical centres to sterilise surgical tools and equipment. They use heat at around 120 °C (20 °C hotter than boiling water) and pressure to steam clean and sterilise equipment. This usually takes about 15 to 20 minutes depending on manufacturer's instructions (MFIs).

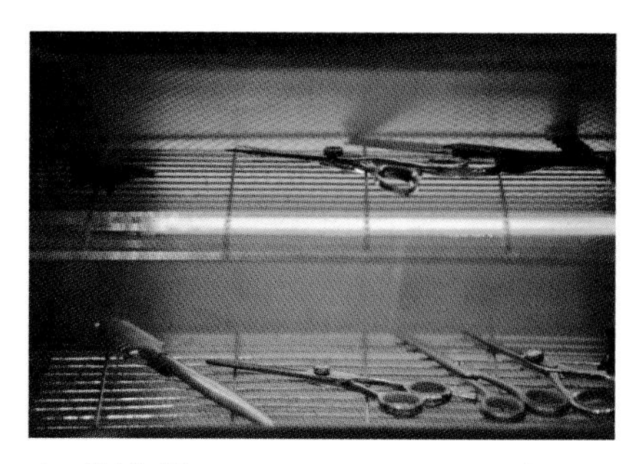

▲ UV light

▲ Autoclave

Methods of sterilising tools and equipment

The table below shows the most appropriate methods of sterilising or disinfecting your tools.

Type of tools and equipment	Liquid disinfectant	Autoclave	UV light
Towels and gowns	Yes – in a washing machine at temperatures of 60–95 °C	No	No
Combs, clips, plastic brushes and clipper attachments	Yes – Barbicide, sprays and wipes	Yes, although not all plastic equipment can withstand the heat of the autoclave	Yes
Wooden handled brushes	No	No	Yes
Scissors and razors	Yes	Yes, this method is the most suitable	Yes
Clippers	Yes – sprays and wipes only	No	Yes
Work surfaces	Yes – sprays and wipes	No	No

HEALTH AND SAFETY

Sterilisers (such as an autoclave) destroy *all* micro-organisms, while other methods will disinfect or sanitise by destroying *most* micro-organisms. It is also very important to adhere to your workplace cleaning, disinfection and sterilisation instructions, as well as those of the supplier or manufacturers' instructions.

Ensure personal hygiene and protection meets industry, organisational and local authority requirements

You must ensure your own personal hygiene meets with your organisation's requirements and meets the needs of the industry. You must also follow the legal requirements for personal protection and ensure you wear personal protective equipment to keep yourself safe.

▲ After showering, wear loose fitting clothes and deodorant to help prevent body odour

Personal hygiene

Start your day after a good night's rest, ensuring you brush your teeth, shower or wash before work, and use a deodorant. Wear clean, ironed clothes that are well presented. If you are a smoker, or enjoy coffee or spicy foods, always ensure you have mints or similar handy to freshen your breath. Your hair should always represent the industry you are in and look clean and tidy. Ladies may choose to wear a little make-up to help them look well groomed, and nails must be clean and not chipped if painted. For men, facial hair should be neatly trimmed. Do not attend work if you have an infectious condition.

Dress in layers that can be taken off so you don't get too hot. Becoming too hot can lead to body odour and cause offence or discomfort to others. This is especially important as hairstyling involves working very close to your clients and often leaning over them.

For safety reasons:

- wear shoes that cover your toes and are comfortable to stand in for long periods of time.
- never wear open-toed shoes, as hair cuttings can penetrate the skin on your feet, and you may injure yourself if you drop any sharp objects such as scissors.
- avoid wearing baggy jumpers that may get caught in equipment
- avoid wearing excessive jewellery. Long necklaces may get caught in equipment and rings could catch in your client's hair, as well as encourage occupational dermatitis.

Wearing several bracelets creates a noise which may affect your client's enjoyment of the treatment, for example when massaging during a shampooing and conditioning service.

HEALTH AND SAFETY

Remember – poor standards of health and hygiene can cause offence to your clients, spread germs and allow cross-contamination.

Protecting your hands and clothes

Personal protective equipment (PPE) is required in many different jobs and can vary from hard hats, steel toe-capped boots and reflective jackets for builders, to gloves and aprons for hairdressing. Your salon must provide you with the PPE you need to carry out your job safely and this may include:

- gloves to protect your skin from chemicals
- an apron to protect your clothes from damage
- eye protection to protect your eyes when mixing up chemicals
- particle masks to protect your lungs against particles found in powder lighteners.

PPE for the stylist and the assistant includes:

- gloves to protect hands from chemicals and staining
- an apron to protect clothes from chemical damage.

If you suffer from asthma or allergies:

- wear a mask when mixing chemicals, particularly when using lightening powders, to prevent inhalation
- wear eye protection when handling chemicals, to prevent chemicals from entering the eyes.

▲ Wear gloves when using or handling chemicals

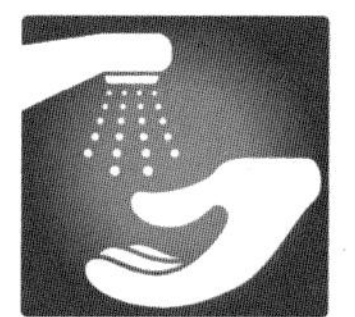

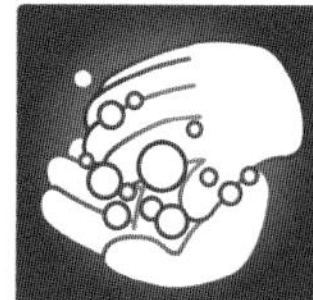

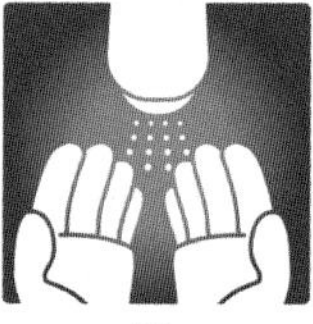

▲ Wash your hands properly

Contact dermatitis

It is important to protect your hands to avoid occupational contact dermatitis. Dermatitis can occur when your skin comes into contact with substances that can irritate the skin and cause allergies. Each person's skin will react differently to substances and dermatitis can occur at any time of your career. Hairdressers are more likely to contract occupational dermatitis than any other profession.

Dermatitis is not contagious to others but it can spread on your own skin. Although most commonly found on the hands, it can appear on the face, lips and arms and cause eye irritation.

The good news is that it can be avoided. Follow these five simple steps to healthy hands:

- Wear non-latex, disposable gloves for shampooing, conditioning, removing colours and neutralising, etc.
- Dry your hands thoroughly after wetting.
- Moisturise your hands regularly.
- Use new gloves for every client.
- Check your hands regularly for signs of contact dermatitis.

Dermatitis can be recognised by any of the following signs:

- dry hands
- itchy hands
- redness of the hands
- cracking of the skin
- bleeding and swelling
- blistering.

HANDY HINT

Dermatitis is a form of eczema and is often referred to as occupational dermatitis and contact dermatitis, as it is caused by your occupation and contact with substances that irritate the skin, resulting in discomfort, itching, a rash and redness.

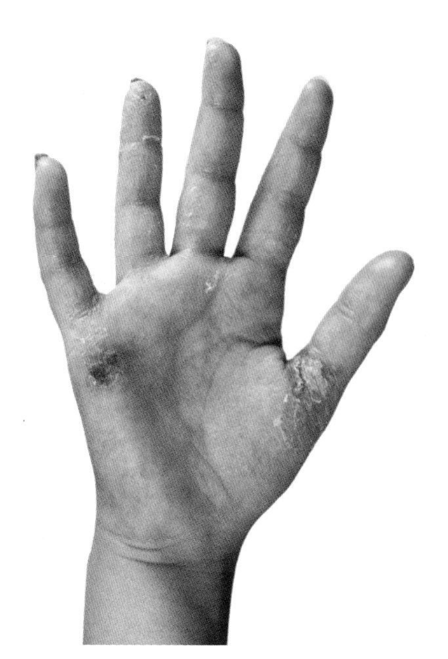

▲ Dermatitis

Keep work area clean and tidy throughout the service

It is important to keep your work areas clean and tidy at all times. Part of your job role is supporting the team of stylists and helping the salon run smoothly. This means that workstations must be prepared for the clients and promptly cleaned and tidied between services. Tools, equipment and work surfaces must be cleaned and sterilised regularly and the salon floor kept free from spillages or slippery surfaces such as hair or other hazards. The shampoo area must be cleaned regularly and ready for continuous use, stocked with clean towels and gowns and free of any colour residue around the neck areas on the basins.

Throughout the service you may also need to tidy up and sweep away hair during a haircut or remove and rinse colouring bowls and materials at the end of a colour application.

Hazards and risks in the workplace

A hazard is something with the potential to cause harm. A risk is the likelihood of the hazard's potential being realised. Trailing wires and hair cuttings on the floor are both hazards. If the trailing wire is neat and tidy against the wall it poses a lesser risk than if it is draped across a workstation where someone may trip over it. Hair cuttings on the floor pose a potential risk to the stylist and the client if not swept up immediately, but there is a lesser risk to the client while they are sitting in the chair.

ACTIVITY

Walk around your salon thinking about the following points and then complete the chart below.

- Identify the potential risks.
- Decide who might be harmed and why.
- Decide what preventative precautions could be put in place.
- Decide who is responsible to carry out the precautions.

Refer to www.hse.gov.uk/hairdressing/ for more information on health and safety and managing risks in a hairdressing salon.

Potential risk	Who is at risk?	Preventative precautions	Who is responsible?

Dealing with spillages

If you notice or cause a spillage you must ensure you mop it up, or others may slip over and injure themselves.

Water spillages can be mopped up and dried more easily and safely than chemical spillages. When dealing with chemicals you must wear gloves to protect your skin and use a mop and bucket to clean the excess from the floor. For any spillage, display a warning 'wet floor' sign until the floor is completely dry and safe.

▲ Warning sign

The importance of risk assessments

A risk assessment of the workplace and its contents is important to protect employees and visitors in the salon, and is required by law. The salon owner is responsible for the salon's risk assessments. Although you may not play a huge part in the risk assessment process, you need to be aware of it. If you, your colleagues or clients are pregnant, have limited mobility, are asthmatic or have ailments that may put you at risk in the workplace, your employer must be informed. Your salon manager is not expected to eliminate all risks, but they must ensure they protect you where possible. It is your responsibility to make your employer aware of any health issues you may have that could put you at risk, so that they can assess the situation.

▲ Water on the floor is a hazard

Minimise risks of cross-infection, injury or fatigue

You must ensure the way in which you work minimises any potential risks.

This includes:

- Cross-infection – be vigilant and check clients for infections and infestations.
- Injury – be careful and do not put yourself at risk of injury, do not run in the salon, always protect your skin, take care with chemicals and sharp objects and remove potentials risks where possible.
- Fatigue – ensure you have plenty of sleep and stand correctly, maintaining a good body position and posture. Drink plenty of fluids and take a break during the day.

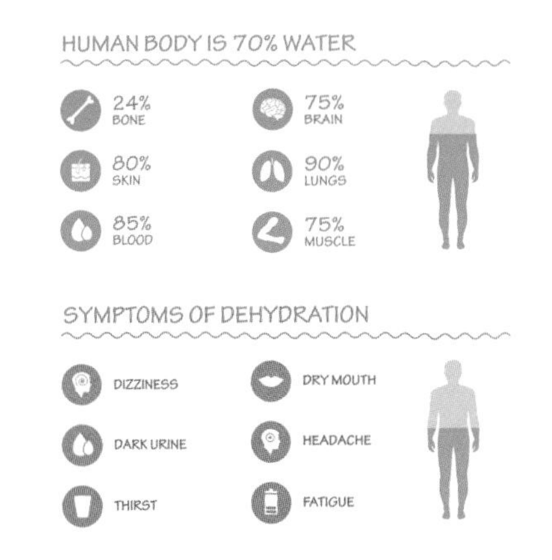

▲ Drinking plenty of water helps you stay hydrated and avoid fatigue

Minimise wastage of products

Wastage of products is bad for business (financially) and the environment (landfill). Use products correctly, following instructions on how to use and amounts to use, taking into consideration the client's hair length and how much hair they have.

HEALTH AND SAFETY

Refer to Chapter 2 Consultation for information on infections and infestations (page: 93–95).

Make effective use of working time

Organising yourself and being prepared help you to make the most effective use of your time. Always check the appointment schedule every morning to ascertain the types of services you need to prepare for throughout the day. This means you can check stock levels, prepare materials ahead of time and assist the team in the most productive way to ensure the salon runs smoothly and to time.

THE HAIR PROFESSIONAL AT WORK

A true hairdressing professional will always ensure they use clean resources, minimise the risk of cross-infection and prevent or minimise the risk of harm or injury to self and others.

Maintain posture and position while working to minimise fatigue and the risk of injury

Both stylists and their assistants work long days and spend many hours standing, particularly when working on chemical treatments. It is very important you stand correctly to minimise fatigue and reduce the risk of injury caused by bad posture. Poor posture can cause back problems and long-term illness, so always stand with your feet slightly apart to maintain your balance and ensure your body weight is evenly distributed. Avoid overstretching or bending unnecessarily.

Client comfort is very important, especially as some services can take several hours to complete. To maintain your client's comfort, ensure their back is straight and supported against the back of the chair at all times throughout the service to prevent neck or back injury. This will also help you to maintain an even balance and meet the needs of the service.

▲ Correct way to stand

▲ Incorrect way to stand

Always ensure that you position your equipment and trolley within easy reach for your comfort and to prevent fatigue. This will also enable you to work efficiently and save time, maintaining a professional image at all times.

▲ Correct way to position your client

▲ Incorrect way to position your client

Protect the client's clothing throughout the service

When your client arrives, sit them comfortably at your workstation and after consultation, protect them suitably for the service required.

Always use:

- a fresh clean towel
- a fresh clean gown
- a plastic/disposable shoulder cape or another fresh clean towel if you are using chemicals or working with long wet hair – this may vary depending on your salon requirements
- a cutting collar for cutting services.

A client must wear a gown during a chemical service; otherwise you may cause damage to their clothes. This could easily lead to a loss of clients or **revenue** if an unsatisfied client charges the salon for damages or takes their business elsewhere.

THE HAIR PROFESSIONAL AT WORK

Maintain your client's modesty by protecting their clothing, rather than having to remove wet clothing after poor and inadequate shampooing. Ensure you maintain client comfort at all times. Protect your client's privacy by keeping their personal and financial details protected and secure.

HANDY HINT

If you are right-handed, keep your trolley on the right-hand side of you and your client, and the opposite if you are left-handed.

KEY TERM

Revenue – income or money received from clients for services provided by the salon.

HANDY HINT

PPE for the stylist consists of gloves, aprons, eye protection and particle masks. Protection for the client consists of gowns, towels, capes.

▲ Protect yourself and your client during a colour service

Promote environmental and sustainable working practices

Consumers and businesses dispose of more than 1.2 million tonnes of waste per year – that's the equivalent of 150 thousand double decker buses! Sadly most of this waste goes to landfill. More and more salons are becoming 'green' salons in attempts to be environmentally friendly. This includes using less energy, managing and reducing salon waste, preventing pollution and using eco-friendly furniture and products

KEY TERM

Organic – produced without the use of artificial chemicals.

where possible. Using eco-friendly (natural and **organic**) products minimises the negative impact on human health and the environment, such as pollution).

Reducing and managing waste

Reducing and managing waste relates to more than just physical stock (such as tubes of tint, bottles of shampoo and towels) – it includes resources such as team members and time, as well as energy.

HANDY HINT

Reducing waste can save money and maximise profit, which is great for business and potentially your salary!

Managing waste is about looking at what you use, how much of it you use and using it correctly. It also includes how you remove the salon's waste.

Reducing the salon's waste will help the environment and attract clients who are environmentally conscious.

You need to look at your waste and identify what can be reduced, re-used or recycled.

Reducing energy and other resources

To reduce the salon's waste you need to monitor where the wastage occurs and identify the causes.

In the salon you can try to reduce waste such as:

- water
- stock and products
- energy
- paper
- money
- time.

ACTIVITY

1. If a stylist mixes up 5% more tint than they need for each colour client, after 20 clients a whole tube of tint has been wasted (5% × 20 = 100% – a full tube).
2. If in one week, six salon stylists all wasted 5% of tint and carried out a total of 50 colour services, how many tubes of tint have been wasted?
3. If these six stylists mixed up half a tube of tint when a quarter of a tube would have been sufficient, how much product has been wasted on the 50 colour services?
4. If one tube of tint costs £6.70 +VAT, how much money has been wasted?

Re-using items

Many of us have developed a 'throw-away' lifestyle, but where possible we should re-use items.

When shopping for salon provisions, re-use carrier bags or use a 'bag for life'. Shampoo and conditioner bottles can be refilled, packaging materials can be re-used for storing items, old towels can be used as cleaning cloths and scrap paper can be used for messages and notes for the team. Your manager may also consider buying 'pre-loved' or second hand furniture, creating a retro or vintage image while protecting the environment too.

Recycling and eco-friendly products

People in the UK throw away enough rubbish to fill Wembley Stadium every day. Buying recycled and greener goods means there is less rubbish for landfill and fewer valuable natural resources are wasted.

For many of us at home, recycling is a way of life and now businesses need to do their bit to reduce the effects of climate change.

Many items are recyclable and your local council can provide you with information on how, where, when and what to recycle. Always follow your local by-laws when disposing of rubbish or recycling.

ACTIVITY

Investigate where you can recycle electrical items and batteries in your area. Visit your local council's website to find out what they do to protect the environment and recycle in your local area.

HANDY HINT

Organise your salon bins into recycling containers and separate your waste. Your salon could increase its profits by selling aluminium cans and waste foil through a cash recycling scheme.

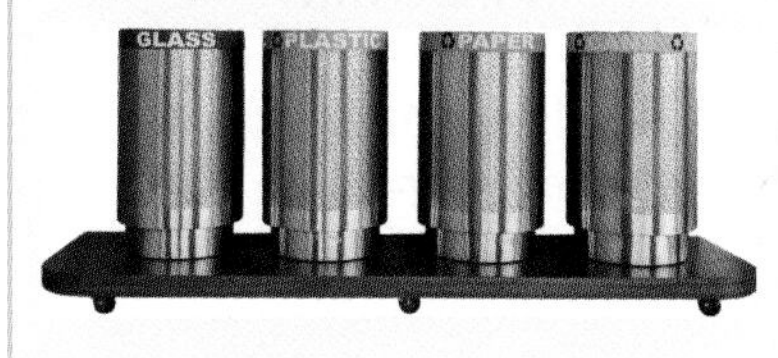

▲ Recycling bins

Electrical waste

Electrical waste is the fastest growing waste in the UK and it increases by 5 per cent every year. Seventy-five per cent of electrical waste ends up in landfill and the lead and other toxins contained in electrical goods cause soil and water contamination. This affects the natural habitat and wildlife and our health. In July 2007 the new 'like for like' Waste Electrical and Electronic Equipment (WEEE) Directive was set up. This meant if you purchased a new item, you could recycle your old item for free. For more information on the WEEE Regulations, see www.hse.gov.uk

Salons can recycle most of their electrical goods such as:

- straighteners
- hairdryers
- clippers
- kettles
- washing machines
- computers
- phones.

Every year an estimated 2 million tonnes of electrical items are discarded by householders and companies in the UK.

▲ Electrical waste

Other recyclable items

Even the salon light bulbs can be recycled. Low energy bulbs contain mercury and should not go into waste bins but be taken to a recycling centre. Fluorescent tubes can be recycled too.

- Batteries should not be disposed of with general waste but recycled correctly and safely.
- Printer toner cartridges can be recycled with the manufacturer.
- Tin cans, paper, cardboard, glass and aerosol cans are all recyclable.
- Some plastics can be recycled depending on their recycle symbol – symbols 1 to 3 are recyclable but 4 to 7 are not due to the mixture of compounds.

Buying recycled and greener goods

You can purchase recyclable and greener everyday salon goods such as paper, stationery, toilet paper, paper towels, rubbish bags and eco-friendly soaps and cleaning supplies.

▲ Benefit your local community – donate hair cuttings to your local allotment group

Food and hair

We all know that food waste is great for composting, but did you know that hair is too? Disposing of hair in a compost bin with food waste helps make healthy rich soil. Some eco-friendly salons are using human hair to insulate the salon and help maintain heat in the winter months – saving energy on heating too.

HANDY HINT

For more information on recycling, go to www.recycle-more.co.uk

Safe disposal

Hairdressing salons and barbers should dispose of waste in the following manner: waste materials must be packaged and stored correctly to prevent **pollutants** escaping into the environment. If disposing of large amounts of **toxic** chemicals, then you must produce a waste transfer note for the company collecting the waste, providing an accurate description of how to handle and dispose of the materials or chemicals safely and appropriately.

General salon waste must be placed in sacks and kept on the premises until the agreed collection day. The public footpaths must be kept clear at all times and the salon area left clean and tidy. The salon should recycle where possible and flatten down or bundle any cardboard boxes ready for collection. No sharp or dangerous objects should be placed in the refuse sacks and chemicals must be disposed of appropriately.

KEY TERMS

Pollutants – toxins or impurities.

Toxic – poisonous.

Reducing energy usage

To reduce energy usage salons should:

- turn lights off when not required
- use energy-saving/high energy efficiency light bulbs
- have sensors fitted for lights in rooms that are not used so often – toilets, storage cupboards, treatment rooms, etc.
- turn off and unplug appliances, for example, straightening irons
- use a 'quick wash' cycle on washing machines
- use airers to dry towels instead of tumble dryers

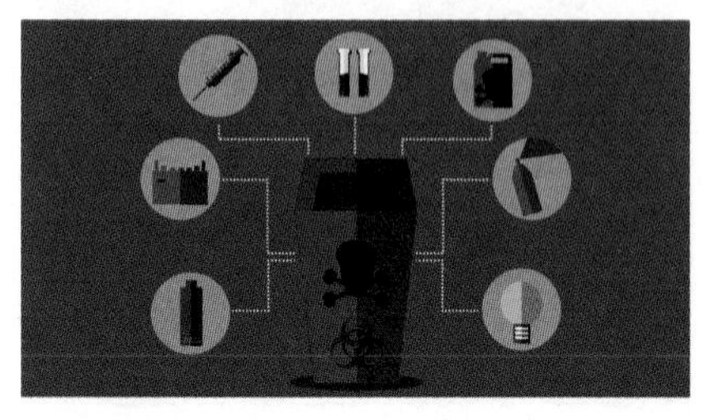

▲ Toxic and hazardous waste

- use 'A' rated appliances (boilers, fridges, heaters, etc.) – A+++ is the highest rate for EU directive labelling, meaning the most energy efficient
- use solar panels for production of electricity and hot water
- use high efficiency heating systems
- use low wattage/high efficiency hairdryers and electrical tools
- thermally insulate building structures.

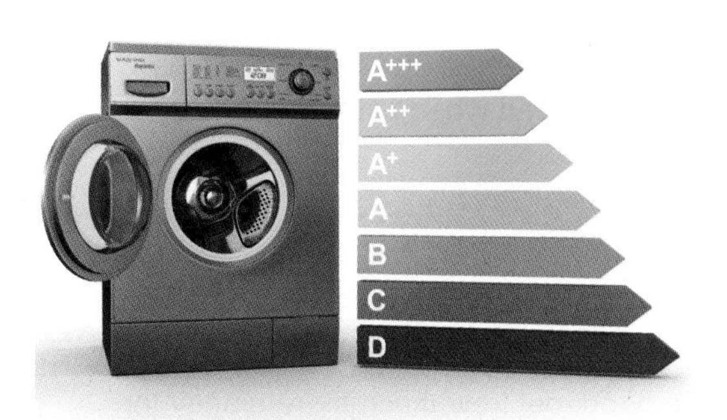

▲ Appliance energy ratings

▲ Low energy light bulb

HANDY HINT

EU directives are legislation that set out objectives for all countries in the European Union (EU) to follow. These directives are often used to enforce free trade, free movement and competition across the EU. They also establish common social policies that can affect employment issues and law, the Working Time Regulations and the Equal Pay Act 1970. EU directives are likely to be replaced by UK legislation by 2019.

Reducing water usage

The most obvious way to save water in the salon is to turn off the taps when massaging during the shampoo service. Although this is important, water usage can be reduced by using low flow showerheads and ultra-low flush systems on toilets too. When washing up or cleaning tools, do not turn the water flow up high or waste water – instead use a washing up bowl and fill it with the right amount of water.

▲ The Ecohead showerhead

ACTIVITY

If you run the tap continuously for 5 minutes when carrying out a shampoo service, you will use at least 37 litres of water.

1. How much water would you use if you ran the tap continuously for 8 minutes?
2. How much water would you save if you turned the tap off when massaging and only had the water running for 2½ minutes?

▲ Do not leave taps running

Reducing other resources

You can reduce the wastage of other resources such as stock and products in the following ways:

- mix colours correctly
- measure products accurately
- judge the hair service correctly, mixing up the right amount of product for the hair length and density and using the correct amount of shampoo and conditioner, and styling products, etc.
- understand and follow the manufacturer's instructions
- rotate stock so it does not go out of date
- avoid over ordering stock.

HANDY HINT

Larger shampoo and conditioner bottles are more cost effective for salon use but always use a pump dispenser to ensure you use the correct amount of shampoo and conditioner.

▲ Shampoo and pump dispenser

Reduce your salon's paper use by:

- asking clients to book appointments in their diaries or on their smartphones, rather than issuing appointment cards
- setting the salon's printer to print on both sides of the paper as default
- using email or the internet to place stock orders
- contacting the mail preference services to have the salon address removed from mailing lists to prevent junk mail – www.mpsonline.org.uk

Reduce your salon's expenses by:

- charging for the products you have used when calculating your client's bill.

Find out from your salon if they charge clients more money for colouring services if they have abundant hair, or if the hair is very long in length.

If your salon does charge more, work out how much more money the salon would make if you had five clients with long hair book in for a colour compared to five clients with short hair.

Reduce your time by:

- organising staff rotas to ensure all staff are busy
- booking appointments correctly so they are timed efficiently for each stylist's working day.

Possible causes of wastage

Generally, wastage is caused by poor usage and can easily be prevented. Poor stock control, poor procedures, bad practice, poorly trained staff, accidental wastage and even dishonest staff may be the cause of some salon wastage.

Walk around your salon and watch the team working. Note down any activity that could be wasting money, products, time, energy or water. Identify what you think are the main reasons for the wastage. If you have any really good ideas that would save your salon time and money, then you could write an email to your employer with your recommendations. Remember to write your email professionally and to check your spellings before you send it.

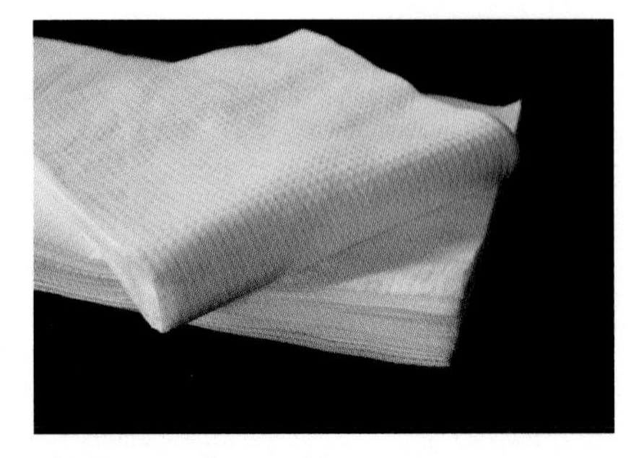

▲ Easydry disposable towels

Disposable towels

Using disposable towels may sound costly, but in fact they are more convenient, absorbent, eco-friendly and hygienic than traditional towels. You can save up to 25 per cent on laundry bills and reduce energy use too. Disposable towels are made from renewable sources and are recyclable and 100 per cent biodegradable within three months. The packaging is often compostable too, as the companies selling these products are environmentally friendly.

Using recycled paper towels in hand washing areas is hygienic and can be better for the environment than some hand dryers. Jet stream dryers are efficient to use but can be noisy and may not suit the environment.

Using recycled, eco-friendly furniture

All salons want their décor to reflect their salon culture and image, as well as looking clean and tidy, but this can be achieved using eco-friendly furniture, fixtures and fittings. You can purchase eco-friendly salon items such as furniture and flooring, basins and taps and white goods (washing machines and fridges) from recyclable or sustainable sources. Unwanted salon furniture can be donated to the homeless or non-profit organisations.

▲ Reclaimed furniture

ACTIVITY

Research online how to 'get rid of stuff for free'. How many sites can you find where you can either recycle or donate items to? How many of these are charities which could help your local community?

Eco-friendly products

Eco-friendly product	How the product helps the environment
Using low chemical paint 	• Eco-friendly salons are opting for VOC-free paint made from natural materials and environmentally managed sources.

Eco-friendly product	How the product helps the environment
Using organic and allergy-free hair products Almond, jojoba and argan oil	• Organic and allergy-free hair products include shampoo and conditioners, styling and finishing products. • They are made with up to 98 per cent naturally derived ingredients that are ethically sourced. • Ingredients may include essential oils, Moroccan argan oil and most plant-based products have UV sunscreen protection too. • Organic hairdressing products are less likely to cause allergies or irritate the client's skin and scalp. However, you must always ask if your client has any allergies, as you may not be familiar with the product's ingredients and a client suffering with a nut allergy may not be able to have nut oil products on their hair.
Using ultra low ammonia hair colourants Goldwell Nectaya ammonia-free colour products	• The salon consumers – your clients – often request eco-friendly and chemical-free products for their hair. This includes colouring products too, but of course they still want vibrant colours and grey hair coverage. • Several manufacturers offer ammonia-free hair colour products, where over 90 per cent of the ingredients are of natural origin, but still cover resistant white hair and achieve up to three levels of lift. These products are kind to the hair, as well as the planet. • Salons are less likely to use products that have been tested on animals or those with animal-derived ingredients. This may be due to consumer demand or the salon's choice.
Using environmentally friendly product packaging	• When salons decide to go green and help protect the environment, they should request that their manufacturers and wholesalers use environmentally friendly packaging. • They could ask if the Styrofoam peanuts that protect products during transit can be returned, re-used or recycled. • Cardboard boxes should be made from recycled paper and after delivery they would ideally be flat packed and recycled. Aveda believe 'We can change the world, by changing how the world does business'. They: • use 100 per cent post-consumer recyclable packaging • reduce the size, weight and processes of packaging • offer packaging that can be recycled • use environmentally sound materials • use renewable energy to manufacturer and fill their packaging • use 100 per cent wind power to manufacturer their products. Visit Aveda's website for further information: www.aveda.co.uk

Eco-friendly product	How the product helps the environment

Choosing responsible domestic products 	• Almost everything you buy has been made; each item is manufactured, processed, packaged and then driven somewhere to be delivered. This process affects the environment and the people who are involved in its production.
	• A simple gesture like offering your client a tea or coffee could probably be improved by using **Fairtrade** tea and coffee.
	• When you clean the salon, the products you use could help to protect the environment:
	  • use eco-friendly laundry detergent, washing up liquid and multi-surface cleaners
	  • check cleaning supply bottles and containers are biodegradable
	  • in bathroom areas use recycled paper toilet roll and eco-friendly hand wash.

ACTIVITY

Look at the ingredients in a retail product from your salon range and identify any ingredients that some clients may be allergic to.

ACTIVITY

Create a mood board and design your eco-friendly salon. You must use:

- re-usable, recycled or eco-friendly furniture and flooring
- VOC-free paint
- eco-friendly and allergy-free hair care products and retail
- ultra low ammonia hair colours
- low energy equipment.

Take a look at the website of Emma Hellier's eco-friendly salon for inspiration: www.emmahellier.co.uk

HANDY HINT

When selling retail to clients you could offer a reward scheme for clients using their own bags and maybe even offer a refill option for shampoos and conditioners.

KEY TERM

Fairtrade – Fairtrade companies guarantee that their products have been made with fairer trading conditions and opportunities for producers in developing countries.

Different working methods that promote environmental and sustainable working

When storing and handling chemicals you must follow the Control of Substances Hazardous to Health Regulations (COSHH). Your salon will have a policy on where to store chemicals, where to mix them up and how to handle and dispose of chemicals in the salon; you must follow these procedures too.

▲ Mix chemicals in the designated area

Disposal of waste

Whatever the size of the business, each owner/employer has a duty of care to protect the environment and dispose of waste on land in an appropriate manner. In fact, every individual has a duty of care, as this act covers dog fouling, litter – including fast food waste, cigarette butts and chewing gum – and fly-tipping and graffiti to name but a few. Not following the Environmental Protections Act can cost you £300 as a fixed penalty and may result in criminal prosecution.

The MFIs will instruct you on how to store, handle, use and dispose of the chemicals or substances; the local by-laws will tell you how to dispose of the chemicals/substances to suit the environment and follow the local authority's guidelines on waste and refuse. Your salon policy will explain where to dispose of them in the workplace.

HANDY HINT

There are two types of waste: contaminated and non-contaminated waste. Contaminated waste consists of hazardous materials such as chemicals.

Non-contaminated waste is not hazardous and goes to landfill; it consists of empty tubes of colour, hair, cotton wool, broken hairbrushes, etc.

Sustainable working practices

You and your salon managers must use sustainable working practices; these include:

- minimising pollution – disposing of contaminated and non-contaminated waste correctly and in ways which do not harm the environment
- reducing and managing waste – using correct quantities of products to reduce waste, disposing of waste correctly and recycling where possible
- reducing energy waste – reducing water use by adapting wash cycle temperatures and ensuring full wash loads only on washing machines and turning off water in between shampoos. Turning off lights and electrical equipment when not in use to save electricity.

▲ Recycle, reduce and reuse

ACTIVITY

1. If assistant Kristian used 45 mls of shampoo on a client with short hair rather than the recommended 25 mls, how much product has been wasted?
2. How much product does Kristian waste per week if he shampoos 75 clients?
3. A litre of shampoo costs the salon £11.75. How much money is wasted per week?
4. If Kristian works 47 weeks per year, how much is this costing the salon yearly?

▲ Smog is a form of pollution

Preventing pollution

Individual businesses do not generate substantial **pollution** but collectively small- and medium-sized salons and individuals working in people's homes produce waste pollution. The use of chemicals such as hair colours, lighteners, perm lotions and relaxers, and aerosol products such as hairspray, contribute to pollution.

KEY TERM

Pollution – contamination of the environment.

Using hairdressing products such as chemicals and aerosol sprays which contain **VOCs** can cause poor indoor air quality and affect the air we breathe, which can affect people's health. On a daily basis we are exposed to:

- ammonia – a chemical used in hair colour
- phenylenediamine (PPD) – also used in hair colours and the ingredient that can cause allergic reactions to hair colour
- hydrogen peroxide – mixed with hair colours to activate them
- sodium hydroxide – used in hair relaxers.

Installing air filtration systems will help to protect clients and staff from poor quality air.

Liquid waste, particularly chemicals, are toxic and banned from landfill, as they pollute the environment. Chemical waste can kill wildlife and, in extreme cases, enter drinking water. Toxic chemicals cannot be poured down the sink or disposed of into natural waters, but small amounts of hairdressing chemicals, such as leftover tints and peroxide, can be diluted with water and rinsed down the drain.

Aerosols have a very long shelf life, so only dispose of them when they are empty. Aerosols can be recycled as they are made from 60 per cent tin-plated steel and 40 per cent aluminium – both of these metals are recyclable. Do not pierce, crush or flatten aerosols before recycling.

KEY TERM

VOCs – Volatile Organic Compounds.

▲ Aerosol spray

▲ Landfill

KEY WORK SKILLS – PROFESSIONALISM, VALUES, BEHAVIOUR AND COMMUNICATION

Every day you will be in contact with other team members and the salon clients, and working within a people-orientated industry. Good professional work ethics and behaviour can accelerate your career and boost your client base, providing you with a loyal clientele and a long future in an amazing, exciting and ever-changing industry.

In order to enjoy your hairdressing or barbering career for many years ahead, you should pay particular attention to this section of the book.

Professionalism and values

Employers expect their staff to demonstrate professionalism on a day-to-day business and these attributes include working with:

- expertise – you need to learn and master your craft
- competence – you need to be capable at your job
- efficient – you need to be a useful team member and make a positive impact
- effective – you need to operate successfully within the salon
- reliable – you need to turn up to work on time, be prepared for the day ahead and manage your time productively.

Alongside professionalism, employers want their employees to demonstrate good personal principles and morals, and professional ethics and values. These attributes include:

- being willing to learn new skills and continually develop your technical talents to a high level
- expressing a positive and professional attitude, by being up-beat, friendly and helpful at all times
- being a flexible team member, adaptable within your job role and tasks you undertake to support the smooth running of the salon
- being a good communicator, adapting how you communicate to suit a variety of people and situations
- showing respect to all by being polite to colleagues and clients, regardless of your or their personal beliefs and differences in views or opinions.

Demonstrate professionalism

It is perfectly natural not to get on with everyone you meet! Personal beliefs and individual interests make people unique, but when it comes to working in the salon, you must work harmoniously with your colleagues and clients, and maintain a professional attitude and working relationship at all times.

Never display any animosity that may be present in the team or engage in a friendly chat with a colleague when you should be focused on your client.

Observe professional ethics and conduct

As soon as a client walks through the door, you must make them feel valued and special. Conversations with your clients should be targeted around them, their interests and activities and, of course, their hair. Always try to engage your client in a neutral, friendly conversation, avoiding views on politics, religion and controversial subjects. Always show respect towards your client's views but minimise expressing your own thoughts if they conflict with your client's opinions.

Client care is paramount in establishing effective relationships, so ensure you always treat clients well. Always remain courteous and never talk to colleagues across your clients.

Diversity of clients

If your client has mobility problems, ask if you can assist them walking to the workstation or shampoo area.

If your client arrives wearing a headscarf or burka, ask them if this is for religious purposes. If so, ask how you can carry out their hair services while respecting their religion. Can you ensure no males are around if a Muslim lady has her hair on show?

If you have a client who is transgender, you may be unsure of how your client would like to be referred to – male or female. It is OK to ask your client how they would like to be addressed, and this will prevent you from offending them.

Industry codes of practice and ethics

The hairdressing and barbering industry focuses on making the client feel valued and special, while maintaining their safety at all times. The industry's code of practice is based around expectations rather than a formal set of written rules. However, your employer may provide you with a contract stating the salon's code of practice. As a guide, the hairdressing and barbering industry follow these 'unwritten rules':

- Maintain health and safety working practices at all times, including cleanliness, sterilisation, client and staff protection and insurances.
- Ensure all staff are suitably qualified and skilled to work in the salon.
- All staff to follow the salon's dress code and expectations on personal hygiene and appearance.
- Consider the welfare of the client at all times.
- Consult with clients and carry out relevant tests.
- Provide a high standard of customer service.
- Carry out services to a high standard to ensure client satisfaction.
- Provide aftercare advice to every client.
- Resolve any client complaints or dissatisfaction as quickly as possible.
- Follow employment law, health and safety Acts and all relevant legislation.

THE HAIR PROFESSIONAL AT WORK

For more information on codes of practice the following websites may be useful:

www.hse.gov.uk/hairdressing/index.htm

www.habia.org/industry-codes-of-practice

www.nhf.info/home

HANDY HINT

Remember that everyone is different, so value everyone's opinion even if you do not agree with them. Treat people fairly and professionally.

Quality assurance systems

Quality assurance systems (QAS) deploy a suite of standard operating procedures (SOPs) to ensure consistency across the salon and among the team members.

Most salons will review their salon systems and want to ascertain ways in which to grow the business or improve the client experience. Having a QAS is great, but it must be reviewed regularly in order to be effective.

Quality assurance systems often include:

- gaining feedback from clients and reviewing the client service experience
- analysing client expectations
- evaluating current standards
- identifying ways to raise standards
- supporting and developing staff and identifying training requirements
- applying policies and procedures
- monitoring and improving quality.

Many employers will identify 'key performance indicators' (KPI) to use as markers to help identify failing or less successful areas of the business. It is important that staff engage with the QAS of the salon, so that everyone is on board with any changes that are required. Employers may set their staff **SMART** targets to help improve sales or raise standards.

KEY TERM

SMART – targets that are Specific, Measurable, Achievable, Realistic and Timely.

Demonstrate a passion for the industry and industry knowledge

Many stylists and barbers remain in this industry for years and their passion for their craft rarely **diminishes**. To be successful in this industry you need a passion for cutting, colouring, styling or creative hair-up, and you have to love working with people. With a thirst for knowledge and a hunger to learn new skills, you can expect to develop your career further and be an asset to any employer.

KEY TERM

Diminishes – fades or reduces.

▲ Be committed to quality

Commitment to quality

No matter how you are feeling, you must provide the best service you can to your client. You must work hard and commit to producing quality results for every client, every day and for every salon visit.

Meet organisational and industry standards of appearance

Within the hairdressing and barbering industry personal appearance and the salon's dress code can vary immensely. Some salons have a uniform or a colour code, such as all black. Some salons encourage the team to express their individuality and personality through their own choice of clothing, as they feel that this style may attract clients with similar tastes and personalities.

Every member of the salon team should look presentable and represent the industry and their salon. Ensure you allow enough time before work to prepare yourself for your working day.

The diagram below shows areas of appearance that are important.

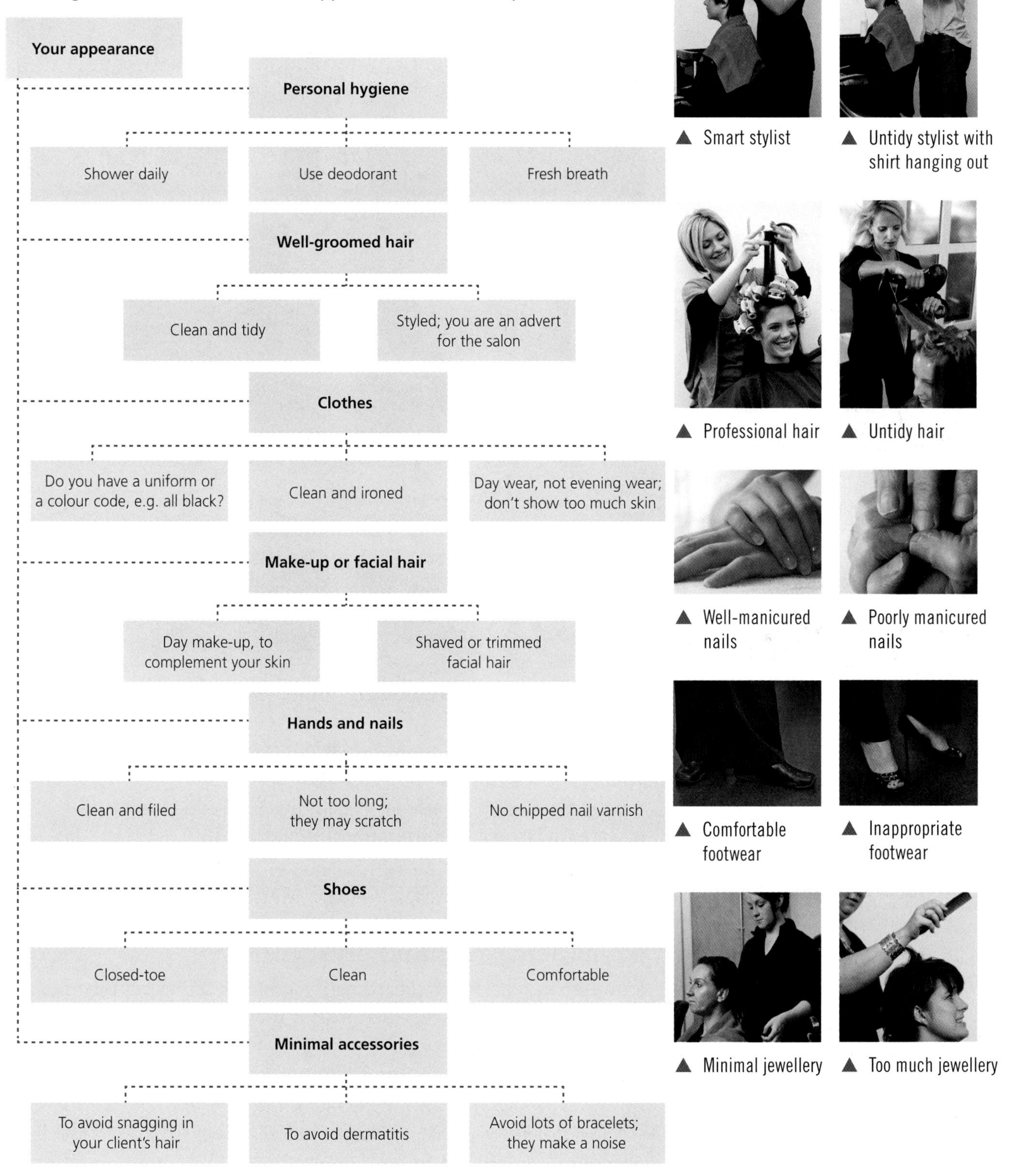

▲ Smart stylist

▲ Untidy stylist with shirt hanging out

▲ Professional hair

▲ Untidy hair

▲ Well-manicured nails

▲ Poorly manicured nails

▲ Comfortable footwear

▲ Inappropriate footwear

▲ Minimal jewellery

▲ Too much jewellery

ACTIVITY

Which of these photos give positive impressions of the salon and which give negative impressions?

HEALTH AND SAFETY

For more information on personal hygiene, refer back to the safe working practices section of this chapter (page 23).

Personal hygiene and protection

You must ensure your personal hygiene and protection meets the accepted industry and organisational requirements.

Adherence to workplace, suppliers' or manufacturer's instructions for the safe use of equipment, materials and products

A true professional never cuts corners and always carries out their duties to the best of their abilities. This includes knowing how to use equipment, tools and products properly.

THE HAIR PROFESSIONAL AT WORK

For more information on the importance of adhering to instructions, refer back to the safe working practices section of this chapter (page 23).

Positive attitude

▲ Remember to display a positive attitude

Your ability to work as part of a team and continually develop are vital to hairdressing. Hairdressing is a fast-paced, ever-changing industry and a positive attitude and the ability to adapt to change will mean that you can develop and maintain your effectiveness at work.

You spend many hours at work, so working relationships are important. Be helpful and friendly to your co-workers; smile, avoid sarcasm, control your reactions, be appreciative and be happy with other people's success. Offer encouragement and give compliments to others, such as: 'congratulations on your promotion', 'your client's hair looked lovely', 'you look nice', and so on.

Hairdressing is a creative and varied industry and a great deal of job satisfaction is possible. Enjoy your job and have fun while working, look your best, remain optimistic and upbeat and get support from a colleague after a setback. Set yourself goals and go after them. Don't complain if things don't go your way – just try again next time.

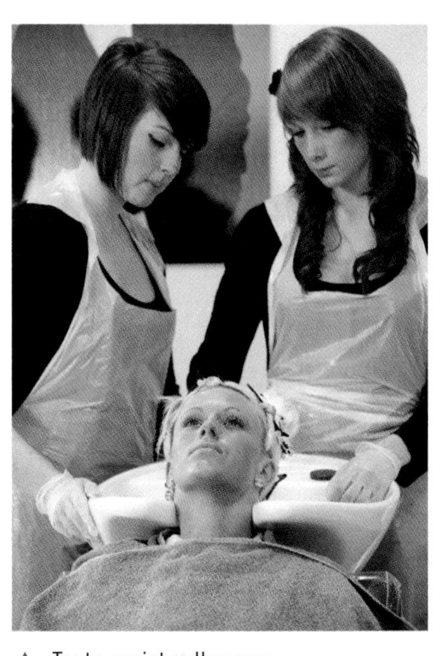

▲ Try to assist colleagues

Flexible working

Where possible, have an adaptable approach to your daily work and always expect the unexpected! Be willing to change your working pattern to suit the needs of the business. Try to be flexible during your working day to meet client demands, without affecting other client services. Be respectful to all staff, visitors and clients and understand that everyone has differences: this includes values and beliefs, religion and culture and personal views. Treat everyone equally, ensuring that you do not make any unsuitable comments regarding age, gender, disability, sexual orientation, race, religion and marital status and so on.

You need to be able to adapt to different situations, such as working under pressure or dealing with a regular client.

Would you treat a regular client differently if the salon were busy or quiet? How would you react if you were short of staff in the salon, or had to deal with a power failure?

HANDY HINT

If someone has upset you, discuss it with them face to face. Always be constructive, communicate clearly and in a friendly manner, and do not talk about them behind their back.

Show willingness to learn

When working in the hairdressing and barbering industry you must be prepared to work hard. Standing all day, working with the general public and learning new skills requires a strong disposition. You'll need motivation and enthusiasm for this kind of work, and eagerness to learn new skills.

You'll need to be ready and prepared for every eventuality, such as:

- clients arriving without appointments
- clients and stylists running behind appointment times
- changes to appointments and services booked
- absent team members
- the ever-changing fashions and skills required to maintain your career.

Being a willing participator in the salon and focusing on the high standards required by your salon will help you to improve your performance and develop your career.

▲ Be willing to learn new skills

You will carry out services on a variety of people: some will have very different values to you, and some will have different backgrounds, upbringing, cultures, religions and beliefs, and may behave unexpectedly. You will need to learn to adapt to these differences and respect other people's values, beliefs and points of view, even if you do not share them.

Respond positively to feedback

It is always easy to respond to positive feedback from a client but some comments may not be positive. When you have to deal with negative comments you must respond in a professional manner at all times. Try to resolve the issue promptly, apologise where necessary and make any suitable arrangements to rectify the issue as soon as you can. Any comments that become complaints should be reported to your manager.

You may receive feedback from the following:

- Clients will regularly give feedback on their satisfaction with their hair service, but you can guarantee that at some point in your career, you will receive some criticism from clients about their hair and the end result not meeting their expectations.
- Your peers will feedback on your day-to-day performance. If you are not pulling your weight in the salon and being a team player, they will criticise your performance.
- Other stylists will offer feedback on your function within the team and the impact your performance has on the salon and their job role.
- Your manager will also feed back to you and critique your performance, letting you know if they are happy with your standards of work and behaviour.

It is important that you react positively to all feedback, even to negative comments about your performance. Feedback helps you to learn and identify your strengths and areas to develop. Reacting positively to all feedback is important for you to grow and realise your full potential.

HANDY HINT

Always react positively to reviews and feedback. Feedback may not always be positive but it should be constructive. You should ensure you act on any advice given.

ACTIVITY

An unhappy client is more likely to leave a negative salon review, than a happy client. Read the salon review below, then answer the questions that follow.

Salon name: Curl me Crazy

Stylist name: Russell Morrison

'I'd heard good things about this salon, so I visited there at the weekend, but sadly I was thoroughly disappointed. Not only was I outraged by the price, but also the stylist was scruffy and did not listen to what I was asking for. He was more interested in telling his work buddy about his Friday night out! The products he put on my hair made my hair greasier than a plate of chips, and I had to go home to wash my hair again before going out that night. I will not be going to this salon again.'

1 What are the key problems the client has **ascertained** in this negative review?
2 Write a professional response to the client's complaint.

▲ Feedback is important

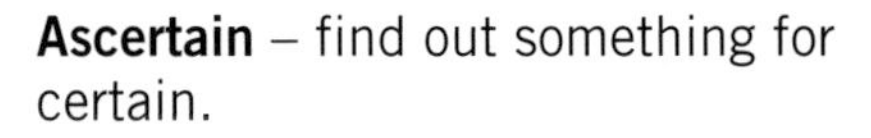

KEY TERM

Ascertain – find out something for certain.

Importance of continuing professional development (CPD)

Continuing to develop professionally is not only rewarding for you as a stylist or barber, but it can also reward you financially too. Client requirements change as often as fashion and trends do, so you must keep up with the times.

Reasons for continuing professional development:

- Achieve job satisfaction
- Fulfil client requirements
- Develop new skills
- Gain career development or promotion
- Earn more money in commission and sales
- Train others and pass on your skills
- Awareness of legislation and product updates.

▲ Regular training is important

Importance of equality and diversity

It is a legal requirement to follow the laws on equality and diversity, but it is important to respect and believe in equality and diversity as well. Your clients and work colleagues could be male or female, pregnant, single, married or divorced, gay, lesbian, straight or **trans**. Some may have mixed cultures and race, or have different faiths and beliefs to you – our world is very diverse and when working with people from different backgrounds our knowledge and experiences are richer because of it.

You may find that you and your clients or colleagues have very different opinions, but you should avoid expressing yours. Let the client voice their opinion; if it has the potential to offend you, move the conversation forward and to a different topic.

You should avoid discussing your personal problems with clients and leave all personal issues at home. The client might use you as a 'counsellor' and tell you all their woes, but they are paying for your service and you should therefore not discuss your problems with them.

KEY TERM

Trans – short for transgender, which means a person's identity and gender does not correspond with their birth sex.

▲ Respect diversity

Work in a team

The day-to-day salon business requires all staff to be supportive of one another and to work in collaboration. Always find co-operative ways of working such as anticipating the needs of others and sharing information which could help your team members. Offer your full support and, if necessary, show that you are willing to help resolve disagreements.

Reporting and dealing with problems

If you make a mistake at work, admit to it. Problems are far easier to rectify if the salon is aware of the problem and the situation can be resolved quickly. It is also less likely to affect the salon services. Your honesty and open apology are more likely to gain you respect from your colleagues, rather than gaining disdain as a result of the error itself.

▲ Anticipate the needs of others to keep the salon running smoothly

▲ Always strive to be a good team player

ACTIVITY

Discuss with a colleague what you would do if you encountered the following scenarios:

1. You have realised after a client has left the salon that you accidentally charged them too much for their hair service.
2. You have accidentally got permanent colour on the collar of your client's shirt.
3. A colleague has confided in you that they have taken some hairdressing products from the retail stand for personal use.
4. A colleague has taken a client's phone number from their record card to use for personal use.

ACTIVITY

Imagine a colleague has upset you at work. Their lack of organisation has caused the salon to run behind and you are now working late on a Saturday night to catch up.

How would you explain to this person why you are upset with them while making sure you were calm and not rude?

Practise your explanation with a colleague, being assertive but remaining polite and professional.

Dealing with differences of opinion and conflict

Working all day in a busy and sometimes strained atmosphere can be demotivating. If you encounter relationship problems at work you must deal with them effectively to prevent the situation from escalating. You might need to be assertive to get your point across and to avoid being ignored. However, you should always treat people in the same manner as you would wish to be treated.

Disagreements

If you have a disagreement with a work colleague, try to follow these guidelines.

- Try to sort it out sooner rather than later. Show a willingness to resolve the disagreement and communicate your concerns clearly, without added drama or malice.
- If you and the individual cannot resolve the situation on your own, then you need to refer the problem to your manager and ask for help.
- A meeting at the end of the day between the two of you and your manager could be the best way forward to air your views.
  - During the meeting, ensure that you remain calm and avoid raising your voice. Issues often arise from misunderstandings, so when it is your colleague's time to talk, it is essential that you listen to their view and do not interrupt them. As you have asked your manager for help, be sure to listen to their view of the situation.
  - When it is your turn to speak, diplomatically and constructively air your grievance, and make suggestions about how the situation could be resolved.
  - If you need to challenge your colleague or ask further questions to aid your understanding of the situation, use open and closed questions that are relevant and show that you are listening to their views. You can show you are listening by using effective body language, such as maintaining eye contact, nodding in agreement and smiling.
- If the situation does not result in an amicable outcome, you may need to refer to the company handbook and the grievance procedure.

- A relaxed and friendly work environment is more motivating, helps to maintain team spirit and ensures good communication between staff. Clients will feel happier visiting a friendly salon, and the professional image is maintained.

Observe self-management

Self-management is about taking charge of your own future, working towards goals, taking and managing risks, dealing with pressure and managing your emotions. It is your contribution to your work – being organised, responding positively to change, planning and managing your time effectively. If you cannot self-manage, you may struggle to advance with your career.

A self-manager is organised and responsive; they manage their emotions and seek out new challenges to develop further. Other skills of a self-manager include being:

- an independent enquirer who explores and resolves problems, plans activities and analyses their results
- a creative thinker who generates new ideas and freely expresses their thoughts, connects previous learning by extending their thinking and adapts well to change
- a reflective person who self-assesses their progress, sets new goals, invites feedback from others and evaluates their work
- a team player who works towards achieving the common goal and reaching agreements, being fair and sharing ideas and good practice for the benefit of everyone.

HANDY HINT

When you need to clarify a situation, challenge a colleague or ask further questions to aid your understanding, you will use your English skills. Open questions require a more detailed response, while closed questions often only require a simple 'yes' or 'no'.

▲ Self-management is a vital skill

Observe time management

Being a good manager of your time is important in work; it helps you organise yourself, take ownership of your responsibilities, and take the initiative with change. To manage your own time effectively you should follow these basic principles:

- Be active and not reactive – know what you need to spend your time on.
- Set goals – plan what you need to do.
- Prioritise actions – what needs to be actioned first?
- Keep focused – if you start a task, stick to it and get the job done.
- Be realistic – ensure you have allowed enough time to achieve the goal and set yourself a limit on how long to spend on it.
- Do it – stop talking about it and get the job done!

Work under pressure

Many salon tasks must be completed in set times, particularly when using chemicals; this often means you are working under pressure. It is crucial you manage your own time if you want a successful career and happy satisfied clients.

▲ Manage your time effectively

Complete services in a commercially viable time and to a high standard

Salon services must run to time for the salon to run smoothly. This means you need to complete the salon services in a commercially viable time. Times may vary from salon to salon and a client's hair can affect the time frames you work to, but you should ascertain the commercial times expected by your salon and employer.

As a guide most salons work to the following time frames:

Service	Time frame
Hair cut short hair (men or ladies)	30 minutes
Blow-dry (long hair)	30 minutes
Cut and blow-dry – ladies	45 minutes
Regrowth colour	20–30 minutes (application only)
1/2 head wovens	30–45 minutes (application only)
Full head wovens	90 minutes (application only)

ACTIVITY

Find out the commercially acceptable times in your salon for the services listed above and five other services not listed.

COMMUNICATION TECHNIQUES AND EXPECTED BEHAVIOURS

Communication is paramount to becoming a 'great' stylist and professional behaviour is expected. In this part of the chapter you will learn how to improve your communication skills and behave in a professional manner.

Customer care and the client journey

You only get one chance to make a first impression, so make sure it is a good one. The client's journey and salon experience start the minute he or she walks through the door, or contacts the salon by phone. From the first phone call or face-to-face contact, you must demonstrate care and respect for your client. Most first impressions are made front of house, so it is important for the receptionist to make a good impression by ensuring the house keeping is in order, the reception area is welcoming and their skills are first class.

▲ Customer service award

Provide a positive impression of yourself and your organisation

Good customer service is vital for building client relationships, ensuring customers return and become loyal to the salon. Providing an excellent service and obtaining a good reputation for client care encourages new clients to visit the salon. It is very important that new clients have a positive impression and experience when they visit, as bad reputations travel faster than good.

Comm… nicating professionally with clients and colleag…

If you ask … ld rate
effective … return to
the same … ith them is
good. A p… s, discusses
how achie… the client
and their … and a valued
customer…

Today, m… omer service
in many i… ns are in a
very fort… ot get their
hair cut a… potential
for a long… they want
to return … at customer
service a…

Greet …

When gr… eous and
respectf… by their first
name or … using their title
and surn…

Be helpful and courteous at all times

Always be helpful and assist clients with their coat – make them feel welcome and valued. Clients are visiting the salon for treatments, so the experience should be a treat!

Industry and salon standards of behaviour

Salon staff should always:

- speak politely
- introduce themselves
- welcome and greet the client by their name
- generally refer to the client by their name
- offer refreshments
- give advice about products and services available in the salon.

Salon staff should not:

- chew gum
- leave the reception unattended
- let the phone ring more than three times
- make a client wait to be attended to
- take personal calls/or respond to personal text messages
- use jargon or technical terms.

ACTIVITY

All of us have entered a store at some point and been poorly greeted by an uninterested staff member. Discuss with your colleagues how that made you feel, what was wrong with the service and whether you have since returned to that store.

▲ Be helpful and respectful to clients

Appropriate ways of communicating with clients

You will mostly communicate with your clients using verbal communication techniques. You will also rely heavily on non-verbal communication, such as reading your client's body language and demonstrating your own positive body language.

Verbal communication

Always speak at a speed your client can understand, be polite, well-mannered and express yourself clearly. If your client is showing signs of uncertainty you can ask more relevant questions to clarify the situation and put them at ease. You will need to adapt your tone of voice and the vocabulary you use to suit your client's needs.

Discussions

During the discussions with your client you must gather specific information about the service requirements and the needs of your client. Some clients struggle with communication, do not always know what they want or how to word their wishes clearly. So it is your job to ask the right questions, in the right way, to draw information from clients who are not forthcoming. Your open questioning techniques will help you to identify their requirements, while using closed questioning techniques will confirm their requirements and conclude your conversation.

▲ Good telephone manners are essential

Open and closed questions

Open questions help you identify requirements and initiate conversation and start with 'what', 'why', 'how' and 'when' – they give you the detail you need.

Closed questions confirm requirements, recommendations and conclude conversations and are answered with a 'yes' or 'no'.

Use open and closed questions to check each other's understanding.

Always read your client's body language and look for signs of uncertainty. If your client is rubbing their neck or behind their ears, it is a sign that they are unsure and further advice/discussion is required.

Use of language

KEY TERM

Exhibits – shows.

It is essential that your client understands what you are saying, so use words they will understand when discussing their hair. In general, avoid using slang and never use bad language in the salon. Also avoid technical words or jargon. Ensure you speak in a way which **exhibits** a professional image.

Tone of voice

Your voice needs to be pitched high enough to project over the noises in the salon, such as hairdryers and music. Speak clearly but with a soft, friendly tone. Smile when you speak as it softens how you sound and look. When emphasising a point or asking a question, raise your voice a little at the end of the sentence.

Listening techniques

Listening to your clients is very important and you will need to use verbal and non-verbal communication and show you are listening. Always give your clients enough time to express their wishes, and smile and nod to acknowledge you understand. Maintain eye contact and show an interest in what is being said.

Always smile and look friendly, ensuring you display open body language that promotes a good impression, and maintain eye contact with your client to aid trust. You should never interrupt a client when they are speaking.

ACTIVITY

1 Which of the following is the best way to answer the phone and why?

'Hello, Cut Above. Can I help you?'

'Good afternoon, Cut Above hair salon. Sarah speaking. How may I help you?'

'Good morning, Sarah speaking. How can I help?'

'Hello, Sarah at Cut Above speaking. Can I help you?'

2 In groups, discuss examples of poor telephone manners and think about your own experiences.

Non- verbal communication

Body language is a method of non-verbal communication and can be positive as well as negative. It can give away secrets about whether you are telling the truth, listening to your client and interested in what your client is saying.

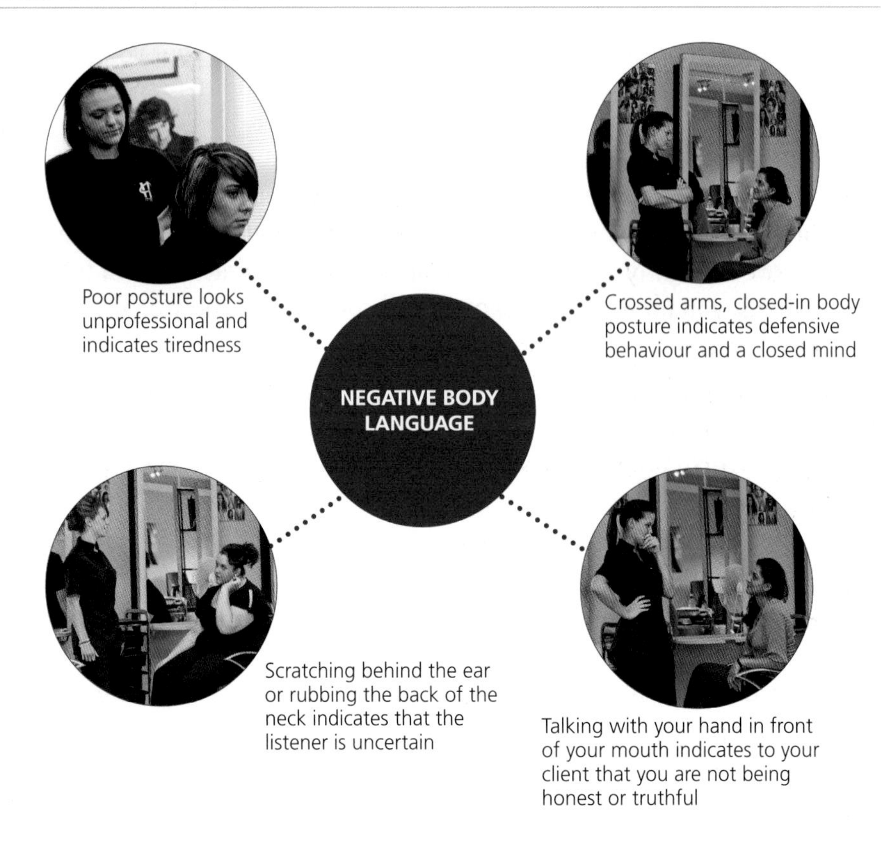

Visual aids

When consulting with your clients about different style choices, hair lengths or colours, you are likely to use visual aids. Visual aids could be images from hairstyling magazines and stylebooks, or images and media online or the use of manufacturer colour charts to show a sample weft of hair colour choices.

Hairstyling magazines are often displayed at reception for the client to look though while enjoying a refreshment and waiting for their appointment time. Many salons have tablets and use Instagram or Pinterest or a PC to save albums of different hairstyles and colouring techniques to show clients during consultations. You can use these apps on smartphones too. Colour charts allow the client (and the stylist) to see the selection of colours and various depths and tones available to choose from when having a colour service.

ACTIVITY

Use Pinterest or Instagram and search for short-layered ladies (or men's) hairstyles. Save these to a folder for future use.

Client care principles and practices

The main principles and practices of client care include:

- keeping the client safe and her belongings secure
- listening to the client's requirements and considering the best option
- advising the client on the most suitable options to meet her requirements
- ensuring adequately trained staff carry out the service
- reassuring and updating the client on the process throughout the service
- checking the client is satisfied with the final result.

Adapt behaviour in response to each client

You will encounter clients who are angry, confused, behave unconventionally and have different needs and expectations; you must be able to adapt to these different situations. This can include what you say, the amount you say and how you say it. You will have to adapt your manner and tone of voice, remain calm and patient and use non-technical and jargon-free terminology.

You may find that you communicate differently with men and women; topics of discussion may vary immensely and personalities too.

To ensure you follow the laws of equality and diversity, always treat clients equally, avoid flirtatious behaviour and be professional at all times. Some of your clients may have disabilities such as sight, hearing or speech difficulties and you must adapt to the needs of these clients and be careful not to cause offence.

HANDY HINT

Avoid discussing topics that involve politics, religion and faith, as some people have very strong views and opinions, and these topics could lead to a heated debate.

Clients with visual impairment or disabilities

- Clients with a visual impairment or those with a physical disability may benefit from being escorted and/or guided through the salon.
- Offer your arm to such clients when moving through the salon and check for any obstacles ahead.
- Be mindful that a client with a visual impairment may take a little while to adjust to different light conditions.
- You may need to adapt your terminology and clarify what you say, as you will not be able to rely on visual aids to confirm your client's requirements.

Clients with hearing impairment

- Clients with a hearing impairment may struggle to hear you over the background noise in the salon – try to lower the noise level in the salon and speak clearly so the client can read your lips.
- Do not shout or exaggerate your words as this can affect your voice patterns and lip movements.
- Stop speaking if you have to turn away from them. Keep to the subject matter and pronounce your words clearly to aid the client's understanding.

Clients with speech impediment

- Clients with a speech impediment may need time to be able to express what they want to say.
- Always show the client respect and patience, and remain relaxed and calm. Listen carefully to your client and never finish their sentences for them.
- Ask them to repeat anything you do not understand.

Clients who are not fluent English speakers

- Clients whose first language is not English may need you to speak a little slower – shouting in English does not translate itself into another language. You need to remain calm and listen carefully.

▲ Build a good rapport with your client

- Ask your client to repeat anything you do not understand – it is important that you do not guess their needs just because you are too embarrassed to ask them to repeat themselves.

> **THE HAIR PROFESSIONAL AT WORK**
>
> There are many disabilities that are not visual such as bi-polar disorder, anxiety disorders and ADHD. Research four other disabilities that you should take into consideration in the salon environment.

Maintain rapport with clients

Always communicate with clients, advise them if the stylist is running a little late and offer them a seat, a magazine to read and a drink to make them feel comfortable and at ease.

The small talk and personal details discussed with your client individualise the treatment you offer. Remembering small details of conversations from previous visits goes a long way to building a good **rapport** with your client.

KEY TERM

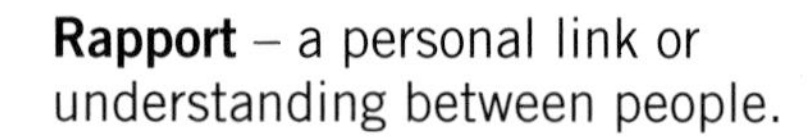

Rapport – a personal link or understanding between people.

ACTIVITY

1 Which of the following forms of communication are good and which are poor?

2 From the poor sentences you identify, how would you rephrase them to make them better?

Establish client expectations and needs

When questioning and talking with clients you are using your communication skills, so remember how communication can make a positive or negative impression on your client of you and your salon.

It is your responsibility to identify and confirm your client's requirements and expectations, and to decide if they are achievable. One of the great features of hairdressing is that not only is every head of hair different, so are your clients. Your clients will have a vision of what they are expecting the result to be; you need to take into consideration their hair type, features and lifestyle to decide the best way to achieve their vision.

Your clients are expecting advice on how to achieve the vision and maintain it. You need to consider the following:

- hair – the density, texture and hair type (abundant, coarse or curly)
- features – prominent ears, sharp jaw line, etc.
- lifestyle – busy mother, full-time worker or sporty.

▲ Allow time for the client to respond

Respond promptly to clients' questions and comments and to clients seeking assistance

Effective communication earns your client's trust in you, builds client and stylist relationships and helps to promote a positive salon reputation too. You must check that your client fully understands what you are suggesting for their hair service and that you have understood your client's requirements.

Before you commence with any service, ensure your client has been given the time to consider their responses and clarify their needs. Always allow additional time if your client is still unsure and offer further information if required.

Explain clearly any reasons why the client's needs or expectations cannot be met

Unfortunately, some clients attend the salon expecting a service or treatment to be carried out, but the resulting consultation and tests prove that these expectations cannot be met. It is essential that you explain to your client why a service cannot be carried out and you should suggest alternatives. Speak clearly, be polite and give the appropriate detail. Remain professional and objective as to why the client's expectations cannot be met.

ACTIVITY

1. List some examples of services that clients might expect to be carried out, which cannot be carried out due to test results or consultation.
2. How would you explain this to your client?

Keep the client informed

If your client is thinking of having a new service in the future or has expressed an interest in purchasing some products, allow them time during the service to consider the benefits. Towards the end of the service, revisit the conversation, show them the products used and repeat the benefits to the client.

HANDY HINT

Always repeat back to your client what you think has been agreed in order to gain confirmation and avoid misunderstandings.

Avoid misunderstandings

It is important to avoid any misunderstandings between you and your client to ensure you have both agreed and understood the same service requirements and to build an effective relationship. You must never talk over your client and should use jargon-free language when discussing services and products to help them understand what is being suggested to them. Listen to your client and nod your head or repeat what is being said so they are clear you have understood.

KEY TERM

Hub – the centre point of an environment; often the busiest point.

Undertake wider salon duties

When the salon is busy, you will be expected to undertake additional duties such as reception and sales. It is of paramount importance that you understand how the salon reception area is run, as this is the **hub** of the salon.

Without a reception you would not be able to meet and greet your clients, book their appointments or receive payment for your services. It is the first area that your clients see, so is where first impressions of the salon begin. Clients may drop in for advice on their hair or to buy products, so it is important that the reception area always looks great. The receptionist's role is an important one, and it is essential that the receptionist is effective and efficient when working.

▲ Salon reception area

Role of the reception area

The reception is the 'front of house' and the first area of the salon that your clients see when they pass the salon or walk through the door. Salon reception areas must always look neat and tidy and be well maintained.

At the start of each day, the receptionist must deal with any answerphone messages that have been left overnight and ensure that the reception area is prepared for the day ahead.

The daily activities of a receptionist might include:

- maintaining a clean, tidy and well-stocked reception area
- meeting and greeting clients

- maintaining the salon's hospitality and offering refreshments to clients
- dealing with enquiries and bookings
- checking that clients have had any relevant hair and skin tests
- solving problems at reception, such as services running late or clients arriving late
- providing information about salon services and retail products
- answering the telephone
- checking emails and any other electronic methods of communication
- organising the salon's post and distributing it to the relevant people
- taking messages and passing them on to the relevant people
- maintaining communication between clients and stylists
- handling payments and promoting the sale of retail products
- preparing client record cards
- maintaining confidentiality of clients' records
- maintaining salon security at the reception area.

▲ Greeting a client at reception

ACTIVITY

Sort the following record cards in alphabetical order by surname:

Mrs Howards	Mrs Harvey
Mr Jackson	Mr Goshi
Mr Singh	Mrs Ohi
Mrs Havard	Mr Henderson
Miss Mackintosh	Miss Hramczuk
Mr Harrod	Mr O'Shaugnessy
Miss Homeworth	Miss McGrady

▲ Smile when you are on the telephone

Displaying a confident attitude

It is important to know what you are talking about in order to be confident in your conversation. If you need some help from a salon stylist/supervisor, ask politely and respectfully.

When you answer the telephone, smile, as it shows in your voice, speak clearly and say good morning/afternoon to the caller. Always state your name, to let the caller know who they are speaking to.

Making appointments

To be able to book your client in for their appointment you will need to know what services they would like and whether or not additional services are required, such as a cut and finish, after a colour service. If you are booking a client in for a colour service, you will need to confirm they have had a skin test and check their age, confirming they are over 16 years of age. You will need to know when the client wishes to attend – date and time – and who their preferred stylist is. You will need to check any skin test requirements too (if relevant).

Confirming and making appointments correctly

If appointments are booked incorrectly then the salon cannot run smoothly, clients may turn up at the wrong times or dates or stylists may not be available. It is therefore important that appointments details are checked and confirmed.

Once you have booked an appointment always repeat back to the client what you have booked, for example:

> 'Okay Janet, I have booked you in for a half head of woven highlights and a cut and finish with Puru on Tuesday 16 December at 1.30 p.m. Your skin test has been carried out today. If you have any problems please contact us and Puru will discuss this with you.'

Some salons may request that you inform the client of the duration of the service and the cost too.

A typical conversation between a receptionist and a client (Sarah) may be similar to this:

Receptionist: 'Hi Sarah, how are you? How can I help you?'

Sarah: 'I'm fine, thank you, Natasha. I'd like to book an appointment for a colour and cut please.'

Receptionist: 'Which stylist do you normally see for your cut and colour?'

Sarah: 'Amraf does my cut and Tina usually does my colour.'

Receptionist: 'When would you like to come in for your appointment?'

Sarah: 'Any chance you can fit me in on Saturday?'

Receptionist: 'Amraf is free and can cut your hair at 2 p.m., but Tina is on holiday. Would you mind if Julia coloured your hair?'

Sarah: 'No, that's fine, thank you.'

Receptionist: 'Great. Are you having your usual colour or do you fancy a change?'

Sarah: 'No, thank you. I would like my usual highlights, but just the top section this time please.'

Receptionist: 'Okay Sarah. Is 12.15 a suitable time for your colour?'

Sarah: 'Yes, perfect, thank you.'

Receptionist: 'Just to confirm then, Sarah, I have booked you in with Julia at 12.15 for your half head of highlights and then Amraf will cut your hair at 2 p.m. Is that okay?'

Sarah: 'Perfect, thank you. See you Saturday. Bye.'

Receptionist: 'Goodbye – have a lovely day!'

▲ Client being booked in for her next appointment

Appointment systems

Common systems available for making appointments include manual appointment systems – where clients are booked in using pencil and a diary page, or electronic systems – where salon staff can book clients in electronically onto the computerised diary page. Some electronic reception application systems even allow the clients to view the booking system online and they can book their own appointments too.

Who to refer to with different types of enquiries or problems and when to seek advice

It is important that you ask for help if and when you need it to ensure the salon runs effectively and problems are solved successfully. Do not try to squeeze in a client for a haircut if the barber is busy, or try to solve a client complaint or a complex colouring problem on your own. If you are out of your depth, work within your levels of responsibility and ask a senior member of the team to help or advise you.

ACTIVITY

List four situations when you may need to ask others for help.

Provide clients with information about salon services and/or products

You will need to ensure that you are knowledgeable on your salon's range of retail products available, in order to promote them effectively to your clients. Although you personally may not be able to offer every service that the salon promotes, they need to be offered and made available to all clients. It will be your responsibility to know which staff members carry out these services and when they are available. Armed with this information, you will be able to offer the best service and make future recommendations to your clients.

Taking payments

It is very important that the receptionist is competent at accurately totalling the client's bill at the end of the service. You must be knowledgeable on the pricing structure for the salon services and retail products. Services and retail products are subject to value added tax (VAT) and prices should be displayed inclusive of VAT. If the prices shown

ACTIVITY

In 2011 the VAT in the UK was calculated at 17.5%. It is currently set at 20% but it may change again in the future. With this in mind, calculate the following bill.

The client's total bill before VAT is £75.00.

1 If VAT returned to 17.5%, what would the total bill be?
2 Calculate the total bill at today's VAT rate of 20%.
3 If VAT increased to 22%, what would the total bill be?

▲ Client buying retail products

HEALTH AND SAFETY

Never put your own safety at risk (or the safety of others) – do not cash up the till with the salon front doors open or unlocked, or in view of the general public.

exclude VAT, you will need to be able to calculate this with a calculator or electronic till. VAT is charged at 20 per cent in addition to the basic cost. If the government changes the VAT amount, you, as the receptionist, will need to be able to revise the prices to reflect this.

Methods of calculating payments

Although working through these tasks and calculating the bills with a calculator is good practice, it is likely that your salon will have an automated computer system that works out the cost for you. To calculate a client's bill you could use:

- a calculator
- a pricing scanner
- a till
- an electronic point of sale (POS) device
- a pen and paper.

Informing clients of costs

When you are confirming the total bill to your client, you should do so politely and courteously. Explain the service cost first, then the cost of any retail products and then give them the overall cost. This will give your client the opportunity to cancel the retail products if the costs are higher than expected. However, with clearly displayed retail product prices and by previously informing clients of the likely charge for the service, you should be able to avoid any embarrassment or surprises regarding the bill.

Handle payments securely

Maintaining salon security is very important, so always keep the till locked and reception desk manned. If the salon has been very busy, then transferring large amounts of cash to the salon safe may be the securest option, or taking the money to the bank and depositing it.

You must ensure that client records and/or credit/debit card payment slips are kept securely in the reception area to keep clients' details confidential. If clients pay by card using a chip and PIN machine, you should discreetly look away as they enter their PIN (personal identification number).

Types of payment

Once you have calculated the cost of the services and any retail goods to be purchased, you will need to establish your client's preferred method of payment and record the sales correctly, following your salon policy.

Payment by cash

If your client chooses to pay with cash, check all notes and coins to verify they are not forged or defaced in any way. There are several ways in which you can check that the notes and coins are genuine:

- The type of paper – does it feel as you would expect?
- Distinct markings on the notes – is the watermark visible? Is the colour accurate? Is the silver strip present throughout the note?
- Is the note still in circulation? Notes are updated from time to time, and there is a period of time where old notes can be used, but after this period, these notes are no longer **legal tender**.
- The weight of a coin – is it heavy enough?
- The markings on the coins – are the correct markings present?

KEY TERM

Legal tender – money that is legal in a given country.

If you are happy that the cash is acceptable, take your client's money and count it, but do not place it in the till until your client has received their change: leave it in sight of both you and the client. Cash payment discrepancies are easier to solve if the money has not been placed in the till, and you can confirm exactly how much money the client gave you.

If you think you have been given a forged/counterfeit note, check the note with your salon manager and inform the client. Politely ask them for an alternative method of payment. Always follow your salon's policy and ensure you know what to do if you encounter cash that is unacceptable or not legal tender.

Once you have calculated the required change, count this out as you hand it to your client, so that you both agree that accurate change has been given. Ask your client to check the change and then issue a receipt.

HANDY HINT

Check your salon's policy for accepting £50 notes and confirming that the notes are genuine.

ACTIVITY

Visit www.bankofengland.co.uk/BANKNOTES/Pages/default.aspx for more information about banknotes.

ACTIVITY

From time to time you will find a forged coin or note. Check your wallet for forged currency and familiarise yourself with the correct markings.

Payment by card

Cards have become very popular and are an easy payment method for clients to use. However, credit cards are costly to the salon and not all salons accept card payments.

If your salon takes card payments and this is your client's chosen payment method, then you need to identify whether your client is using a debit or credit card.

With debit cards the payment is taken immediately from the client's bank account and issued to the salon's bank account when the payment system is processed at the end of the day. Credit card companies request payment from the client on a monthly basis, but pay the salon when the payment system is processed at the end of the day. Therefore, banks often charge salons for this service.

▲ Chip and PIN cards

HANDY HINT

Chip and PIN cards are designed to prevent fraud. Only the cardholder knows the PIN and they are the only person who needs to touch the card, unless there is a query. Remember to look away discreetly when your client enters their PIN.

Gaining electronic authorisation for payment

Your salon will have a floor/salon limit, which states the amount of money the salon can take in one transaction. To accept payments above this, your salon will require authorisation from the card company. You will need to know what the salon's limits are before you process any credit card payments.

The procedure for paying with a debit or credit card is the same, and you will use a chip and PIN machine called either a 'merchant machine', a 'card reader' or a 'chip and PIN terminal'.

Once you have agreed the cost with the client:

1. Key in the amount and press enter.
2. Hand the merchant terminal to the client to insert their card.
3. Ask the client to check the amount, type in their PIN and press 'enter'.
4. Once the card has been authorised, ask the client to remove their card.
5. Issue the client with their copy of the receipt and place the salon copy in the till.

You may need to obtain authorisation from the relevant person when accepting non-cash payments at reception.

ACTIVITY

A walk-in client sees an advert in your window stating 'Buy three products and receive a 25% discount on all three'. If this client buys the products shown below, what is her bill before and after the discount?

Funk Sticks £6.49

Funk Paste £6.99

Funk Gel £5.99

Payment by cash equivalents

Your client may wish to pay with cash equivalents such as:

- gift vouchers
- discount vouchers
- special offer promotions – 'buy three, pay for two' or 'buy one get one free'
- introductory offers
- loyalty card points
- travellers' cheques.

Sale of Goods and Services Act

The Supply of Goods and Services Act 1982 required traders to provide services to a proper standard of workmanship within a reasonable time and for a reasonable charge. In addition, any materials used or goods supplied in providing the service had to be of satisfactory quality.

This Act was replaced with the Consumer Act on 1 October 2015.

HANDY HINT

Before you sell any item of retail, check the item for defects to ensure you are selling a product that is fit for purpose.

Data Protection Act

When working at the reception you are responsible for following those Acts relevant to selling retail and services, ensuring you abide by the salon rules and regulations for confidentiality, as well as following the Data Protection Act. You must also check that your client has had any relevant hair and skin tests to ensure that services can go ahead as planned once the client arrives.

The receptionist has access to the client service records and may prepare the record cards for the stylists. For paper- and computer-based record card systems you and the salon must comply with the Data Protection

Act (DPA). If the salon stores staff or client information on a computer the salon must be registered with the Data Protection Registrar.

The other rules of the DPA state that all records must:

- be kept up to date
- hold accurate information
- be kept in a secure location
- be used for professional purposes only
- not be shared with unauthorised personnel or a third party
- only be kept for as long as the client remains a client
- be disposed of securely, for example, shredded.
- be available for clients to see and access their own client record.

THE HAIR PROFESSIONAL AT WORK

Following the DPA and the salon's policy for client confidentiality maintains professionalism, enhances the salon image and avoids a bad reputation and unnecessary loss of clients. Clients can take legal action against the salon if their personal information is not kept confidential.

Test your knowledge

Question 1

List three types of PPE for the stylist and three types of client protection and state when you would use them.

Question 2

Nina is looking unsure about the services you have discussed with her. What signs and body language is she displaying for you to think this? How will you reassure her and put her at ease?

Question 3

Devon and Jade have had a disagreement. There is conflict and the salon atmosphere is tense and uncomfortable. What advice would you give them to improve their working relationship and ensure the salon is harmonious again?

Question 4

What is the legal significance of completing client records?

Multiple choice questions

5 Are the statements below true or false?
Statement 1: The employer's responsibility, under the Health and Safety at Work Act, is to ensure all staff, clients and visitors are safe.
Statement 2: It is the employee's responsibility to make sure their actions do not put others at risk.

a True True
b True False
c False True
d False False

6 Which two of the following identify what is contained in a CO_2 fire extinguisher and the type of fire it is best used on?

1 Carbon dioxide
2 Carbon monoxide
3 Paper or wood
4 Electrical items

a Carbon dioxide and carbon monoxide
b Carbon monoxide and paper or wood
c Paper or wood and electrical items
d Electrical items and carbon dioxide

7 The acronym SHUD stands for:

a Store, handle, use and dispose
b Stain, hands, use and dispose
c Safe, health, union and directive
d Stain, hands, union and directive

8 Are the statements below true or false?
Statement 1: The Environmental Protection Act requires employers to dispose of waste responsibly.
Statement 2: Information on the health and safety laws can be found at: www.heathandsafety.co.uk

a True, true
b True, false
c False, true
d False, false

9 Are the statements below true or false?
Statement 1: It is better to recycle than to reuse.
Statement 2: Using second hand furniture in a salon can give it a vintage look and also help to save the environment.

a True, true
b True, false
c False, true
d False, false

10 What does the term 'values' refer to?

a Culture and age groups
b Ethnicity and religion
c Possessions and money
d Morals and ethics

11 Which two of the following best describe the term self-manager?

1 Being the first in the salon everyday
2 Taking ownership of responsibilities
3 Being flexible
4 Working safely

a 1 and 2
b 2 and 3
c 3 and 4
d 4 and 1

12 Which of the following is the best way to deal with a client with different values to you?
  a Avoid talking to them so that they don't get upset.
  b Ask detailed questions to try and understand them.
  c Debate with them and try to change their mind.
  d Respect them and adapt to their needs.

13 Why is it important to have commercially viable timescales when working in a salon?
  a To make sure the salon operates smoothly
  b To make sure the salon closes on time
  c To make sure all clients are satisfied
  d To make sure no clients turn up late

14 Why is it important to have a flexible working attitude?
  a To secure a pay rise
  b To keep the salon busy
  c To be able to work under pressure
  d To meet changing demands

CHAPTER 2

GEORGIA FIELDER – FRANCESCO GROUP, NEWPORT

I qualified as an Apprentice in 2015, and it has led me on to many wonderful things including winning the accolade of Newcomer of the Year at the Francesco Group Awards.

When my little sister was diagnosed with leukaemia, I was in low spirits and so went to get my hair done at a Francesco Group salon to feel better. I realised how a simple haircut could make such a difference to a person's emotional state. I've always been a very creative person so I decided that I wanted to use my creativity in a positive way to give people the same feeling I experienced when I left the salon that day.

While training, my biggest challenge was learning how to balance my time between gaining my qualification and my general work within the salon. No matter how busy you are with your own clients, there are always opportunities to learn.

Being an Apprentice allowed me to build relationships with both staff and clients in the salon. I began blow-drying on the shop floor very early in my training; this allowed me to retain my clients as they became my cut and colour clients once I qualified, which made my transition to stylist easier.

Passion and hard work really pay off – if you're passionate and love hair then you'll enjoy your training which makes it much easier. Becoming a hairdresser is difficult, but the job satisfaction makes it all worth it!

Remember, practice makes perfect. When I began hairdressing I was quite an impatient person and I was just desperate to get stuck in. Sometimes it is worth holding back and just practising a few more times; it may be the difference between you passing or failing an assessment. In the long run, you'll be a better hairdresser for taking your time and mastering that skill.

This chapter maps to:

- Unit 1 Consultation (Level 2 Diploma for Hair Professionals – Hairdressing)
- Unit 1 Consultation (Level 2 Diploma for Hair Professionals – Barbering)

INTRODUCTION

If you asked clients what makes a good hairdresser and barber, many would say that effective communication skills are as important as creativity. Most clients return to the same stylist consistently if the relationship between them is strong. The most popular and successful stylists and barbers listen to what their client really wants, discuss how achievable the result is and show a genuine interest in the client and their needs.

Making a client feel good about themselves and a valued customer is as important as making the client look good. Being able to identify barriers to services and products is as important as making recommendations to the client on how to change their image or enhance their look.

After reading this chapter, you will:

- know how to identify the requirements of the client
- be able to carry out consultation services
- know how to examine the hair, skin and scalp
- know how to advise your client and agree services and products.

IDENTIFY THE REQUIREMENTS OF THE CLIENT

Communication is paramount in becoming a 'great' stylist or barber and in this chapter you will learn how to communicate effectively throughout the consultation process and service.

Communicate effectively when carrying out consultation services

You will need to be effective and skilled in your communication with your client from the very beginning of the consultation. Identifying your client's requirements is the most important part of every service, because without this knowledge you cannot meet the client's needs.

▲ Communicate with your client about the services required

Why effective communication is important

The more effective your communication is, the more successful you will be as a stylist or barber. From the moment your client walks through the door, you and the salon staff should make the client feel valued and comfortable. Greet your client warmly and be interested in what they have to say.

You should discreetly look at your client before they are covered with a gown to ascertain their choice of clothing and sense of dress. Some clients will arrive at the salon in their 'comfy' clothes or clothes they think can be spoiled by hair clippings or colour drips without too much upset – so this may not be their normal style of dress. Some may arrive in work wear, which may be very different to their non-work wear, and others may arrive wearing clothing that expresses their outgoing or confident personality.

THE HAIR PROFESSIONAL AT WORK

A professional stylist will observe a client's dress sense but be open minded about their chosen style and not make judgements or assumptions about their appearance.

Your client may be nervous about their hair appointment or excited about a new look; it is your job to fulfil their wishes and effective communication is vital for this to happen. A happy client is highly likely to become a regular visitor to the salon and a loyal customer, whereas an unsatisfied client is likely to tell their friends, which could be damaging to the salon's reputation.

▲ Unsatisfied clients can affect the success of the business

Effective consultation techniques

Every single head of hair you work on will be different, as will every single client.

What makes people unique?

- Personalities – people can be laid-back, excitable, anxious or even difficult and **cantankerous**
- Cultural background – nationality, ethnicity, race, up-bringing, **socioeconomic factors**
- Religious background
- Life experiences as people grow up and become older
- Health and life barriers
- Gender.

We live in a diverse world and when you are communicating with your clients you may be from a different background, social class or ethnicity, or you may hold different beliefs to your client. Under no circumstances should you show disrespect to your clients, however they differ from you.

KEY TERMS

Cantankerous – argumentative, difficult or unreasonable.

Socioeconomic factors – factors related to an individual's income, health status, environment, education level, social class, etc.

Different cultural and religious backgrounds

Some people have very strong views and opinions on religion or politics. Avoid discussions around these topics as they can quickly become heated if there are differences of opinion, making it uncomfortable for other clients and staff nearby. You should keep your personal views to yourself and respect the views and opinions of your clients. Ideally, steer conversations away from politics and religion.

Age, disability and gender

Your clients will vary in age, from young children having their first haircut in the salon/barbers to elderly clients who may need assistance moving around the salon environment or hearing what you are saying. Always adapt how you speak to suit the client you are communicating with: be jolly and use simple words with children, but more professional and discuss more topical subjects with mature clients.

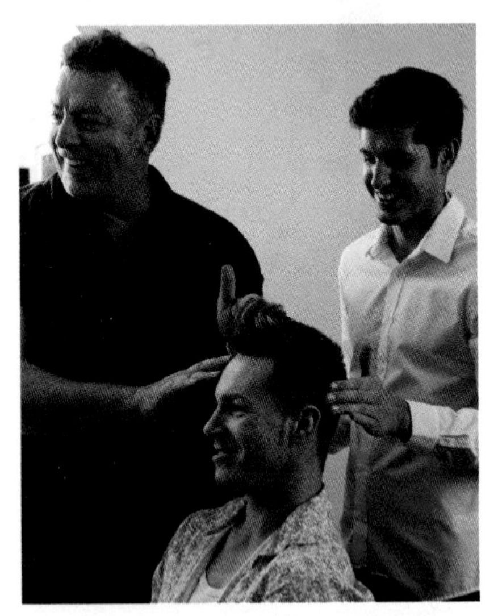

▲ Barber shop banter

Some clients may have mobility issues or use a wheelchair. Always explain how you can assist these clients and advise whether the salon can adapt a service for a client using a wheelchair. Many disabilities are not visual, but clients may still need support and a patient stylist. A client with a stutter or speech impediment will be made to feel worse if you are impatient or try to finish their sentences for them. Be respectful and patient and ask how you can help your clients.

You will have male and female clients, or if you are a barber your clients will be male, but some of their partners may be female, so your topics of conversation need to suit both genders. Banter is often used in a barber shop, more so than a salon, but conversation should be professional and not offensive to those nearby.

Questioning and listening skills to find out information

Most of your client communication will be through verbal discussion as you question your clients on their service needs. However, you will also use non-verbal communication as you use body language to enhance your interaction.

Verbal communication

Questions to ask your clients include:

- What service would they like and why?
- How would they like their hair to look and why?
- What restrictions do they have, for example, wanting to keep the length, lifestyle restrictions such as a need for hair that is long enough to be able to put it up for work, or short enough to wash and go after a morning gym workout?
- Whether they have any problems with their hair, for example, their current style, curls, waves, straightness of hair, length or layers, coarse wiry hair, fine flyaway hair, white hair, oily hair, abundant or sparse hair, previous colour or chemical service, condition of hair.
- Whether they have any problems with their scalp – this may include allergies, sensitivities, ailments, irritations, disorders or general concerns.

Always speak clearly and politely to your client and ask questions in client-friendly language, avoiding jargon and complicated hairdressing terminology.

▲ Speaking face to face with a client

Non-verbal communication – body language

When speaking to your client you will need to show you are listening to what they are saying by exhibiting positive body language:

- Smiling indicates you are friendly, happy and approachable, and are positive about what is being said or agreed.
- Nodding your head and maintaining eye contact shows you are listening to your client; an open body posture shows you are alert and ready for the task in hand.
- Using hand gestures can help to clarify key points and give clearer meaning to the conversation.

THE HAIR PROFESSIONAL AT WORK

Remember to read your client's body language for signs of uncertainty. Crossed arms and a closed-in body posture indicate defensiveness and a closed mind – your client is not agreeing to what you are suggesting.

Talking with hands over the mouth can indicate dishonesty: maybe there is colour on the client's hair despite what they say and you should carry out hair tests to be certain.

Scratching behind their ear or rubbing the back of the neck suggests your client is uncertain and really not sure this is what they want.

ACTIVITY

Write down three open questions and three closed questions you could ask the following clients:

- Frederique has dense, wavy, coarse hair and has booked in for a cutting service.
- Jade has shiny type 1 dense hair and has booked in for a colouring service.

▲ Read your client's body language for signs of uncertainty

Why it is important to encourage and allow time for clients to ask questions

During your consultation, allow time for your client to ask questions; you should encourage them to do so, so they are clear on what has been suggested and agreed. Allowing your client a chance to ask questions should ensure they are happy with the ideas and recommendations put forward and are aware of the process to follow.

HANDY HINT

For more information on effective communication, look at Chapter 1 'Appropriate way of communicating with clients'.

Explain the importance of following current relevant legislation

You are required to comply with the requirements of all Acts and regulations relating to health and safety:

- Health and Safety at Work Act – to maintain your own safety and the safety of those around you, avoid taking risks that put you in danger and report any concerns to your manager.
- Personal Protective Equipment Regulations – to ensure you always wear PPE when appropriate.
- Reporting of Injuries, Diseases and Dangerous Occurrences Regulations – to report any accidents that you or your client have in the workplace/salon.
- Regulatory Reform (Fire Safety) Order – to evacuate yourself and your client and to raise the alarm and call the emergency services in the event of a fire.

▲ Take action if you see a hazard!

ACTIVITY

List one rule for each of the Health and Safety Acts and regulations – if you need a refresher on this information refer back to Chapter 1.

▲ Only sell products that are fit for purpose and of satisfactory quality

▲ Protect your client's information at reception and follow the requirements of the Data Protection Act

- Manual Handling Operations Regulations – to remember to bend your legs and keep your back straight when lifting a bulky box; if an item is too heavy to lift, ask for help – do not strain your back.
- Control of Substances Hazardous to Health Regulations – to store substances correctly, use and handle them according to instructions and dispose of them in the correct manner.
- Electricity at Work Regulations – to check wires and electrical equipment prior to use, turning them off afterwards, and to ask for training on equipment if required.
- Environmental Protection Act – to avoid wasting water and energy and to follow correct methods of disposal of waste.

THE HAIR PROFESSIONAL AT WORK

As your confidence and experience grows, your job will become ever more exciting and you may wish to increase your working hours. However, you must remember the rules of the Working Time Directives:

- Those aged 16 to 17 years can only work an 8-hour day and a maximum of 40 hours per week and cannot opt out of this.
- Those aged 18 and over are not expected to work more than 48 hours per week, but can choose to opt out of this ruling.

When carrying out hairdressing services or providing advice and recommendations you must adhere to the following Acts and regulations:

- Cosmetic Products Regulations
- Sale of Goods Act
- Consumer Contract Regulations
- Trade Descriptions Act
- Consumer Protection legislation
- Date Protection Act

Salon rules for maintaining confidentiality and privacy

The salon holds data from client records and the Data Protection Act protects these personal details. Always update client records and keep them secure so a third party does not have access to them. Only authorised staff should have access to a client's details and they must be used for official use only.

Avoid discriminating against clients with illnesses and disabilities

As mentioned earlier, you may have clients with visual or non-visual disabilities or illnesses and it is important that you do not discriminate against them. Disability is one of the protected characteristics under the Equality Act, which means it is illegal for a salon to discriminate against a client because of a disability.

Salons and their staff are expected to do whatever is reasonable to ensure a client with a disability can receive the same service (where possible) as a non-disabled person. However, if a client is a wheelchair user and the salon is located above ground level with no lift access, then it is acceptable to turn the client away, provided a clear explanation why is given. If the salon is at ground level and the client's wheelchair can safely move around the salon space (for example, it is possible for the wheelchair to easily exit through the fire exit in the event of a fire), then a salon should accommodate the client. If the client were unable to leave the wheelchair for a shampoo service, it would be reasonable to ask the client to come to the salon with pre-shampooed hair and offer cutting and drying services only.

ACTIVITY

Research visual and non-visual disabilities and identify how your salon could adapt a service or make improvements in the salon to accommodate a potential client with these disabilities.

Visual aids that can support client consultation

Clients may bring in images, photos or magazines to show you a style or colour they would like to have. The salon could use a tablet, PC or mobile phone to show images to a client. Internet searches for hair images will bring up many style options. These images will be forever changing, so you could save images to a virtual pin board by subscribing to Pinterest or opening an Instagram account. These are popular ways to hold and store images in folders and to follow like-minded people posting photos of their work on the application.

▲ For more information visit https://uk.pinterest.com or https://www.instagram.com

▲ Use a tablet to search the internet for images or use an app like Instagram

The use of colour charts is very important when discussing a colouring service with your client. Most manufacturers have colour charts with removable samples that you can drape through the client's hair and against their skin to check that the colours suit their skin tone and their existing hair colour.

EXAMINE THE HAIR, SKIN AND SCALP

When you examine the hair, skin and scalp you will need to follow health and safety and work within the limits of your authority, referring problems you cannot deal with to your manager, such as hair disorders or suspected infections/infestations. You will carry out visual tests on the hair and checks on the scalp, as well as be able to identify some infections and infestations.

Responsibilities for health and safety

As you progress with your career you will take on additional responsibilities. As an assistant you have very little responsibility but when you become a stylist or barber you have a greater responsibility towards your clients to keep them safe.

Your responsibilities under current health and safety legislation

You must follow all the health and safety Acts and regulations to ensure you keep yourself and those around you safe from harm. If you notice a problem you must act quickly to solve the problem or refer it to your manager. You are expected to respect the rules and responsibilities of the employee under the terms of the Health and Safety at Work Act (see Chapter 1 for more information).

▲ Ensure your image reflects well on the salon

Maintaining your own personal hygiene, protection and appearance

Your personal hygiene is important since poor hygiene can cause offence to your clients, reflect badly on the salon image and risk cross-contamination if you attend work with an infectious condition.

You should always protect your clothes from damage and your hands from dermatitis by wearing gloves and using barrier cream and hand cream. If you are asthmatic you should use a particle mask when mixing up chemicals to protect your lungs. You have a duty of care to your clients and you must always protect their clothes and skin too. When attending work you should ensure your appearance is appropriate and upholds your salon's expectations to enhance their image.

Salon procedures and manufacturer's instructions in relation to conducting tests

Salon procedures and manufacturers' instructions will vary, but whichever salon you work in and whichever manufacturer's products you use, you must familiarise yourself with the rules and instructions. Every product or substance has its own COSHH data sheet, which must be followed; the instructions will either be in the box or on the side of the box, bottle or tub.

When carrying out tests on the hair and skin you must be particularly careful and follow the instructions accurately – an incorrect test for the skin could be fatal if a client has a severe allergic reaction.

When and how tests are carried out

You must carry out tests before and during all services. These tests must be completed following the manufacturers' instructions to ensure that you follow health and safety guidelines. You must record the results on the client record card and seek guidance from the relevant person if any **adverse** reactions occur. Remember to work within the limits of your authority and report all adverse reactions.

The tables below describe the necessary tests.

Test	When to carry out the test	How to carry out the test	Why is it important to carry out the test?
Porosity test	Before any service on dry hair.	Take a few hairs and slide your fingers up the hair shaft from point to root.	To test the cuticle layer to identify if the cuticles are smooth or rough.
Elasticity test	Before any service on wet hair.	Take one or two hairs and mist them slightly with water. Then stretch the hair a couple of times between your finger and thumb.	To test the strength of the cortex.
Incompatibility test	Before chemical services, if you suspect **metallic salts** are present in the hair.	Take a small cutting of the client's hair and place it in a solution of 20 ml liquid 6% peroxide and 1 ml of perm solution (or a solution of 20:1 liquid peroxide and ammonium hydroxide). Leave for up to 30 minutes.	To identify if any metallic salts are present which would react with professional chemical products.

→

Test	When to carry out the test	How to carry out the test	Why is it important to carry out the test?
Strand test	During the colouring or lightening service	Wipe off the colour or lightener from a few strands of hair.	To see if the colour result has been achieved, or if the lightener development is sufficient.
Skin test	24–48 hours before most colours.	Always follow the manufacturer's instructions as these may vary. As a guide only: Clean an area in the inner elbow or behind the ear. Then apply the client's chosen colour (mixed with peroxide if stated in the manufacturer's instructions) to the area and leave it exposed to dry.	To test for an allergic reaction or sensitivity to the product.
Development test (curl or curl reduction)	During perming or relaxing services.	Wipe off or rinse the product from a few strands of hair. Check the degree of curl or straightness.	To see whether the curl or relaxing result is sufficient

KEY TERMS

Adverse – unfavourable, poor, difficult or not suitable.

Metallic salts – these can be found in products which contain lead compounds or a variety of other metals, depending on the shade of colour required.

HANDY HINT

Follow the rules of the EU directive – before you colour the hair, remember to ask the age of your client and check their ID. This will ensure you are following your MFIs and the law by confirming your client is aged 16 years or older.

How test results influence services

Test	Expected results of the test	Influence and impact on services
Porosity test	Hair cuticles will feel smooth if the hair is non-porous, or rough or raised if the hair is porous.	Impacts on all services: Damage to client's hair might occur or the desired outcome might not be achieved. Porosity levellers may be required prior to any chemical service such as a perm, colour, relaxing service. Hair may snag and tangle during hair extensions, cutting and styling services.
Elasticity test	As a guide, normal straight/wavy hair, when wet, should stretch about 30 per cent more than its original length and then return when released.	Impacts on all services: Damage to client's hair might occur or the desired outcome might not be achieved. Penetrating treatments may be required for a period of time prior to and after the service. Use semi-permanent or quasi-permanent colours only. Take care with tension during hair extensions, cutting and styling services.
Incompatibility test	If metallic salts are present the hair may change colour, the solution may bubble and fizz and/or give off heat.	Impacts on chemical services: Damage to and/or disintegration of client's hair could occur. Chemical services may not be carried out, but a semi-permanent product could be used.
Strand test	If permanent colour is developed, then the desired result should be achieved. If the bleach is regularly checked, the level of lift should be achieved without damage to the hair. Further development may be required if the colour result has not been achieved.	Impacts on colour services: Damage to and/or disintegration of client's hair could occur if colour left on for too long. The desired outcome may not be achieved if the colour is not left on long enough.
Skin test	A positive reaction is red skin and/or sore areas that may weep and itch. A negative reaction is no change to the skin area.	Impacts on colour services: An allergic reaction, anaphylactic shock, contact dermatitis or damage to the client's skin could occur. Services may not proceed; re-test with quasi-permanent and semi-permanent products to identify if these services can be carried out instead.
Development test (curl or curl reduction)	If desired level of curl/relaxing has been achieved, the result is positive. If it has not been achieved further development time may be required.	Impacts on perming and relaxing services: Damage to and/or disintegration of client's hair could occur if perm solution is left on for too long. The desired outcome may not be achieved if the solution is not left on for long enough.

Identify factors that may limit or affect services

It is important to identify factors that may limit or affect services to ensure that the hair, skin and scalp are suitable for the service required.

The following factors can impact on the services you recommend, as well as the products, tools and equipment you may use:

- hair classification
- hair characteristics
- adverse hair, skin and scalp conditions
- incompatibility of previous services and products used
- test results
- client's lifestyle.

Impact of hair classifications on services

Classifications refer to the type of hair the client has, such as straight, wavy, curly or very curly hair.

Hair classification	Impact on services
Straight hair – type 1    ▲ Asian hair	Can be difficult to curl and may affect the styling of hair. May be resistant to chemicals such as colour and perming products. When cutting the hair, straight hair can show cutting marks on the hair.
Wavy hair – type 2   ▲ Caucasian hair	Can be great hair to work with, but coarse wavy hair can make styling more challenging at times. When cutting the hair use products which may reduce any frizziness and aid control. Coarse hair may be a little resistant to chemical processes.

Hair classification	Impact on services
Curly hair – type 3	The styling of curly hair needs products and control with styling tools. Hair will appear shorter once cut, so less tension will be required. Hair may be delicate and take quickly to colour and chemical processes.
Very curly hair – type 4 ▲ African-type hair	Very curly hair needs lots of control when styling and products designed for curly hair. Hair will tangle easily and spring up when cutting. Hair is fragile and care must be taken with chemical processes.

Hair classifications will affect various hair services, from drying and styling, setting, dressing and cutting to colouring and perming the hair.

Impact of hair characteristics on services

Hair characteristics include density, texture, elasticity, porosity, condition and hair growth patterns.

Hair characteristic	Impact on services
Density ▲ Sparse	Hair density refers to the amount of hair and is described as **sparse**, average or abundant. Sparse hair often means the hair is fine and there is not a lot of it covering the head. The scalp may be visible through the hair, less product will be required and the types of hairstyles that will suit this density of hair will need to be considered.
▲ Abundant	Abundant hair means the client has a full head of hair; this may be fine or coarse in texture but there is lots of it. Abundant hair requires more products, more drying time and will take longer for services to be carried out. Cutting techniques will need to be considered as the hair may need to be thinned out.

Hair characteristic	Impact on services
Hair texture  ▲ Fine	Hair texture refers to the thickness of each strand of hair and is described as fine, medium or coarse. Fine hair has a small circumference and fewer layers of cuticle scales.
 ▲ Medium	Medium hair is greater in circumference than fine hair with an average number of layers.
 ▲ Coarse	Coarse hair has a large circumference and the most layers of cuticle scales. Fine hair will absorb chemicals much faster than coarse hair because there are fewer cuticle scales. Coarse hair can often be resistant to chemicals. A porosity test can be carried out on all hair textures to check whether these cuticle scales are rough and open, or smooth and closed. 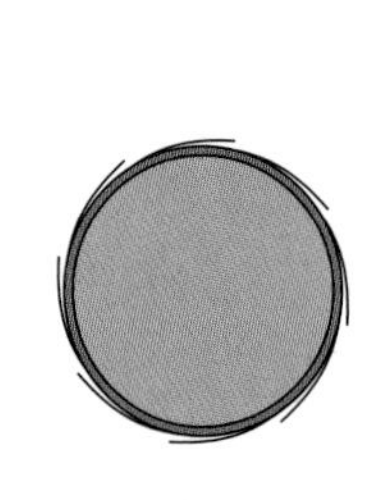 Very fine hair 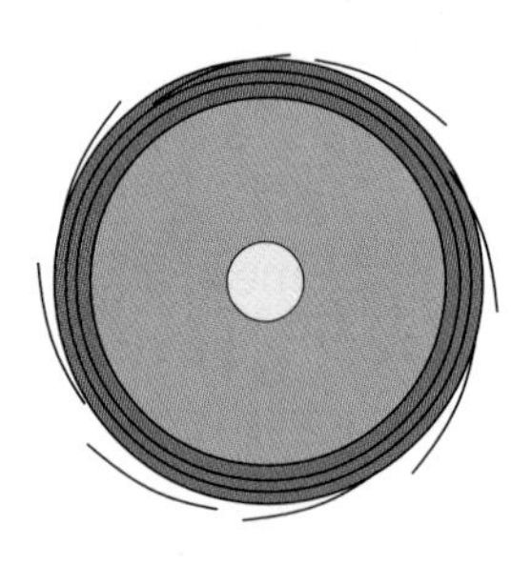 Average hair 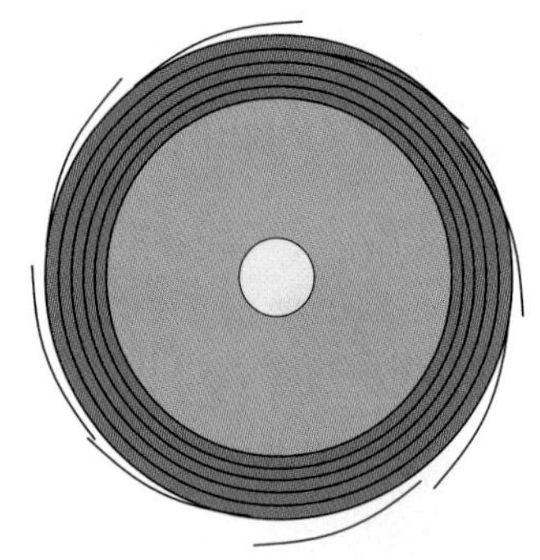 Very coarse hair
Elasticity 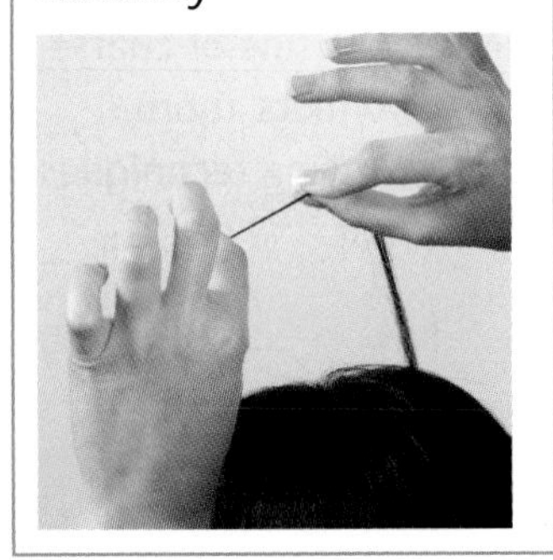	Elasticity of hair refers to how weak or strong the hair is and whether the cortex layer has been damaged. When working with hair that is of weak elasticity you will need to consider whether the hair is strong enough to take additional chemicals or whether to advise on an alternative product, such as a semi-permanent colour. You will also need to consider the choice of styling products and decide on how much tension can be applied to the hair when cutting and styling.

Hair characteristic	Impact on services
Porosity 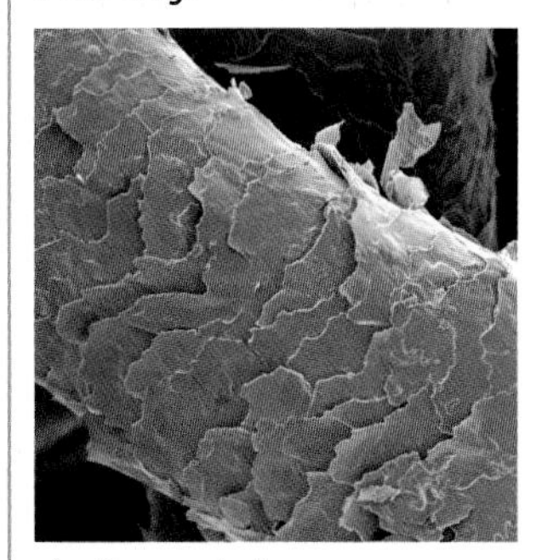 ▲ Porous hair	Porosity of hair refers to the cuticle layers – if the cuticles are damaged and open then hair is **porous**; the cuticles can also be normal/non-porous or closely compacted/resistant. Porous hair will absorb chemicals much faster and may not be able to handle any additional chemicals. As the cuticles are open the hair will tangle more easily and you must consider this when combing or styling the hair.
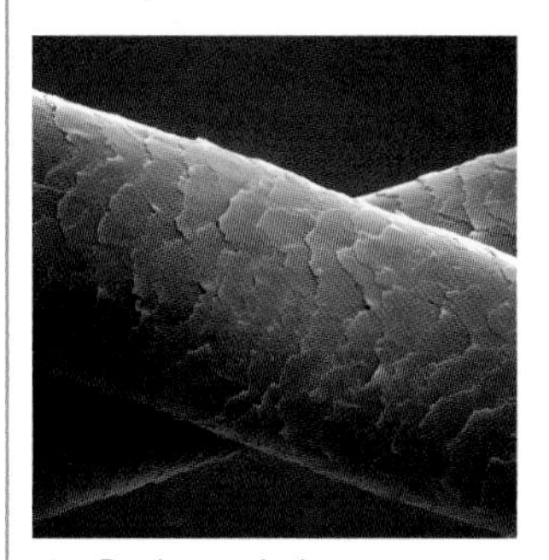 ▲ Resistant hair	Resistant hair may be resilient to some colouring or perming products and suitable techniques will need to be considered. Hair may be coarser and it will take longer to dry as it holds on to moisture.
Condition  ▲ Chemically damaged hair	The condition of your client's hair can vary greatly; it may be normal, naturally dry, oily or damaged (by chemicals, environment, heat or lifestyle). If hair is damaged you will need to identify how it has been damaged and advise your client on how to prevent further damage and improve their hair condition. Consider whether the hair is able to have any further chemical services or whether a course of treatments is required. Damaged hair is likely to be either porous or have weak elasticity – or both.
Hair growth patterns  ▲ Cowlick	Hair growth patterns consist of cowlick, widow's peak, double crown and nape whorl. Cowlick – found at the front hairline, this hair stands straight or lies at an odd angle and affects whether a fringe can be worn and how it is worn.

→

Hair characteristic	Impact on services
 Widow's peak	Widow's peak – also found at the front hairline, the hair grows into a point near or at the centre of the front hairline. This can affect choice of hairstyles and fringe options.
Double crown	Double crown – found at the crown area and can also be one crown whorl. This affects how the hair will sit around the crown area. The length of the crown must be considered when cutting and styling.
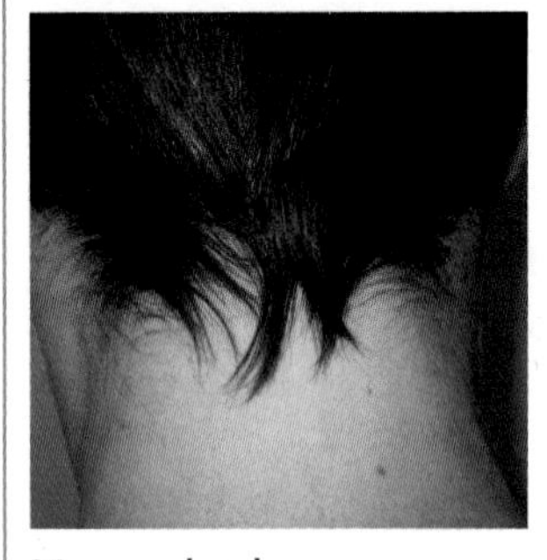 Nape whorl	Nape whorl – found at the nape area, the hair grows into a whorl direction and can affect shorter hairstyles. Sometimes one side of the nape hairline sits differently to the other, so always check both sides of the nape before cutting hair short, or styling hair into up dos.

KEY TERMS

Sparse – thin or scarce.

Porous – absorbent.

ACTIVITY

Consider how the above characteristics would affect the following services:

- Restyle
- Woven highlights with lightener

Adverse hair, skin and scalp conditions

If hair is physically or chemically damaged, further services could make the condition of the hair deteriorate or cause breakage. Physical damage can be caused by backcombing the hair, overuse of electrical heat appliances or excessive brushing. Chemical damage can be from colouring, bleaching and perming the hair, but also from chemicals like chlorine if your client swims regularly.

Adverse skin and scalp conditions such as psoriasis, cysts, impetigo, scars and moles, infections and infestations can all affect whether a service can be carried out, especially if the client's condition is infectious. Some non-infectious conditions do not affect the service but extra care must be taken to avoid causing discomfort or aggravating a condition, such as avoid catching your comb on moles and skin tags and applying styling products near the scalp areas for clients with psoriasis and eczema.

Incompatibility of previous services and products

There may be factors that affect potential services because treatments and products have already been used on the hair. For example, tint will not lift tint, so if a client wants a full head permanent colour but already has tint on their hair, the desired look might not be achieved.

Although it is rare, some products will react with other products on the hair and could cause the hair to break and disintegrate. Metallic salts that are found in a few hair colouring products available in high street shops will react with the chemicals in professional brands. If in doubt about what is on the hair, always carry out an incompatibility test.

Some clients' hair may not be suitable for further chemical treatments, for example if the hair is in poor condition as a result of previous services or products.

ACTIVITY

In pairs, discuss which services could cause barriers to future services and may not be compatible with the client's requirements.

Test results

The results of all hair and skin tests need to be considered. If a client has had an allergic reaction to a colour then alternative services need to be discussed. A client whose hair has been identified as porous, weak or incompatible will also need to be offered alternative services such as a semi-permanent colour and further discussions on what service is most suitable for their hair.

HANDY HINT

Factors are anything which could influence or affect the hairdressing service.

THE HAIR PROFESSIONAL AT WORK

You should always refer to a client's records to check if there are, or have been, any factors that may affect the service.

Lifestyle

For most services, you should consider your client's lifestyle to identify whether they will be able to maintain their hair between visits.

It may be inappropriate to recommend a vibrant fashion colour service to a client whose workplace would not allow it, so ask about your client's work or lifestyle and if there are any restrictions you need to know about. Equally, if your client has a shy personality, a vibrant fashion look that draws attention to them would not be suitable.

A mother with a hectic lifestyle might not have the luxury of the time needed for a high-maintenance hairstyle, so a quick-style look is what is really required. A keen swimmer should not be advised on colouring services that would affect the condition of the hair in chlorinated water.

▲ Outdoor activities can be hard on the hair

KEY TERM

Psoriasis – a non-contagious skin disease, which causes patches of red, itchy, flaky and scaly skin.

ACTIVITY

Consider the products and/or services that may be affected by the following lifestyles:

- a busy parent
- an avid sportsperson
- a student
- a flight attendant
- a salesperson.

Recognise hair, skin and scalp problems and the necessary actions to take

A client with a scalp problem, such as **psoriasis**, can have a cut and blow-dry but you may decide that colouring treatments are best avoided. Other hair, skin or scalp problems may require further treatments and services may need to be avoided.

You must be able to recognise most hair, skin and scalp problems to prevent the spread of infections and infestations and to avoid making conditions worse by adding chemicals to damaged hair or a sensitive scalp. You must be careful not to diagnose a condition to your client, however; instead refer them to either a pharmacy, GP or trichologist (a person who specialises in the care of the scalp and hair).

Hair problems

Hair problems may consist of damaged hair caused by physical or chemical treatments or hair defects. The table below describes some hair problems and possible treatments.

Adverse hair problem	How to recognise the hair problem	Cause	Symptoms	Possible treatment
Fragilitas crinium	Split ends	Physical damage or chemical treatments.	Dry, split ends, damage to cuticle and cortex at the end of the hair shaft.	Regular use of surface conditioners and deep-penetrating conditioners improve the condition. Cutting the hair removes the split end.

Adverse hair problem	How to recognise the hair problem	Cause	Symptoms	Possible treatment
Trichorrhexis nodosa	Swollen, hardened areas of the hair shaft	Physical damage or chemical treatments.	The hardened swelling can break off and cause the hair to split.	Regular use of surface conditioners and deep-penetrating conditioners improve the condition. Cutting the hair may help to remove the damaged area.
Monilethrix	Beaded hair shaft	A rare hair defect that is hereditary and caused by an uneven production of keratin.	Very weak hair that may break off near the root. The hair feels bumpy where the 'beads' are formed.	Treat with caution and care. Conditioners and treatments may help. Refer to a GP.

Recognise non-infectious skin and scalp problems

Skin and scalp problems include infections or infestations as well as non-infectious conditions such as alopecia.

Adverse skin and scalp problems	How to recognise the problem	Impact on services
Eczema	Red, inflamed, itchy skin, sometimes split and weeping.	Refer client to GP or dermatologist. Salon services can be carried out but avoid chemicals on any broken skin. (If weeping, then the eczema is infected and services must not be carried out.)

Adverse skin and scalp problems	How to recognise the problem	Impact on services
Alopecia	There are many types of alopecia: Alopecia areata usually starts with one or more small round areas of smooth bald patches, which can be on the head or anywhere on the body. Scarring alopecia/cicatricial alopecia is caused by scarring from burns, injuries or infections. Male pattern baldness (androgenic alopecia) also referred to as the Hamilton pattern of baldness. This occurs as a result of changes in the hormone androgen. Female pattern baldness (female pattern hair loss) is also referred to as Lugwig's classification hair loss – this hair loss is genetic and not generally related to the androgen hormone.	When working on a client who has alopecia areata you will need to consider the hair length and layers to help disguise the hair loss. Where possible, avoid chemical treatments while the client has this disorder. Clients with male or female pattern baldness may prefer to keep the hair length long enough to disguise the hair loss or go shorter around the thinning area to give the rest of the hair the appearance of being thicker.
Psoriasis	Silvery yellow scales and thickening of the skin.	Psoriasis can cause discomfort to the client and the scales of skin overlap the hair and may cause uneven haircuts. If the skin is open and weeping do not carry out any services.
Scars	Healing tissue that has become thickened and raised.	During the healing process this area may be tender, delicate and open to infection. Once healed, proceed with normal services.
Keloid	Overgrown area of scar tissue that encases the original wound. More common on people with darker skin.	Generally normal services can resume, but extra care should be taken with tools and equipment in case the area is sensitive or protrudes slightly.

Adverse skin and scalp problems	How to recognise the problem	Impact on services
Moles	Dark coloured skin lesions, either under or on the skin. Most moles are caused by skin growths; changes in moles should be examined by a doctor.	Normal services can be carried out, although take care not to catch the mole with hairdressing tools, as this will cause discomfort to your client and the mole could then be susceptible to infection.
Cysts	A small pea-sized, non-cancerous lump that is filled with pus or fluid. The most common cyst is a non-infectious sebaceous cyst.	These are often painless and rarely affect services. However they can be painful when knocked, so take care with clippers, combs and tools, etc. Avoid services if the cyst has become infected.
Skin tags	Small, flesh-coloured or brown growths that hang off the skin – common around eyelids, neck and folds of skin.	These are generally painless and rarely affect services. However, take care with tools to prevent catching the skin tag and causing discomfort to the client.

Recognise infections and infestations which must be reported

If your client has an infection or infestation, you will need to report this to your manager/supervisor diplomatically. You do not need to report any conditions that are not contagious.

Infection or infestation	How to recognise the problem	Impact on services
Ringworm/tinea capitis	Ringworm – red ring surrounding a grey patch of skin, sometimes seen with broken hairs.	Fungal infection – no services can be offered or provided. Refer client to their GP.

→

Infection or infestation	How to recognise the problem	Impact on services
Impetigo	Yellow crusty spots on the skin.	Infectious condition caused by a bacterial infection. No services can be carried out.
Scabies	A very itchy rash in the folds of the skin, normally the midriff or inside of arms and thighs.	Infestation of an itch mite, burrowing into the skin and laying its eggs. Treatments cannot be carried out in the salon.
Folliculitis	Inflammation of the hair follicles.	A bacterial infection, which can be caused by harsh physical or chemical actions. No salon services to be offered. Refer to GP.
Dandruff/pityriasis capitis	The most common type is dry dandruff which is recognised as a white, dry, scaling, flaky dead skin cells. Fungal or yeast dandruff is recognised by the appearance of yellowy flakes accompanied by a smell. It is sometimes referred to as seborrheic dermatitis.	Dry dandruff is non-contagious and non-infectious and is caused by an over-production of skin cells. It can also be stress-related or caused by irritants. Dry dandruff can be treated in the salon using a moisturising shampoo. Fungal dandruff is non-contagious to the stylist but can be infectious and spread around the client's face and skin. The condition is a fungal/yeast infection in the sebaceous gland areas and will require a medicated or an antifungal shampoo or cream. Treatment from the client's GP should be recommended to prevent the condition spreading to their face.

Infection or infestation	How to recognise the problem	Impact on services
In-growing hair	Also known as razor bumps, these are hairs that grow inwards and cause a mild infection or discomfort.	Non-infectious as long as the blocked follicle has not become infected. Generally a normal service can continue if it is not infected.
Head lice/pediculosis capitis ▲ Microscopic view: nits ▲ Microscopic view: louse	Head lice and nits (eggs)	Contagious – risk of infestation and cross-contamination. The head louse feeds off the blood in the scalp and lays its eggs on the hair close to the warmth of the scalp. No salon services to be offered. Refer client to pharmacy.

ACTIVITY

Identify hair and scalp factors that you could deal with by yourself and could advise the client on the best outcome. Then identify factors that you would need to refer to the appropriate person.

ACTIVITY

Using your salon's list of services, identify which products you could use and which services you could recommend to clients who have the following adverse hair, skin and scalp conditions:

- allergic reaction to permanent tint
- metallic salts identified during an incompatibility test
- weak elasticity
- alopecia areata
- infected scalp cyst
- scalp moles
- impetigo

HANDY HINT

'Infectious' means 'contagious', so these conditions can be passed from one person to another. Infestations are parasites living on the body in large numbers and are also contagious. Salon services must not be carried out on clients with infectious conditions.

ACTIVITY

Research other infectious and non-infectious conditions, such as furunculosis, sycosis, tinea pedis, herpes simplex and herpes zoster.

▲ Advise your client on services and products

THE HAIR PROFESSIONAL AT WORK

Once you have listened to the client's wishes and discussed the best outcomes for their hair, you should make your recommendations. Your suggestions should be based on what will produce the best results, taking into consideration the client's hair characteristics and classifications.

ADVISE YOUR CLIENT AND AGREE SERVICES AND PRODUCTS

To be able to advise your client and agree on the best service to carry out and the products to use, you must be able to understand the:

- different characteristics and classifications of hair
- basic structure of hair and skin
- growth cycle of hair
- services and products available in your salon
- legal requirements you must follow when advising on products and services
- salon pricing system and how to calculate for services
- importance of providing aftercare
- importance of completing record cards accurately.

HANDY HINT

The different types of hair characteristics include density, texture, elasticity, porosity, condition and hair growth patterns. These were covered in depth earlier in this chapter.

Different hair characteristics and classifications

Every client is unique and every head of hair is too. When you identify the characteristics and classifications of the hair in front of you, you equip yourself with the most important knowledge of your client's hair. That knowledge empowers you with a clearer understanding of what would work best for this particular head of hair.

Hair classifications

Hair classification	Definition	Characteristics of the hair type
Straight hair – type 1	Fine/thin straight hair which tends to be very soft, shiny and oily; it can be difficult to hold a curl. Medium hair generally has lots of volume and body. Coarse straight hair is normally extremely straight and difficult to curl.	Asian hair is very straight and grows directly up from the hair follicle. It is round shaped and has about 11 layers of cuticle scales. The more cuticle scales the hair has the more resistant the hair will be to chemicals and to styling. Straight hair is often more oily in condition than other hair types, because oil from the sebaceous glands can travel more easily along the hair shaft.

Hair classification	Definition	Characteristics of the hair type
Wavy hair – type 2	Fine/thin wavy hair has a definite 's' pattern and you can normally accomplish various styles. Medium wavy hair tends to be frizzy and a little resistant to styling. Coarse wavy hair is also resistant to styling and normally very frizzy; it tends to have thicker waves.	**Caucasian** or European hair is generally referred to as wavy; this is because of the way the hair grows out of the hair follicle. The hair shaft is oval with around four to seven layers of cuticle scales. In straight and wavy hair, the follicles are more or less vertical to the surface of the scalp. The angle of the hair follicle determines the natural wave pattern of the hair.
Curly hair – type 3	Loose curls – the hair tends to have a combination texture. It can be thick and full with lots of body, with a definite 's' pattern. It also tends to be frizzy. Tight curls – the hair also tends to have a combination texture, with a medium amount of curl.	Caucasian or European hair can be naturally curly, as well as the hair of people with mixed race or **dual heritage**. Curly hair has hair follicles that grow from the scalp almost parallel to the surface of the scalp.
Very curly hair – type 4	Soft curly hair tends to be very fragile, tightly coiled and has a more defined curly pattern. Wiry hair also tends to be very fragile and tightly coiled; however, it has a less defined curly pattern and instead has more of a 'z' pattern shape.	African-type hair is very curly and grows out of the follicle at an acute angle. The hair shaft is kidney shaped with around seven to eleven layers of cuticle scales. As the hair's oil cannot travel so easily along the hair shaft, the curlier the hair, the drier the hair tends to be.

The shape of the hair shaft is determined by the shape of the hair follicle:

- people with straight or wavy hair have typically round or oval shaped hair follicles
- people with curly or very curly hair have follicles which are kidney shaped or **elliptical**.

Your hair shape is determined by your hair follicles, which vary in size, shape and thickness due to genetics.

Straight hair	Wavy hair			Wavy-curly hair		Tight-curly hair	Kinky-curly hair	Kinky hair	Z-pattern hair
1	2A	2B	2C	3A	3B	3C	4A	4B	4C

▲ Hair types

KEY TERMS

Caucasian – description of people of Northern European origin with lighter skin tone.

Dual heritage – having parents from two different ethnic or cultural backgrounds.

Elliptical – oval shaped.

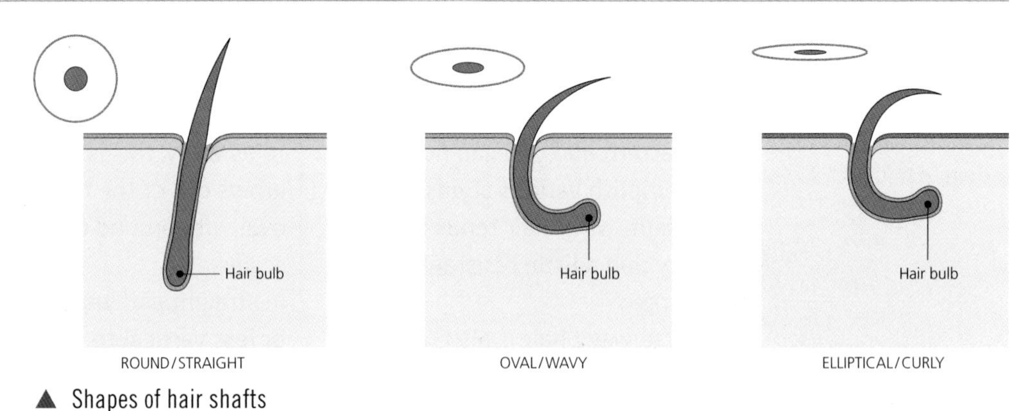

▲ Shapes of hair shafts

HANDY HINT

When referring to clients' skin colour and hair type you must ensure you use terminology that will not offend your clients. Clients with dual heritage are often referred to as 'multi-racial', 'mixed race' or 'bi-racial' and these terms are deemed to be politically correct and non-offensive. Clients with African-type hair often self-identify as 'black'.

The more kidney shaped/elliptical the shaft is, the curlier the hair. The cross-sectional shape also determines the amount of shine the hair has. Straighter hair is shinier because sebum from the sebaceous gland (an oily substance that protects the hair from becoming dry, brittle and cracked) can travel along the hair shaft more easily. The curlier the hair, the more difficulty the sebum has travelling along the hair shaft and therefore the drier or duller the hair looks.

Basic structure of hair and skin

Before you can begin to fully understand how and why you analyse the hair, skin and scalp, you must first understand the structure of the hair, skin and scalp.

Structure and function of the hair

KEY TERMS

Vellus hair – fine, downy hair that appears all over our bodies except the palms of the hands and soles of the feet.

Terminal hair – the hair on our heads, underarms and genital areas of the body.

Hair covers the entire body except for the palms of the hands and soles of the feet. Body hair is called **vellus hair**; the hair on the head is referred to as **terminal hair**.

Hair shaft

The hair shaft is made up of three main layers: the cuticle layer, the cortex layer and the medulla layer. It is vital you are familiar with the cuticle and cortex layers as they play a huge part in all areas of hairdressing and can affect the outcomes of services and products available for use.

Cuticle layer

The outer layer of the hair is called the **cuticle** and is made up of many layers of transparent overlapping scales which protect the hair. The cuticle scales lift when chemicals are added to the hair to allow penetration of the chemicals into the layer underneath. Heat can also open the cuticle layer.

KEY TERMS

Cuticle – outer layer of the hair.

Lacklustre – drab.

Ideally the cuticle scales should be closed and lie smoothly from root to tip. Shiny, healthy hair that reflects light does so because the cuticle scales are closed and smooth, and therefore non-porous. Dull, **lacklustre**-looking hair appears flat and absorbs the light because the cuticle scales are damaged or open, and the hair is therefore porous.

HANDY HINT

Cuticle scales are often described as 'fish scales' or 'overlapping roof tiles'; they overlap from root to point.

HANDY HINT

Different hair types have varying layers of cuticle: Caucasian hair types have four to seven layers, African hair types have seven to eleven layers and Asian hair types have up to eleven layers.

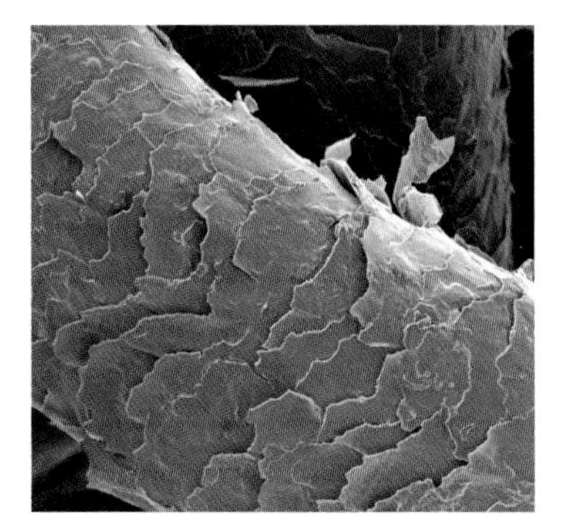

▲ Damaged cuticle absorbing light

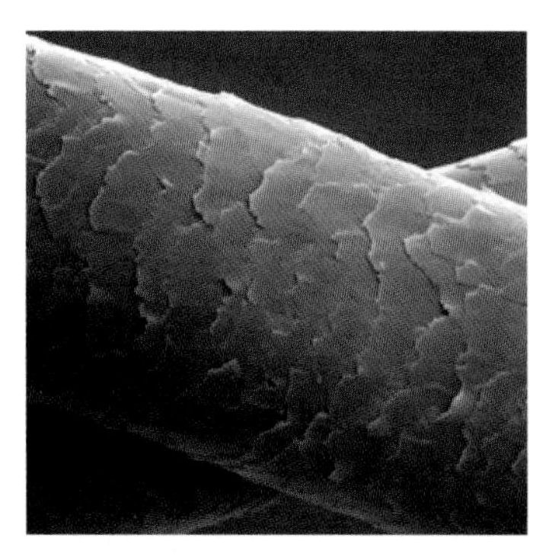

▲ Smooth cuticle reflecting light

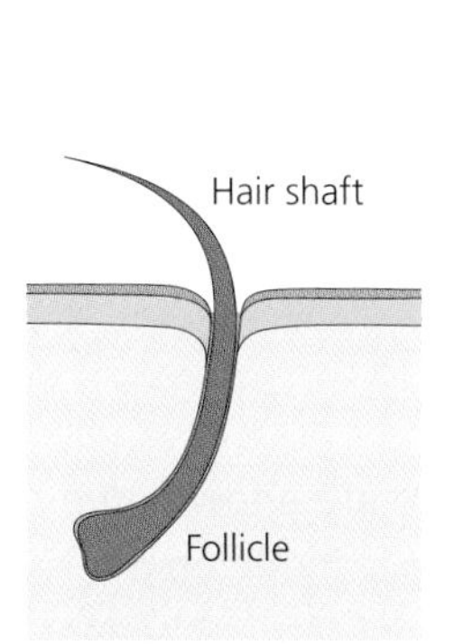

▲ Caucasian hair

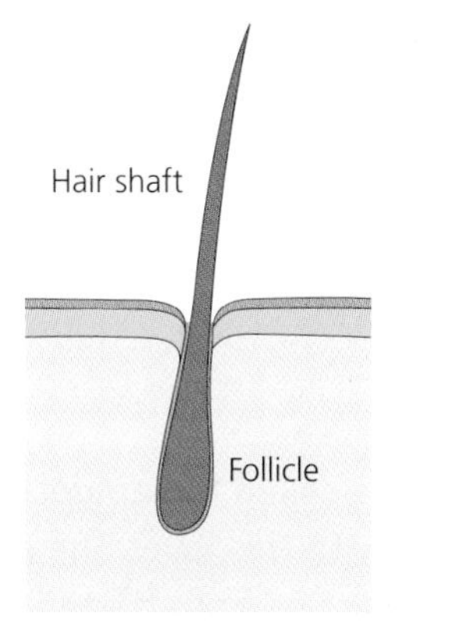

▲ Asian hair

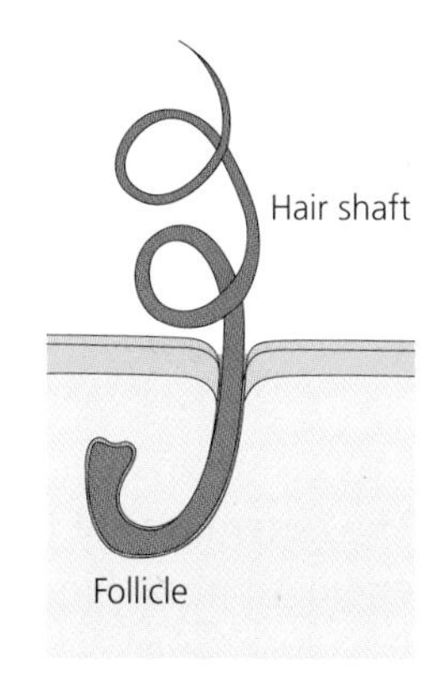

▲ African-type hair

Cortex layer

The **cortex** is the section under the cuticle and the most exciting layer of the hair. Your natural hair colour is determined in the cortex and it is here that artificial colouring takes place. The cortex layer holds the bonds which hold your hair in place and determine whether your hair is naturally curly, wavy or straight. When hair is temporarily or permanently changed from curly to straight or straight to curly, this takes place in the cortex. The cortex is the main body of the hair, giving the hair its strength and elasticity.

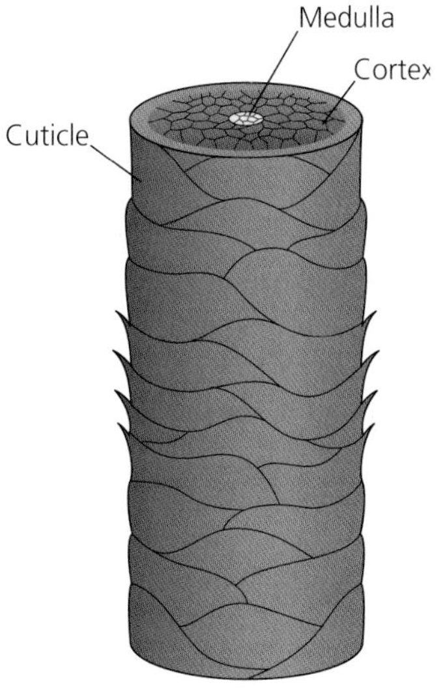

▲ Structure of the hair

KEY TERM

Cortex – layer of the hair under the cuticle.

KEY TERM

Medulla – central layer of the hair.

HANDY HINT

To help you remember the three layers of the hair, think of a pencil. The cuticle is like the varnish/paint on the outside of a pencil and this area sometimes gets a little flaky. The cortex is like the main body of the pencil, which gives it its strength, and the medulla is like the graphite.

ACTIVITY

Draw and label the three layers of the hair and list two or three facts about each layer.

KEY TERMS

Epidermis – outermost layer of the skin.

Stratum – layer.

Mitosis – cell division.

Medulla layer

The **medulla** layer does not play any real part in hairdressing. It is the central layer of the hair but it is not always present. Little is known about what the medulla is for or its significance. In a single strand of hair the medulla may fade in and out, be present the whole way through or not be there at all. In thicker hair it appears to be present more often than not.

Structure and function of the skin

The hair on our head helps to protect our scalp and keeps us warm. The skin and scalp have three main layers, each with a role to play.

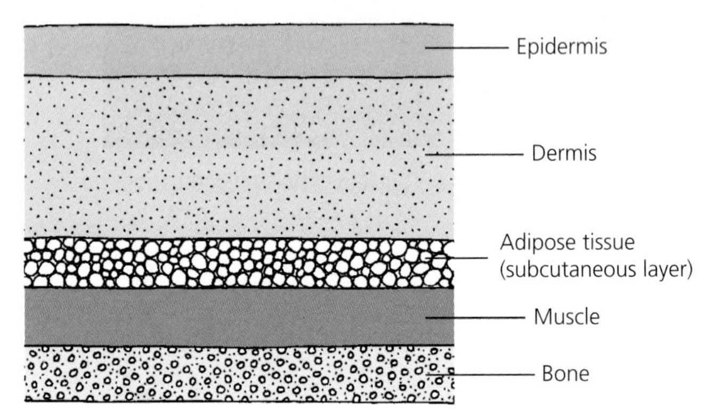

▲ Cross-section of the body's tissues

Epidermis layer

The outer layer of the skin is called the **epidermis.** There are a few nerve endings but no blood supply to this layer. The epidermis is made up of five main layers which protect us from bacteria and temperature changes and are regularly replaced. House dust is partly made up of the epidermis that our bodies have shed. Our whole body is covered with the epidermis, which varies in thickness; it is thickest on the soles of our feet and thinnest on our eyelids.

The top three layers of the epidermis contain dead cells, one layer contains old cells and the bottom layer is constantly producing new cell growth.

The **stratum** corneum is the outer top layer and provides us with a waterproof 'coat'. This 'horny' layer flakes and dries out easily. We remove the dead skin cells from here when we exfoliate.

The stratum lucidum is a clear layer present only in thick skin, helping to protect it from the force of friction.

The stratum granulosum is a granular layer which contains most of the skin's protein called keratin.

The stratum spinosum is the prickle cell layer. These cells are formed as new cells grow and the old ones are pushed up to create a new layer. The cells interlock and are capable of **mitosis** under friction or pressure, for example, on our feet or on the palms of our hands.

The stratum germinativum is the base and deepest layer of skin. It is the primary site of mitosis which produces new cell growth. This can take 28–30 days to move through the five layers of the epidermis before it is shed. This layer contains a pigment called melanin which gives the skin its natural colour.

HANDY HINT

The function of the epidermis is to protect the dermis.

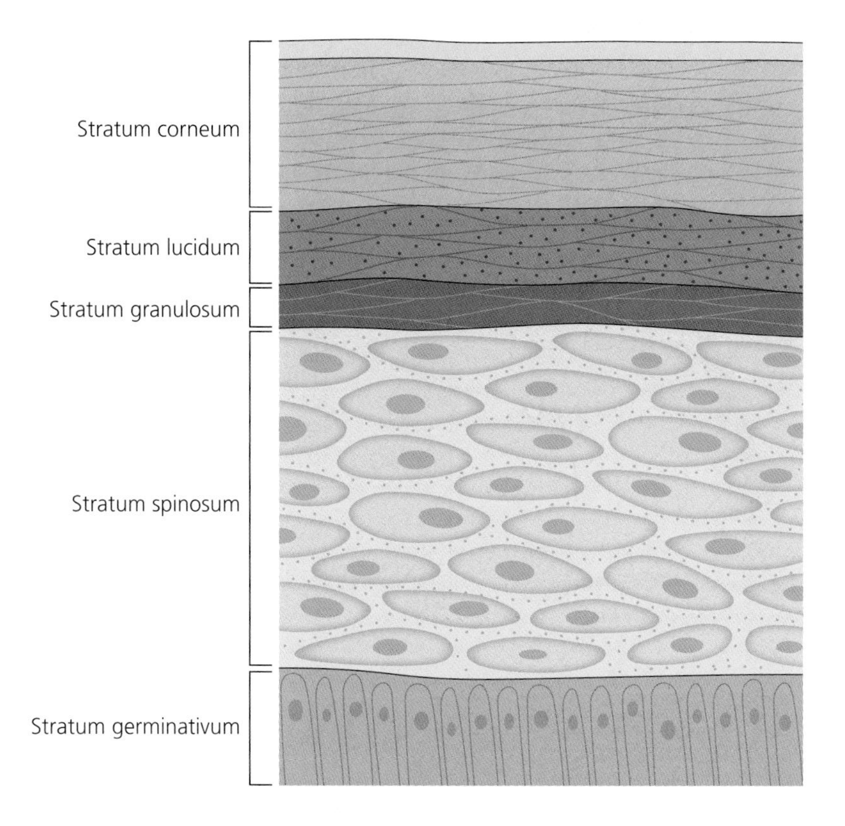

▲ Strata of the epidermis

Dermis layer

The **dermis** attaches the epidermis to the subcutaneous layer and passes nutrients between the two layers. It is this layer that provides strength and elasticity to the skin.

Subcutaneous layer

The **subcutaneous layer** is fatty tissue that is attached to the dermis layer. Its functions are to keep us warm and supply nutrients via the blood supply. All the nerve endings, hair follicles, **arrector pili muscles**, sweat and **sebaceous glands** travel through here to the dermis. It is much thicker on the body than on the head.

KEY TERMS

Dermis – middle layer of the skin.

Subcutaneous layer – fatty tissue layer.

Arrector pili muscle – muscle attached to the hair follicle at one end and dermal tissue on the other.

Sebaceous glands – glands in the skin that secrete oil.

HANDY HINT

You need to know the functions of the skin structure. The main activities of the skin structure take place within the dermis and subcutaneous layer.

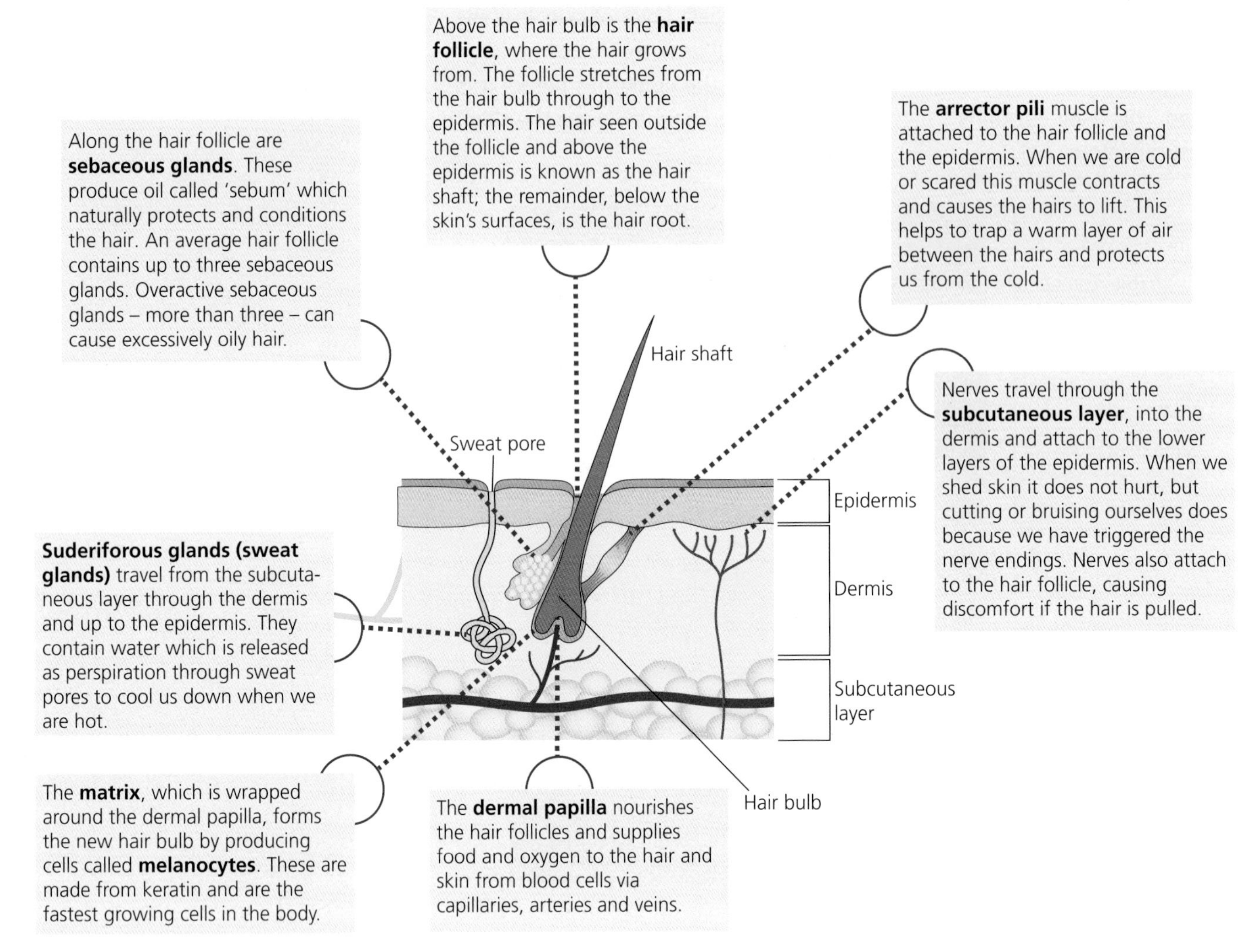

▲ Cross-section of the skin

Growth cycle of hair

The hair grows in three stages, known as cycles.

- Anagen – during this part of the growth cycle up to 80 per cent of the hair follicles are active and the hair is growing. The blood and oxygen from the capillaries form the hair follicle in the dermal papilla and can grow for up to seven years or stop growing after as little as one-and-a-half years. Clients trying to grow their hair may find it stops when it reaches a certain length; this could be due to the limited hair growth in their anagen cycle.
- Catagen – during this part of the cycle the hair growth slows down for a couple of weeks. The follicle starts to shrink and detaches from the dermal papilla.
- Telogen – during this phase the hair is resting; it can last for 10–12 weeks.
- New anagen – towards the end of the resting cycle, new activity and cell division take place in the dermal papilla and the anagen cycle begins again. The new hair growth pushes the old hair further up the hair follicle, which is often then completely removed from the follicle when the hair is brushed or combed.

HANDY HINT

To help you remember the order of the three stages of hair growth, use the word **ACT** – **A** for active and anagen, **C** for changing and catagen, and **T** for tired/resting and telogen.

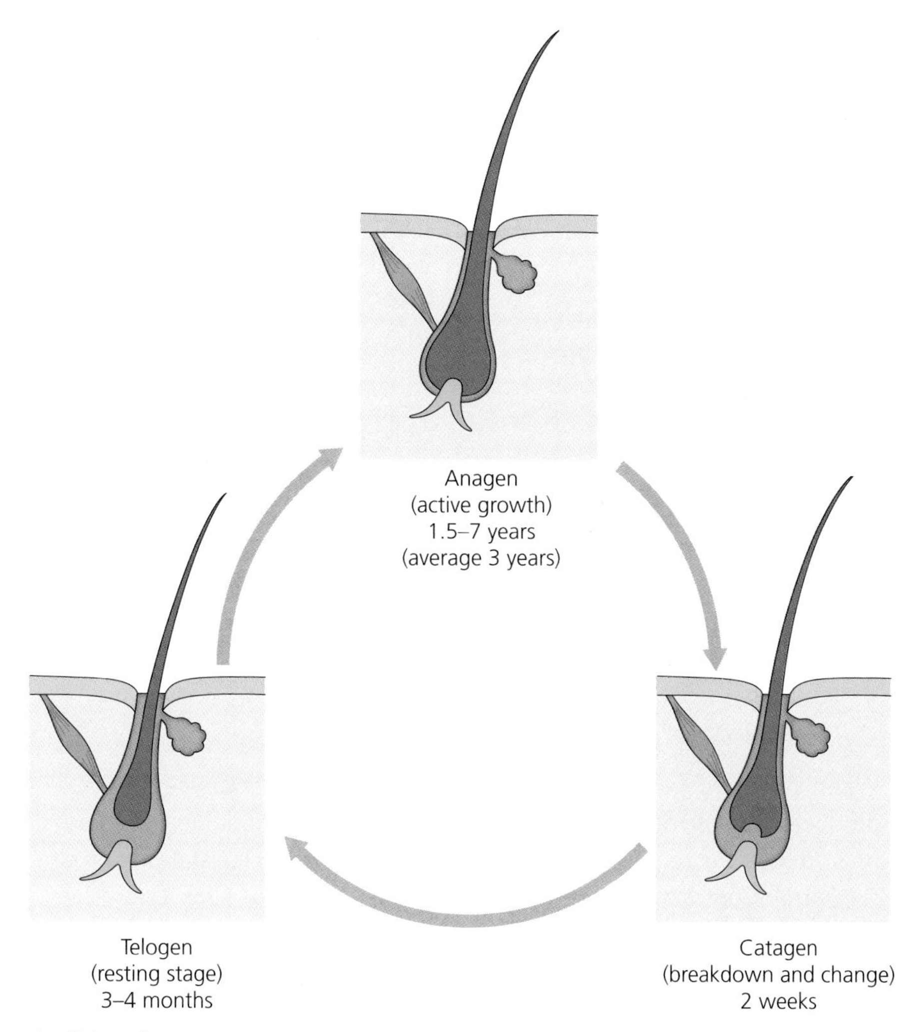

▲ Hair cycle

Average rate of hair growth

Our hair grows on average 1.25 cm (½ inch) per month. We have thousands of hairs on our heads, all at different stages of the hair growth cycle; we each lose on average 100 hairs per day.

Explain the services and products available in your salon

To be able to offer a full service you need to know what services your salon offers and the products available for use. You should ask your salon manager about this, but you could look at the salon price list to familiarise yourself with the services and prices and watch the stylists using a variety of products.

ACTIVITY

Using your salon pricelist, make a list of all the services your salon offers. Next to this, add a column of the products you could use for each service. Use the example below to help you.

Service	Products available
Blow-dry – straight and smooth	Smoothing balm, serum, heat protector, hair spray
Blow-dry – curly round brush blow-dry	
Regrowth colour	Wella Koleston and 6% hydrogen peroxide
Woven highlights	

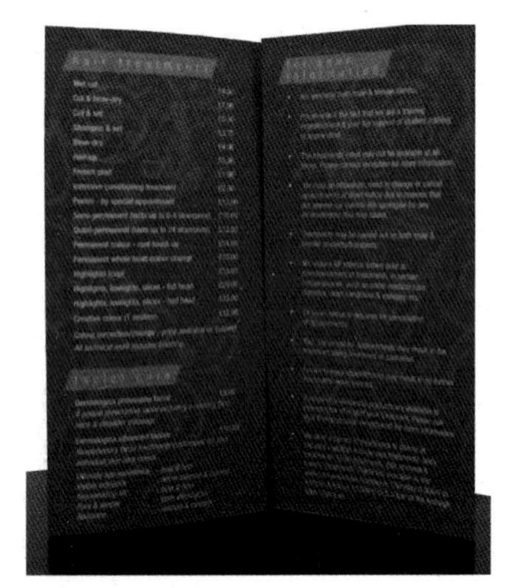

▲ Salon price list

ACTIVITY

Compare the prices of three salons in your local area to three salons in London, or compare prices in rural and urban areas. Explain how and why they differ.

Your legal responsibilities for describing the features and benefits of products and services

When you are describing the features and benefits of a service or products – what the product does or why the client should use it – you must follow the requirements of Consumer Protection legislation and the Consumer Contracts Regulations. Refer back to Chapter 1 for a refresher on your legal responsibilities.

Your salon's pricing structure

Every salon's pricing structure will be different and will vary in the range of services offered. Some salons will have a structure reflecting the level or expertise of the stylist and may have set prices for Stylist, Senior Stylist, Manager or Director level; other salons may charge a set price per stylist but have a price range for short, medium and long hair services to ensure they cover the cost of extra products or time required for longer hair lengths.

How to calculate the likely charge for services

It is important that services are charged for accurately in order for the salon to cover costs and make a healthy profit. Towards the end of the consultation period, you will have a clear idea on the service you are going to carry out, the products required and how long it will take. From this consultation the salon and you can calculate the correct cost of the service. It is important to inform your client of the likely costs and for them to agree the price and the service before you begin.

1 Using your salon's pricing structure calculate the following client bills correctly:

Client 1: Aaron	Cost of service/ product	Client 2: Shauna	Cost of service/ product	Client 3: Ellie	Cost of service/ product
Men's cut and blow-dry	£	Long graduation cut	£	Short graduation cut	£
Facial beard trim	£	Wet set and hair-up	£	Woven highlights	£
Beard oil	£	Hair spray	£	Protective conditioner	£
Total cost	£	Total cost	£	Total cost	£

2 If the salon pays 60% commission on stylist's services and 10% commission on retail sold, how much commission would Aaron, Shauna and Ellie have earned?

Provide clients with advice and recommendations

Before you commence a service you must provide your client with advice and recommendations about their hair. This advice should include explanations regarding:

- how to maintain the look you are going to complete – your client must understand the potential costs, time and effort that may be required for maintenance
- the time interval between services – your client should know how often to return to the salon and how costly the service will be to maintain their look
- present and future products and services – advise your client on additional products they may need for home maintenance and any future services required, such as recommended colours or treatments.

When providing advice make sure you follow Consumer Protection legislation at all times.

HANDY HINT

Always ensure you charge the correct price; if your salon charges separately for a cut and blow-dry after a colour service, make sure you add all the services to the total bill.

Using your salon price list, work out the costs for four different services adding 20% to the bill for an artistic director and reducing the bill by 10% for a newly qualified stylist. Add a different retail product to each bill.

HANDY HINT

Always check the total bill with a senior staff member if you are unsure of the costs.

Give the client realistic expectations

You must explain to your client if their hair is too damaged to be permanently coloured, or too fine to achieve a chosen style, so that they understand why their expectations cannot be met. Always try to offer an alternative solution so that your client is not too disappointed, but make sure your client has a realistic expectation of what is achievable.

Provide advice and recommendations on salon services and products

Any advice that you give to your client should be based around the services and products your salon can offer. By providing advice, you will encourage your client to return, helping you to build a solid clientele.

Complete client records

Client records may be completed and stored on a computer or be handwritten and stored securely at reception. These records should include the client's contact details, details of tests carried out and by whom, the products used and the service carried out. You must always record the results of any hair and skin test, including the advice you provided to your client and confirmation of their consent for the service. At the end of the service, record the outcome and if the client was satisfied with the end result. These records provide reference for future use and could be used as evidence of good practice, should something go wrong and your client take legal action.

HANDY HINT

Some consultations might be carried out a few days before the service is booked; this enables you to carry out the relevant hair and skin tests.

WHAT YOU MUST DO

Identify the requirements of the client

An effective consultation must take place before every hairdressing service. This includes services such as shampooing and conditioning treatments, cutting hair and facial hair, styling, setting, colouring and perming.

You should complete the consultation process in a relaxed environment and your client must have plenty of time to express their views and wishes. It is not unusual for consultations to take up to 20 minutes for new clients, as this gives you both time to clearly understand what is required and whether or not it is achievable. When carrying out a consultation on a regular client it is important to confirm whether your client wants a repeat service or if they are looking for a new service or style.

▲ Consultation is an essential part of every service

Carry out consultation services

You must:

- consult with your client to determine their requirements
- allow your client sufficient time to express their wishes

- ask relevant questions in a way your client will understand
- use visual aids to present clients with suitable alternative ideas to help them reach a decision
- encourage your client to ask about areas of which they are unsure
- identify and confirm your client's wishes for services and products.

▲ Use visual aids

THE HAIR PROFESSIONAL AT WORK

With a visual image in mind, you can discuss with the client how feasible the outcome will be. Remember, as the expert, it is up to you to suggest alternative ideas if the style will not suit the client's face shape, hair type or texture, or even their lifestyle. Always be prepared to suggest other positive options.

THE HAIR PROFESSIONAL AT WORK

Always ensure you ask relevant questions and listen to your client's responses in order to find out all the information required to carry out the desired service.

Always *listen* to what your client is asking of you. Allow them time to express their wishes before suggesting your ideas and recommending services.

HANDY HINT

See Chapter 4 for specific information on how characteristics such as face shapes, hair types or hair textures affect cutting or styling services.

ACTIVITY

Try to list up to:

- six questions you could ask your client if they were booked in for a styling or dressing service
- eight questions you could ask your client if they were booked in for a cutting service
- ten questions you could ask your client if they were booked in for a colour service.

HANDY HINT

As you gather information from your client and answers to your questions, encourage them to ask questions, particularly if they are unsure about any areas discussed.

Examine the hair, skin and scalp

You must:

- apply safe and hygienic methods of working throughout the service, ensuring your personal hygiene, protection and appearance meet accepted industry and organisational requirements.
- carry out relevant tests:
  - conduct visual checks and any necessary tests on the hair, skin and scalp to meet specified procedures
  - identify from your client's previous records, when available, any factors likely to affect future services – such as hair classifications and characteristics, adverse hair, skin and scalp conditions, incompatibility of previous services and products used, test results and client's lifestyle
  - promptly identify and report any problems which cannot be dealt with to the relevant person.

Advise your client and agree services and products

You must provide clients with advice and recommendations including:

- making recommendations on the outcomes of your identification of your client's hair characteristics and their hair classification:
  - Type 1 – straight hair
  - Type 2 – wavy hair
  - Type 3 – curly hair
  - Type 4 – very curly hair
- explaining how their hair characteristics may impact on the hairdressing services in a way your client can understand
- agreeing services, products and outcomes that are acceptable to your client and meet their needs
- stating the likely cost and duration of the agreed products and services to your client
- conducting all communications with your client in a manner that maintains goodwill, trust, confidentiality and privacy
- offering your client advice and recommendations on the service provided such as:
  - how to maintain their look
  - time interval between services
  - present and future products and services.

Test your knowledge

Question 1

Under the Working Time Directive, how many hours per day can a 16–17 year old work?

Question 2

Which Act regulates the selling of goods online?

Question 3

Describe the best way of communicating with a client with a hearing impairment.

Question 4

Provide three examples of positive and three examples of negative body language.

Question 5

Describe the signs of tinea capitis.

Question 6

Which test is the following describing?

Put a small piece of hair in a mix of 20 parts H_2O_2 and 1 part ammonium hydroxide.

Multiple choice questions

7 Not all disabilities can be seen. Which of the following may not be obvious but still needs to be considered when ensuring equality and diversity?
   - a A client in a wheelchair
   - b A client with a broken leg
   - c A client with a mental health illness
   - d A client with a contagious skin condition

8 Which of the following legislation requires the seller to give details of their geographical location?
   - a Consumer Contracts Regulations
   - b Trade Descriptions Act
   - c Cosmetic Products Regulations
   - d Consumer Protection legislation

9 Which of the following hair classifications is type 4b?
   - a Medium texture and frizzy
   - b Very straight and fine
   - c Very curly and fragile
   - d Medium texture and wavy

10 Which of the following best describes the cuticle?
   - a Overlapping coils inside the hair
   - b Overlapping, translucent scales
   - c The centre of the hair
   - d Polypeptide chains

11 The anagen stage usually lasts for between:
   - a 1.5 and 4 years
   - b 1.5 and 5 years
   - c 1.5 and 6 years
   - d 1.5 and 7 years

12 The best advice to give a client with suspected scabies is:
   - a to visit their GP
   - b to visit a trichologist
   - c to use antibacterial cream
   - d to use an antifungal cream

13 What is the hair on the head called?
   - a Vellus hair
   - b Terminal hair
   - c Lanugo hair
   - d Androgenic hair

14 The *stratum germinativium* is the layer of the epidermis where:
   - a new cells are produced
   - b new cells die off
   - c cells are pushed from the basal layer
   - d cells are thick and replaced every month

DRY DAMAGED HAIR
PAUL MITCHELL

SHAMPOO, CONDITION AND TREAT THE HAIR AND SCALP

ABI BRITT – HQ HAIR & BEAUTY SALON

My name is Abi and I am a graduate stylist working and building a clientele in HQ Hair & Beauty Salon, a busy salon in Bristol, specialising in creative cutting and hair up techniques. I also support and co-ordinate salon training to upskill our new apprentices and pass on my own knowledge and experience to our growing team.

I have just completed my Advance Hairdressing Level 3 Apprenticeship at Reflections Training Academy where I enjoyed the benefits of a work-based Apprenticeship, gaining knowledge alongside real-life employability skills in the salon environment.

While training, I was able to focus on creative cutting and advanced colour knowledge which has allowed me to take part in competition work during my Apprenticeship. I reached the final of both the Hair Council Student of the Year Award with a creative cut model and the Wella Xposure student competition, where I won the Gold Award for demonstrating my colour expertise and finishing skills. Through the support of my Apprenticeship, I have gained confidence in these skills and my success in these competitions has opened up opportunities to work alongside top industry experts, shadow art teams at live shows and meet my idols.

I've certainly faced challenges, particularly with my English and Maths skills, but the support I received alongside embedded, practical functional skills training that was related to my employability in a salon really helped me to improve. I am now calculating bills, delivering full consultations and ordering salon stock.

My advice to anyone training in the hairdressing industry would be to grab every opportunity given to you, believe in yourself and use the time during your Apprenticeship to get support with challenging areas. I believe this will allow you to achieve your goals and build a successful career in this creative and exciting industry.

This chapter maps to:
- Unit 2 Shampoo, condition and treat the hair and scalp (Level 2 Diploma for Hair Professionals – Hairdressing)
- Unit 2 Shampoo, condition and treat the hair and scalp (Level 2 Diploma for Hair Professionals – Barbering).

INTRODUCTION

The shampoo and conditioning process is often a favourite with clients, because of the massage techniques used and the resulting clean, conditioned feel of the hair. It can be relaxing and therapeutic if the scalp is massaged correctly and the client is positioned comfortably. The hair and scalp must be checked for any damage or disorders and the most suitable products recommended. The client's enjoyment is a key factor, but treating the hair and scalp are the most important reasons for shampooing and conditioning.

After reading this chapter you will:
- know how health and safety policies and procedures affect the service
- understand how to apply safe working practices
- be able to shampoo, condition and treat the hair and scalp.

HEALTH AND SAFETY POLICIES AND PROCEDURES

As with all services, you must always follow the rules and regulations of the ten health and safety Acts.

KEY TERM

Treatment – a process to improve condition; it could refer to a penetrating conditioner that improves the condition of the cortex, or a scalp treatment that remedies a scalp disorder.

Outline own responsibilities for health and safety

The four most relevant Acts affecting shampooing, conditioning and scalp **treatment** services are:
- Health and Safety at Work Act
- Control of Substances Hazardous to Health Regulations (COSHH)
- Environmental Protection Act
- Electricity at Work Regulations.

ACTIVITY

How do the above health and safety Acts relate to your job role when you are carrying out shampoo services?

HEALTH AND SAFETY

Refer to Chapter 1 for further information on each of the ten health and safety Acts.

Your responsibilities for health and safety

The shampoo and conditioning service is often the first part of any service, so it is important to give a positive impression of yourself and your salon. Always follow health and safety legislation and behave in a manner that will not put you or your client at risk of injury or harm. Mop up any spillages that occur at the shampoo area and always protect your client throughout the service.

When you use shampoos and conditioning products, you must do so safely and economically. Always ensure you follow COSHH Regulations – controlling the substances that could be hazardous to your health. Store substances correctly, handle them carefully, use them correctly and dispose of them in a non-harmful way.

Make sure you follow the manufacturer's instructions (MFIs), local by-laws and your salon policies. Following the MFIs ensures you use the correct amount and achieve the best results. Using too much product is wasteful and the salon will lose profit; excessive use of products can overload the hair, affecting further services. You must dispose of any waste correctly, ensuring you follow the rules of the Environmental Protection Act.

If using electrical equipment for treatments you must avoid wasting energy and use the equipment correctly, following the Electricity at Work Regulations. If equipment is used or stored incorrectly, it may cause injury to others or cause electrical faults in the salon, which will impact on the business. Equipment should be used for its intended purpose and you should read the provided instructions before use – particularly for new equipment, which is unfamiliar to you.

▲ Wearing an apron and gloves helps to protect your hands and clothes

Protective clothing for yourself and clients

You should prepare your hands for the service ahead and use barrier or hand cream. It is good practice to protect your hands and wear gloves during the shampoo service, but not every client enjoys having their hair shampooed by a gloved stylist.

An apron can help to protect your clothes from splashes of shampoo and conditioner, ensuring you look well presented all day.

You should use a clean towel and gown for every client, and a disposable cape to keep the protective clothing dry, when carrying out treatments on longer hair.

HANDY HINT

It is a good idea to use a disposable or reusable plastic protective cape on clients with shorter necks as their necks do not always fit snugly into the curve of the salon basin and the cape may help protect their clothes from getting wet.

Importance of personal hygiene and presentation

During the shampooing and conditioning service, you will be leaning over your client, so it is very important that your personal hygiene is maintained and you do not have any body odour. Your salon will lose business if clients are offended and choose to go elsewhere because staff have poor personal hygiene and body odour. You must shower or bath, use deodorant and wear clean clothes every day. Brush your teeth regularly and always represent the industry and salon's image by having clean, well-groomed hair.

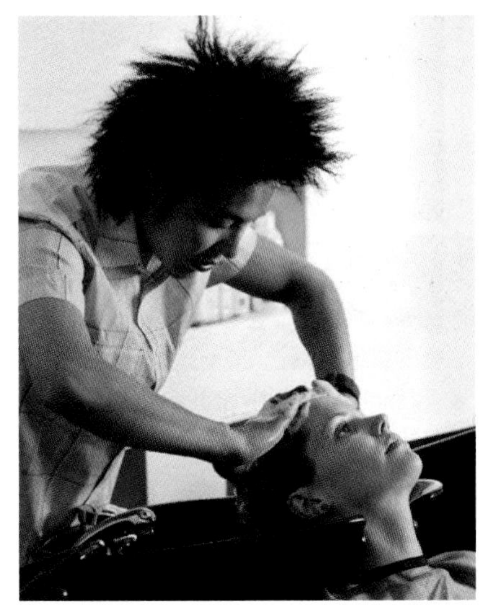

▲ Ensure your personal hygiene is tip top

Hazards and risks in the workplace

It is important that you always act in a manner that does not put you or your client at risk of injury or harm. The salon environment can present plenty of hazards that could become a risk to someone's health and wellbeing if not prevented.

ACTIVITY

Complete the 'Prevention/safe working practice' column in the table below.

Can you list any other potential hazards and risks?

Hazard	Risk	Prevention/safe working practice
Water on the floor	People could slip over	
Shampoo and conditioner	Product could get into the client's eyes	
Shampoo and conditioner	Dermatitis	
Hot water	Could burn self or client	
Infection/infestations	Cross-contamination	

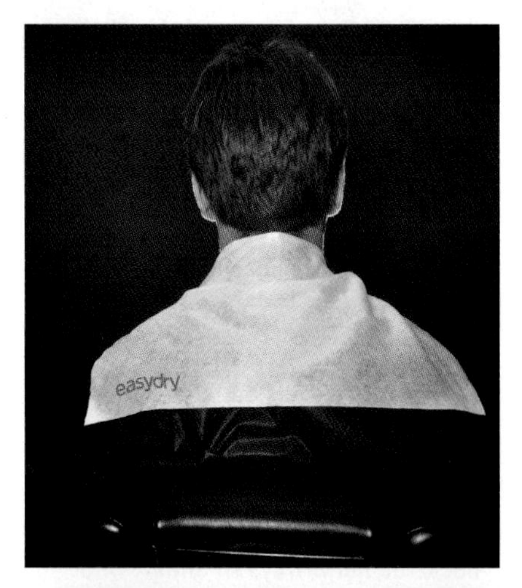

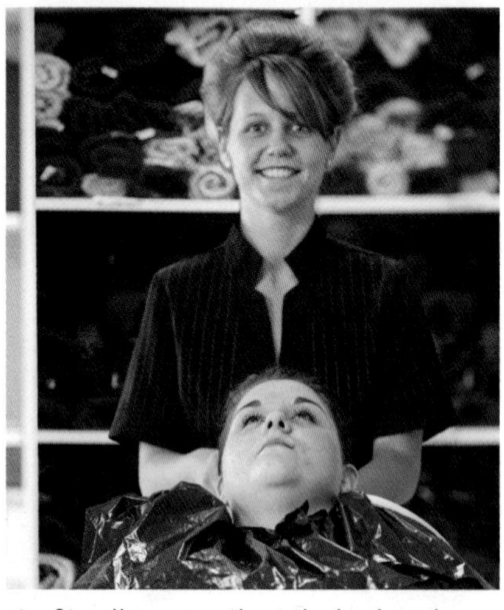

▲ Standing correctly at the basin reduces the risk of fatigue

KEY TERM

Hyperextension – over extension/over stretched.

Safe and hygienic working methods and practices

Throughout the service you must keep yourself and your client safe, by behaving professionally and following safe working practices. You must ensure that you, your tools and the working environment are hygienic at all times. Poor standards of health and hygiene can cause offence to others, lead to cross-contamination and present a poor professional and salon image.

THE HAIR PROFESSIONAL AT WORK

A good apprentice demonstrates professionalism at all times and ensures their personal hygiene meets their organisation's and the industry's standard of appearance.

Your salon's requirements for client preparation

Most salons protect the client's clothing during a shampoo or conditioning treatment with a fresh, clean gown, a disposable cape and a towel.

Position of your client and yourself

Poor client positioning can affect the desired outcome, cause the client to get wet and cause discomfort. Poor stylist positioning can cause fatigue and the risk of injury or long-term damage to spine.

Client position

To ensure the comfort of your client, sit them upright with their back and neck supported at the basin area. When the client's head and neck are positioned backwards for a period of time at the shampoo area, it can cause **hyperextension** of the neck. Hyperextension of the neck can lead to an injury, tear or blood clot in one the four main arteries that go to the brain and any one of these symptoms can cause a stroke. While this can happen to anyone, it is extremely rare, but it is of paramount importance that your client's neck is supported sufficiently throughout the shampoo and conditioning service.

Always check that the hair is not caught between the shampoo basin and your client's neck as you position your client. Push the hair back away from the forehead, so that water does not drip on your client's face. Ensure that the water is directed away from your client's face. For the client's comfort, ensure you use your finger pads and not your fingernails on the scalp.

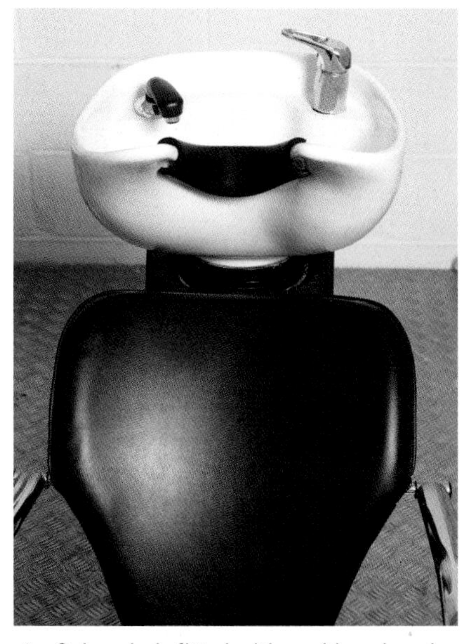

▲ Salon chair fitted with cushioned neck protectors to support the client's neck

HEALTH AND SAFETY

Never allow your client's neck to be hyperextended at the shampoo area for longer than 15 minutes, and less if possible.

Your position and posture

During the shampoo process you will need to lean over the client, and if shampooing from a side basin you will also need to twist your body slightly. Make sure your balance is evenly distributed; stand with your feet slightly apart and avoid stretching and twisting where possible to prevent back problems and fatigue. You can sometimes be standing over the basin for as long as 15 minutes, for example, when shampooing long hair or applying conditioning treatments, and this is a long time to spend leaning over. You need to ensure that you stand correctly to avoid risk of injury.

ACTIVITY

Research 'beauty parlour stroke syndrome' or strokes caused by shampooing in the salon. You will see from your research that clients can sue the salon for thousands of pounds, if they are held responsible for not protecting the client's neck during the service.

Working methods that promote environmental and sustainable practices

Along with the more obvious ways of working in an environmentally friendly way, such as turning off water in between shampoos and using disposable towels, there is so much more the salon can do to help preserve the planet.

ACTIVITY

Complete the chart below and identify what you can do in your salon to promote environmental and sustainable working practices.

Environmental practice	What can you do in your salon?
Reduce and manage waste	
Reduce energy	
Use disposable items	
Use organic hair products	
Use products with environmentally friendly packaging	
Offer responsible catering products such as Fairtrade tea and coffee	
Reduce carbon footprint	

▲ Excessive twisting and leaning at the basin can cause back problems for the stylist

Correct methods of waste disposal

Dispose of any plastic capes in the waste bin and ideally recycle where possible. Empty shampoo and conditioner bottles should be refilled, if suitable, or disposed of in an environmentally friendly manner. Most plastic bottles are suitable for recycling.

Preventing contact dermatitis

Contact dermatitis is a common workplace disease which can be recognised by inflamed skin that is red and sore and may weep and crack. Contact dermatitis can leave you unfit for work and in the worst case scenario you may need to leave the industry. To avoid contracting dermatitis, you must rinse and dry your hands thoroughly after every shampoo and conditioning treatment, and wear gloves when necessary. Using moisturising hand cream can also help.

HANDY HINT

Always protect your hands with hand cream and/or barrier cream to prevent dermatitis.

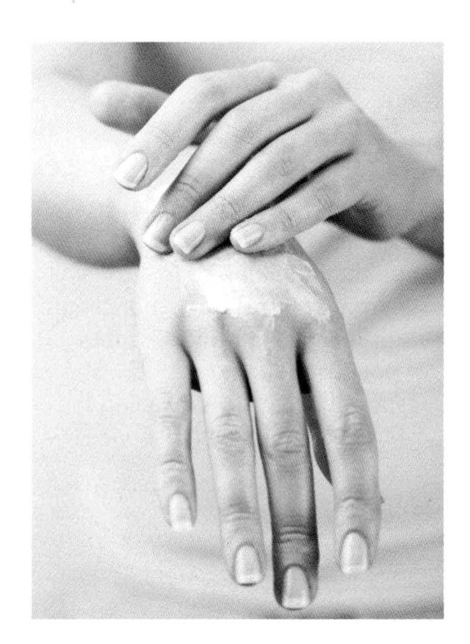

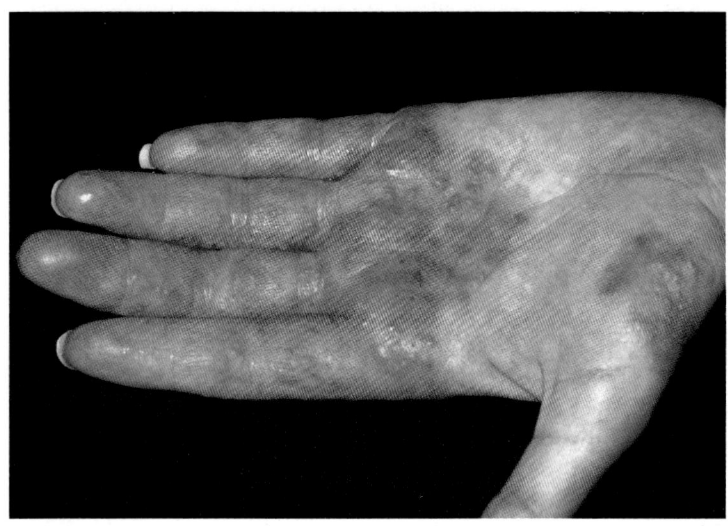

▲ Dermatitis

Importance of questioning clients prior to and during services

Good language and communication skills are very important in hairdressing. The way you ask questions and the types of questions you ask your clients will affect the information you receive.

Questioning clients to establish any contra-indications

You must consult with your client and ask suitable questions to identify their service requirements and establish if they have any contra-indications which could affect the service carried out, or the products used. You also need to check for:

- cuts and abrasions
- infections/infestations
- skin/scalp disorders
- allergies to products
- recent scar tissue or injuries to the scalp area.

Preventing cross-infection and cross-infestation

You must ensure that all client protective clothing and salon tools and equipment are cleaned and then disinfected, sterilised or sanitised to prevent **cross-contamination**, **cross-infection** or **cross-infestation** from one person to another.

KEY TERMS

Cross-contamination – cross-infection or cross-infestation.

Cross-infection – spread of germs and bacteria.

Cross-infestation – transfer of mites and lice from one person to another.

Keep your work area clean and tidy

Keeping your work area clean and tidy promotes a professional image of the salon to clients and visitors, and assists with preventing cross-contamination.

Working safely and hygienically

Safe methods of working when you complete shampoo and conditioning treatments include:

- cleaning and preparing your tools and work areas
- checking the scalp for contra-indications and infections/infestations
- carrying out the relevant hair tests
- protecting your client's clothing
- reading and following instructions
- following health and safety policies and procedures
- working within the limits of your own authority
- maintaining a clean and tidy environment
- sterilising, disinfecting or sanitising tools and equipment.

Cleaning, disinfecting and sterilising

Always spray your work areas and shampoo basins with a chemical solution to disinfect them in between clients. Towels and gowns should be washed at low temperatures (30 °C) to help protect the environment, but if an infection or infestation is suspected, then towels and gowns should be boil washed on a high temperature (around 95 °C). Any tools used should be cleaned and sterilised in readiness for the next client.

HEALTH AND SAFETY

Refer back to Chapter 1 for more information on disinfecting, sterilising and sanitising.

SHAMPOO, CONDITION AND TREAT THE HAIR AND SCALP

Before you can successfully shampoo hair you must understand the following:

- hair and scalp conditions and their causes
- underpinning science of shampoo
- massage techniques used
- importance of detangling hair correctly
- range of products available
- importance of using products cost effectively
- potential effects of using the incorrect products
- importance of removing products correctly
- importance of removing excess water from the hair
- effect of heat on the hair
- importance of providing clients with advice and recommendations.

HANDY HINT

Refer to Chapter 2 to remind yourself about hair and scalp conditions, and their likely causes.

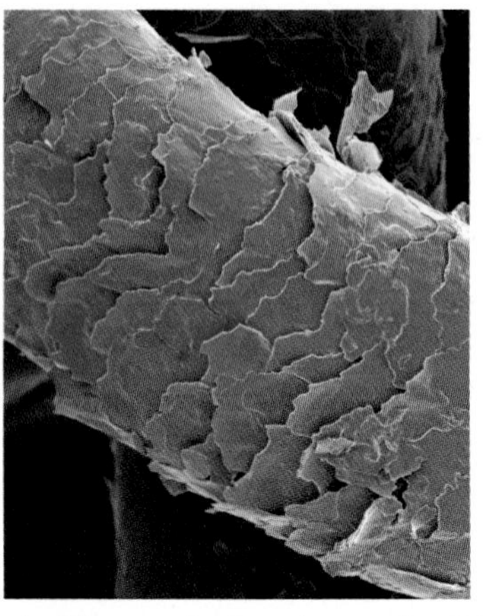

▲ Microscopic view: damaged cuticle

Hair and scalp conditions and their causes

You must analyse the hair and inspect the scalp to establish whether your client has any contra-indications and to identify the condition of their hair and scalp before the service commences. Once you have the information required you should make recommendations for the service.

As the stylist, it is your responsibility to identify which products should be used to suit the client's requirements, the following service, and the client's hair and scalp condition.

The tables below show common hair and scalp conditions that you must be able to recognise and treat.

Common hair and scalp conditions

Hair/scalp condition	Identified by?	Likely cause	Effect on products to use
		Damaged hair	
Chemical damage	Porosity testing and identifying damaged cuticles. Elasticity testing and identifying weakness to the hair's cortex. The hair may also be dull in appearance and lacklustre as the light is being absorbed and not reflected due to the damaged cuticles.	Chemical damage – too many harsh chemical treatments leave the hair dry and porous and the cuticle scales open and rough. The cortex may be weak with poor elasticity. This can affect further services and may cause the hair to tangle easily.	Use a moisturising shampoo for coloured or chemically treated hair and a penetrating conditioning treatment to strengthen the cortex and smooth the cuticle scales.
Heat damage	As above	Heat damage – the continued daily use of hairdryers, straightening irons or curling tongs can damage the cuticle scales and remove moisture from the cortex layer, destroying the bonds. Excessive heat from appliances, incorrect usage and/or failure to use heat protector products when styling can cause the hair to be porous, with the cuticle scales open and rough and decreased elasticity in the cortex.	Use a moisturising shampoo and surface conditioner. A penetrating conditioning treatment may also be required.

Hair/scalp condition	Identified by?	Likely cause	Effect on products to use
Environmental damage	As above	Environmental damage – the sun and wind can affect the hair's condition, causing colours to fade and the cuticle scales to open, resulting in porous hair. Chlorine and seawater can also affect the hair. Use a moisturising shampoo and surface conditioner.	A penetrating conditioning treatment may also be required. You should advise your client about wearing a hat and protecting their hair against the effects of the environment.
		Product build-up	
Product build-up on the hair/scalp	The hair may look oily, or 'crunchy' with excess products visible on the hair. The hair may also appear dull and lacklustre, because the cuticles are filled with products and the light is being absorbed rather than reflected. The scalp may have the appearance of being dry and flaky or oily, depending on the products used.	The overuse of some products, applying too much or using an incorrect product can cause a build-up on the hair or scalp. An incorrect shampoo may also prevent the products from being effectively removed from the hair. Oil-based products, such as wax, do not mix with water and need a good detergent to break them down. Excessive hairspray, sprayed too closely to the hair, can often leave a coating on the hair that is difficult to remove. Product build-up can create a barrier to the subsequent service.	A thorough shampoo process with a clarifying shampoo will be required, as this shampoo will deeply cleanse the hair and scalp. A light surface conditioner is recommended after shampooing.

Hair/scalp condition	Identified by?	Likely cause	Effect on products to use
Common hair conditions			
 Normal hair/scalp	Hair should appear shiny and cuticles smooth. A normal healthy scalp will look pinky-white in appearance, without any dry or oily patches present.	Note that hair can be normal and scalp can be dry, oily or dandruff affected, or scalp can be normal and hair can be dry or damaged.	For normal hair, use a shampoo suitable for the scalp condition or a normal shampoo and surface conditioner. For normal scalp conditions, use a normal shampoo and a light surface conditioner if required.  
 Dry hair	The hair may appear dull in appearance and lacklustre as the light is being absorbed and not reflected due to the dryness of the hair; the cuticles may be raised slightly.	For damaged dry hair – see the previous section on damaged hair. Very curly hair is often naturally dry, as the sebum cannot travel along the hair follicle and shaft as easily as it can on straighter follicles and hair shafts.	A moisturising shampoo and conditioner is required, but if the hair is fine as well as very curly, be careful not to overload the hair and cause it to be weighed down with product.  

Hair/scalp condition	Identified by?	Likely cause	Effect on products to use
Oily hair (seborrhoea)	Hair will appear wet-looking at the root area and slightly along the hair shaft. Oily hair can also 'clump' together rather than lie as single hairs.	You must identify whether the hair and scalp area are oily because: • the hair is due to be shampooed • a poor shampooing service – the hair and scalp were insufficiently cleansed • the client has been sweating (for example from exercise) • the client has overactive sebaceous glands • the client's diet has contributed to oily hair.	If the hair is in need of a good cleanse, use a shampoo for oily hair and a surface conditioner on the mid-lengths and ends only. If the client has seborrhoea, use a shampoo for oily hair, a surface conditioner or penetrating treatment on the mid-lengths and ends and a leave-in scalp treatment to aid seborrhoea control. You may also wish to advise your client that eating healthily can help reduce oily hair and scalp conditions.
Common scalp conditions			
Oily scalp (seborrhoea)	The scalp area will look shiny in appearance and slightly damp-looking. Excessively oily scalps can also smell quite pungent.	See above.	See above.
Dry scalp	A dry scalp looks whiter than normal and has white flakes close to the scalp.	There are many causes of dry scalp, such as: • a natural moisture imbalance • change in seasons and temperature • product and chemical reactions • diet • health issues and underactive sebaceous glands.	Use a moisturising shampoo and a dry scalp treatment. You may need a surface conditioner or treatment on the mid-lengths and ends of the hair too.

→

Hair/scalp condition	Identified by?	Likely cause	Effect on products to use
Dandruff scalp (pityriasis capitis)	Dandruff can be yellow in appearance and often smells if caused by fungi, or appear dry, white and flaky if it is stress-related dandruff.	You must identify whether the dandruff is caused by fungi or stress, as treatment will vary.	For fungus-related dandruff you can refer your client to their GP for prescription treatments. For stress-related dandruff, caused by an overproduction of skin cells, then a medicated shampoo can be used. Use a conditioner to suit the hair condition and a leave-in scalp treatment to aid dandruff control.
Sensitive scalp	A sensitive scalp may appear whiter than oil normal and have white flakes close to the scalp, or appear pink/red and be tender to touch.	A sensitive scalp can be caused by many factors – allergies, chemical hair treatments, hair extensions, traction, sunburn, insect bites, infections or infestations, changes in weather temperature and even from a change of hairdressing products. Ask your client if they have any allergies or have changed their products recently and try to ascertain the reason and cause of the sensitivity.	Use products for a sensitive scalp and avoid heavily perfumed shampoos, conditioners and styling products.

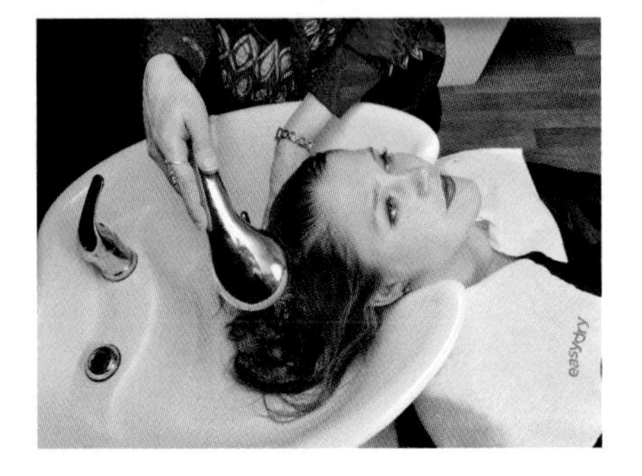

HANDY HINT

When porous hair is shampooed, it will absorb and hold on to the moisture and therefore take longer to blow-dry. Porous hair has open and damaged cuticles that may catch in brushes and combs, so extra care must be taken.

HANDY HINT

Advise your client that their diet can affect how oily their scalp and hair can become and that eating healthily can reduce oiliness.

Repeating the shampoo process is recommended for oily/dirty hair.

Effect of contra-indications

Contra-indications, such as skin and scalp disorders or product allergies, can affect the treatment being carried out, the type of product that can be used and the massage technique used. You must ask your client appropriate questions to find out the information required, if you cannot see a visible contra-indication. You should look at and feel the hair and scalp and listen to your client's responses to be sure which treatment is most suitable.

The table shows the contra-indications that you must consider and the **implications** these may have for the service.

KEY TERM

Implication – a likely effect or consequence.

Contra-indication	Possible implication for the service
Infections, infestations, and skin and scalp disorders	If your client has a disorder that is infectious, it will prevent the treatment being carried out. If it is non-infectious, check that the scalp is not tender, adapt the massage movements and be gentle.
Product allergies	Always ask if your client has experienced any reactions to previous treatments. Ask about other known allergies, such as allergies to nut products or aloe vera, as these are common ingredients in shampoos and conditioning treatments. If your client has a known allergy, check the ingredients on the container and use alternative products if required.
Recent scar tissue	If there is evidence of scar tissue, check it has healed and is not tender or open. Use gentle massage movements over the scar tissue area.
Injuries to the area	If your client has had a recent bump to the head, it may not be visible through the hair but could cause the client discomfort if the massage is too firm. Use gentle massage movements.
Cuts and abrasions	If the cuts are open, then the treatment should not be carried out. If they are healed but sore and tender, be aware of where they are on the head and use gentle massage movements. Avoid scalp treatments containing alcohol, as these may cause a stinging sensation to the wound.

Always follow your salon's policies and procedures for dealing with infections and infestations. If you encounter an unrecognised scalp disorder, you must refer this to a senior staff member to prevent possible cross-infection and infestation.

When asking your clients about the above contra-indications, always record their responses to your questions clearly and accurately on their client record card, so that these details can be referred to when your client visits the salon for their next treatment. Should any problems arise which lead to legal action, you will have a clear record of the service and treatment you carried out and evidence of the client's responses.

HANDY HINT

Some clients with nut allergies may be allergic to products containing Argan or almond oil – so always ask if they have any allergies.

ACTIVITY

Write down at least five open questions that you could ask to obtain relevant information from your client about their hair and scalp condition or any contra-indications.

HANDY HINT

Always follow the Data Protection Act and never disclose a client's personal information to a third party or unauthorised personnel. When discussing personal information, remember to speak quietly to maintain this confidence.

ACTIVITY

List the information that should be recorded on a client's record card. Practise completing a record card, recording all the information from your list. Double check your spellings, punctuation and grammar, and write neatly and accurately.

The science underpinning the services provided

When shampooing and conditioning the hair it is important that you understand the relationship the shampoo has with water and how it removes the dirt and oils from the hair. You also need to understand how water temperature affects the hair and scalp, and how the pH level of products and product build-up affects the structure of the hair.

How shampoo and water act together to cleanse the hair

Oil and water don't mix! We know this from washing greasy roasting dishes in the kitchen, where we have to use plenty of washing-up detergent. Shampoos work in the same way as washing-up detergents. We will look at this in more detail to understand the scientific effects of shampoo.

KEY TERM

Surface tension – the skin-like surface layer of a liquid.

Water is made from both hydrogen and oxygen atoms (H_2O). There is a strong attraction between the hydrogen and oxygen atoms. This attraction causes a skin-like surface to the water molecule. This is commonly known as **surface tension** and can be seen by the way water forms droplets and the way they pool together.

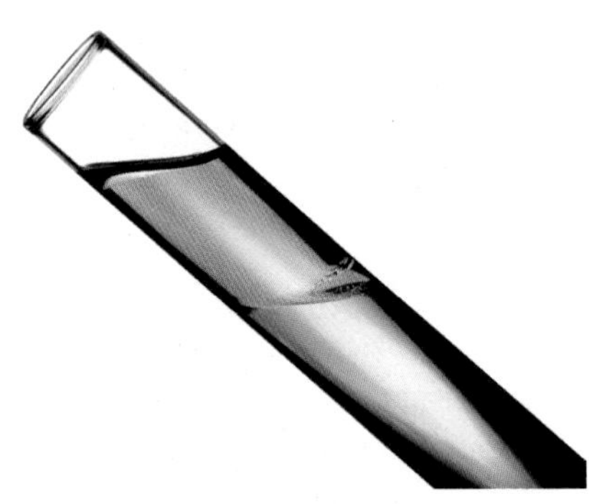

▲ Water and oil do not mix

ACTIVITY

Completely fill a glass with clean, fresh tap water until it is overflowing. You should be able to see that the water's surface is dome shaped and the level is higher than the glass! This is due to the surface tension of the water. Gently lay a small metal paperclip on the surface of the water. It should float on the surface of the water, again because of the surface tension. Now add another small metal paperclip that has been coated lightly in detergent. What happens when you add the second paper clip?

▲ Ripples form on surface tension

Shampoos are made from cleansing agents called surfactants (the name surfactant is derived from surface, active and agent). A surfactant is an agent that actively reduces the surface tension. Surfactants contain molecules that are attracted to water at one end and oil at the other.

A surfactant molecule has a hydrophilic (water-loving) 'head' and a lipophilic (oil-loving) 'tail'. (We also refer to this as hydrophobic – a water-hating tail.) A surfactant molecule dissolves in both oil and water and joins them together, enabling the breakdown of oils within water.

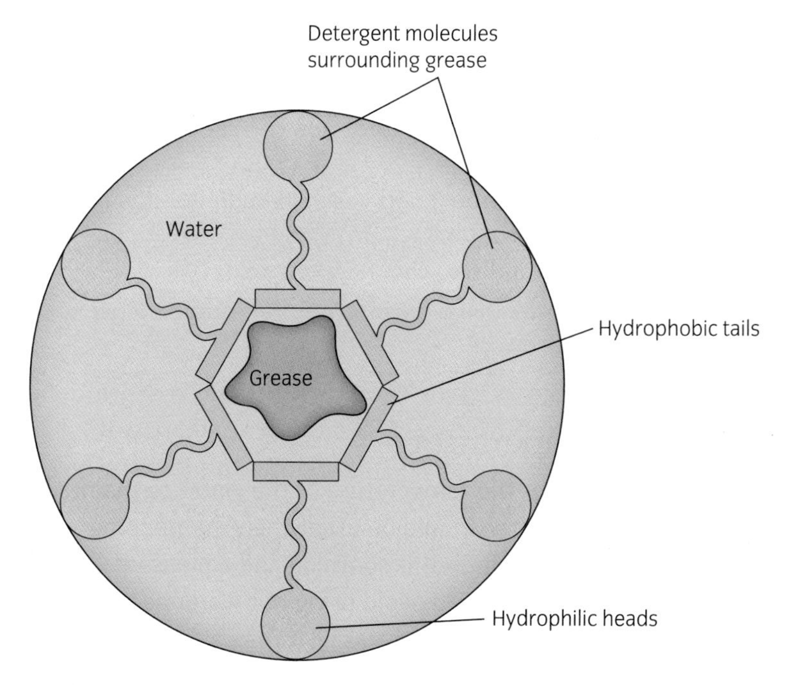

▲ Surfactant (detergent) in water, surrounding grease

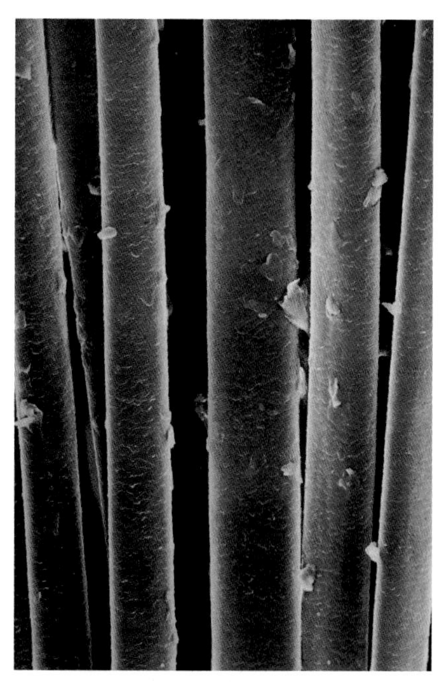

▲ Microscopic view: grease and dirt on the hair

When you apply a shampoo and water mix to the hair you create lather. The hydrophilic head of the surfactant is drawn to the water, while the hydrophobic tail is drawn to the oil and grease on the hair and scalp.

The oil and grease contain dirt and skin particles. The lathering action of the 'head' and 'tail' of the surfactant creates a push and pull effect on the oil and grease, lifting it from the hair shaft. The more oil and grease there is to bond with the surfactant molecules, the less the shampoo will lather. This is why a second shampoo always lathers more richly, because the majority of the oil and grease has already been removed by the initial shampoo.

When you use fresh water to rinse away the shampoo's lather, which now contains the oil and grease from the hair, it leaves a clean, oil-free hair shaft.

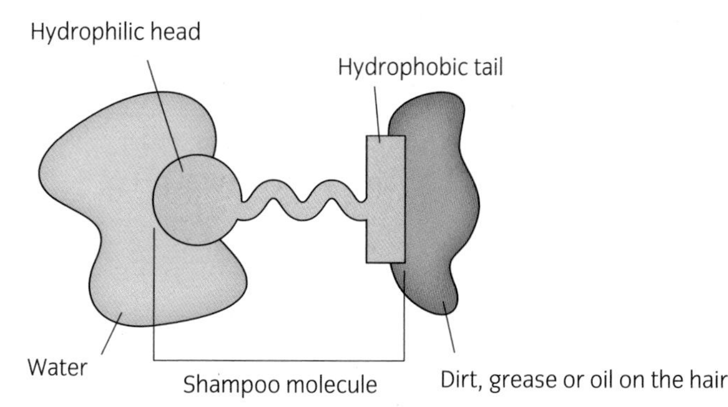

▲ Hydrophilic head attached to the water and hydrophobic tail attached to the grease and dirt

HANDY HINT

To help you remember which end of the surfactant molecule is water-loving, think of ducks! Ducks go underwater head first (hydrophilic – water-loving head), leaving their tails poking out of the water (hydrophobic – water-hating tail).

ACTIVITY

1. Almost fill a glass with fresh tap water and add a couple of tablespoons of oil (cooking oils work best as you can see the colour difference). What happens?
2. Now add a small squirt of detergent and watch through the side of the glass and look at the oil pattern on the top. What happens?
3. Give it a stir, wait a while, and see what happens next.
4. Now try it in a different order. Fill a glass with water, add detergent, then add the oil. What happens?

Effects of water temperature

It is essential that you consider the temperature of the water to maintain your client's comfort. Warm water should be used when shampooing and conditioning the hair and scalp as it is soothing and a pleasant temperature for your client. You should avoid using hot water as this opens the cuticle scales so hair may tangle easily; it may also scald the client and can make the scalp oily.

Cold water is unpleasant and may cause the client some discomfort; however, after shampooing and conditioning, a cooler rinse may benefit the client by closing the cuticle scales or soothing a sensitive scalp

HANDY HINT

Heat and hot water opens the cuticle scales while cool and cold water close the cuticle scales.

HANDY HINT

pH stands for 'power of hydronium ions' – the measure of how acid or alkaline a material is.

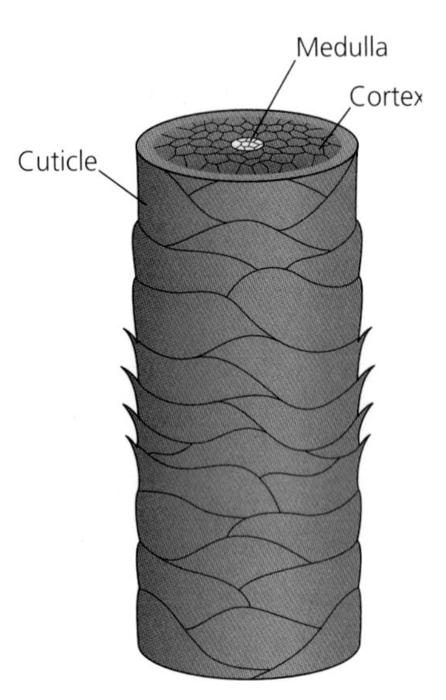

▲ Structure of the hair

How products affect the hair

Our hair and skin are acidic and have a natural pH of 4.5–5.5. Therefore the day-to-day shampoos and conditioners we use must be pH-balanced to our hair and skin – also pH 4.5–5.5. This ensures that the hair and skin's natural moisture is maintained and the cuticle scales are closed.

The pH scale has a range of pH 0–14. Acid products (pH 0–6.9) close the cuticle. Alkaline products (pH 7.1–14) open/lift the cuticle scales.

Acid products, pH 0–pH 6.9:

- pH 0–1 – strong acids, which would destroy and dissolve the hair completely
- pH 1.5–4 – mid-strength acids, which would cause the outer cuticle layer to shrink and harden while the body of the hair would swell (and eventually the hair could disintegrate)
- pH 4.5–6.9 – weak acids, such as those found in shampoos and conditioners that are balanced to the hair and skin's natural pH of 4.5–5.5.

pH-neutral (pH 7):

- water
- soapless shampoos – shampoos used to cleanse and clarify the hair before a perm are pH 7, which lifts the cuticle scales slightly to aid the perming process.

Alkaline products, pH 7.1–14:

- pH 7.1–7.9 – weak alkali, which slightly lifts the cuticle scales

- pH 8–10 – mid strength alkali, which swells the hair and causes cuticle scales to open, allowing penetration into the cortex
- pH 10–14 – strong alkali, which causes **depilatory** action, destroying and dissolving the hair completely.

KEY TERMS

Depilatory – causing hair removal.

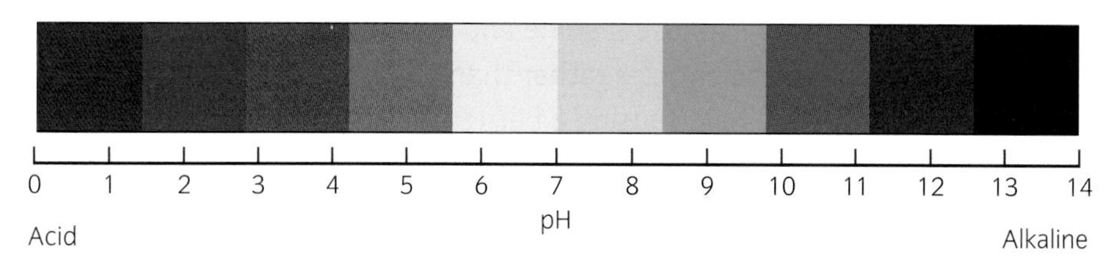

▲ The pH scale

The diagram below shows the effects of acid and alkali products on the hair shaft. You would most commonly use alkaline products when you need to lift the cuticle scales so that chemicals can **penetrate** the cortex layer.

KEY TERMS

Penetrate – enter into.

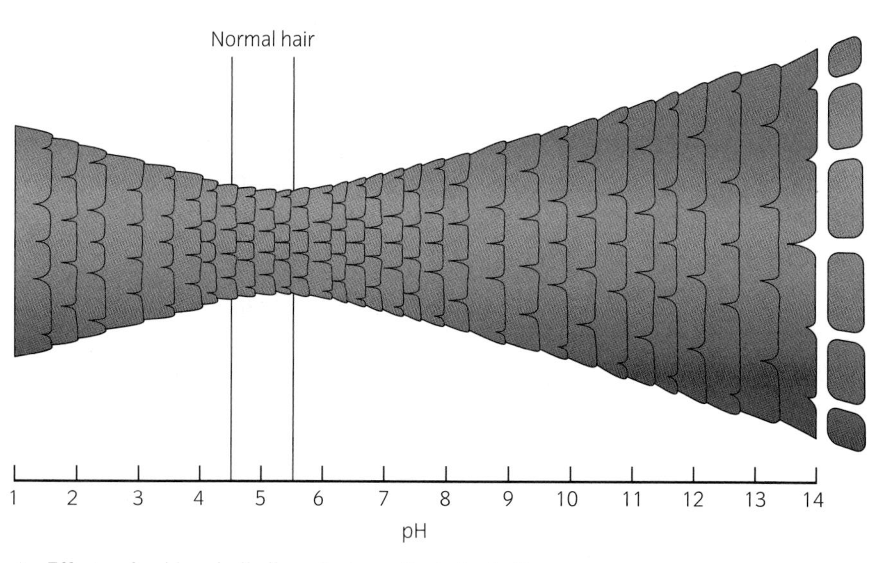

▲ Effects of acid and alkali products on the hair shaft

HANDY HINT

Alkali perm solutions are pH 7.5–9.5.

Permanent colouring products are pH 8–9.5.

HANDY HINT

To help you remember which products lift or close the cuticle scales:

ACID	ALKALINE
L	**I**
O	**F**
S	**T**
E	**S**
S	
The '**C**' in 'aCid' helps you to remember they 'Close' the cuticle scales.	The 'L' in 'aLkaline' helps you to remember they 'Lift' the cuticle scales.

HANDY HINT

If the hair is coated with oil-based products, you could apply a cleansing shampoo directly onto the hair, prior to wetting it during the shampoo process. This will give the hydrophobic tails in the shampoo molecule a chance to break down the oils and attach themselves before the water is added.

Product build-up and its effects

Some products are more difficult to remove from the hair and scalp and can build up over time. Daily applications of products build up in between shampoos and can then coat the hair and the cuticle layer. Product build-up can cause hair to lose it shine and look lacklustre, as the light is being absorbed into the cuticles rather than being reflected. A build-up of products will coat the hair, causing a barrier, which may affect styling and chemical services too. Product build-up on the scalp will make the scalp appear oily and may block the follicles and pores.

Using equipment during conditioning and treatment processes

Before shampooing, you should use a bristle brush through the hair to remove tangles and loosen products. After shampooing, you can detangle the hair with a wide-tooth comb before applying a surface conditioner. While the surface conditioner is on the hair, comb through again with a wide-toothed comb. A bristle brush should not be used on wet hair because it can cause the hair to overstretch and break.

You can apply a penetrating treatment to the hair with a tint brush, then comb the product through. Long hair should be clipped up to prevent moisture from the hair soaking through the towel to the client's clothes. Always follow your MFIs to ensure that the correct product is chosen to achieve the best result and that you use an adequate amount. If heat is recommended to allow the treatment to open the cuticle scales and penetrate into the cortex, use the appliance safely.

Using electrical equipment

When you use electrical equipment near water or on wet hair, be aware of the potential hazards and follow the Electricity at Work Regulations. Always ensure your equipment is in good working order and fit for use, to prevent the risk of harm or injury to you or your client. Use equipment correctly, following the manufacturer's instructions (MFIs).

Steamers can be used to add heat to open the cuticle scales. This method uses moist heat.

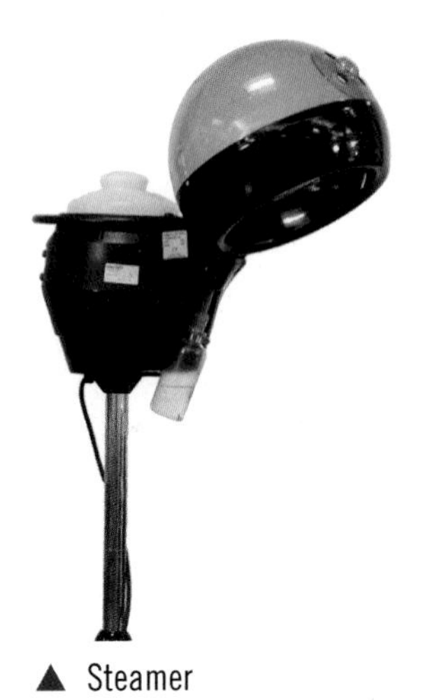

▲ Steamer

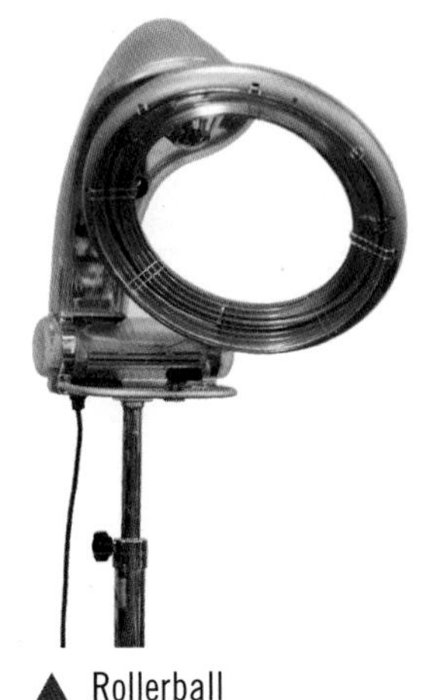

▲ Rollerball

▲ Climazone

Climazones or rollerballs can be used to apply dry heat to the hair to open the cuticle scales. Plastic caps can be secured to the client's head to help keep in the hair's moisture during the dry heat treatment.

Massage techniques used during shampooing and conditioning

A variety of different massage techniques can be applied during the shampooing and conditioning process.

Purpose and benefits of scalp massage

The main purposes of scalp massages are to:

- increase blood supply
- stimulate and tone the underlying tissues
- stimulate the nerves.

The body's circulatory and lymphatic systems benefit from massage. The main function of the circulatory system is to carry blood and nutrients to the **body tissues**. One of the main functions of the lymphatic system is to take away carbon dioxide and other waste. Both systems enable the body to stay healthy.

KEY TERM

Body tissues – for example, the skin and muscles.

Shampoo massage techniques

Technique	When to use and purpose	How to perform
Effleurage	During shampooing – it is particularly good for long hair to prevent tangles.	Effleurage massage is a gentle stroking massage movement used to apply the products to the hair.
Rotary	During shampooing – this massage movement benefits the client by stimulating the blood supply and relaxing the client. For clients with long hair, ensure that you remove your hands from the head regularly and comb through with your fingers, as continued rotary movements could cause tangles.	Rotary massage is a firm circular movement using the pads of the fingers over the surface of the scalp.
Friction	During shampooing for normal to dry scalps only, as it is stimulating, rather than relaxing, so is not always carried out. It is only done for a few minutes, working from the front to the back. This method enables the sebaceous glands to be stimulated and the fast, firm, plucking movements helps to stimulate the blood flow. This method must not be used on oily scalps or long hair.	A vigorous rubbing movement using the finger pads.

Conditioning massage techniques

Technique	When to use and purpose	How to perform
Effleurage	During conditioning – used to apply products to the hair and is particularly good for long hair to prevent tangles.	Effleurage is a gentle stroking massage movement.
Petrissage	During conditioning – this can be very relaxing for the client, but must be avoided on oily scalps. For long hair, your hands must be removed from the head regularly to prevent tangles, and you should return to the effleurage technique in between to detangle and soothe the scalp.	Petrissage is a slow, firm, deep, circular kneading massage movement, which stimulates the scalp and the sebaceous glands.

HANDY HINT

For clients with fine hair, you will need to use less product and more gentle movements, as the head is not protected by dense hair. For dense hair you may need to use more product to cover the head and enable the shampoo to remove oil, dirt and debris from the hair.

ACTIVITY

Misha has type 1, fine, medium-length hair. Describe the massage techniques the stylist should use.

The following are some things to remember when performing a scalp massage on your client:

- When massaging, do not rub the hair as this will cause friction on the cuticle scales and tangle the hair.
- Ensure the hair is free from excess moisture so that when the client sits up they will not get wet and uncomfortable.
- Ask the client to sit up, and support their head and back as they rise.
- Care must be taken when using petrissage massage movements on long hair to avoid tangling the hair and causing discomfort to your client.
- Do not use petrissage massage movements on oily scalps as it will activate the sebaceous glands and make the hair greasy.
- For long hair and oily scalps only use effleurage massage movements.
- For oily scalps use a surface conditioner on the mid-lengths and ends only.

HANDY HINT

Brush dry hair before shampooing to detangle, but use a wide-toothed comb when the hair is wet. Always comb or brush the hair following the directions of the cuticles.

▲ Use a wide-toothed comb on wet hair to detangle, but a brush on dry hair

Detangling hair from point to root

The cuticle scales overlap each other and lie flat from root to point when closed. When you detangle the hair after shampooing and conditioning you should always use a wide-toothed comb. Start combing at the ends of the hair (points), in a downwards direction, and start each new stroke further up so you work progressively up towards the root area. This ensures that you work with the direction of the cuticle scales. Hair stretches when wet, so always use a wide-toothed comb so you do not damage the hair and to prevent the hair from snagging.

HANDY HINT

If you notice there is still conditioning product in the hair, rinse the hair again; otherwise it may cause a barrier on the hair, making it lank and limp.

ACTIVITY

How long does your salon allow for:

- shampoo and surface conditioning service on above-shoulder-length hair?
- shampoo and surface conditioning service on below-shoulder-length hair?
- shampoo and penetrating conditioning service on below-shoulder-length hair?
- shampoo and scalp treatment on above-shoulder-length hair?

ACTIVITY

Based on your answers in the previous activity, how many of the following could you do in 1 hour and 30 minutes?

- Shampoo and surface conditioning service on above-shoulder length hair
- Shampoo and surface conditioning service on below-shoulder length hair.

In 2 hours and 30 minutes, how many of the following could you do?

- Shampoo and penetrating conditioning service on below-shoulder-length hair
- Shampoo and scalp treatment on above-shoulder-length hair.

Shampoo and conditioning products

There are hundreds of shampoo and conditioning products available for clients to buy. Manufacturers make the most of this selling opportunity by providing a variety of shampoo and conditioning products that look vibrant and interesting, smell great and promise to enhance the hair's condition, add volume and fullness, and prolong colours. Conditioning products are available as surface conditioners, penetrating conditioners and scalp treatments.

How shampoos and conditioning products affect the hair and scalp

Shampoo products cleanse the hair and scalp, and prepare the hair for the following service. Conditioning products provide shine by smoothing the cuticle scales, which improves the handling of the hair and makes combing and brushing easier.

The table overleaf shows the types of shampoo and conditioning products available, how and when to use them and what equipment to use.

Hair and scalp condition	Ingredients in shampoo and conditioner and their effects on the hair and scalp	Shampoo and conditioner product and how to use them	Equipment
Normal hair/ scalp	Rosemary, soya, aloe vera and jojoba oils are often key ingredients in all shampoos and conditioners. These ingredients help to maintain the hair's condition and moisture levels.	Normal/everyday shampoo – use effleurage and rotary.  Normal shampoo Surface conditioner (rinse-out or leave-in) – use effleurage and petrissage  Rinse-out conditioner for normal hair  Leave-in conditioner	Wide-toothed comb

Hair and scalp condition	Ingredients in shampoo and conditioner and their effects on the hair and scalp	Shampoo and conditioner product and how to use them	Equipment
Dry hair/ scalp	Coconut oil, jojoba oil, honey and almond or brazil nut oil are some of the main ingredients found in shampoos and conditioners to help treat dry hair and scalps. These products are naturally moisturising and nourish the hair.	Moisturising shampoo – use effleurage, friction and rotary, depending on hair length. Moisturising shampoo Moisturising surface conditioner (rinse-out or leave-in) – use effleurage and petrissage. Penetrating conditioner (rinse-out or leave-in) – effleurage. Penetrating treatment	Wide-toothed comb Optional bowl and brush for application Steamer Rollerball or climazone used with a plastic cap to lock in the moisture
Dandruff-affected	Tea tree oil, medicated ingredients, zinc pyrithione, selenium sulphide, ginger, eucalyptus, lavender and sage are used to treat dandruff. Ginger, eucalyptus, lavender and sage may help to soothe the scalp.	Dandruff-affected scalp shampoo or sensitive scalp shampoo – use effleurage, friction and rotary, depending on hair length. Scalp treatments (rinse-out or leave-in) – sprinkle onto the scalp and massage in.	Wide-toothed comb

→

Hair and scalp condition	Ingredients in shampoo and conditioner and their effects on the hair and scalp	Shampoo and conditioner product and how to use them	Equipment
		Scalp treatment	
Oily	Lemon, camomile, egg and citrus fruits are often the main ingredients, as these help break down the oils and slow down the production of sebum from the sebaceous glands.	Shampoo for seborrhoea/oily scalp. Cleansing shampoo – use effleurage and a gentle non-stimulating rotary movement. Shampoo for oily hair Scalp treatments (rinse-out or leave-in) – sprinkle onto the scalp and massage in. Scalp treatment	Wide-toothed comb

ACTIVITY

1 List the range of shampoos, conditioners and treatments available in your salon for dry, normal, oily and dandruff-affected hair and scalps.
2 What conditioning product would you recommend for dry, type 4 very curly wiry hair?

ACTIVITY

Create a poster for your clients providing information about one or two of the products listed above. Make sure you check your spellings and that your grammar and punctuation are also correct. Make it colourful and appealing for your clients.

Using products cost effectively

Shampoo and conditioning products are costly to the salon, so using the correct amount is important. If you use too much product, not only are you wasting money for the salon and harming the environment with more product container waste, you also risk overloading the hair with products which can affect the service and the longevity of the style.

Repeating the shampooing

Repeat the shampooing process only if required; if the hair does not lather on the first shampoo, it indicates that oil or products still remain within the hair and therefore further shampoo applications are needed.

Potential effects of using incorrect products

Shampoos and conditioners are available for every hair type and scalp condition. Using the incorrect shampoo/conditioner can create a barrier by coating cuticle scales and preventing penetration of chemical services. They can also cause irritation to the scalp or the hair to become lank.

When shampooing the hair prior to a perm you should use a pre-perm shampoo, as it is pH neutral and lifts the cuticle scales, ready for the perm solution to enter the cortex. Never condition the hair and smooth the cuticle scales before a perm, as this will cause a barrier to the perm solution.

Always ensure that you use the correct shampoo and conditioning product for the hair and scalp condition to prevent problems occurring:

- Fine hair – excessive conditioner or deeply moisturising products can cause fine hair to become limp and lank.
- Oily scalps – using a moisturising shampoo will coat the hair with a layer of moisture and could activate the sebaceous glands, producing more sebum.
- Type 4 hair, dry hair and scalps – using a shampoo for oily scalps may cause the hair to feel drier with rough cuticle scales. The product is designed to break down the natural oils needed for the hair, which may cause irritation to dry scalps and cause damage to dry hair.

You must always refer to the MFIs:

- for the correct use of products
- to check how much to use
- to find out how to apply the product
- to check whether heat is required
- to know how to remove the product from the hair.

Removing conditioning and treatment products

Rinse-out conditioning products and treatments must be thoroughly removed from the hair; otherwise the hair will be left feeling overloaded and lank. The conditioning residue remaining in the hair will affect the subsequent service and the style will not hold.

HANDY HINT

After chemical processes you must always use a pH-balancing conditioner to smooth and close the cuticle scales and lock in the moisture to prevent the hair from drying out and becoming brittle.

HANDY HINT

Avoid wastage and use products cost effectively – only use the amount you need for the hair length and density of your client's hair.

Importance of removing excess water from the hair

At the end of the service, gently squeeze the hair to remove the excess water from the hair to ensure the client is not left with water dripping from their hair, which may cause them discomfort. You can also gently squeeze the hair with the towel, but avoid pulling on the roots of the hair. Do not rub the hair excessively with the towel to remove excess moisture, as the hair will tangle and matt together.

Effect of heat during conditioning treatments

Temperature affects the cuticle scales in a similar way to acid and alkaline products. Heat aids the opening of the cuticle scales and is often used to reduce the processing time of chemical services. Heat is used to open the cuticle scales during a penetrating treatment so that the product can enter the cortex to strengthen the hair and aid repair.

Excessive heat, either from an **accelerator** used during a treatment, or from very hot water, can cause damage to your client's hair and scalp. Hot water should be avoided when shampooing oily scalps as the heat can activate the sebaceous glands and produce more sebum.

KEY TERM

Accelerator – appliance used to apply heat to the hair and speed up a service, for example steamers, rollerballs and climazones.

▲ Providing advice to a client

▲ Protect hair from environmental damage with a hat

Providing clients with advice and recommendations

It is important that your knowledge of the salon's product range, both at the shampoo area and available for retail, is sound and up to date. You should advise your client of the most suitable shampoos, conditioners and treatments available in the salon and to purchase for use at home.

Clients with damaged hair should be given advice on how to detangle their hair, and how to comb and brush their hair correctly to avoid further damage. You will need to know your salon's available brands of products to be able to give the most effective aftercare advice to your client. Give them advice for maintaining the condition of their hair and scalp between salon visits, and include how the products should be used and how often.

For clients who are going on holiday, offer advice on hair protection from the sun and wind, and perhaps the benefits of wearing a hat.

The products you use in the salon to shampoo and condition the hair and scalp should be explained, demonstrated and recommended to your client for use at home. When advising your clients about retail products you must give clear and accurate information about why you are recommending these products, and their benefits. Openly and constructively discuss the condition of the client's hair and scalp and how these retail products will help to improve or maintain the condition.

When giving aftercare advice, use positive body language that promotes an open and trusting relationship. Use eye contact and check the client's body language to identify any areas of uncertainty. Use open and closed questions to really understand your client's needs for home haircare.

Always consider your client's lifestyle. Does your client have time for further salon treatments, or would they be best suited to maintain the condition of their hair at home? Would your client prefer the convenience of surface conditioners, rather than having to find 20 minutes to develop a penetrating conditioner and heat some towels to aid the process?

If your client's hair had product build-up, you should suggest alternative products that will still suit their particular hairstyle, but will work more effectively on the hair and scalp. If your client wants to continue with their current styling product, offer advice on how they could improve the removal process; perhaps suggest that your client uses neat shampoo on the hair if wax products have been used. Neat shampoo will attach to the oil-based product prior to wetting the hair and enable a more thorough removal.

HANDY HINT

When providing aftercare make sure you:

- provide clear and accurate information
- give feedback and advice that is open and constructive
- use positive body language
- use open and closed questions.

ACTIVITY

What advice would you give the following clients?

Pauline has long, fine, coloured hair and is going on holiday next week in the sun.

Lenka has very curly short dry hair and dandruff caused by an allergic reaction to chemicals.

Roxanne has oily, medium-length hair that is a little dry at the ends from previous colour treatments.

Gita has a dry scalp, medium-length red-tinted Asian hair, and swims regularly.

Anita has long, abundant hair that is very dry on the mid-lengths and ends.

Dave loves sport and washes his hair regularly.

Suzie enjoys going for a spin on her motorbike, but her long hair suffers in the wind.

Paul has oily-looking hair and uses a lot of wax products to support his hairstyle.

WHAT YOU MUST DO

For your practical assessments you must:

- apply safe working practices when shampooing, conditioning and treating the hair and scalp
- shampoo, condition and treat the hair and scalp.

Apply safe working practices when shampooing, conditioning and treating the hair and scalp

Throughout the shampooing, conditioning and treatment services you must ensure you prepare for the service ahead. The shampooing and conditioning service is the starting point for main services – such as cutting and styling – so it is important that you are prepared in order to help keep the salon running smoothly and to time.

▲ A stylist working in a clean, tidy manner

Preparing for shampooing, conditioning and treatment services

Ensure you prepare your client to meet the salon's requirements using a gown and towel and a plastic cape if required.

In order for you to be ready and prepared for the service, you need to ensure your own personal hygiene and appearance meets your salon's standards and your client's expectations. Do not attend work if you have a contagious condition, such as influenza, a common cold or an eye infection. Ensure you cover any open wounds and refer any potential cross-infection, hazards or risks to your manager.

▲ Work safely

Apply safe and hygienic methods of working

You must always follow the law, as well as your salon's rules and regulations for health and safety. Always read the instructions on products and tools and use them properly and for their intended use. Take care when using electrical appliances, mop up spillages or slippery surfaces and eliminate all possible risks by removing any hazards.

To keep yourself safe, wear personal protective equipment – gloves and aprons are available for the assistants and stylists to protect their hands and clothing.

Make sure your client is positioned comfortably and that you also maintain a good body posture throughout the treatment service to prevent injury or fatigue.

Working safely and keeping your work area clean and tidy minimises the risk of harm and injury to yourself and others and prevents cross-contamination. It also ensures a professional image is presented to the client and visitors.

Use working methods that minimise the risk of cross-infection

Ensure the basin area is clean, free of waste and ready for your client's service. Clean basin areas and work surfaces with detergent and water, disinfect the basin and your equipment using either suitable chemical liquids or a UV light, and sterilise tools in an autoclave. If you have encountered an infection or infestation, remove all infected waste immediately and dispose of it in the dedicated salon bin, boil-wash the towels and gowns and sterilise tools thoroughly.

Use working methods that minimise the risk of harm or injury to yourself and others

The diagram below shows the safety considerations and areas of good practice you should follow:

HANDY HINT

Cover any open wounds to prevent cross-contamination.

Maintain your responsibilities for health and safety

Wear personal protective equipment if required

Consider your posture and your client's body position for health and safety, and comfort

Keep your work area clean and tidy

Minimise risks of damage to tools

Use clean resources and minimise the risk of cross-infection

Promote environmental and sustainable working practices and minimise waste

Ensure your personal hygiene, protection and appearance is up to salon standard

Minimise risk of injury to self and others and follow manufacturers' instructions

Use your time effectively and complete the service in a commerically acceptable time

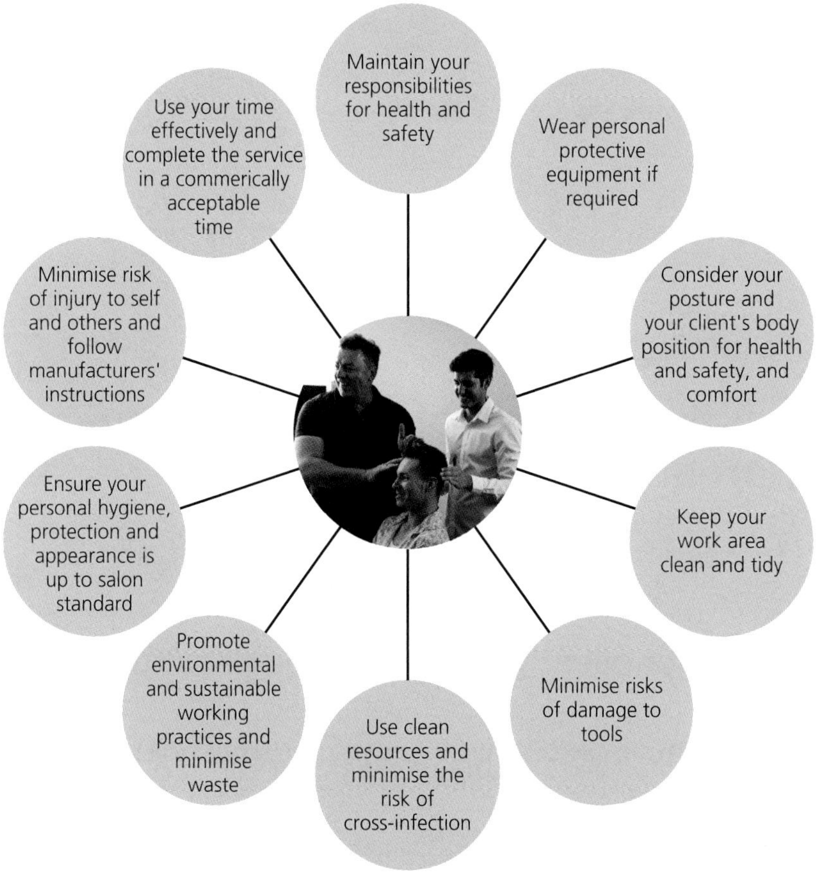

▲ Good practice and safety considerations to follow when shampooing and conditioning hair

Use working methods that ensure the use of clean resources

You must ensure you have a supply of fresh clean towels and gowns. If you are using a trolley and applying a treatment at the workstation, you must ensure you have the trolley to your favoured side of working, to suit if you are left- or right-handed. Always make sure that your trolley and tools are clean.

HEALTH AND SAFETY

Use a clean gown and towel for every client to prevent cross-contamination and to promote a professional working environment.

HANDY HINT

Always replenish stock without causing a disruption to the client's service and report shortages to the relevant person.

HEALTH AND SAFETY

Minimise the risk of damage to tools by reading and following the instructions supplied by the manufacturer. If you do not know how to use tools or equipment, always ask your supervisor or a stylist to help you.

THE HAIR PROFESSIONAL AT WORK

Be prepared and deliver a quality service by ensuring there is sufficient stock of shampoos and conditioners and that hair treatments are available. If you notice you are running low on resources, such as towels and gowns, you must inform the relevant person or reload the washing machine/dryer to ensure a plentiful supply in advance of the service. If stock such as shampoos needs re-ordering, inform the relevant person or note it on the stock list.

HANDY HINT

Every day you must ensure your own hygiene, personal protection and salon appearance meet accepted industry and organisational requirements.

Follow instructions for the safe use of equipment, materials and products

You must always follow instructions supplied by your manager and the workplace regarding storage of stock and equipment. Suppliers and manufacturers will provide instructions on how to use and store products and equipment correctly and safely.

At the end of the service, maintain health and safety and help protect the environment by disposing of any waste materials correctly in the designated lidded waste bin and recycling or refilling product bottles where possible.

Carry out shampooing, conditioning and treatment services

It is important to apply your knowledge of health and safety and put it into practice when you carry out a shampoo or conditioning treatment service.

Protect your client's clothing throughout the service

During the shampoo and conditioning service you should use the following items of protective clothing for your clients to ensure they remain dry and clean throughout:

- gown
- towels – disposable or reusable and washable
- plastic cape – disposable or reusable and wipe clean.

Use working methods that make effective use of your working time

It is vitally important that basic services, like the shampoo and conditioning service, keep the salon running to time, so you need to be prepared for the service. Always make sure the shampoo area is ready to greet the next client, ensure tools and resources are readily available and prioritise your time effectively.

▲ If it's not dirty, wash at 30 °C

Use working methods that promote environmental and sustainable working practices

Throughout the service turn off the water supply in between shampoos, and avoid water and product wastage. Only wash towels and gowns when there is a full load for the washing machine and where possible wash at lower temperatures. Hang up towels to dry if you can to avoid using energy on tumble drying.

Complete the service within a commercially viable time

An average time frame for a short hair shampoo and conditioning service is around 10 minutes, and up to 15 minutes for longer hair that requires more rinsing and detangling time. Treatments will add extra time to the service, as they are often left on and placed under heat to work more effectively. It is important that you work to an industry and commercial time frame to ensure the salon runs a viable service.

Shampoo, condition and treat the hair and scalp

To effectively complete the service you will need to consult with your client, select suitable products, tools and equipment to use, carry out the shampoo, condition and treatment services and provide aftercare advice.

Consult with clients about services and outcomes of tests

You must carry out a porosity test to identify whether the cuticle scales are open or closed and if the hair is porous or non-porous. If the cuticle scales are open, the hair is porous and will need more conditioner and maybe even a treatment. You must also test the strength of the cortex with an elasticity test, as weak hair will need treating.

Always ask your client questions to identify if they have contra-indications to hair and scalp treatment services.

HANDY HINT

Refer back to Chapter 2 for a recap on how and why you carry out porosity and elasticity tests.

Select suitable products, tools and equipment

Once you have consulted with your client and carried out the relevant hair tests, you are ready to choose the most suitable products for the client's hair and scalp condition, to prepare the hair for the service and to achieve the best result. You will need to use the most suitable massage techniques for the hair and scalp type and to ensure client comfort.

Always use products, tools and equipment suitable for your client's hair condition and scalp condition – these products include surface, penetrating and scalp treatment products. Tools may include bowls and

HANDY HINT

Make sure you monitor and time the development of conditioning products, so that the salon runs to time and the hair is not overloaded with conditioning products, leaving the hair unmanageable.

brushes for treatments, and heat accelerators as equipment used for penetrating conditioners.

Carry out shampooing, conditioning and treatment services

The diagram below shows ways of adapting the service to meet the needs of your clients' hair, scalp and comfort.

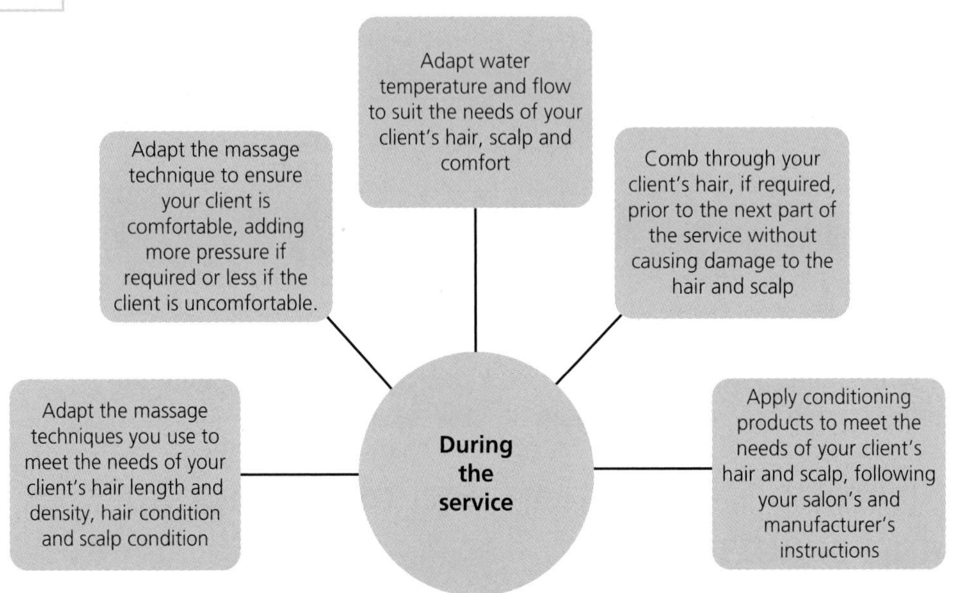

Adapt your massage techniques to suit the client's hair and scalp

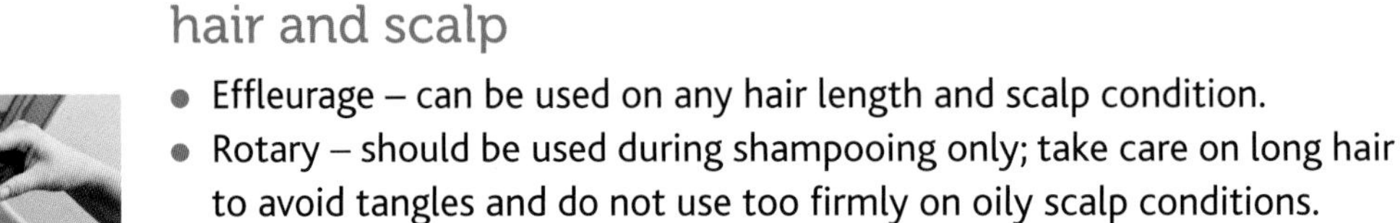

- Effleurage – can be used on any hair length and scalp condition.
- Rotary – should be used during shampooing only; take care on long hair to avoid tangles and do not use too firmly on oily scalp conditions.
- Friction – should be used during shampooing only. Avoid on long hair, oily scalps and fine hair.

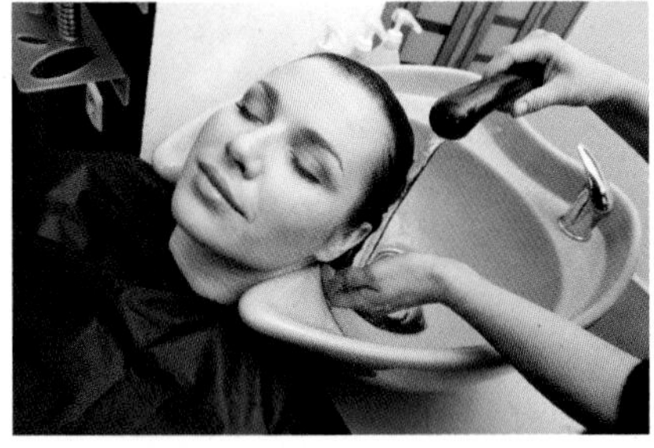

▲ Check the water temperature on your hands before applying water to the scalp

Adapt water temperature and flow

You must always check the water temperature on your hands or wrists before you apply it through the hair to avoid scalding the scalp or causing discomfort to your client.

The flow of water must be controlled – if it is too high it may splash your client and if it is too low it may not rinse sufficient suds or debris from the hair. You should angle the tap head away from the hairline and ensure the hair is not over the client's face, as water will always travel to the lowest point! Always ensure the water flow is angled in the direction of the cuticles.

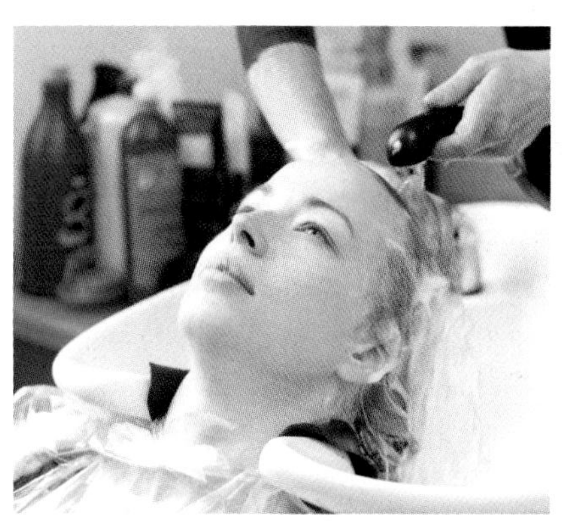

▲ Ensure the hair and water flow are away from the client's face

HANDY HINT

Ensure the water flow follows the direction of the cuticle scales to help smooth them.

HEALTH AND SAFETY

Promote environmental and sustainable working practices while carrying out a shampoo and conditioning service by turning off the tap in between shampoos and not wasting water.

Comb through your client's hair

Comb through your client's hair, if required, prior to the next part of the service, without causing damage to the hair and scalp.

▲ Comb through your client's hair

Apply conditioning products, adapt your techniques and monitor development

Apply conditioning products to meet the needs of your client's hair and scalp, following your salon and manufacturer's instructions.

Adapt your conditioning massage techniques to meet the needs of your client's hair and scalp condition and following manufacturer's instructions:

- Effleurage – can be used on any hair length and scalp condition.
- Petrissage – should be used during conditioning; take care on long hair to avoid tangles and do not use too firmly on oily scalp conditions.

Monitor and time the development of the conditioning product and apply heat at the correct temperature, if required.

The diagram below explains the process to follow to prepare the hair.

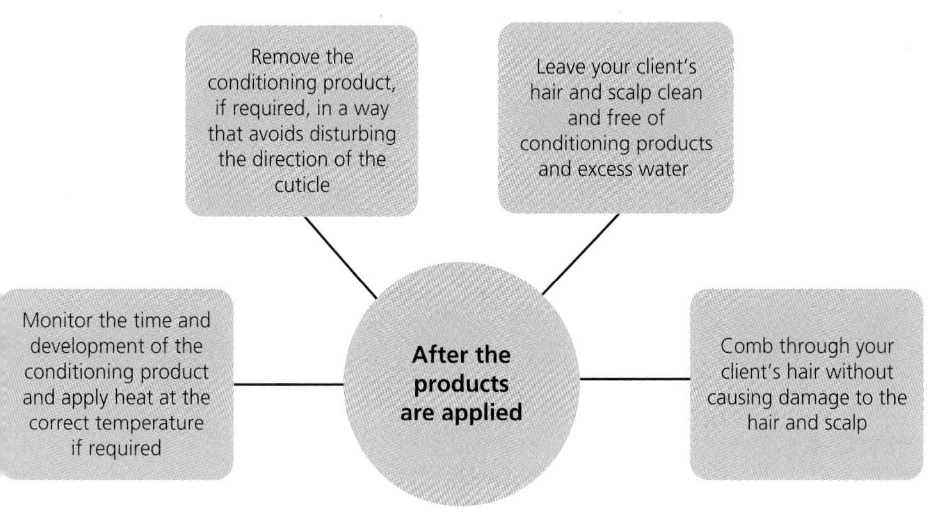

▲ How to prepare the hair for the next service

HANDY HINT

Ensure you always remove shampoo and conditioning products thoroughly from the hair and scalp. Shampoo residue left in the hair can cause scalp irritations and failing to remove the conditioner from the hair can leave it unmanageable and oily.
At the end of the shampoo service, squeeze out and remove excess water from the hair before you apply the conditioner. This will prevent the conditioner from being diluted.

After the conditioning process, remove any excess water from the hair to prevent the hair from dripping and causing the client to get wet.

Remove conditioning products and excess water from the hair

After development, remove the conditioning product, if required, and gently squeeze out the excess moisture from the hair. Do not rub the hair as this will disturb the direction of the cuticle. Always make sure the hair is ready for the next service.

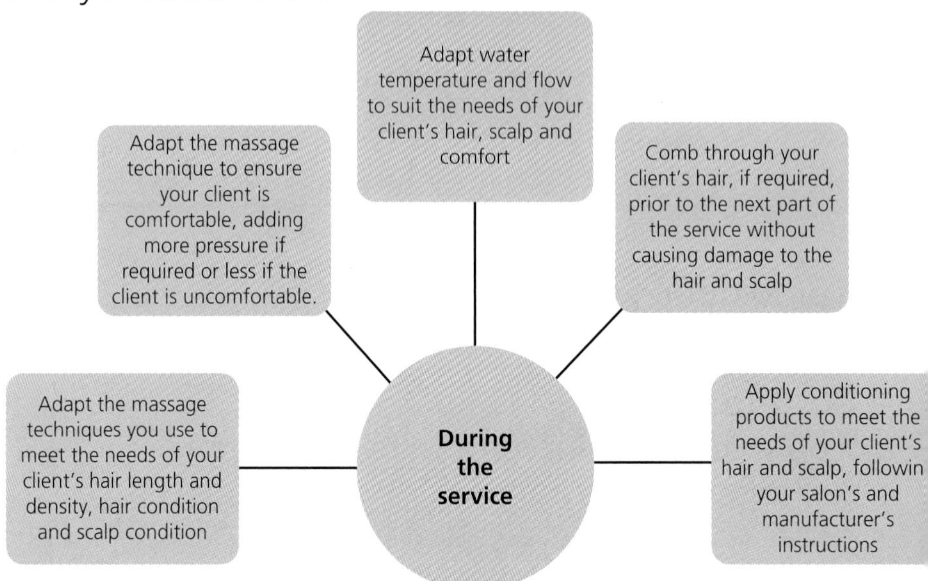

▲ During the conditioning service

Comb through your client's hair without causing damage to the hair and scalp

Comb through your client's hair using a wide-toothed comb, starting detangling the hair at the points and gradually work up towards the roots.

Provide clients with advice and recommendations on the service

At the end of the service always provide advice and recommendations to your client – this should include:

- correct detangling techniques
- suitable shampoos, conditioning products
- time interval between services
- present and future products and services.

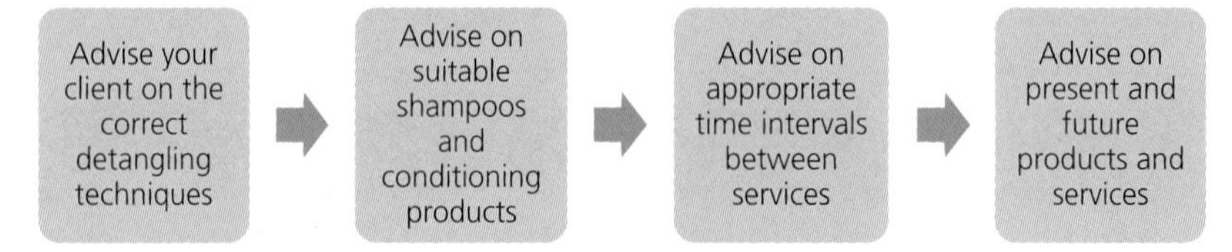

STEP BY STEP

In this part of the chapter you will look at how to shampoo the hair and scalp using the correct massage techniques.

Shampoo the hair and scalp using massage techniques

Once you have decided on the correct tools, equipment and products required to achieve the desired result, you can begin the shampoo process. You will need to use the effleurage massage technique to apply the product to the hair. Effleurage is a gentle stroking movement, using the palms of your hands. Once the product is applied you would use rotary massage movements to cleanse the hair. Rotary is a quick, small, circular movement used to loosen the dirt from the scalp and hair. Your hands are positioned in a claw-like manner and you use your finger pads to work around the head in a methodical way to cleanse the whole head. Friction – a fast plucking movement – can be used to stimulate the scalp, if the hair is short and abundant and the scalp is not oily.

STEP 1 – Apply a protective gown, towel and a disposable cape under the towel.

STEP 2 – Support the client when moving back into the backwash, adjust the basin and check that the client is comfortable. Remove clips and ensure all the hair is in the backwash.

STEP 3 – Wet your hands and shake off any excess water. Gently wet the hairline to gather in flyaway hair. Protective gloves may be worn.

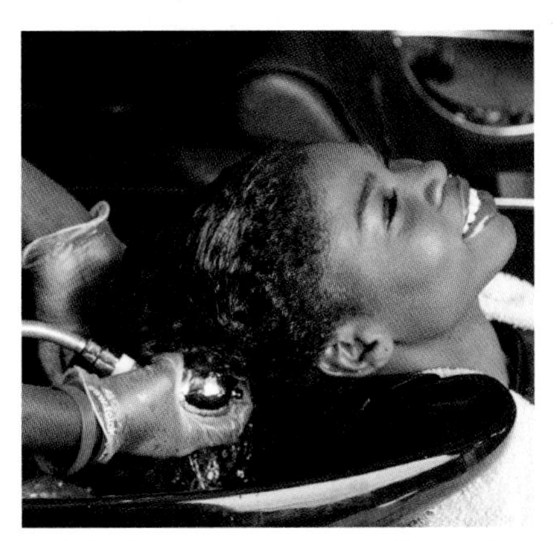

STEP 4 – Apply water to the crown first. Apply the water on and off the scalp and check client is happy with the temperature.

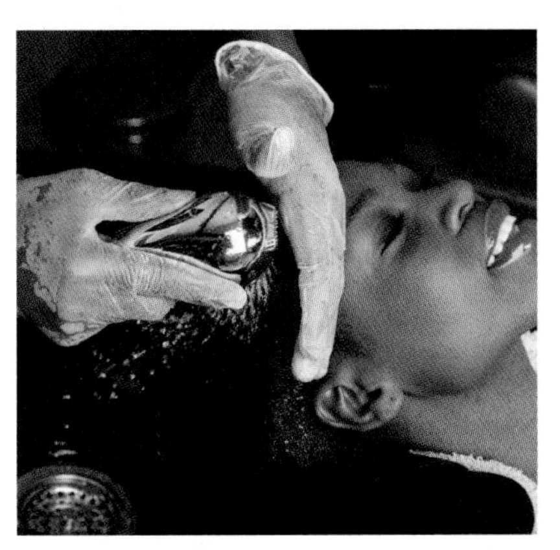

STEP 5 – Protect the client from drips onto the face using your hand as a guard. Ensure that all the hair is saturated including hairlines and lengths. Move the water flow nearer to the hairline, stroking away excess water as you work.

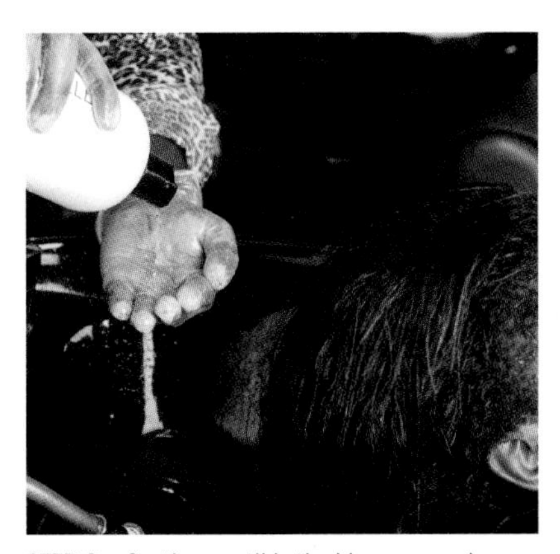

STEP 6 – Continue until both sides are evenly damp. Use your hand as a guard around the ear area, directing the water away. Lift the head and check the underneath for saturation. In order to evenly soak the back of the head cup one hand along the hairline and apply water with the other to guard the water from soaking the client. Brush away or wring the excess water from the hair before applying the shampoo. Depending on the manufacturer's instructions, use approximately a 3 cm diameter of shampoo in the palm of the hand.

STEP 7 – Massage the product in your hands and, with your palms flat, work from the front hairline to apply the shampoo with an effleurage technique. Make sure you apply the product to all of the hair, especially around the hairlines and throughout long hair. Lift the head to apply shampoo to the underneath.

STEP 8 – Use your fingers and thumbs and a rotary technique to work the shampoo into the hair. Start from the front hairline to the top of the head.

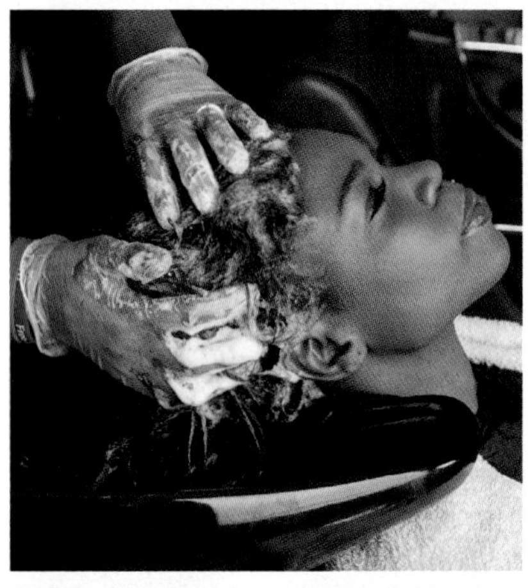

STEP 9 – Work from the centre front hairline into the side hairlines. Then work behind the ears into the nape and up through the centre of the head. (If the hair is short you could also use the friction massage technique through the sides and back.)

STEP 10 – Rinse the product from your hands, check the water temperature and rinse the hair, guarding the face, ear and neck areas. Rinse the longer lengths in the basin first.

HANDY HINT

The same process is used for a male client. With shorter hair be aware that the saturated hair can spring back and splash the client.

Condition the hair and scalp using massage techniques

Having completed the shampooing procedure, you can now apply a surface conditioner.

Before applying surface conditioner, ensure the hair is free from excess moisture, as the water will dilute the product. Apply the product to the palms of your hands (about the size of a 50 pence piece) and use effleurage massage techniques followed by petrissage to apply the conditioner to the hair. To carry out petrissage massage movements, spread out your fingers and use slow, deep, circular, kneading movements.

This slow massage movement is very relaxing if carried out correctly and stimulates the blood flow and the sebaceous glands. After petrissage massage, return to effleurage for a few seconds before continuing.

Using a wide-toothed comb, comb the product through the hair starting from the points and follow the direction of the cuticle scales, working in sections towards the roots. Ensure all tangles are removed, without causing any discomfort to your client.

HANDY HINT

Surface conditioners add moisture to the surface of the hair and smooth the cuticle scales. Penetrating treatments can help to repair the hair's structure and strengthen the cortex. Scalp treatments treat scalp conditions.

STEP 1 – Apply conditioner using an effleurage technique to work the product into the hair. This will relax your client and will stimulate the blood supply.

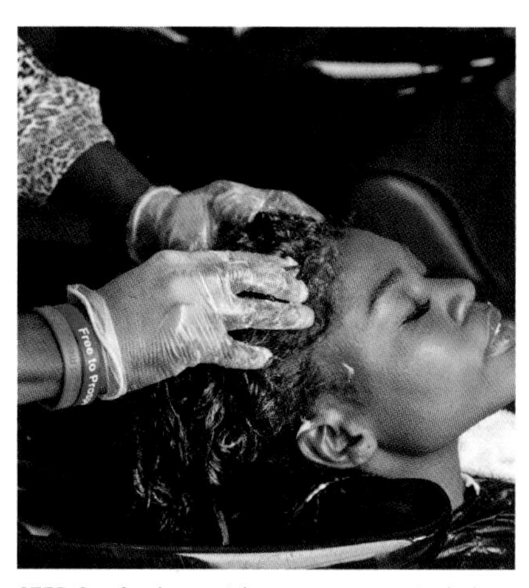

STEP 2 – Apply a petrissage massage technique to the sides and work in to the top. Apply the same technique down the centre, ensuring coverage of lengths, hairline and the nape.

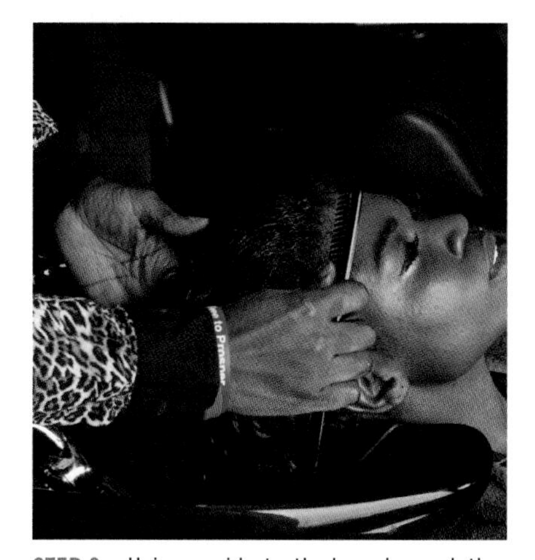

STEP 3 – Using a wide-toothed comb, comb the conditioner through the hair from roots to point and then rinse thoroughly from the hair.

STEP 4 – Apply a folded towel over the front hairline, wrap it down over the ears, under the back and pass one side over the other. Wrap up and over and secure into the fold.

HANDY HINT

With longer hair, use the wide end of the comb and comb the product through for even coverage and to eliminate tangles. Start with the ends and work upwards to avoid damage to the hair. Separate the hair into panels to avoid tangles and damage.

Scalp and penetrating conditioner treatments

Most scalp treatments come in the form of tonics and are applied directly to the scalp. If the product is very watery, then apply it at the basin and ensure your client keeps their head back. If it is sprinkled onto the hair then it can be applied at the workstation. These products are not washed out of the hair and can be applied after a surface or penetrating conditioner.

Before applying penetrating conditioner, ensure the hair is free from excess moisture, as the water will dilute the product. Section the hair from the centre to each side. Each section should be approximately 2 cm in depth apart.

The treatment can also be applied to mid-lengths and ends only, if this is more suitable for the scalp. If you are applying the product to the scalp, and when you have coated the product through the entire surface of the hair, use petrissage massage movements to stimulate the blood flow to the scalp.

Steamers are the preferred method of applying heat with penetrating treatments as they add moisture and are kinder to the hair. Always accurately monitor the time a steamer is used, following the MFIs.

HANDY HINT

Surface conditioners and penetrating treatments can be used alongside a scalp treatment, as one conditions the hair and the other treats the scalp.

Test your knowledge

Question 1

Describe how you would reduce energy usage and encourage sustainability in a salon during a shampoo service.

Question 2

Describe when you would use friction massage techniques.

Question 3

State the importance of detangling the hair correctly.

Question 4

A client has yellowy oily dandruff.

- Explain the likely cause of this adverse scalp.
- Explain how the stylist should deal with this adverse scalp.

Multiple choice questions

5 Which of the following is the most likely consequence of incorrect positioning at the basin?

a Client could get wet and be uncomfortable
b The stylist may suffer allergies
c Contact dermatitis
d Slippery surfaces

6 Which two of the following describe product build-up on the hair?

1 Dull hair
2 Flaky deposits on hair
3 Smooth cuticle scales
4 Seborrhoea

a 1 and 2
b 2 and 3
c 3 and 4
d 4 and 1

7 A detergent molecule is partly hydrophilic. What is the meaning of this term and which part is hydrophilic?

a Water loving; the head
b Water loving; the tail
c Water hating; the head
d Water hating; the tail

8 Which of the following is the best conditioner to recommend for a client with dry damaged hair?

a A surface conditioner
b A penetrating conditioner
c A scalp treatment conditioner
d A conditioner containing zinc pyrithione

CHAPTER 4

CUT HAIR USING A VARIETY OF TECHNIQUES TO CREATE A VARIETY OF LOOKS

STAR APPRENTICE: BETHAN POLLEY – TONI&GUY CHELMSFORD

My name is Bethan Polley and I am an apprentice at Toni&Guy Chelmsford. I'm now one year into my Apprenticeship placement at the Toni&Guy salon and I have loved every moment, from shampooing clients to passing each of my assessments. I started at Toni&Guy working Saturdays and this experience assured me that hairdressing was the career path I wanted to take – the vibrant salon environment is an exciting place to work, where you're constantly dealing with people, problem solving, and using your communication skills to ensure the customers get the experience and end result they came into the salon for.

Since starting my training, I've definitely had to face some challenges, like passing an assessment that involved technical skills I found difficult. But if you're determined and prepared to work hard, you can definitely overcome these. I now have more confidence in my abilities and know I can work hard and succeed.

Joining an Apprenticeship needs commitment if you're going to achieve the most you possibly can. It can open up endless opportunities because you gain a qualification and experience in a work environment; it also shows your passion and determination to succeed in your chosen career.

I hope to become a technician for Toni&Guy and one day be a colour specialist and work on London Fashion Week, and I know the Apprenticeship route is the best way for me to achieve this.

This chapter maps to:

- Unit 3, Cut hair using a range of techniques to create a variety of looks (Level 2 Diploma for Hair Professionals – Hairdressing).

INTRODUCTION

Cutting hair is the foundation of all styles and at the centre of your role as a stylist. Having learnt the art of a good consultation, you can now focus on how to style and cut the hair. The cut and shape of every style is fundamental to a successful end result, so learning basic and creative techniques will be of paramount importance for the rest of your styling and cutting career. So what are you waiting for? Get your scissors and let's get started!

After reading this chapter you will:

- understand how health and safety policies and procedures affect cutting services
- be able to apply safe working practices when cutting hair
- know how to cut hair to achieve a variety of looks
- be able to creatively restyle hair.

HANDY HINT

Use your time effectively to ensure you work to commercially viable times and prepare your tools in advance.

HANDY HINT

Always protect your client's clothes from hair cuttings by gowning them and using a clean towel or cutting collar to ensure client comfort throughout the service.

▲ Cutting collar

HEALTH AND SAFETY RESPONSIBILITIES AND PROCEDURES

When cutting hair, you will be working with sharp tools, electrical appliances and walking on slippery surfaces due to fallen hair cuttings. Throughout the service you must pay attention to health and safety matters that may affect you and your clients.

Your responsibilities for health and safety are defined by the specific legislation covering your job role and this includes following all the health and safety Acts and regulations. You must ensure a range of protective clothing is available for your clients and maintain your personal hygiene and presentation while maintaining health and safety in your workplace.

Potential hazards and risks

You must wear closed toe shoes and clothing that allows for easy removal of hair clippings to ensure health and safety and personal comfort.

You must correctly clean and prepare your workstation and trolley in advance of your client's arrival. Throughout the whole service you must maintain your responsibilities for health and safety and ensure that you, your client and others are not at risk of injury. Take care when handling your tools and use them for the correct purpose, following your workplace and the suppliers' and manufacturer's instructions for use. Make sure you carry scissors and razors with their blades closed and keep them safe in a carry pouch when not in use. Sweep the floor during and after the service and correctly dispose of any waste in an environmentally friendly manner.

HANDY HINT

Refer back to Chapter 1 for more information on maintaining your personal hygiene and following your salon's dress code.

HEALTH AND SAFETY

You must ensure you sweep up hair clippings during and after the service, as both wet and dry hair is slippery and could cause accidents.

HEALTH AND SAFETY

Take care with scissors so as not to cut yourself or your client. If you do cut yourself or your client, cover any open wounds and take care not to cause any cross-contamination. Remember to record the details in the salon's accident book.

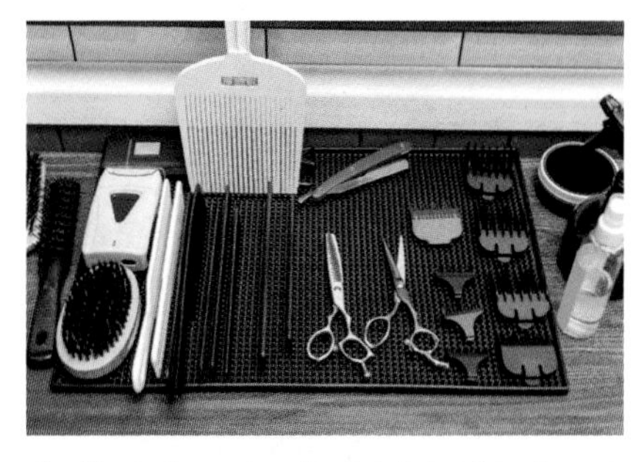

▲ Hygienic and well-maintained tools and products

Safe and hygienic working methods and practices

Throughout the cutting service you must ensure your working methods promote environmental and sustainable working practices – you can donate hair to a local composting site or dispose of it in a lidded bin. You must meet your salon requirements for client protection, protecting their clothes and skin from hair clippings and discomfort at all times.

Positioning

The positioning of you and your client is important when cutting hair, as the result and balance of the finished look can be affected.

Your body position

Stand with your body weight evenly distributed throughout the entire cutting process. This will not only prevent fatigue and back problems but will ensure the hairstyle is balanced. Sit on a cutting stool while cutting hair short or for working on the back of the client's head. This will prevent you from bending and overstretching, and help to maintain your comfort, which is essential during the cutting service.

▲ Keep your back straight when cutting hair

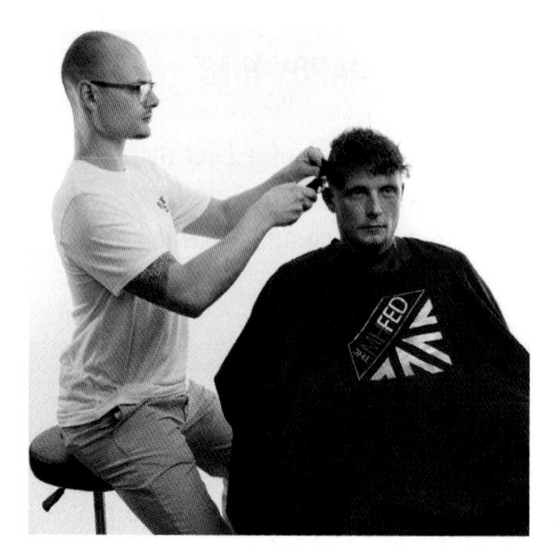

▲ Stylist sitting on a cutting stool to cut hair

▲ Good client positioning

▲ Saloncide spray

Your client's positioning

Once gowned and protected, you must ensure that your client sits comfortably with their back supported in the chair, in an upright position with their legs uncrossed and evenly balanced.

HANDY HINT

If your client's posture is unbalanced or they are sitting with their legs crossed, your resulting haircut may also be unbalanced as your client may have a tendency to lean to one side. Always ensure your client is sitting upright with their legs uncrossed.

THE HAIR PROFESSIONAL AT WORK

Suppliers' and manufacturer's instructions must be followed for the safe use of equipment, materials and products.

HANDY HINT

Refer to Chapter 1 for more information on maintaining effective, hygienic and safe working methods and on hazards and risks in the workplace.

Preventing cross-infection and cross-infestation

You must disinfect or sterilise your cutting tools after every service, to maintain a good reputation, ensure a professional image and to prevent cross-infection and infestation. You must ensure that you protect yourself and your client from the risk of cross-contamination.

To prevent cross-contamination, work safely and hygienically, cleaning and sterilising your workstations, trolley, tools and equipment.

The tools you are likely to use during the cutting service are:

- scissors
- thinning scissors
- razors
- combs
- sectioning clips
- clippers/trimmers.

Make sure all your cutting collars, towels and gowns are contamination-free, and scissors and combs are sterile. Towels and gowns should be machine-washed after every client, and cutting collars cleaned with hot soapy water. If you encounter any infections or infestations you will need to sterilise your tools and boil wash all towels and gowns. Use heat such as boiling water or an autoclave for scissors and combs and remember that a UV light will only maintain sterilisation; it is not an effective method of removing infections or infestations from your tools. Use chemical disinfectant sprays on trollies and cutting collars before and after use.

Methods of cleaning, disinfecting and sterilising

The table below shows the most appropriate methods of sterilising or disinfecting your tools.

Cutting tools	Appropriate method of disinfecting/ sterilisation
Scissors and thinning scissors	Autoclave – moist heat UV light cabinet Chemical solutions (Barbicide or saloncide; oil the blades after disinfecting)
Razors	Autoclave – moist heat UV light cabinet
Combs	UV light cabinet Chemical solutions (Barbicide or saloncide)
Sectioning clips	UV light cabinet Chemical solutions (Barbicide or saloncide)
Clippers and trimmers	Chemical wipes or sprays (oil the blades after disinfecting) Oil your blades after disinfecting them

HANDY HINT

Always clean your non-electrical tools prior to disinfecting or sterilising, using detergent with warm water. Toothbrushes or nail brushes work particularly well for removing hair cuttings and scalp debris from between the teeth of combs and clipper blades.

HANDY HINT

Saloncide can be sprayed directly onto tools and used immediately without rinsing, making this type of disinfectant quick and popular with stylists, and visible to the clients in the salon.

CUT HAIR TO ACHIEVE A VARIETY OF LOOKS

To understand how to cut hair and achieve the desired result you will need to be able to:

- identify factors that may influence the service
- understand the importance of applying correct techniques to services
- question clients prior to and during the service
- understand the types of problems that may occur and identify ways to resolve them
- provide advice and recommendations.

Factors that may influence the service

You must consider the following factors prior to and during cutting and understand how these may impact on the cutting service:

- hair classifications
- hair characteristics
- features, head, face and body shape.

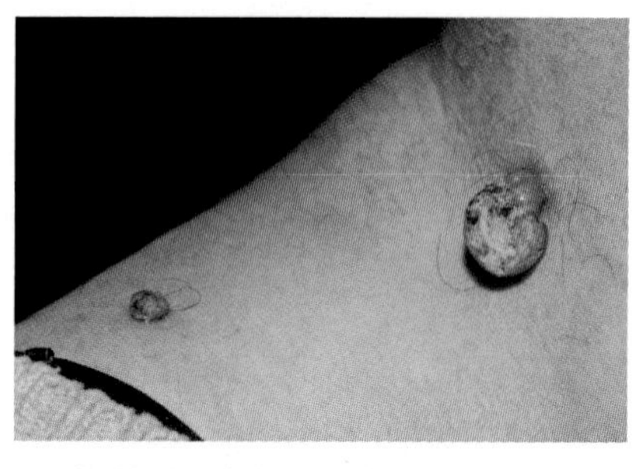

▲ A skin tag is a skin disorder a client may want covered up

Some scalp disorders may require consideration, depending on the style recommended, as the client might want them covered up. Always ask about scalp disorders during your consultation and check for infections and infestations which would prevent the service from being carried out.

Hair classifications

The following table explains how hair classifications might affect the service.

Hair classification	Description	Impact on service
Type 1 – straight hair Fine/thin hair	Fine/thin – hair tends to be very soft, shiny and oily, and it can be difficult to hold a curl.	Fine/thin straight hair might not achieve the desired result. Avoid using texturising techniques that will make the hair thinner Use club cutting techniques and choose styles to suit the hair type.
Medium hair	Medium – hair has lots of volume and body.	When cutting fine and medium straight hair, every 'scissor cut' can show in the hair, so accuracy is very important and subtle texturised cuts, such as point cutting, can help to prevent the cutting lines from being so apparent.
Coarse hair	Coarse – hair is normally extremely straight and difficult to curl.	Coarse straight hair may benefit from texturising and thinning out techniques to remove some bulk, and improve the end result and style.
Type 2 – Wavy hair Fine/thin hair	Fine/thin – hair has a definite 'S' pattern. Normally you can accomplish various styles.	Wavy hair can be great to work with. It is easy to mould it straighter or enhance the body. Most techniques work well with this hair type. Fine/thin wavy hair – you may need to leave some length to aid body within the cut.

Hair classification	Description	Impact on service
 Medium hair	Medium – hair tends to be frizzy and a little resistant to styling.	Medium and coarse wavy hair can be frizzy so avoid texturizing techniques that will enhance a fluffy appearance such as razor cutting. Club cutting can help, by keeping all hair lengths the same.
 Coarse hair	Coarse – normally very frizzy; tends to have thicker waves.	Coarse wavy hair can be resistant to styling. It may benefit from being texturised or thinned out but avoid using the razor on the hair.
Type 3 – Curly hair  Loose curls	Loose curls – the hair can be thick and full with lots of body, with a definite 'S' pattern. It also tends to be frizzy.	Soft loose curly hair can have a combination of textures to consider: it may be frizzy in appearance and have lots of body. Avoid using razors or heavily texturising the hair if the hair tends to be frizzy.
 Tight curls	Tight curls – often combined textures resulting in a medium amount of curl.	Tight curly hair can also have combined textures and will spring up after the hair has been cut when it is dried – particularly fine curly hair. Consider the amount of tension you place on the hair during the cutting service and use a wide-toothed comb.
Type 4 – Very curly hair  Soft very tight curls	Soft – tightly coiled and has a more defined curly pattern.	Soft very curly hair is often fragile, so be careful of using razors or clippers. Comb the hair gently using a wide-toothed comb and use a conditioning spray to prevent client discomfort. Choose a style to suit and work with the curls, rather than try to fight them.

→

Hair classification	Description	Impact on service
Wiry very tight curls	Wiry – tightly coiled but with a less defined curly pattern. The hair has more of a 'Z' pattern shape.	Wiry curly hair is also very fragile but can have less of a defined curly pattern. Avoid techniques that texturise the hair and use mostly club cutting and freehand techniques. Take care with tools if using razors or clippers. Comb the hair gently using a wide-toothed comb and use a conditioning spray to prevent client discomfort and damage to the fragile hair.

HANDY HINT

Equality and diversity – you will work on many different hair types to cover the range required. Some of the hair types you may cut could be European hair, Asian hair or African type hair. Clients will come from different ethnic groups and, have different cultures and have different religions. Make sure you respect other people's culture and religion, even if they differ from your own personal views.

Hair characteristics

The following table explains how hair characteristics might affect the service.

Factor	Impact on service
Density Abundant hair	Density can affect the choice of style and cutting technique. Abundant hair may need to be thinned out to create the desired look. Consider whether abundant hair will complement the look and suggest alternatives.
Sparse hair	Sparse hair will need to be blunt cut/club cut to maintain as much thickness as possible. Avoid cutting the hair too short, but equally avoid suggesting keeping fine hair long.

Factor	Impact on service
Texture  Coarse hair  Fine hair	Texture can affect the choice of style and cutting technique. Coarse textured hair may not suit the desired look; you will need to recommend smoothing products to help achieve the result. Texturising techniques may help to remove some of the coarseness, but razor cutting the hair can make the hair look coarser and more frizzy. Fine hair may also need supporting hair products and style recommendations to enhance the finish.
Elasticity   Elasticity test	Elasticity can affect the cutting technique. If the hair is weak avoid using razor blades and fine-toothed combs to detangle the hair. Wet hair has more elasticity than dry hair. If the hair is weak avoid overstretching the hair. Spray the hair with water throughout the cut to maintain an even moisture balance which helps avoid the hair tangling and snagging.
Porosity and hair condition  Porous hair	Hair that is damaged is likely to be porous. This can affect the cutting technique and client comfort. If the hair is porous and the cuticles are open, then the hair is more likely to tangle during the cut, and this may cause client discomfort. You should use a wide-toothed comb and spray the hair with leave-in conditioner to aid the combing process. Avoid using a razor on porous hair and take care if using clipper grades, as they may get caught in the dry porous hair.

Hair growth patterns

Hair growth patterns can affect the choice of style and cutting technique.

▲ Cowlick

For cowlicks avoid fringes; instead, suggest a side half fringe that works with the cowlick. Cut this area of the hairline once dry to clearly see the jump and length of hair remaining.

▲ Widow's peak

For widow's peaks avoid fringes completely and suggest styles that are created with the top area of hair going over to one side or straight back.

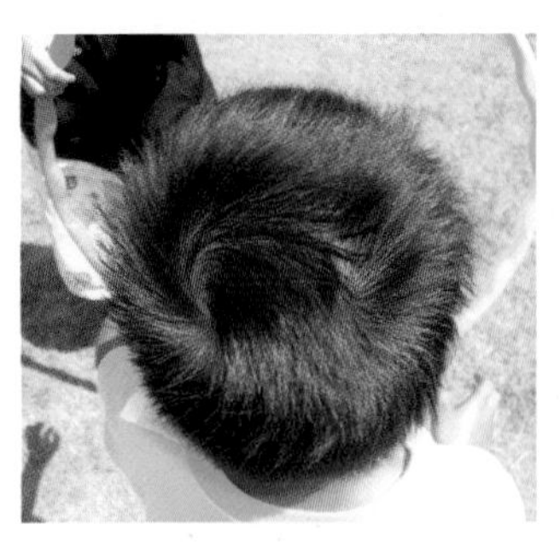

▲ Double crown

For double crowns suggest maintaining a little length around the crown area and ideally work the natural fall into the style.

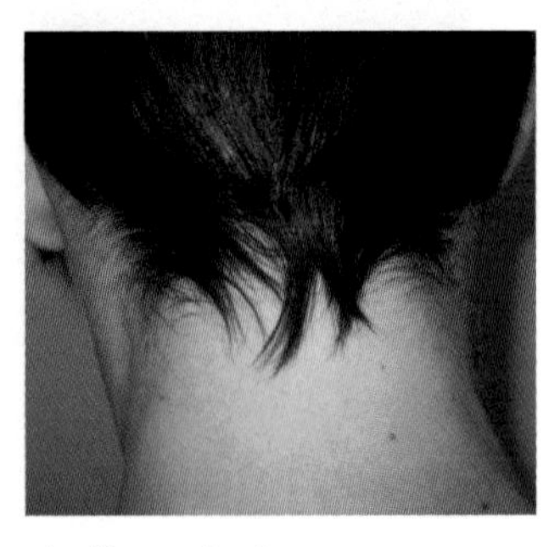

▲ Nape whorl

For nape whorls suggest maintaining the length at the nape area, or at least a little weight. Avoid cutting into the hairline, unless you take the hair very short.

For more detail on these hair growth patterns, see the hair characteristics table in Chapter 1.

HANDY HINT

Always check the hair for growth patterns prior to shampooing the hair – when the hair is wet, some growth patterns are not as easy to detect.

Alopecia

There are many types of alopecia which need to be considered when cutting hair. Clients may prefer to keep the hair longer and try to cover the area of hair loss, or have the area cut shorter to give the rest of the hair the appearance of thickness.

Alopecia areata

Alopecia that usually starts with one or more small round areas of smooth bald patches, this can be on the head or anywhere on the body. This type of alopecia can be temporary.

Scarring alopecia (cicatrical alopecia)

As the name would suggest, caused by scarring – burns, injuries, or infections. This hair loss is permanent, as the hair follicles have been damaged beyond repair.

Male pattern baldness (androgenic alopecia)

Also referred to as the Hamilton pattern of baldness. This occurs as a result of changes in the hormone androgen and the hair loss is permanent.

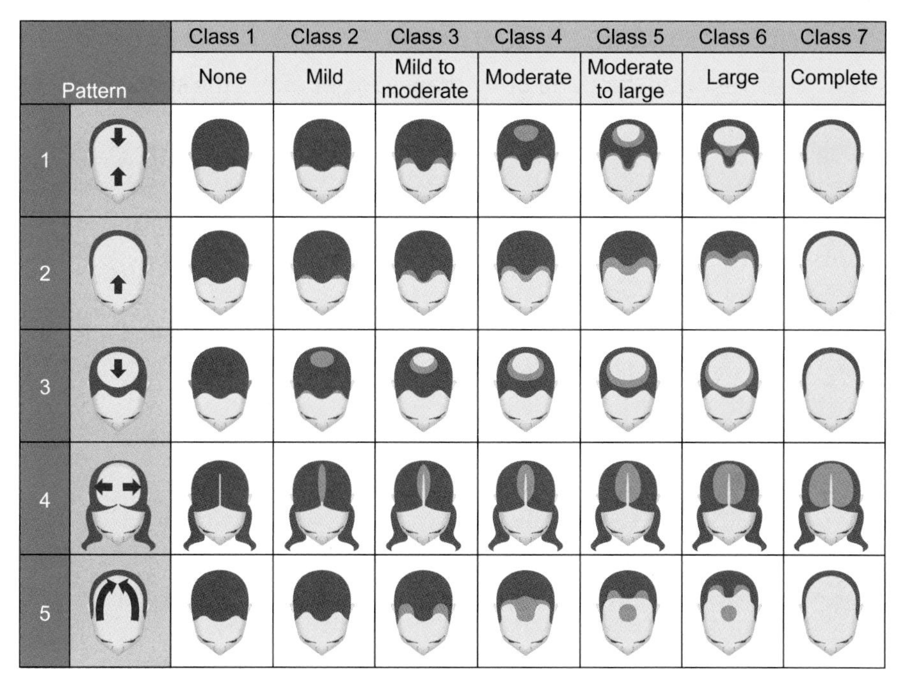

▲ Hamilton pattern

Female pattern baldness (female pattern hair loss)

Also referred to as Lugwig's classification hair loss, this hair loss is genetic and not generally related to the androgen hormone. The hair loss is not always permanent but can be made worse by stress and depression.

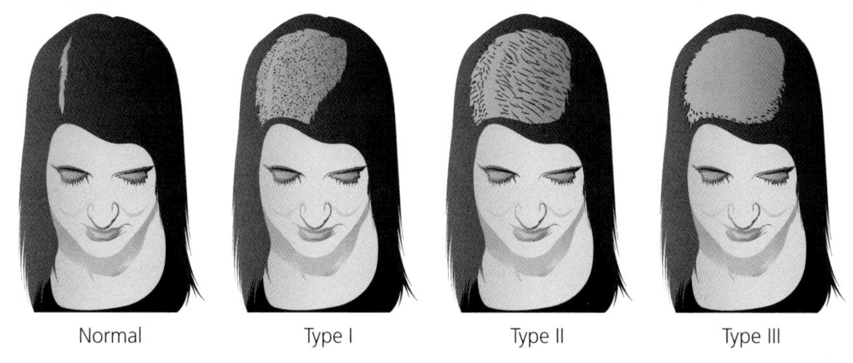

▲ Lugwig classification

ACTIVITY

Research the causes of these types of alopecia:

- Telogen effluvium
- Tricotilomania
- Traction alopecia

Client lifestyle

When consulting with clients you should always ask about their lifestyle to ascertain how much time they have to spend on their hair. Busy clients will need a style that is quick and easy to maintain, whereas clients with more free time may prefer to visit the salon on a weekly basis for you to maintain their style.

Features, head, face and body shape

How features, head, face and body shapes might affect the service

Factor	Impact on service
Client features  Take care with your scissors and combs, and check for piercings	Always ensure that you check the hair and scalp for any lumps and bumps that could cause discomfort to the client when you are combing or cutting the hair. Check the eyebrows and ears for piercings that could cause an injury if you were accidentally to catch them with the comb.
Facial features  Protruding ears  Strong nose or jaw features	**Prominent** facial features can affect the choice of style. For clients with **protruding** ears, suggest styles that cover the entire ear. For strong nose features or jawlines, avoid centre partings that encourage the eye to follow down from the parting to the nose and chin.
Head and face shape  Round face	The head and face shape can affect the choice of style. Always aim to achieve a style which makes the face look oval-shaped. For round face shapes, avoid styles that add more roundness, such as too much width or height. Try to suggest styles that come onto the face.

Factor	Impact on service
 Oblong face	For oblong face shapes, encourage width, avoid height and suggest a fringe to shorten the impression of a long face shape.
 Square face	For square face shapes, suggest softer styles that soften the jawline.
 Heart face	For heart face shapes, avoid width at the temple area and add width near the jawline area; try to avoid the finished length being at jawline level.
 Question mark head shape	Head shapes vary widely but should be considered within the overall shape of the style. Short styles that flatter the head shape will look a little like a question mark from the side view. The head should emphasise a rounded crown to the occipital bone and then dip in slightly towards the nape.
Body shape	When considering the style and shape of the hairstyle consider your client's body shape. Avoid suggesting small hairstyles for larger clients and large hairstyles for clients who have a slight build.

ACTIVITY

To aid your development in maths it is important you understand and recognise different shapes.

Draw and label the different face shapes, and then add sketches of hairstyles that will complement each one to give the illusion of an oval face.

KEY TERM

Prominent and **protruding** – sticking out.

▲ Check through the dried hair cut after styling to remove any scissor marks from fine hair

HANDY HINT

When checking dry hair before the service, you will be looking at a styled head of hair which may have products on or have been styled to change the natural fall and make the hair feel thicker. Always recheck the hair type, and the natural movement and fall of the hair when it has been shampooed.

▲ Set up your trolley or workstation before each client

Factors to be considered when cutting hair

Cutting the hair wet or dry will affect the tools you use, the technique used and the end result. Hair should be checked while dry and rechecked after shampooing.

Dry haircutting

You must check the hair while it is dry to see how the client currently wears their hairstyle, to identify any natural hair growth patterns and to feel the density and texture of the hair. Always carry out a porosity test on dry hair prior to the service and an elasticity test on wet hair.

Freehand and scissors over comb cutting techniques are best carried out on dry hair. Thinning scissors and clippers must only be used on dry hair.

Wet haircutting

Once the hair has been shampooed and prepared for the service, check through the hair to identify the natural parting. On wet hair, you will be able to see the hair type in its natural state, such as curly or straight, and recheck the movement of the hair.

The elasticity in the hair allows wet hair to be stretched up to 50 per cent of its original length. You must consider this when you are cutting the hair wet, as the dried result could be much shorter than you or your client have anticipated. Always carry out an elasticity test on wet hair. Razors and any slice cutting techniques should only be used on wet hair.

Apply correct techniques during services

During cutting services, you will use a range of tools for techniques such as club cutting, freehand, scissor over comb, texturising and precision cutting.

Controlling your tools and equipment

You must control your tools and equipment to reduce the risk of damage to your client's hair and scalp. When using the products, tools and equipment, always follow the instructions and ensure you use, handle and store them correctly and safely.

When cutting your client's hair, your most commonly used tools will be:

- scissors
- cutting comb
- thinning scissors/razors
- clippers
- sectioning clips.

Choosing suitable cutting tools

For most basic cutting techniques, you will use scissors with an average blade length of 5 inches (12.5 cm), depending on the size of your hands. Choosing the right scissors for you to work with comfortably is important. As you become more experienced you are likely to want a selection of scissors for a variety of techniques, and you will probably buy more expensive scissors as your skill level increases.

ACTIVITY

Convert the following imperial size scissors to centimetres (cm):

- 4.5 inch scissors
- 5.5 inch scissors
- 6 inch scissors.

Scissors

Although, at a glance, all scissors look the same, they are indeed very different. They can vary in size and weight due to the metals they are made from, and the type of cutting blade may also vary. At varying costs, you can purchase scissors that have a movable thumb area, which can make it more comfortable for you to cut baselines and achieve exaggerated angles. Scissors are available with serrated or straight blades.

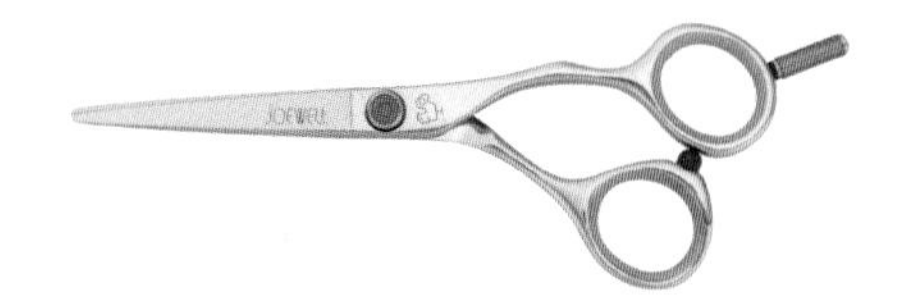

▲ Straight edge blades

Serrated scissors

Serrated scissors (or scissors with bevelled blades) are most suitable when you first start cutting hair, as they aid control and grip the hair as you cut. However, if you wish to use texturising techniques and slide or slice cut the hair, these will not be suitable as they pull the hair, affecting the cut, and may cause discomfort to your client.

Straight scissors, or non-serrated blades, are the sharpest for cutting, slicing and chipping. You can use these for most techniques and can buy them from £30 up to a few hundred pounds.

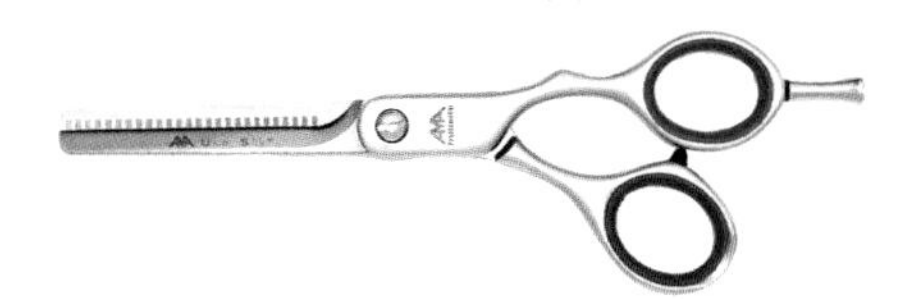

▲ Thinning scissors – one blade with notches

Thinning scissors

Thinning scissors are used to remove bulk at the end of the haircut and have 'teeth' or 'notches' all the way up one or both blades. Thinning scissors with notches on both blades remove less bulk than those with only one notched blade.

▲ Thinning scissors – two blades with notches

Texturising scissors

Texturising scissors can be used to add texture to a finished haircut. These have wider notches along the blades and remove weight from the hair section as you cut.

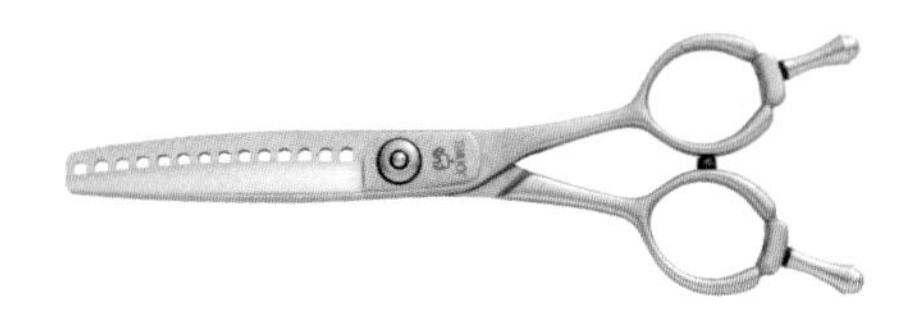

▲ Texturising scissors

HANDY HINT

Shorter-length scissors are good for chipping into the hair; 5 inch (12.5 cm) scissors are good for most techniques; and longer-length scissors are ideal for scissor over comb techniques used by many barbers.

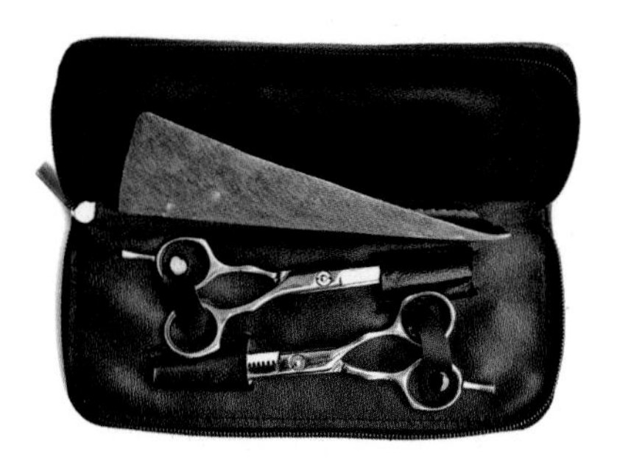

HANDY HINT

Storing your scissors securely in a cutting pouch will ensure they are kept safe, the blades are closed and protected, and they will remain sharper for longer.

ACTIVITY

Practise holding your scissors correctly, moving only your thumb.

ACTIVITY

Use the internet to research the types of scissors available. Decide which ones would be most suitable for you and consider the following:

- How much can I afford to spend?
- What size do I need?
- What size is most suitable?
- What type of blade would I like?
- What cutting techniques do I need my scissors for?
- How am I going to store them when they are not in use?

Look at colours and styles that are available too.

What size scissors should I buy?

To help you choose the correct size scissors, rest the scissors in the palm of your hand, starting with a 12.5 cm blade length. If they are slightly shorter than the length of your hand, from middle finger to wrist, then these should be suitable. For smaller hands try a 10–11 cm length and for longer hands try a 14–15 cm length.

The thumb and finger holes vary in size, too; try them for size before buying, and ensure they are comfortable but not so loose that you could lose control over the cut.

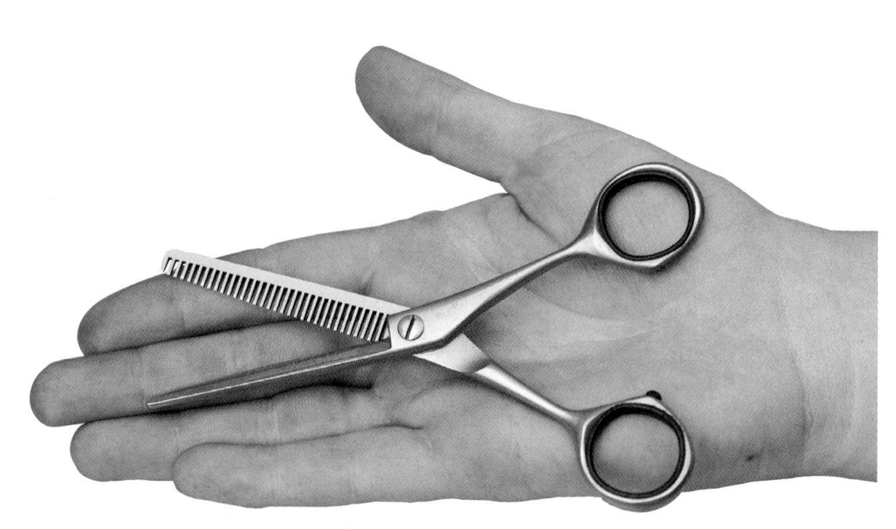

▲ These scissors are the correct size for this hand

The parts of your scissors

1 The points of the scissors – used for point cutting or chipping techniques and freehand.
2 The cutting blade edges – used for all club cutting techniques, scissors over comb and some freehand angles.
3 The blades – outside of blade edges.
4 The heel – the strength of the scissors.
5 The pivot – an adjustable screw to loosen or tighten the movement of the blades.
6 The shanks – give the length from the blades to the handles.
7 The handle – thumb and finger holes.

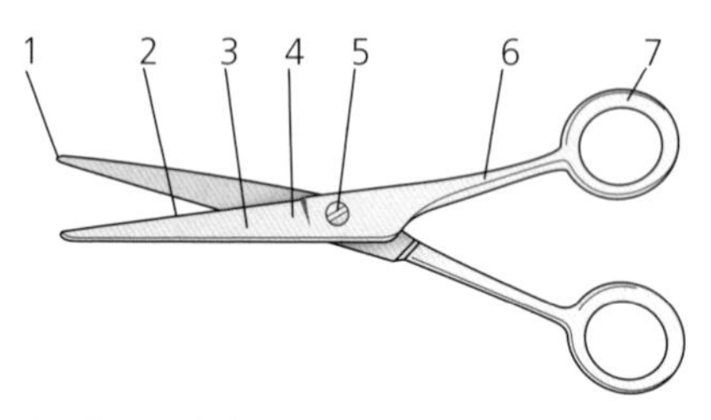

▲ Parts of the scissor

HANDY HINT

Scissors are held with your thumb and your ring finger – not your middle finger. Your little finger supports the scissors, often on the finger rest attached to the scissors; your first and middle fingers support the shanks. You move only your thumb when you cut the hair, as this gives you the greatest control when cutting.

ACTIVITY

To help you to decide on how tight or loose your blades should be, try this simple exercise. Do not have your thumb in the hole during this exercise.

Place your ring finger in the finger hole and support your scissors with your other fingers; lift and open the thumb blade and let the thumb blade drop towards the finger blade. Ideally, the thumb blade, when dropped, should stop just short of the finger blade. If the blades touch, they may be too loose; if there is a large gap between the blades, they are too tight. This can be adjusted by loosening or tightening the pivot screw.

Razors

Razors can be used once you are confident with your cutting techniques. They are used to add texture or definition to your style and to taper and remove bulk from the hair.

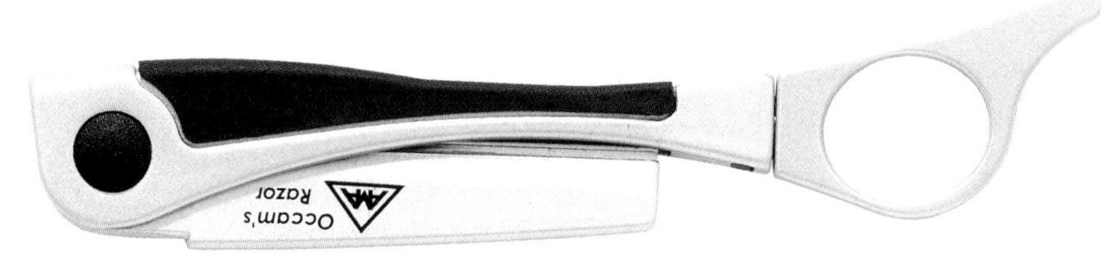

▲ Razor

▲ Razor being used on wet hair

Clippers

Clippers can be used to blend in hair on the back of the neck, create outlines and definition, or for clipper over comb techniques. Trimmers can also be used to blend or remove neck hair. These are mostly used for cutting men's hair. They can be mains electrical or rechargeable battery-operated clippers.

▲ Clippers – using mains electricity

▲ Clippers – rechargeable

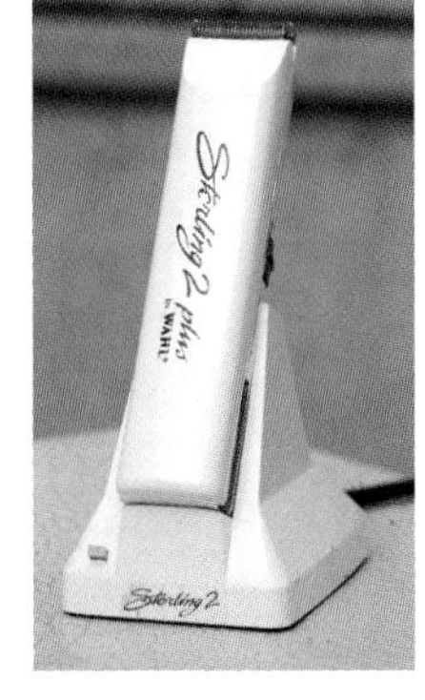

▲ Trimmers

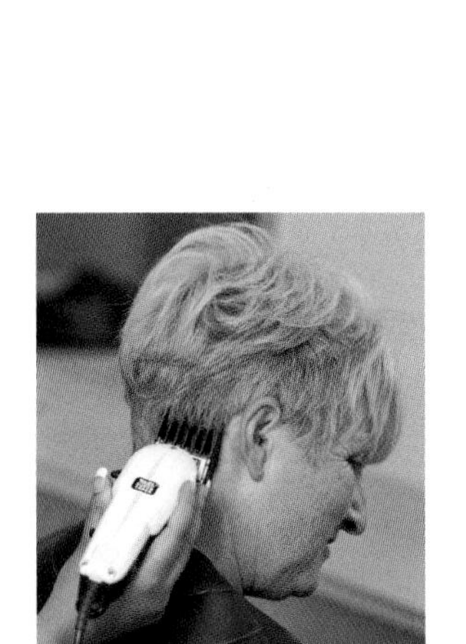

▲ Clippers being used on a client

HANDY HINT

Control your tools and use them safely to minimise damage to your client's hair and scalp, and to avoid accidently cutting yourself or your client and maintain client comfort.

Section clips

A variety of section clips can be used to securely hold the hair in place and aid methodical working. Some stylists prefer clamp-type section clips that grip the hair firmly in place after the stylist has sectioned the hair with a comb. Others prefer using clips that help to section the hair with the clip itself and then clip the hair out of the way. Whichever style you prefer, always ensure you wash them with hot soapy water and sterilise them after use.

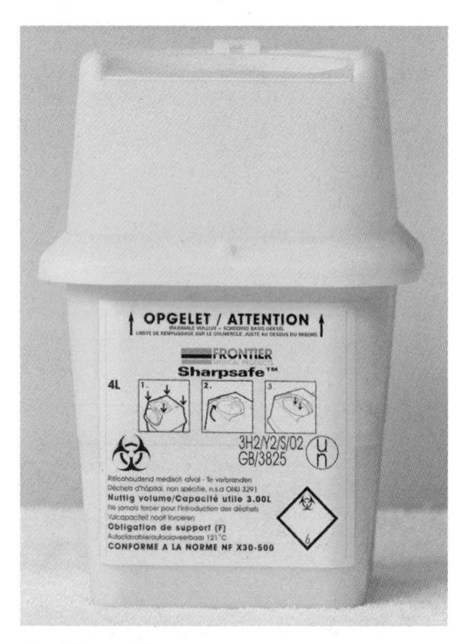

▲ Sharps bin

Methods for maintaining tools and equipment

You must always use your tools correctly. Scissors are extremely sharp and accidents can occur. Always carry your scissors with the blades closed and keep them safe from harm by storing them in a cutting case. Your scissors are likely to be the most expensive item in your tool collection and dropping them with the blades open or pointing downwards can be very costly and affect the position of the blades.

Instructions for the care of scissors:

- use them only for their intended purpose – cutting hair
- do not carry them in the pockets of your clothes
- carry them in a safe manner and store them after use
- ensure they are fit for purpose
- use the correct type of scissors for specific styles
- clean and sterilise them after use
- remove all hair cuttings and oil them regularly
- have them professionally sharpened when required.

Care of razors should include:

- using them only for their intended purpose
- carrying them in a safe manner and storing them after use
- ensuring they are fit for purpose and using a new blade when required
- cleaning and sterilising them after use
- removing all hair cuttings and oiling them regularly
- disposing of used razor blades in a sharps bin.

You might, on occasions, use clippers. These must be maintained by removing all excess hair from the blades and oiling the blades. Adjusting the blade settings while oiling helps lubricate the entire blade area.

HANDY HINT

Working safely with cutting tools is very important: you must ensure that your tools and equipment are well maintained and fit for use.

HEALTH AND SAFETY

Throughout the service, it is important to control your tools to minimise the risk of damage to hair and scalp, client discomfort and to achieve the desired look.

Apply the correct degree of tension to the hair when cutting

As part of the consultation process you must touch and feel the client's hair and carry out elasticity and porosity tests to ascertain the condition and strength of the hair. The results of these tests may affect the haircut you recommend and how much length you advise the client to have removed. They will also affect the tools you use, and how much tension you apply to the hair when cutting.

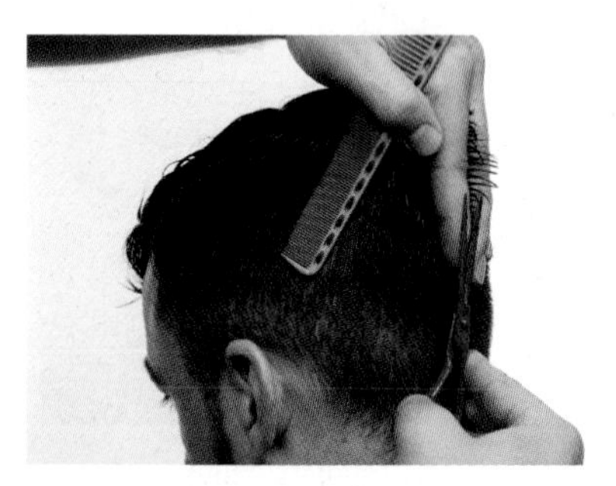

▲ Stylist using tools correctly

Throughout the haircut you must maintain the tension evenly and remember that wet hair stretches more than dry hair. Ensure you keep even moisture balance throughout the haircut too, so the hair is not of mixed porosity or elasticity, as this may cause tangles and damage to the hair, particularly on longer hair. Uneven tension, porosity and elasticity can cause the end result to be uneven or be shorter than expected.

HANDY HINT

With any cutting technique you must always work with the natural fall of the hair, taking account of the weight distribution to ensure the expected shape can be achieved.

Different cutting techniques

The looks that you will create may involve a number of techniques, including:

- club cutting
- freehand
- scissors over comb
- texturising – including razoring
- precision cutting techniques – including disconnection
- fringe cutting
- clipper work.

You will use these techniques to achieve one-length, uniform layers, short-graduation and long-graduated-layer looks. Some of these techniques may be cut on dry hair, but most are carried out on wet hair.

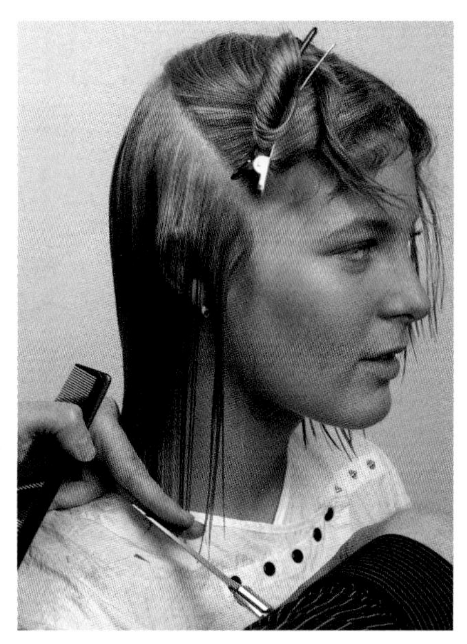

▲ Holding the hair for club cutting

Club cutting

Club cutting is also known as blunt cutting and involves cutting the hair straight across while holding the hair with tension between your fingers. This technique will reduce the length of the hair and layers but will retain the thickness and bulk of the hair. Club cutting can also reduce movement in curly and wavy hair.

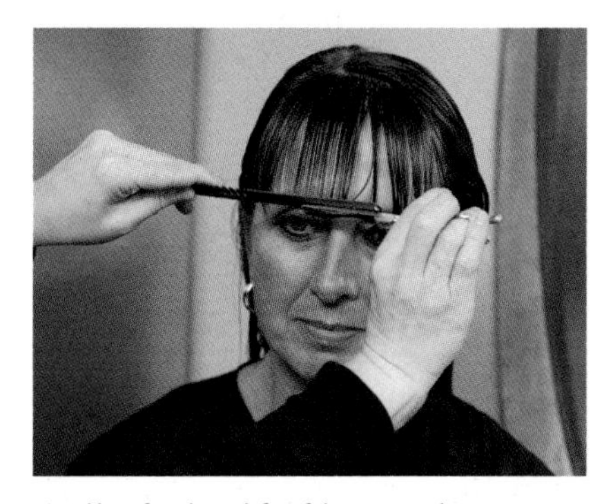

▲ Use freehand for fringes and one-length cuts to allow for natural fall

Freehand

When using the freehand technique, you must not hold the hair with any tension, but instead comb the hair into position and cut. This technique can be used when tension is not required, such as when cutting fringes, or allowing for the natural fall of the hair over the ears when cutting hair one length.

Scissor over comb

When using the scissor over comb technique, run the comb up the hair and use it to lift and support the hair to be cut. The hair is cut with the scissors over the comb. This technique gives a graduated effect into the contours of the head and the cut blends or fades short hair into the neck.

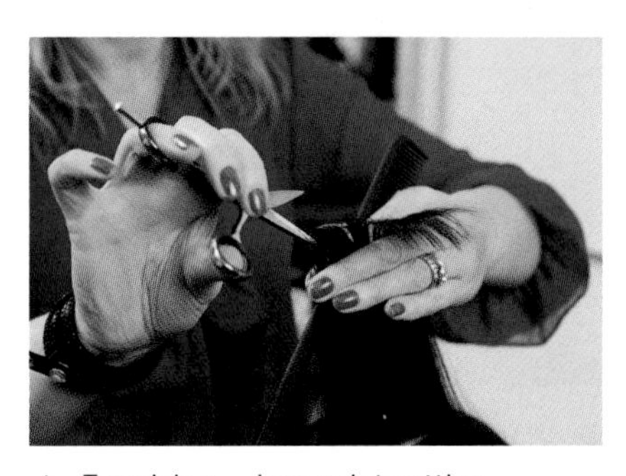

▲ Texurising – deep point cutting

Texturising with scissors – deep point cutting

Texturising the hair reduces the bulk at the ends of the hair. It helps to soften the shape of styles internally and externally, adds personalisation and encourages movement throughout the style. A large section of wet or dry hair is taken about 5–7cm below the fingers, and carefully cut

▲ Scissor over comb technique

inwards and slightly vertically towards the fingers. This removes bulk but maintains length (unlike club cutting where the hair is taken to the ends of your fingers and then cut straight across horizontally).

Texturising with scissors – shallow point cutting

A type of texturising which reduces lines and removes bulk on the ends of the hair. Wet or dry hair is cut in a similar way to club cutting, but the ends of the hair are removed vertically rather than horizontally.

▲ Texurising – shallow point cutting

Texturising with scissors – slice cutting

Wet hair is pulled outwards and sliced vertically through the hair several times to remove bulk or blend differing lengths of hair. Scissor blades must not be serrated or bevelled for this technique.

Texturising with scissors – tapering

Wet hair is sliced vertically downwards from one point to another, blending different lengths together, producing a tapered effect. Scissor blades must not be serrated or bevelled for this technique

▲ Texurising – slice cutting

Texturising with scissors – twist cutting

Small sections of wet hair are twisted and scissor blades are carefully run up the hair section with the blades slicing through the hair to remove bulk and add texture. This works well on wavy hair, but is less suited to fine hair.

▲ Texurising – tapering

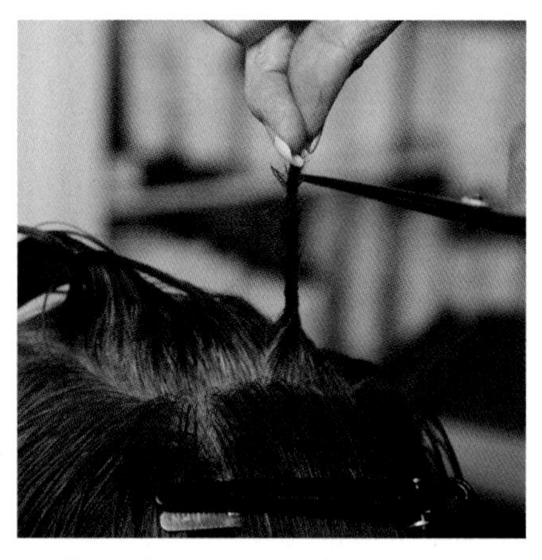

▲ Texurising – twist cutting

Texturising with thinning scissors – thinning the hair

Small sections of dry hair are held out and thinning scissors are used away from the root area, to remove bulk but maintain length.

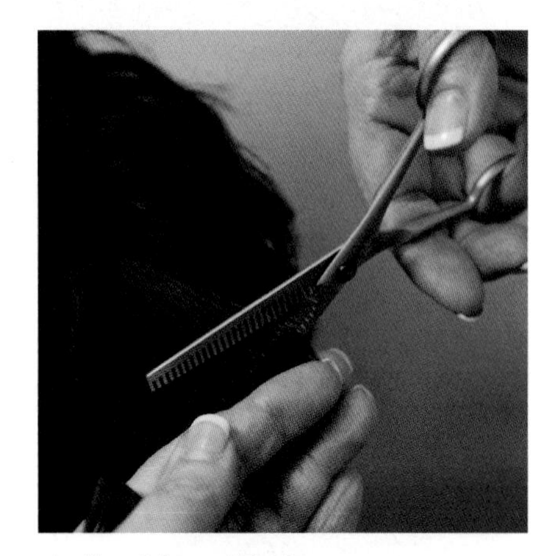

▲ Texurising – thinning

Texturising with razors – razoring

Small sections of wet hair are held outwards and the razor is used from midway to the ends, slicing through the top section of the held hair and removing the bulk. This adds softness and accentuates texture, but should not be used on curly or fine hair.

▲ Texturising – razoring

Precision cutting – blunt lines

Techniques used to create strong, bold, sharp, precise cuts in the hair, such as short, blunt fringes and vertical or diagonal angled lines.

Precision cutting – disconnection

A variety of techniques used to create different lengths within a cut and to accentuate facial features.

Fringe cutting

Fringes are often disconnected from the rest of the style and can be cut with a variety of techniques, including club cutting, freehand, point cutting, slice cutting, precision cutting and disconnection.

HANDY HINT

Remember, texturising introduces differing lengths in areas of, or throughout, the haircut to soften a hard line or to create root lift.

Clipper work

When using the clipper over comb or clippering techniques, the hair is cut with the clippers to create a sharper finish, similar to scissor over comb techniques. This technique gives a blunt, graduated effect into the contours of the head and the cut blends or fades short hair into the neck.

▲ Precision cut – blunt lines

▲ Precision cut – disconnection

▲ Fringe cutting

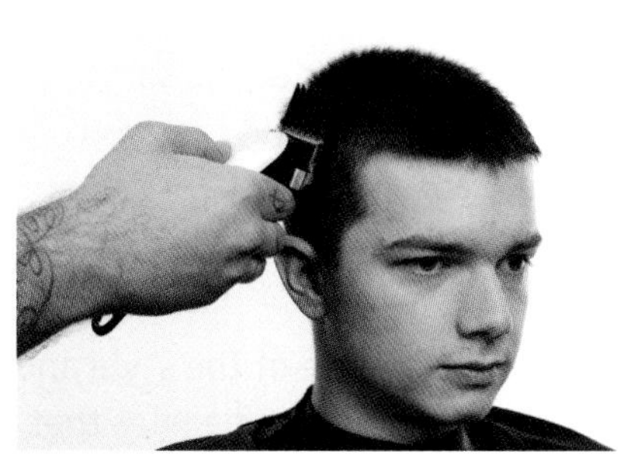

▲ Clippering techniques – clippering with grades

▲ Clippering techniques – clippering over comb

Methods of working when cutting hair

Establishing and following guidelines when cutting hair

The guideline is the most important part of the haircut. If you are cutting and lose your guideline – STOP! The guideline determines the finished length of the cut and the overall shape and balance. Following these guidelines is of paramount importance to ensure you work methodically through the haircut and maintain accuracy and balance. Even the most experienced stylists will follow a guideline.

Guidelines are the first cuts of every hairstyle. Generally you first cut in a baseline length; once the length has been agreed with your client, this becomes your guideline for the length of the haircut. After the baseline length has been cut, you add internal guidelines from crown to nape and ear to ear, to follow the internal lengths of the layers created.

Once the baseline length has been agreed and cut, you are ready to begin the guideline for the internal layers of the hair. This internal guideline will help you achieve the shape of the style. Again, agree the desired length of the layers with your client and then cut in your internal guideline to suit the angle at which the hair will be cut. You can either cut in your internal guideline from front to back and ear to ear, or work in stages, cutting the back first from crown to nape, and then working towards a front guideline.

▲ Internal guideline crown to back

▲ Stylist following guideline when cutting

Once you have cut your guideline, every section you cut afterwards will follow this guideline to the same length and hold the hair at the same angle. Always ensure that your cutting sections are clean and that you take manageable size sections.

Cutting angles

Cutting angles impact on weight distribution, the balance of the style and the degree of graduation created. The weight distribution and angles that the hair is held at will vary for every haircut and style. It is the angles that the hair is cut at that give the weight distribution.

▲ Baseline guideline (one length)

HANDY HINT

If you cannot see your guideline, stop cutting, go back a few sections and find it. Or you can section the hair the opposite way to work out where you have cut up to.

HANDY HINT

Your baseline cut is the foundation of the style – just like a house the foundations are important, while the layers are like the internal decoration.

HANDY HINT

Ask your client where they wear their parting, but always check visually for the natural fall of the hair.

HANDY HINT

Remember, if the one-length look, short graduation or long layers have been cut with a side parting, then the balance of the look may be **asymmetric** and the weight distribution could be heavier on one side, with an uneven balance.

KEY TERM

Asymmetric – unequal, not symmetrical.

The table below shows the angles at which the hair is cut and where the weight distribution falls.

Look	Angle of graduation	Weight distribution	Balance of style
One length	The hair is pulled down at 0°.	The weight of this hairstyle sits at the **perimeter**.	The balance of this style is even all around the perimeter.
Uniform layers	The whole haircut is pulled out at 90°.	The weight distribution of this haircut is even throughout the style.	The balance of this style is even throughout.
Short graduation	The hair on top may be cut at 90°. The back and sides are tapered in and cut at 45°.	The weight distribution of this style would be where the shape changes from 90° to 45° – around eye level at the sides and the **occipital** bone at the back.	The balance of this style is even on both sides.
Long graduation	The layers are cut between 90° and 180°.	The weight distribution for this style would be at the back and sides, where the length is mostly around the neck and below.	The balance of this style is even on both sides and around the head.

ACTIVITY

Use a magazine (or print out images from the internet) and cut out a variety of hairstyles. Draw the cutting angles used for each hairstyle.

KEY TERMS

Occipital – the bone between the crown and the nape area that normally sticks out a little bit.

Perimeter – length or baseline of the cut.

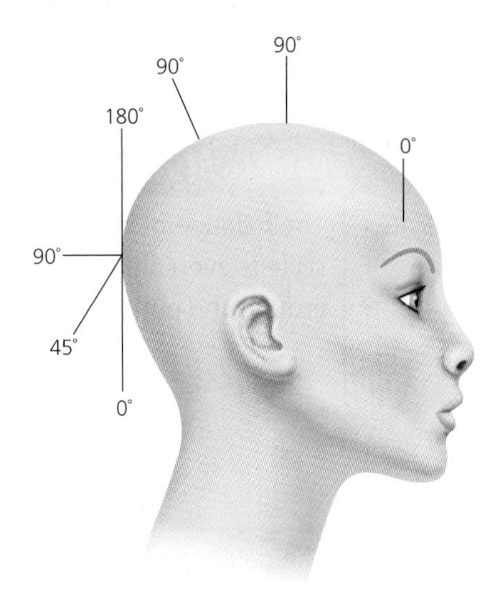

▲ Angles to hold the hair while cutting

Create different looks

To achieve one-length, uniform layers, short-graduation and long-graduated-layered looks you will hold the hair at different angles. We will explore the looks achieved in more detail in the step-by-step part later in this chapter.

The diagram shows the most common angles that you hold the hair at while cutting, for creating one-length, uniform layers, short-graduation and long-graduation looks.

- One length – the hair is pulled directly down at 0°.
- Uniform layer – use 0° for the baseline, and for the layers the hair is pulled out at a 90° angle throughout the entire haircut.
- Short graduation – the inner layers of the hair lengths are longer than the outline shape and generally pulled out at 45°.
- Long graduation – use 0° for the baseline, and between 90° and 180° for creating the longer layer effects.
- Fringes – often cut freehand to allow for the natural movement and fall of the hair growth patterns, but fringes can be cut under tension and pulled down to 0°.

ACTIVITY

Understanding angles is important in maths and is essential in hairdressing. The angles at which you cut the hair will determine the overall shape and accuracy of the haircut.

Practise sectioning and pulling the hair out at the angles described in the diagram.

Personalise and adapt cutting techniques

How you personalise and adapt your techniques will vary from one client to another and depends on the needs of the required look. Texturising techniques are used greatly to personalise a look, soften edges and lines, remove bulk but maintain length and add texture and lift to a cut. You will need to adapt your choice of techniques and how much texturising is required as this will depend on the style requirements and the condition, texture and classification of your client's hair.

Combine and adapt cutting techniques

Once you master the basic techniques and your confidence and experience grow, it is highly unlikely you will use just one technique to create your client's hairstyle.

For a one-length look, you are likely to use club cutting but you may personalise a fringe and use disconnection.

For short graduation, you may use point cutting and scissor over comb techniques, or razor cut the hair if it is thick and abundant.

For long graduation, you may use club cutting to remove the overall length but texturise the internal layers to remove bulk, add texture and create movement.

Cross-check and balance the cut

Cross-checking the haircut during the service and at the end ensures an accurate finish. You can cross-check the haircut at any point during the service to check for balance and even cutting lengths. Using a mirror will help you to check for balance.

For layered haircuts you can cross-check the evenness of the whole cut by sectioning the hair in the opposite direction to which you cut the layers. If you cut the layers in vertical sections, then cross-check horizontally and vice versa.

The final and most common method of cross-checking is used as you progress through the haircut. Pull out sections of cut hair on both sides to feel if the lengths are the same. For longer hair you can pull sections forward and see if they meet evenly under the chin.

KEY TERM

Cross-checking – checking the haircut for balance and evenness throughout.

▲ Cross-checking in the mirror

▲ Cross-checking horizontally

▲ Cross-checking long hair

▲ Cross-check short hair cut

▲ Poor sitting position could cause a poor end result

▲ Try to ensure your back is straight, although not rigid, and your shoulders are relaxed

HANDY HINT

Always ensure your client is sitting up straight with their legs uncrossed to achieve an even, balanced haircut.

▲ Ensure your client is sitting straight

HANDY HINT

As hair only grows about 1.25 cm (½ inch) each month, it is important that you do not cut the hair too short.

HANDY HINT

Keep the hair damp when cutting wet hair to ensure even elasticity and porosity. Failure to do so may mean the result is uneven and the hair could snag and tangle when you comb through.

HANDY HINT

It is important to follow guidelines and apply the correct degree of tension to ensure you achieve an accurate balanced result.

ACTIVITY

1. If a client had her hair cut every three months, how much would her hair have grown between cuts?
2. How much does your hair grow on average over a six-month period?
3. How much does your hair grow on average over a year?

Removing unwanted hair outside the desired outline shape

At the end of the haircut, make a final visual check of the hair to ensure the finished cut is accurate, remove any unwanted hair outside the desired outline shape and confirm your client's satisfaction with the finished cut.

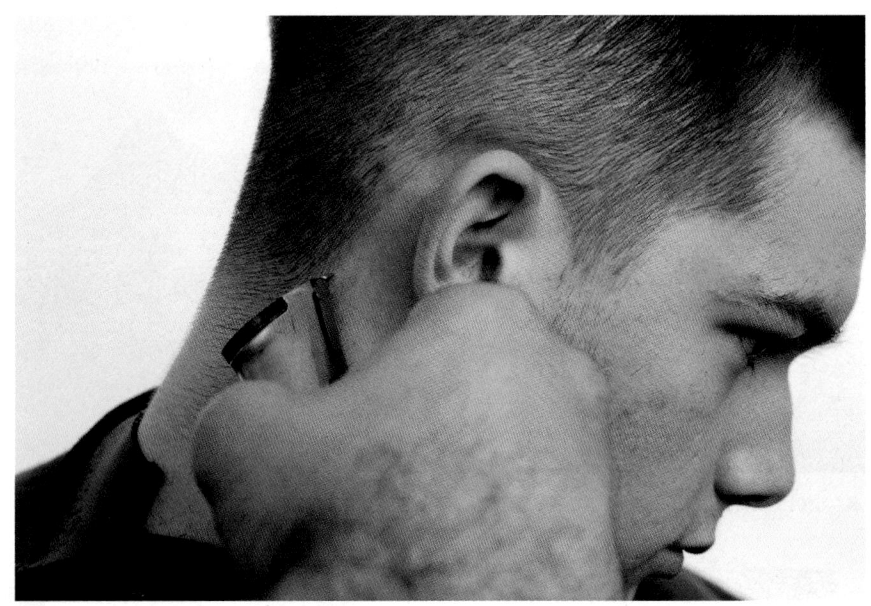

▲ Removing hair outside the desired outline shape

Importance of questioning clients

It is importance to consult with your clients prior to the service and throughout the cutting process to ensure they are happy with what is being agreed and the process of the cutting service.

Initial consultation

It is advisable to begin the initial consultation before you gown your client, to see their style of dress and overall image. You should ask your client about their day-to-day lifestyle and available time to commit to styling their hair. Always listen to what your client is asking of you, and be honest but tactful with the advice you give them. You should use open questions to obtain as much information as possible and finish with closed questions to confirm what has been agreed.

In-depth consultation

Always carry out an in-depth consultation with your client to ascertain what they would like. Your questions must be specific to achieve an accurate account of their needs. Show the client in the mirror how much hair you are going to remove to confirm what you assume to be the agreed lengths and amounts. Use visual aids such as magazines or images on Instagram or Pinterest to agree on styles and shapes. Always give your client the option to try something different from their current style and give them the opportunity to express what their vision of the finished look should be.

Before you commence the cut confirm with your client the look you have both agreed. Use client-friendly language, ensuring you avoid jargon and too many technical terms such as the techniques and angles you are planning to use. Instead describe the look with the use of visual aids or by showing the client in the mirror how and where their hair will sit or look.

Agree the service and time frame

During the consultation you should tell the client how long the service should take and how they can maintain the look between salon visits. The consultation process should continue throughout the cutting service, as you should update them on the progress of the haircut and check you are cutting to the agreed lengths.

When you have decided on a style together, ask your client which products they currently use to style their hair to identify whether you need to recommend any alternative products for their new image.

ACTIVITY

When using your consultation skills, you are also developing and maintaining your English speaking and listening skills. These skills are vital in hairdressing, so always speak clearly, avoid jargon and listen to the key details of the consultation.

Reasons why clients leave their hairstylist

- The hairstylist did not recommend anything new or interesting.
- The hairstylist did not listen to the client's request.
- The hairstylist created a style which was not suitable for the client.
- The hairstylist cut the hair too short, even after consultation and agreeing the lengths.

ACTIVITY

Ask a colleague to pretend to be your client. Ask them to visualise a style and then ask the relevant questions to identify the image and look they require.

HANDY HINT

Establish any factors that may affect the service – check the hair classifications, hair characteristics, head and face shape, and any hair growth patterns.

▲ Agree and check with your client how much length to remove

HANDY HINT

Revisit Chapter 1 for more in-depth information on consulting with your client and on client care and effective communication.

Problems that may occur

The table below describes the types of problems that can arise when cutting hair and ways in which they may possibly be remedied.

Problem	Cause	Possible remedy
Unhappy client	Poor consultation. Style requirement not achieved. Did not listen to client requirements. Did not question and check the progress of the cut with the client during the service.	If not too short, discuss the problem and re-cut the hair.
Hair is too short or left too long	Poor consultation. Did not listen to client requirements. Did not question and check the progress of the cut with the client during the service.	Apologise and wait for the hair to grow longer. Recut the hair and remove the unwanted length.
Hair is too thick and heavy	Retained bulk.	Texturise the hair to remove thickness, bulk and unwanted weight within the cut.
Hair is too thin, fine, fluffy or flyaway	Too much texture added and too much bulk removed. Hair type or texture was not suitable for chosen texturising technique.	Use club cutting to blunt and thicken the hair and prevent fluffy flyaway areas.
Haircut is unbalanced	Stylist posture may be unbalanced and/or client is not sitting straight with legs uncrossed.	Check balance and posture of client. Amend uneven areas and re-balance the cut.

Provide advice and recommendations

During and at the end of the service, give your client advice and recommendations on products used and the service provided. Your client will also value advice on how to maintain their style and is more likely to become a regular client to the salon.

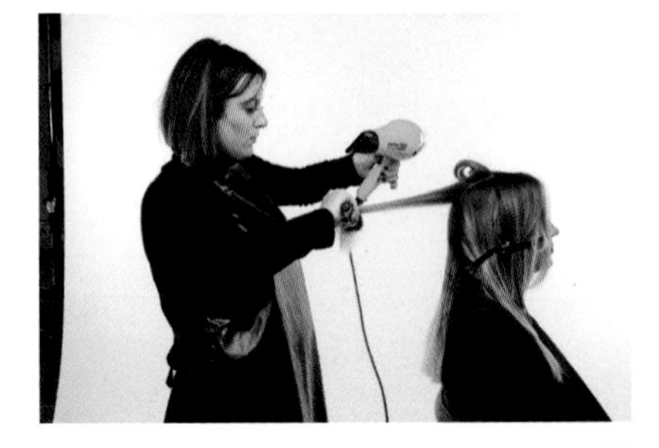

▲ Show your client how to achieve root lift

How to maintain look

You have just created a fabulous haircut for the client – when they leave, they are an advert for you and your salon. Not only does your client want the new style to look great every day until their next visit, so do you! Every compliment the client receives about their hairstyle could be a potential new client for you or the salon. Therefore, it is essential that you provide suitable aftercare for your client on maintaining the look you have created.

Throughout the styling service you should advise your client on which tools to use at home to recreate their look, and during the blow-dry service demonstrate what you are doing and why. This gives the client a thorough understanding of what they will need to do when styling their hair at home. Talk to them about how to create root lift if required or how to prevent it. Discuss which brushes are needed and the correct sizes to use. Remember to discuss the health and safety side of styling and the use of electrically heated styling equipment on the hair and the damage it could cause.

▲ You could recommend enhancing a haircut with subtle colours to add depth, tone and shine

Time interval between services

You should advise your client on when to book their next cutting service. To help guide them, explain that it depends on how quickly their hair grows. You should suggest that they return to the salon when the style grows out of shape and when they have trouble maintaining the style, as this may mean it is ready for a cut.

Present and future services

During the cutting and styling service is a good time to recommend colouring services to your clients to enhance the image created. Adding colour and highlights to a haircut helps to add texture and definition to the shape. A modern block colour can add a striking finish to any cut. Without doubt, colour enhances and complements every look you create.

Retail opportunities

If your client has had a full cut and blow-dry service, you should have discussed the products that you used during the styling service and explained why you used them. If the service was a wet cut, then a discussion should take place on how the client should finish the look themselves.

Advise your client which styling and finishing products would enhance and support their finished look. Explain how particular styling products will aid the drying and styling process, help control the hair and provide longevity to the finished result. You should advise them on how much product to use and how to apply it. If the product could cause a build-up on the hair, make sure you advise your client on how to remove the product effectively.

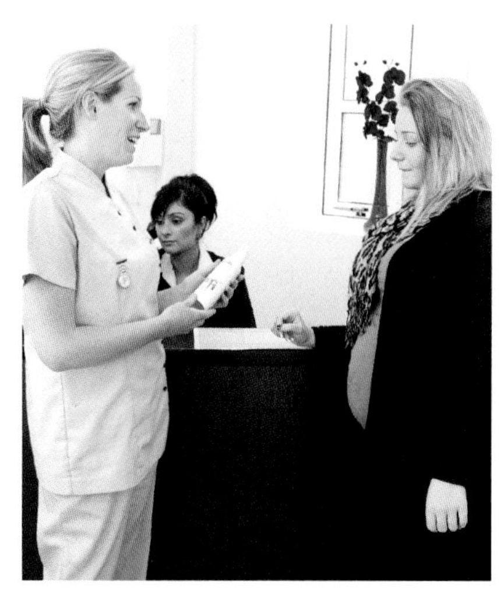

▲ Recommend aftercare to your clients

WHAT YOU MUST DO

For your practical assessments you must:

- apply safe working practices when cutting hair
- cut hair to achieve a variety of looks
- creatively restyle hair.

Apply safe working practices when cutting hair

You must:

- Prepare for cutting services by making sure you have showered/bathed and have clean clothes and are ready for the day's work; prepare your client to meet salon requirements by using clean gowns and towels and ensuring tools and equipment are sterilised.

- Apply safe and hygienic methods of working during services and maintain your responsibilities for health and safety throughout the service.
- Throughout the service protect your client's clothing and keep their skin free of excess hair cuttings by removing excess hair with a neck brush.
- Position your client to meet the needs of the service without causing them discomfort – they should sit up straight and rest their feet on the floor or a foot rest. Ensure your own posture and position minimises fatigue and the risk of injury by keeping your back straight and avoid twisting.
- Follow workplace and suppliers' or manufacturer's instructions for the safe use of equipment, materials and products and dispose of waste materials correctly.
- Keep your work area clean and tidy throughout the service and use working methods that:
  - minimise the risk of damage to tools
  - minimise the risk of cross-infection
  - make effective use of your working time
  - ensure the use of clean resources
  - minimise the risk of harm or injury to yourself and others
  - promote environmental and sustainable working practices.
- Select suitable products, tools and equipment.
- Carry out cutting services and complete the service within a commercially viable time.
- Provide clients with advice and recommendations on the service(s) provided.

Cut hair to achieve a variety of looks

You will be assessed on:

- a one-length haircut
- a uniform layer haircut
- a short graduation haircut
- a long graduation haircut.

At least one of these haircuts *must* have a fringe. While carrying out these haircuts you must use:

- club cutting
- freehand
- scissor over comb
- texturising, fringe cutting
- clipper work techniques.

You must:

- Consult with clients to confirm the desired look to establish the factors likely to influence the service and confirm with your client the look agreed at consultation prior to beginning the cut.
- Carry out cutting services and create and follow the cutting guideline(s) to achieve the required look:

- Control your tools to minimise the risk of damage to the hair and scalp, client discomfort and to achieve the desired look.
- Use cutting techniques suitable for your client's hair type and to achieve the desired look.
- Adapt your cutting techniques to take account of the factors that influence the service.
- Change your own position and that of your client to help you ensure the accuracy of the cut.
- Cross-check the cut to establish accurate distribution of weight, balance and shape and remove any unwanted hair outside the desired outline shape.
- Continue to consult with your client during the cutting process to confirm the desired look. Make a final visual check of the hair to ensure the finished cut is accurate and confirm your client's satisfaction with the finished cut.

- Provide clients with advice and recommendations on the service(s) provided.

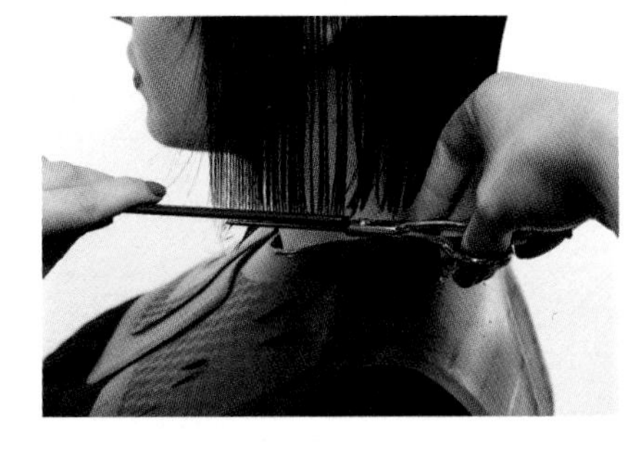

▲ Cut hair

CREATIVELY RESTYLE HAIR

When carrying out your creative restyle assessments you may be assessed on layered cuts or long or short graduation as well as club cutting, freehand, scissor over comb and texturising techniques. You will also need to use precision cutting techniques that will include some disconnection within the haircut. As well as creatively restyling the hair, you must apply safe working practices throughout the service.

You must:

- Consult with clients to confirm the desired look and explore the variety of looks with your client using relevant visual aids.
- Recommend a look that is suitable for your client, basing your recommendations on an accurate evaluation of your client's hair and its potential to achieve the look.
- Prepare for creative hair cutting services.
- Carry out creative hair cutting services, confirming with your client the look agreed at consultation before commencing the cut.
  - Create and follow the cutting guideline(s) to achieve the required look.
  - Personalise your cutting techniques and effects to take account of factors that will influence the desired look while combining and adapting your cutting techniques and effects to achieve the desired look.
  - Change your own position and that of your client to help you ensure accuracy and cross-check the cut to establish accurate distribution of weight, balance and shape.
  - Create outline shapes that are accurate, defined and achieve the look required by your client.
  - Remove any unwanted hair outside the desired outline shape, consulting with your client during the cutting service to confirm the desired look.

▲ Restyle hair

- Take suitable remedial action to resolve any problems arising during the cutting service and making a final visual check to ensure the finished cut is accurate.
- Use creative finishing techniques that complement the cut and ensure the finished, restyled look complements your client's features and enhances their personal image and that of the salon.
- Confirm your client's satisfaction with the finished look.

- Provide your client with advice and recommendations on the service(s) provided.

STEP BY STEP

You will need to be able to create the following looks:

- One-length cut – the hair is cut the same outside length.
- Uniform layers – all sections of the hair are the same length.
- Short graduation – the inner layers of the hair lengths are longer than the outline shape.
- Long graduation – the inner layers of the hair lengths are shorter than the outline shape.
- With a fringe – one of more of your haircuts must include the cutting of a fringe.
- Creatively restyle hair – one or more of your haircuts must include precision cutting techniques and disconnection.

Creating a one-length look

When cutting the hair to create a one-length look, you need to take very thin sections to enable you to follow your guideline, and take into consideration the natural fall of the hair. The hair is pulled straight down at 0°.

One length above shoulders

STEP 1 – Before the cut the client is protected

STEP 2 – Starting at the nape and using a slightly curved horizontal section, cut a square line with tension.

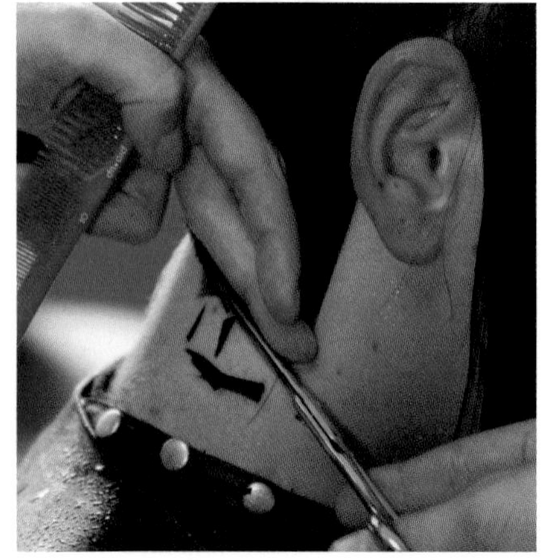

STEP 3 – Start in the centre and work out on both sides.

STEP 4 – After cutting your line, comb the hair and assess your shape **aesthetically**. Constantly check and clean your line.

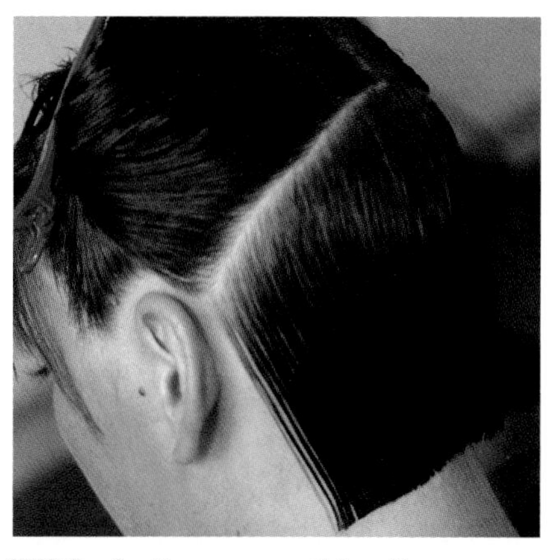

STEP 5 – Continue your parallel sections up the head with the same tension and using your previous section as a guide. Note that with the head tilted, it is important to follow the square line in relation to the head angle.

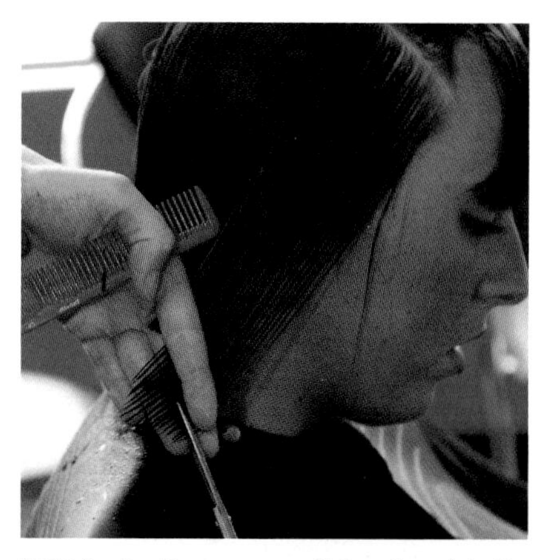

STEP 6 – Continue your parallel sections into the front hairline, and use your scissors to pick up and lay the hair over the ear, tapping the bottom of the ear before cutting to allow for **protrusion**.

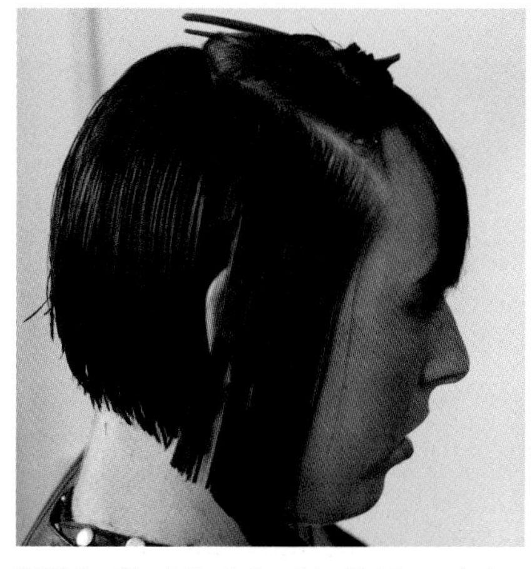

STEP 7 – Check the hair cut is slightly angled downwards when the chin is down.

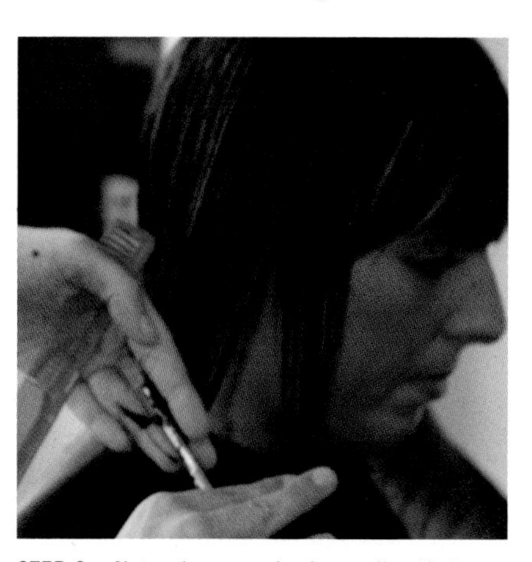

STEP 8 – Note when you check your line that there is a small corner that allows for the ear protrusion which must not be cut off.

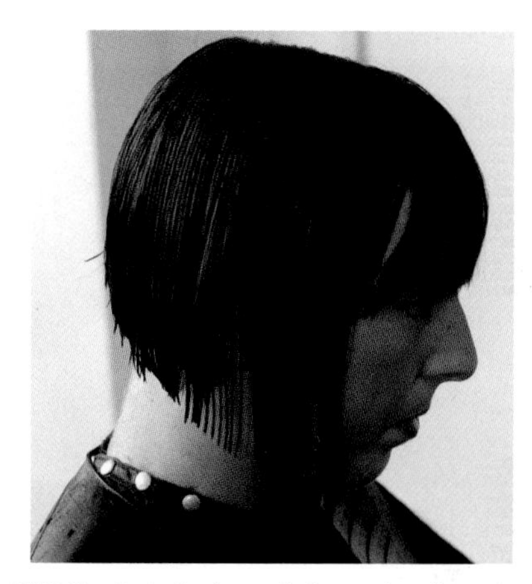

STEP 9 – Next check your balance visually and technically on both sides.

STEP 10 – Bring down the fringe area. Use a curved horizontal section with the bridge of the nose and the corner of the temple as a guide. Club cut the fringe using light tension.

STEP 11 – Continue with parallel sections throughout the triangular fringe area.

STEP 12 – The result: a balanced bespoke one-length defined shape.

KEY TERMS

Aesthetic – beautiful
Protrusion – overhang

One length below shoulders

STEP 1 – Gown the client, position the head and section the hair. Use the horizontal section at the back for the guideline.

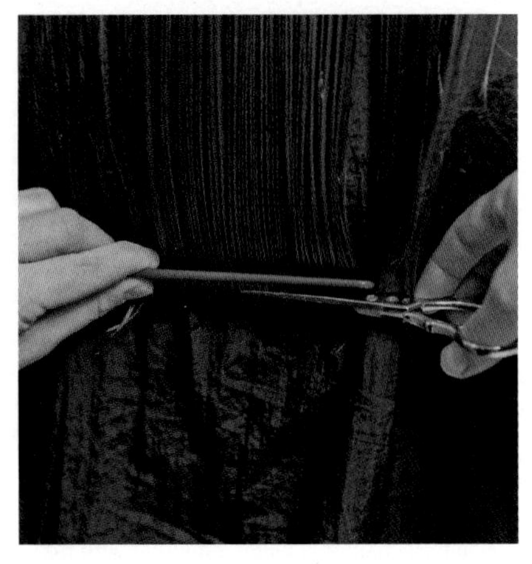

STEP 2 – Club cut following the horizontal cut guideline.

STEP 3 – Club cut the next horizontal section. Check for balance regularly. Remove any graduation after checking.

STEP 4 – Blend in the sides section and take a guideline. Then cross-check the cut, pulling sections down evenly.

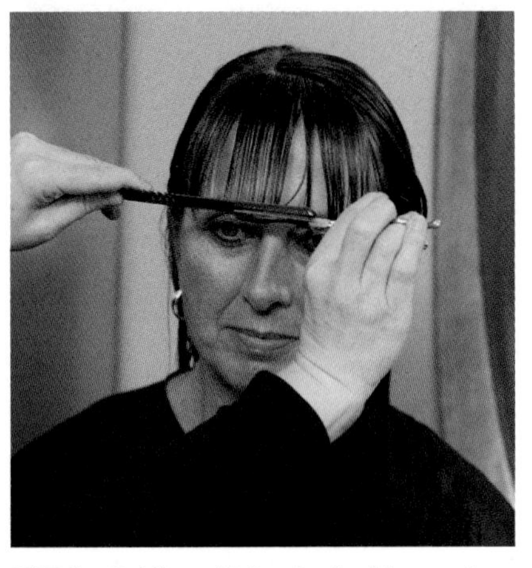

STEP 5 – Cut the guideline for the fringe, using a freehand technique

STEP 6 – When balanced, apply finishing products and style the hair.

ACTIVITY

Create a mood board of varying one-length looks and write up how to achieve one of the images.

Creating a uniform layer look

When cutting the hair to create a uniform layer look, you will need to make a guideline section for the length of the hair and one for the internal layers of the hair. The hair is cut at 90° all over.

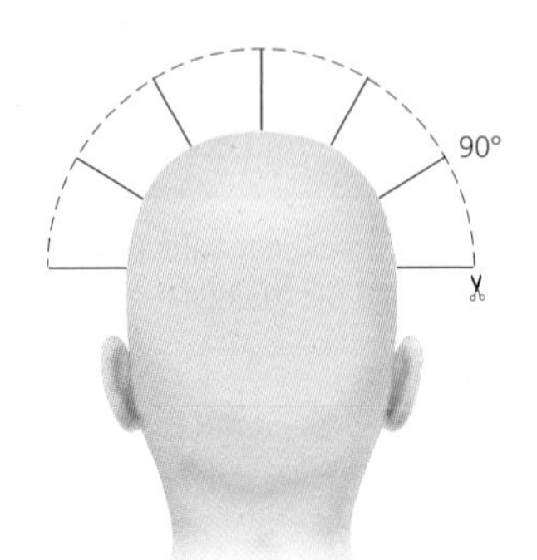

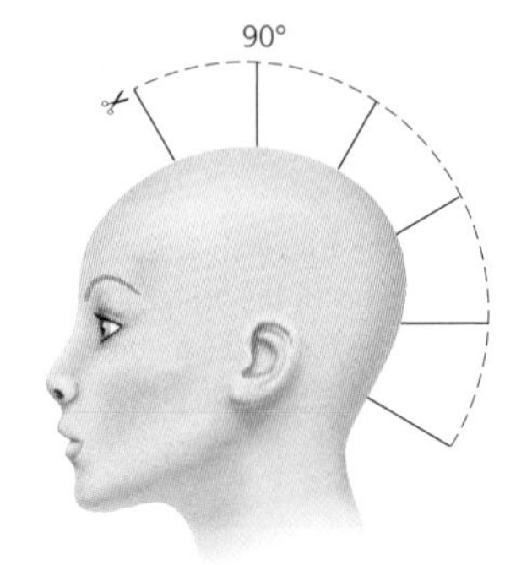

STEP 1 – Take clean vertical sections of hair and pull the hair up at 90°.

STEP 2 – Cut the hair in sections from the top to the back, following the head shape.

STEP 3 – Ensure you pull the hair directly away from the head, maintaining a 90° angle.

STEP 4 – Blend the length into the base guideline.

STEP 5 – Cut the internal guideline using club cutting techniques.

STEP 6 – Work around the back sections, taking hair at 90°.

STEP 7 – Cross-check the hair using a horizontal section.

STEP 8 – Cross-check the cut, pulling sections out evenly to the sides.

STEP 9 – The completed look.

ACTIVITY

Create a mood board of varying uniform layer looks and write up how to achieve one of the images.

Short graduation – creating an asymmetric look

Asymmetric means unequal or unbalanced, so the look will not be symmetrical. You will need to use different cutting angles and guidelines to create this look.

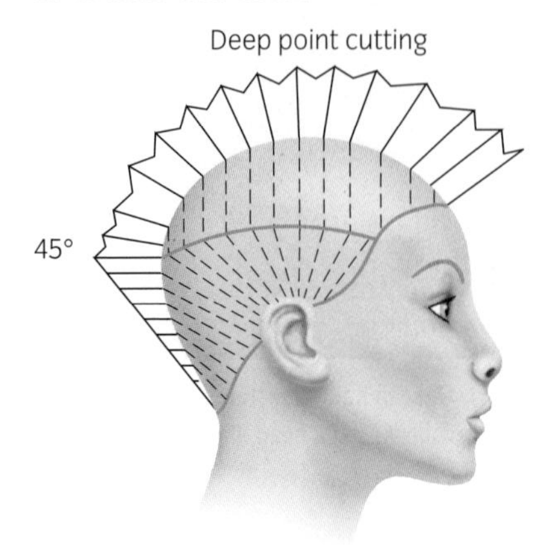

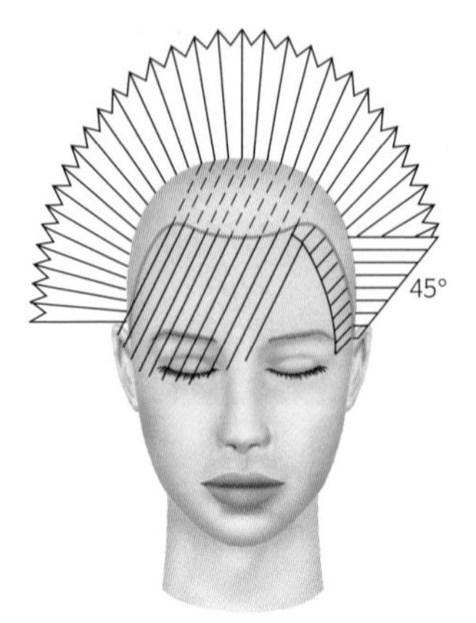

Step 1 – Client's hair before asymmetric hair cut.

Step 2 – Completed sectioning for asymmetric cut and to reflect the parting worn

Step 3 – Start hair cut at nape of neck and taking sections straight down at 0°, and point cut the baseline, as the client's hair is abundant and this provides a softer finish

Step 4 – Take down the next section of hair, but ensure you can clearly see your guide

Step 5 – Continue to the crown and check the baseline shape.

Step 6 – Continue round to the sides and following the shape through using point-cutting techniques. (The entire perimeter is point cut.)

Step 7 – Section the hair from below the occipital bone to the nape taking sections vertical sections

Step 8 – Holding the hair at a 45° angle, point cut to remove length and bulk from the occipital bone to the nape

Step 9 – Continue with the graduation to just below crown

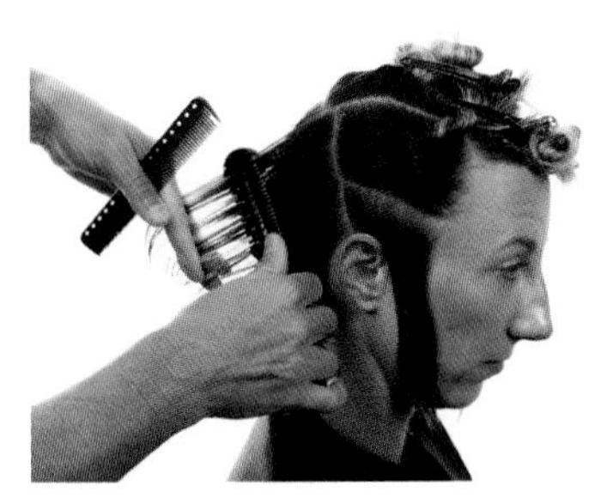

Step 10 – Razor cut (using a 'carving comb') through the back section to remove extra bulk and add movement and texture to the style

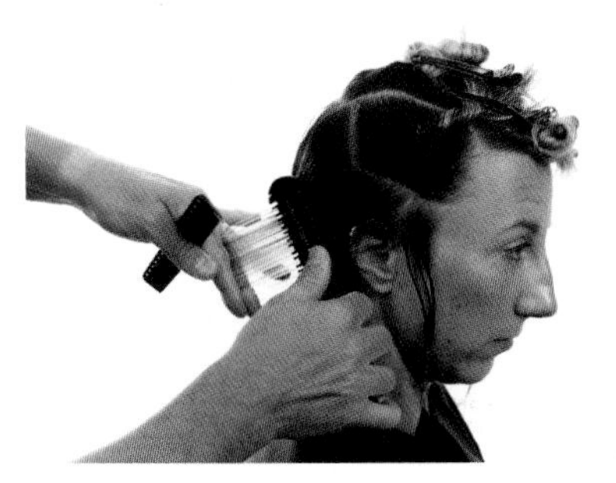

Step 11 – Maintaining the same cutting angles and over directing the hair backwards, progress through to the side sections and razor cut to remove weight.

Step 12 – Through the top sections, to create disconnection elevate the sections to a 90° angle and take off the corners with club cutting techniques. Chip in the corners of the layers to remove bulk

Step 13 – Dry the hair and check the back for balance

Step 14 – Personalise the haircut and cut a triangular section diagonally using freehand techniques.

Step 15 – Add finishing products to complete the look

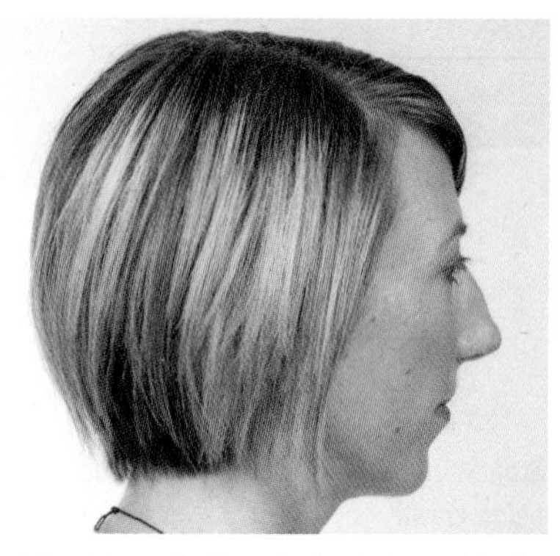

Step 16 – Alternatively style the hair straight for a different image

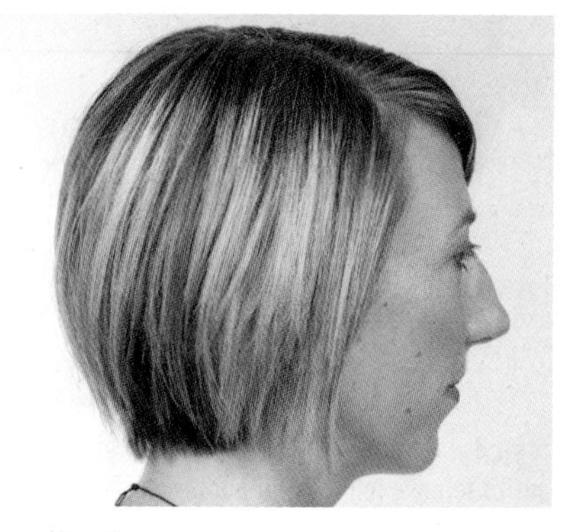

Step 17 – The short side dried smooth and straight

Step 18 – The longer side finished result.

ACTIVITY

Draw the correct cutting angles used to create this look.

Short graduation – creating a textured graduated bob

Step 1 – Section the hair into the natural parting and take a concave section from just below the occipital bone.

Step 2 – Comb the hair onto the skin and cut following the sectioning pattern using a freehand technique. Take the next section, working up towards the occipital area, following the concave section.

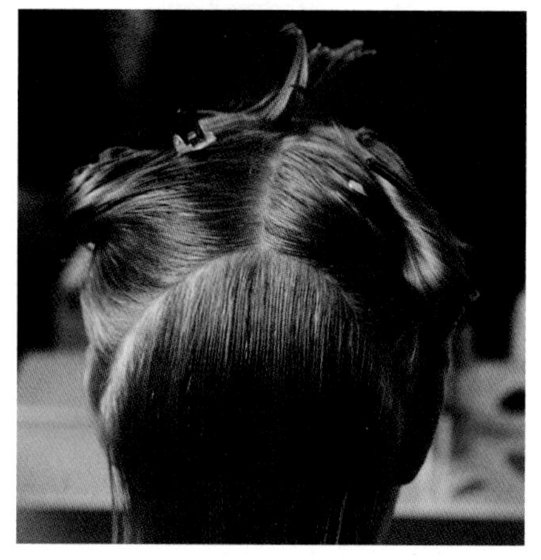

Step 3 – Keep your sections clean and continue with the concave sectioning pattern as you work towards the crown.

Step 4 – Take a centre profile section and pull out at 90°, then cut a square layer through the back sections using club-cutting technique.

Step 5 – Cross-check the back section for balance using your fingers and horizontal sections.

Step 6 – Take a horseshoe section from crown to low recession. Working through the side, over direct to maintain length. Repeat on the other side.

Step 7 – Continue through the front, following the guidelines and over-directing the hair.

Step 8 – Take a radial parting and elevate at 90° to the head. Use a point cutting technique to blend the crown in with the previously cut sections.

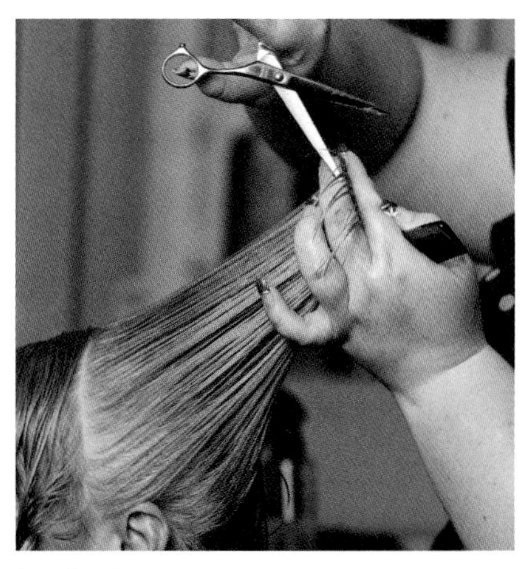

Step 9 – Follow through to the side sections, over directing everything to the ear to maintain length through the front.

Step 10 – Check the baseline and comb down at 0°, following the previous section and increasing length towards the face.

Step 11 – Working through the front section, over direct to blend the fringe with the sides. When the hair is dried into style, personalise the cut using a deep point cutting technique and apply finishing products.

Step 12 – The finished look.

ACTIVITY

Draw the correct cutting angles used to create this look.

ACTIVITY

Create a mood board of varying short graduated layer looks and write up how to achieve one of the images.

Creating a long graduated layer look

When you create a long graduated layer look, the hair must gradually get longer. This style maintains the length of the hair. The layers are held out between 90° like the uniform layer and up to 135° or 180°, depending on the length of the hair and the layers.

Long graduation including texturising techniques

Step 1 – Shampoo and condition, comb through, identify the natural parting and section hair methodically. Take a back section and club cut the base line length as agreed at consultation.

Step 2 – Continue cutting the back sections, removing length.

Step 3 – Use the comb to check the line is straight.

Step 4 – Pull the hair down on both sides to check the back length is balanced, level and even.

Step 5 – Continue around the side. Bring the side length into the back sections and remove the length.

Step 6 – Complete both sides and check the front sections are level and balanced.

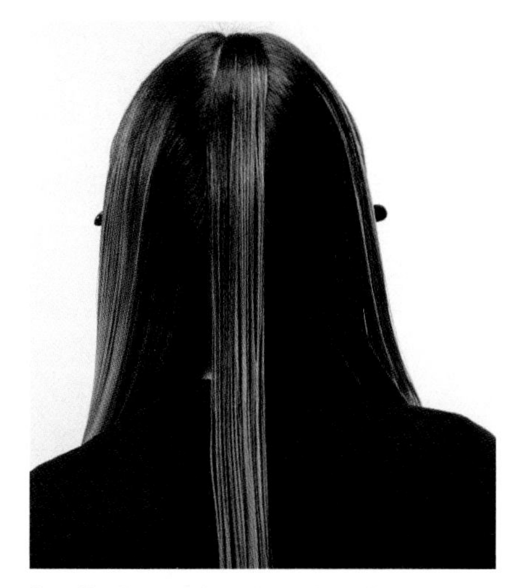

Step 7 – Section the hair vertically from the lower crown area to length.

Step 8 – Elevate the hair to maintain the length and cut the layers.

Step 9 – Continue cutting the layers around the back sections and cross-check horizontally.

Step 10 – Over direct the top section and blend into the back layers.

Step 11 – Use point cutting texturising techniques to remove length and add texture to the front sections.

Step 12 – Check the balance of lengths on both sides by pulling sections of hair upwards and checking both sides are the same lengths.

Step 13 – Razor cut the sides to soften edges and texturise.

Step 14 – Disconnect a long fringe area and texturise to remove length and bulk.

Step 15 – Add styling products and blow-dry hair to achieve the finished look.

ACTIVITY

Draw the correct cutting angles used to create this look.

ACTIVITY

Create a mood board of varying long graduated layer looks and write up how to achieve one of the images.

For an example of a uniform layer cut, see chapter 5.

Creating a precision cut

Precision cuts with clear sharp edges work well on long or short styles. On a long look, it may be the sides or fringe that are not connected to the rest of the style. On shorter hair the disconnection could be an undercut or as part of an asymmetric look, or a creative style designed by you.

STEP 1 – Shampoo, condition, comb through and section the hair. Use a horseshoe section on top. Section the front and centre section down the middle with the fringe separated from the rest of the hair.

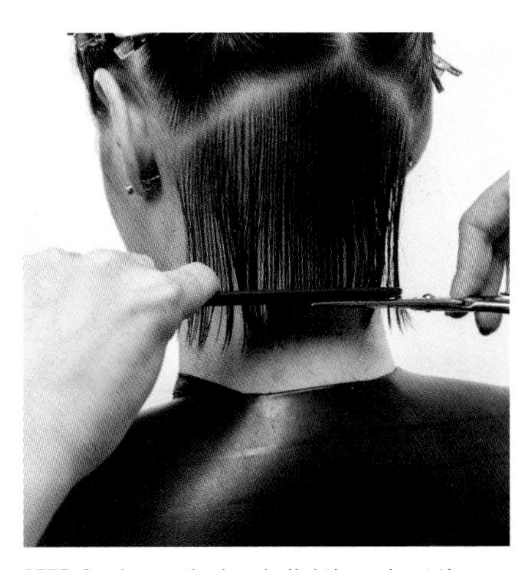

STEP 2 – Lower the head slightly and cut the first section at the back at 0° using freehand and club cutting techniques without tension.

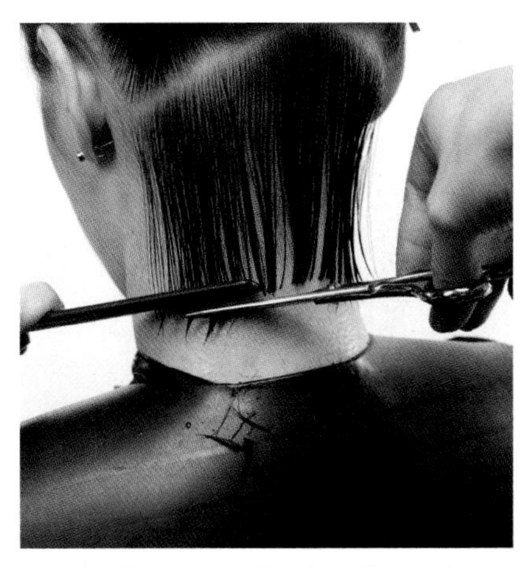

STEP 3 – Complete the first base line cut for your future guide.

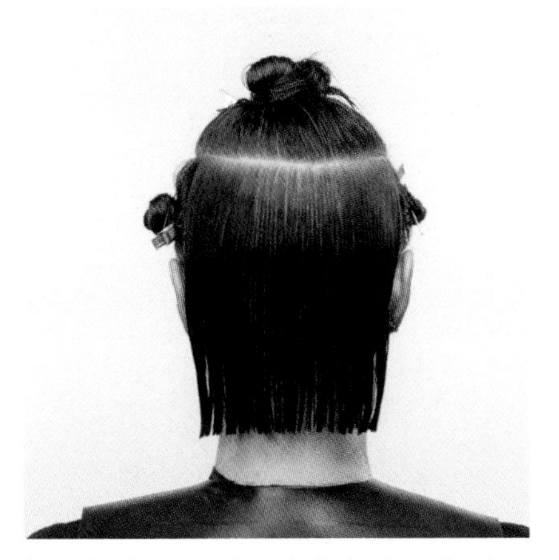

STEP 4 – Continue through the back section to below the crown.

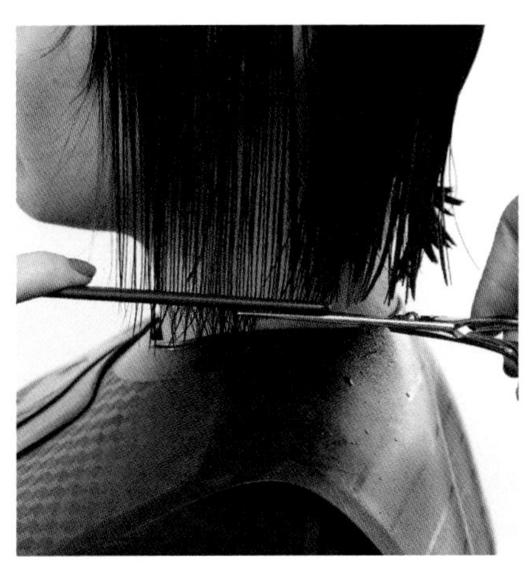

STEP 5 – Lift the head slightly to cut and blend the left side section into the back.

STEP 6 – Continue to cut the right-hand section.

STEP 7 – Check the balance of both sides.

STEP 8 – Create a smaller horseshoe parting. Cut this section of hair slightly longer than the previous guide to ensure the hair tucks under when styled (reverse graduation).

STEP 9 – Continue with the horseshoe section, cutting slightly longer throughout.

STEP 10 – Cut the remaining section to a centre parting.

STEP 11 – Personalise the look and add texture.

STEP 12 – The finished result.

Test your knowledge

Question 1

Asme mentions to you that he is upset with the hair loss around his recession area. Name and describe the cause of this disorder.

Question 2

State four influencing factors that should be considered before carrying out a cut and blow-dry service.

Question 3

Why is it important to maintain tension during a haircut?

Question 4

Describe three cutting techniques that could be used during a long graduation.

Question 5

How would you adapt a short haircut for a client with a double crown?

Question 6

Why is it important to consider whether to cut the hair wet or dry?

Multiple choice questions

7 Which of the following is recommended for sterilising clippers?

- a Ultra Violet light – UV cabinet
- b Chemical – Barbicide
- c Chemical – wipes/sprays
- d Moist heat - steam

8 The characteristics of curly hair can make it difficult to cut because:

- a it is usually coarse and needs thinning
- b it has more growth patterns and can spring up
- c it seems shorter during the cut and longer when finished
- d it is often fine and lacks volume

9 Look at these two statements:

Statement 1: Clients with a large face will always suit a short crop as this will accentuate their features.

Statement 2: A fringe or side parting will disguise a narrow forehead.

Which of the following is correct for the above statements?

- a True, true
- b True, false
- c False, true
- d False, false

10 Which of the following techniques should be used to create a textured look?

- a Club cutting
- b Point cutting
- c Scissor over comb
- d Clipper over comb

11 A disconnected cut will show:

- a a solid perimeter
- b graduations and soft layers
- c bulk at the mid-lengths
- d various lengths within the style

12 A style that adds width would suit a client with a:

- a heart-shaped face
- b long face
- c round face
- d square face

13 Which one of the following describes the result of using a razor on dry hair?

- a Hair will rip and become weak
- b Hair will stretch and break
- c The layers will become more visible
- d The layers will be softer

14 Which of the following tools and techniques should only be used on dry hair?

- a Freehand, club cutting, razors and clippers
- b Texturising, club cutting razors and thinning scissors
- c Texturising, slicing, scissor over comb and thinning scissors
- d scissor over comb, thinning scissors and clippers

15 Straight hair is classified as:

- **a** Type 1
- **b** Type 2
- **c** Type 3
- **d** Type 4

16 Look at these two statements:
Statement 1: Fine hair should be kept long to avoid it looking too sparse.
Statement 2: Fine hair should be texturised with a razor to give support.
Which one of the following is correct for the above statements?

- **a** True, true
- **b** True, false
- **c** False, true
- **d** False, false

This page intentionally left blank.

CHAPTER 5

CUT HAIR USING BASIC BARBERING TECHNIQUES TO CREATE A VARIETY OF LOOKS

EVIE SPENSLEY – DASH SALON

I'm Evie Spensley. I'm 17 years old and live in Newton Aycliffe, a town in County Durham. I've been working in the same salon, Dash, in Shildon, since I left school a year ago to begin my NVQ Level 2 Hairdressing Apprenticeship.

I applied for the BL Hairdressing Training last summer. I attended interviews and trial days at various salons close to my home, and was thrilled to win an Apprenticeship with Dash salon. I was inducted straight onto the Level 2 Hairdressing course and started attending BL for classes. I'm really enjoying the variety of working in the salon as well as getting the support at college. Learning in both environments, I'm making so much progress. In the Dash salon I'm gaining invaluable, real-life work experience and I continually have the opportunity to practise the hairdressing skills I've been developing in the classroom by completing in-salon training and off-the-job training.

Dash also encouraged me to attend a Wella Colour ID course where I received expert training in Colour ID, with the chance to practise on models. Through my BL Hairdressing course, I've also completed a THS Introduction to Colour workshop, which gave me important basic knowledge of colour theory. A Curl Formers workshop was also invaluable in improving my curling technique in a different environment than the one I'm used to.

The biggest difference I've noticed is not just the improvement in my technical abilities, but in my self-confidence. I feel capable and supported and I know I'm constantly improving and developing into the stylist I always dreamed I'd be. I feel ready to take on my NVQ Level 3 Hairdressing course and I'm even considering expanding my skillset by completing an NVQ Level 2 in Barbering qualification.

As you start to think about your next steps from school, just never give up on your dreams of finding a salon placement, always try and never be afraid to try new things and skills.

This chapter maps to:

- Unit 9 Cutting hair using barbering techniques to create a variety of looks (Level 2 Diploma for Hair Professionals – Barbering)

INTRODUCTION

Barbering has a long and historical tradition and cutting men's hair is one of the most popular services provided by barbershops. It is considered to be the cutting edge of male grooming and is a huge area of growth in today's market.

Outlines and detailing is sometimes referred to as hair tattooing and incorporates a variety of techniques, enabling barbers to create unique and artistic designs that demonstrate their skill. This service is popular, particularly with the masculine finish created with detailing and outlining around the hairline. It also allows the client to express their individuality and image via a personalised hair design.

Learning a variety of techniques will give you the knowledge, skills and confidence to generate a clientele that you can build on. Enhancing your skills will give you the opportunity to produce a variety of different styles and become a professional barber.

After reading this chapter you will:

- understand how health and safety policies and procedures affect cutting hair using barbering techniques
- be able to apply safe working practices when cutting hair using barbering techniques
- understand the factors that may influence cutting hair using barbering techniques
- be aware of the tools, equipment and products used when cutting hair using barbering techniques
- know how to cut hair using basic barbering techniques
- know how to creatively cut hair using a combination of barbering techniques
- be able to create basic outlines and detailing design in hair.

HEALTH AND SAFETY POLICIES AND PROCEDURES

As with all services, you must follow the requirements of health and safety legislation when cutting men's hair and minimise the risk of harm to you and others.

Personal hygiene

Make sure you are ready for work and your personal hygiene is excellent – shower, have clean hair and fresh breath, use deodorant and wear ironed clean clothes. When preparing for the service always wear gloves to prevent cross infection, maintain hygiene throughout service and to ensure client comfort.

Prepare and protect your client

It is advisable to begin the initial consultation before you gown your client, to see his style of dress and overall image. You should ask him about his day-to-day lifestyle, work patterns and available time to commit to styling his hair. If your client works outside in all weathers, his job can seriously affect the condition of his hair, as it will be exposed to sunlight or wind and rain. For clients who love the gym and regular sport, quick and easy to style hair may be preferred. Always listen to what your client is asking of you and be honest yet tactful with the advice you give him. You should use open questions to obtain as much information as possible and finish with closed questions to confirm what has been agreed.

It is your responsibility to protect your client during the service with a gown, towel and cutting collar. You may also use neck strips to protect the neck and collar from hair clippings and discomfort; some barber gowns have a neoprene edged collar which is highly effective in preventing hair clippings travelling further down the neck area.

▲ Always listen to your client and be honest yet tactful with advice

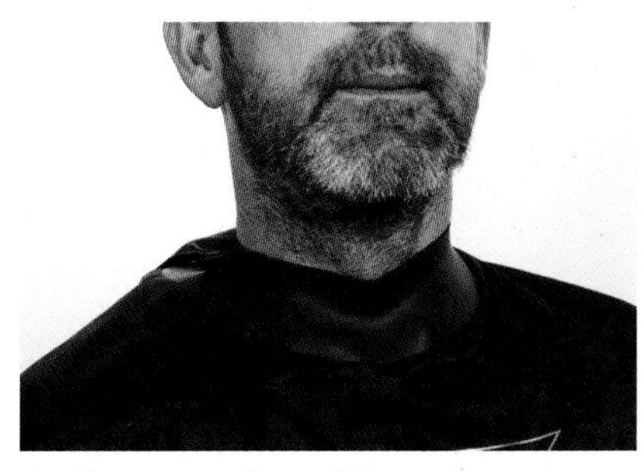

▲ Neoprene collar cutting gown

Positioning

The positioning of you and your client is most important when cutting the hair, as the result and balance of the finished look can be affected.

When he is gowned and protected, you must ensure that your client sits comfortably with his back supported by the chair, in an upright position with his legs uncrossed and evenly balanced.

THE HAIR PROFESSIONAL IN THE WORKPLACE

Sit on a cutting stool while cutting hair short or working on the back of your client's head. Adjust the height of the barber's chair to ensure you work comfortably. The headrest on a barber's chair should be lowered for cutting and drying services and raised for the neck during shaving and facial hair services. This will prevent you from bending and over stretching and help to maintain your comfort, which is essential during the cutting service.

HANDY HINT

If your client's posture is unbalanced or he is sitting with his legs crossed, the resulting haircut could be unbalanced, as your client might have a tendency to lean to one side. Always ensure your client is sitting upright with his legs uncrossed.

▲ Sit on a stool when cutting hair around the neck line

▲ Adjust the neck rest when using the barber chair for hair cutting services.

HANDY HINT

During the service you will need to adapt and change your body position, and that of the client, to ensure you maintain a balanced, even and accurate haircut throughout.

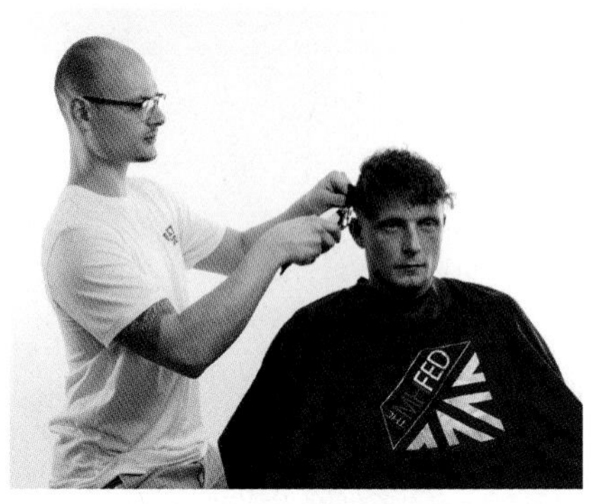

▲ Client and barber at suitable height

THE HAIR PROFESSIONAL IN THE WORKPLACE

During detailing and outlining services, it is important that your client's neck is supported, particularly if it is positioned awkwardly, to enable you to carry out the design work. Clients are at risk of neck pain and discomfort from hyperextension and prolonged periods of time spent with the neck extended and unsupported can lead to a stroke.

Potential hazards and possible risks

The hazards and risks in your workplace include slippery surfaces, spillages, sharp items, electrical equipment and chemical substances.

Safe working practices

Throughout the service ensure that you take care when using tools and equipment to minimise the risk of damage. Use sustainable working practices, such as turning off electricity and taps after use, avoiding waste and recycling where possible. When using a razor on the skin, wear gloves to prevent any cross-contamination and dispose of the blades safely in a sharps bin.

At the end of the service remove any waste, ensuring you protect the environment. Turn off all electrical items and prepare your tools and work area for the next service.

SAFE AND HYGIENIC WORKING METHODS AND PRACTICES

Safe and hygienic working methods include:

- client preparation and protecting client from hair cuttings
- using personal protective equipment
- following safety considerations
- using working methods that promote environmental and sustainable working practices
- correctly disposing of waste
- minimising the wastage of products.

Methods of working when cutting men's hair

It is important to follow health and safety, as well as working hygienically and methodically when cutting men's hair. Monitor and check your safe methods of working by following this diagram.

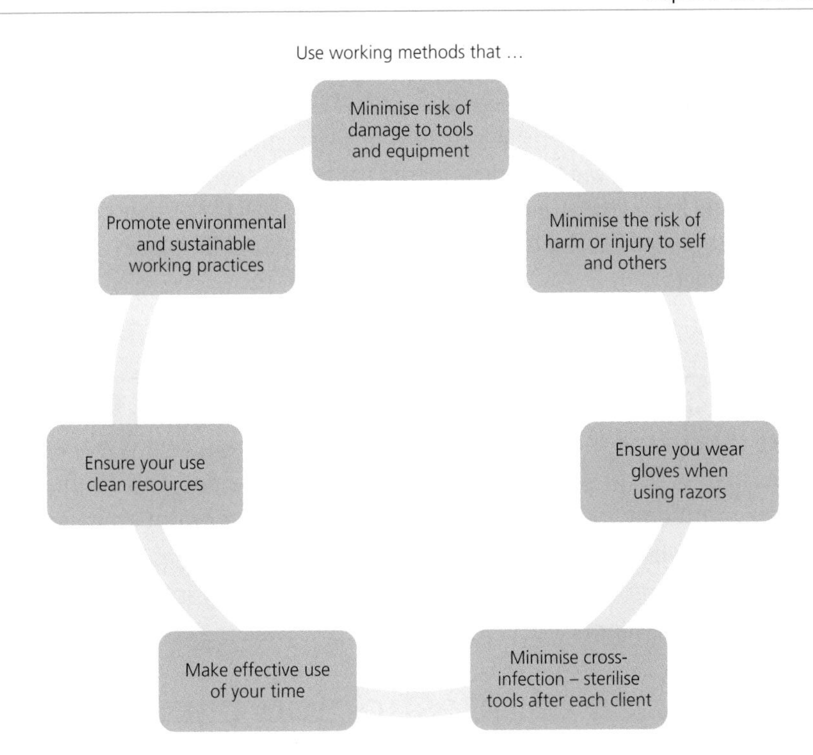

Prevent cross-infection and cross-infestation

It is important to keep your work area clean and tidy to prevent hazards, risks and cross-contamination, which would give a poor barbershop image. You must wear gloves when razor cutting directly onto your client's skin to minimise the risk of cross-infection.

Cleaning, disinfecting and sterilisation

To minimise the risk of cross-infection always ensure that the salon has a plentiful supply of clean, washed gowns and towels, and check if any need to be washed or dried. You should change your Barbicide solution regularly, so that it can be used between every client for disinfecting your combs and scissors; use clippercide on your clippers and trimmers. Clean and sterilise your cutting collars and check your cutting stool and trolley are free of hair, wiped clean and disinfected.

HANDY HINT

Refer back to Chapter 1 for more information on health and safety, preventing hazards and risks, and safe and hygienic working practices.

HANDY HINT

Keeping your work area clean and tidy prevents accidents, injuries and risks of cross-contamination.

HANDY HINT

Control and maintain your tools and equipment correctly, and always clean tools and sterilise them after use. Remember to oil the blades on your scissors and clippers to ensure they are in good working order.

HANDY HINT

Refer to Chapter 1 for a recap on preparing the barbershop for your client's arrival and ensuring you are ready to commence the service.

ACTIVITY

Discuss with a colleague how you think a client would feel if you used combs, scissors or clippers with the previous client's hair still on them.

HANDY HINT

Always dispose of used razor blades in a sharps box and take care when removing blades. Refer to Chapter 1 for a recap on generic salon waste disposal.

▲ Barbicide

▲ Clipper oil

HANDY HINT

You could refer to the following websites for barbering images:
www.britishbarbers.com
www.thelionsbarbercollective.com
www.mhfed.com (Gallery)

HANDY HINT

Always clean your non-electrical tools prior to disinfecting or sterilising, using detergent with warm water. Toothbrushes or nailbrushes work particularly well for removing hair cuttings and scalp debris from between the teeth of combs and clipper blades. To maintain the life of your clippers, oil the blades after cleaning them.

CONSULT WITH YOUR CLIENT

Prior to the start of the service, explore different looks using visual aids, such as Instagram or Pinterest, magazines or the internet, and confirm the look required with your client. You will need to carry out an in-depth consultation with your client and analyse their hair to be able to make recommendations based on their requirements and any influencing factors you have identified.

Importance of questioning clients

During the consultation you should ask questions about how much hair your client would like taken off the length and the layers. You must ask specific questions to achieve an accurate account of your client's needs. Does he want an easy-to-manage style, or does he have time to dry and style his hair? Does he use tools and equipment or buy styling products? Show him in the mirror how much hair you are going to remove to confirm what you assume to be the agreed lengths and amounts. Encourage your client to put forward his own ideas on the design, give him the opportunity to express his thoughts about the finished look and/or give him the option to try something different from his current style.

When you have decided on a style together, ask your client which products he currently uses to style his hair, to identify whether you need to recommend alternative products for his new image. You should then confirm the agreed outcome requirements and explain the duration and likely cost of the service.

Relationship between barber and client

Barbers and their clients often build a special relationship and strong bonds, which can in turn help clients to open up about their personal problems.

The Lion's Barber Collective is an international collection of top barbers who have come together to help raise awareness for the prevention of suicide. The Collective began with a comment on a Facebook group and now members donate their time to demonstrate their skills and raise awareness about the mission of BarberTalk, as well as other charities. Their aim is to create training that will enable barbers to 'Recognise, Talk, Listen and Advise' their clients when they are sitting in their chair.

The Lion's Barber Collective state:

> ... as Barbers we have a unique relationship of trust and friendship crossing personal space which often creates a strong bond between barber and client allowing many people to open up and discuss subjects they wouldn't usually talk to friends or family about. We don't want barbers to become councillors, however we would love our industry to embrace the trust we have earned to make a difference and be able to become that first step on that journey, directing people in the right direction to where they can receive the help they need.

Visit www.thelionsbarbercollective.com/about-us for more information.

Talk to your client throughout the cutting process to ensure they are happy with the style or design as it develops and make changes if required. At the end of the service you should always confirm your client's satisfaction with the finished cut.

THE HAIR PROFESSIONAL AT WORK

You will use different communication skills with male clients, which may involve banter, and varied topics of conversation. You will, however, need to remain polite and professional throughout the service and ensure your communication skills and instructions are effective and clear. Repeating back what your client has asked of you will help you to gain the client's confidence during the service.

HANDY HINT

Reasons why clients leave their barber:

- The barber did not recommend anything new or interesting.
- The barber did not listen to the client's request.
- The barber created a style which was not suitable for the client.
- The barber cut the hair too short/left it too long, even after consultation and agreeing the lengths.
- The service took too long.

HANDY HINT

Use a smartphone or tablet to search for men's styling images online.

▲ The internet is a great source of ideas for men's styles

ACTIVITY

Ask a male colleague to pretend to be your client. Ask him to visualise a style and then ask him relevant questions to identify the image and look he requires. Use at least three open and two closed questions to obtain as much information as possible about his requirements. (For more information on open and closed questions refer to Chapter 1.)

HANDY HINT

Revisit Chapter 1 for more in-depth information on consulting with your client.

Factors that may influence barbering techniques

As with every service, before you can make recommendations on the hair service, you need to test the condition and strength of the hair. Carry out a porosity test to identify the condition of the cuticle layer and an elasticity test to test the strength of the cortex.

If the hair is porous or of poor elasticity, you will need to consider the tools you use to cut the hair and how much to recommend you cut off. You may also need to advise your client on:

- shampoo and conditioning products to use in between visits
- styling products to use

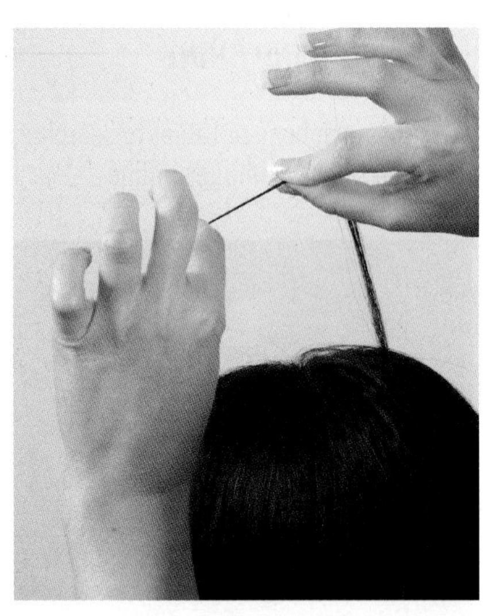

▲ Elasticity test

- tools to use or avoid
- how to protect his hair against the elements and environment if he works outside
- future services.

Factors that influence services include:

- hair characteristics
- hair classifications
- head and face shape
- presence of male pattern baldness
- presence of added hair
- piercings
- adverse skin conditions.

Expected service times

In addition to the above factors, you must consider how long your salon expects the service to take. Although salon and services vary, as a guide allow the following times for barbering services:

Service	Time allocated for service
Gent's cut and finish	About 30 minutes
Basic detailing or outlining on previously cut hair	10 to 30 minutes depending on the detail required
Creative cutting and restyle services	Up to 45 minutes.

▲ Feel the head for lumps and bumps prior to cutting

Factors to consider before and during cutting

Men working manual jobs can be prone to bumps on the head; if they wear their hair short then the head is not as well protected. Always check the hair and scalp for any lumps and bumps that could cause discomfort to your client when you are combing through the hair.

There are many factors that could affect how you cut the hair, the tools that you use and the styles that you recommend. You must consider these factors prior to and during the service. The first factor that you must take into consideration is what your client wants! His requirements are what your whole consultation is about, so now you must determine whether there are any factors that might affect the desired result. Ask your client about his lifestyle to ensure that he does not have any barriers that could prevent him achieving the desired result. Is the chosen style easy to maintain and does it fit around his work requirements?

Hair classifications

The hair classifications fit into four types and can affect the choice of style and cutting technique. You will need to consider whether you should cut the hair wet or dry, when considering the hair classifications.

The table below shows how various factors may impact on the cutting service and the end result.

Classification	How it can affect the service
Type 1 – straight hair 	When cutting fine and medium straight hair every '**scissor cut**' can show in the hair. Accuracy is very important and subtle texturised cuts can help to prevent the cutting line's form being so apparent. Fine/thin straight hair might not achieve the desired result. Avoid using texturising techniques that will make the hair thinner; instead use club cutting techniques and choose styles to suit the hair type.
	Medium straight hair can have lots of volume and body and suits most techniques.
	Coarse straight hair can be difficult to curl or add movement to. It may benefit from texturising and thinning out techniques to remove some bulk and improve the end result and style. **Detailing/outlining** – for straight hair you would generally hold the clippers at 45° and the design will be clear to see. You would need to adjust the thickness of the lines created for fine/thin hair compared to coarse hair.
Type 2 – wavy hair 	Wavy hair can be great to work with as it is easy to mould straighter and to enhance its body. Most techniques work well with this hair type. Fine/thin wavy hair may need to have some length left to aid body; use club cutting techniques to give the appearance of thicker hair.
	Medium and coarse wavy hair can be frizzy so avoid texturising techniques that will enhance a fluffy appearance, such as razor cutting. Club cutting can help by keeping all hair lengths the same.
	Coarse wavy hair can be resistant to styling, so may benefit from being texturised or thinned out but avoid using the razor on the hair. **Detailing/outlining** – wavy hair is generally good to work with, but adjust the thickness of the lines depending on the coarseness of the hair.

→

Classification	How it can affect the service
Type 3 – curly hair	Soft curly hair can have a combination of textures to consider. It may be frizzy in appearance and have lots of body. Tight curly hair can also have combined textures and will spring up after the hair has been cut when it is dried – particularly fine curly hair. When cutting curly hair consider the amount of tension you place on the hair during the cutting service; use a wide-toothed comb and use freehand cutting techniques. **Detailing/outlining** – the clipper angle is slightly adjusted to nearer 90° to ensure the design can be seen clearly.
Type 4 – very curly hair	Soft, very curly hair is often fragile, so be careful if using razors or clippers. Comb the hair gently using a wide-toothed comb and use a conditioning spray to prevent client discomfort. If the client does not want to encourage the curls, then clipper cuts would be the most effective recommendation. Wiry curly hair is also very fragile but can have less of a defined curly pattern. Avoid techniques that texturise the hair and use mostly club cutting and freehand techniques. Take care with tools on the fragile hair. **Detailing/outlining** – the clipper angle is at 90° to ensure the design is clear and crisp and can be seen in the very curly short hair.

KEY TERM

Scissor cut – marks made in the hair when cutting with scissors.

Hair characteristics

Characteristics	How they can affect the service
Elasticity	Elasticity can affect the cutting technique. For medium to longer hair with poor elasticity you should avoid pulling with too much tension during the cutting process. Ensure the hair has an even moisture balance when you cut it – either all wet or all dry – to ensure the effects of poor elasticity are not worsened.

Characteristics	How they can affect the service
Porosity and hair condition 	Hair that is damaged is likely to result in porous hair – this can affect the cutting technique and client comfort. If the hair is porous and the cuticles are open, then hair is more likely to tangle during the cut and this may cause client discomfort. You should use a wide-toothed comb and spray the hair with leave-in conditioner to aid the combing process. Avoid using a razor and take care if using clipper **grades** as they may get caught in the dry, porous hair.
Density  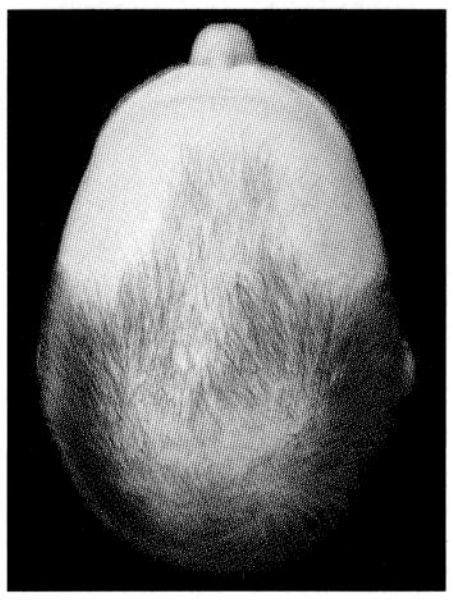	Density can affect the choice of style and cutting technique. Abundant hair might need to be thinned out to create the desired look. Consider whether abundant hair will enhance the look; if not, suggest alternatives. Sparse hair will need to be blunt cut/club cut to maintain as much thickness as possible. Avoid cutting the hair too short. **Detailing/outlining** – the greater the density, the more intricate and detailed the design can be. For fine hair, however, the design needs to be bolder with thicker lines to show off the detail. 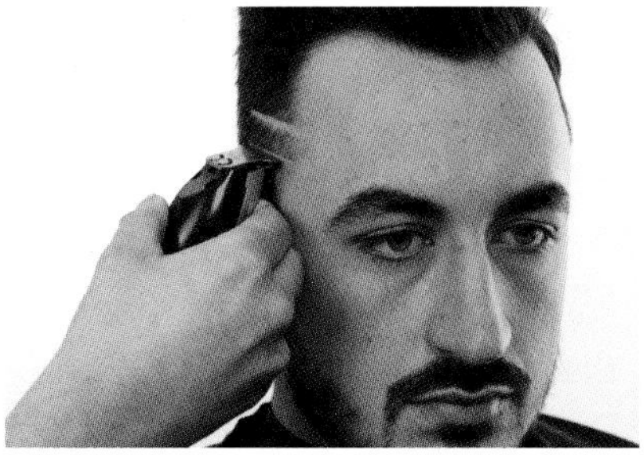
Texture 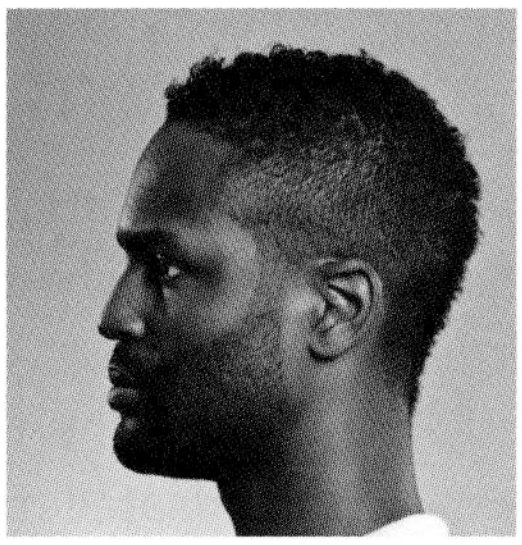 	Texture can affect the choice of style and cutting technique. Coarse-textured hair might not suit the desired look; you will need to recommend styling products to help achieve a smoother result. Fine hair might not suit clipper cuts or very short cuts; you might also need to use supporting hair products.

KEY TERM

Grade – an attachment placed on to the clipper blades to cut hair at varied fixed lengths.

Other characteristics

Hair growth patterns 	Hair growth patterns can affect the choice of style and cutting technique. For cowlicks avoid fringes; instead suggest a side half fringe that works with the cowlick.
	For widow's peaks avoid fringes completely and suggest styles that are constructed with the top area going over to one side or straight back.
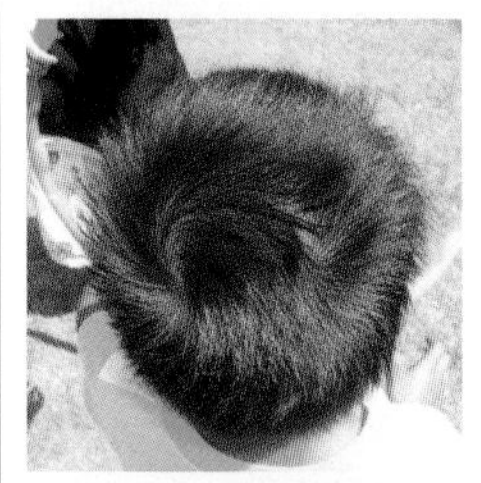	For double crowns suggest maintaining a little length around the crown area and ideally work the natural fall into the style. Alternatively, very short haircuts around the crown area will prevent the hair from sticking up.
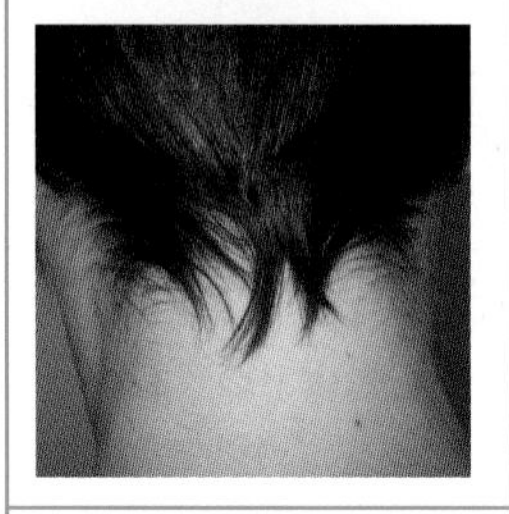	For nape whorls suggest maintaining the length at the nape area, unless you are using the clippers or cutting the nape area very short. **Detailing/outlining** – as hair can be finer in the centre of a hair growth pattern, particularly whorls, they can sometimes cause a problem. Generally a design can be worked around them; move and adjust the design to suit the area and try to incorporate the hair growth pattern into the design.
Male pattern baldness and alopecia 	If your client wants to cover the hair-loss area, then suggest leaving the overall style slightly longer, particularly on the top. Some clients prefer to have the hair cut short around the thinning area, to make the rest of the hair look a little thicker. **Detailing/outlining** – clients with male pattern baldness are still able to have the service but the location or detail of the design may need to be moved or adapted to suit the hair loss areas.

Head and face shape 	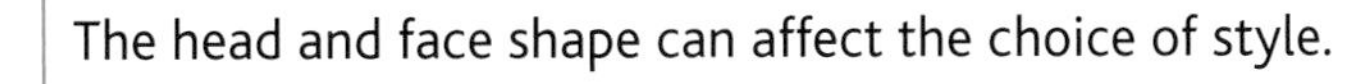 The head and face shape can affect the choice of style. For round face shapes, avoid styles that add more roundness, such as too much width or height.
	For oblong face shapes, avoid height but add width if you can, and suggest a fringe to shorten the illusion of a long face shape. The shorter the haircut, the more **prominent** the oblong shape will appear.
	For square face shapes, avoid square styles, such as 'flat-tops', that will accentuate his features.
	The head shape should be considered within the overall shape of the style. The head should be rounded from the crown to the **occipital bone** and then dip in slightly towards the nape. Some crowns are flatter than others and very short styles could make the back of the head look too flat. Others have very pronounced crown areas and need the cut to make the shape look flatter.
Prominent facial features 	Facial features can affect the choice of style. For clients with **protruding** ears, you can suggest styles that cover the entire ear or are not cut too short around the ear.
	For strong nose features or jaw lines, avoid centre partings that encourage the eye to follow down from the parting to the nose and chin.

	For high foreheads, suggest the haircut has a fringe or some hair styled forward over part of the forehead.
Piercings and tattoos  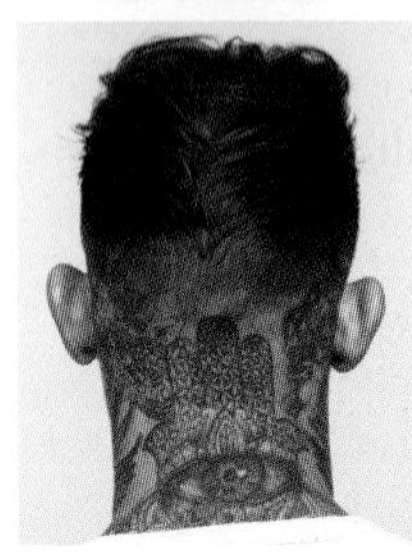	Check the skin, eyebrows and ears for piercings that could cause an injury if you accidentally caught them with the comb. If your client has tattoos on the face or head area, check how recent they are, to ensure they are not tender or at risk of infection. Your client may wish for the hair to be very short to show off his body art, equally it may be something he would like covered up, so always discuss the options during your consultation. **Detailing/outlining** – tattoos can be integrated into the design and enhance the overall look. However, avoid detailing and outlining on areas of the head where tattoos are fresh and the skin is still healing.
Adverse skin conditions 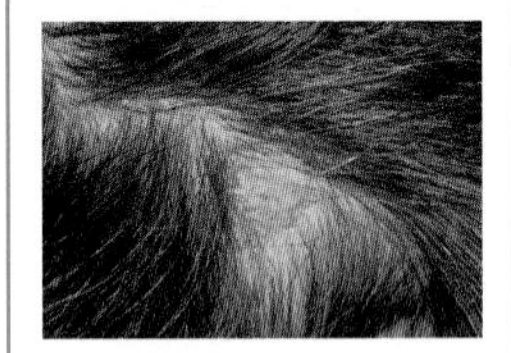	Some scalp disorders might require consideration in the style recommended, as your client might want them covered up. Always ask about scalp disorders during your consultation and check for infections and infestations, which would prevent the service from being carried out. Refer to Chapter 1 for more information.

KEY TERM

Occipital bone – the bone between the crown and the nape area that normally sticks out a little bit.

KEY TERMS

Prominent or protruding – sticking out.

HANDY HINT

If your client has male pattern baldness, designs can still be carried out but in the area where hair is thickest. As you create the design you must think about the balance of style and work this around the area of baldness.

HANDY HINT

Scar tissue can affect the balance and look of designs; it may require the repositioning of the design and can affect the repeated look of a design pattern. Always take care with your clippers around scar tissue.

HANDY HINT

Excessive use of the razor and intricate detailing can cause razor bumps or pimples. If your client is showing these signs do not carry out the service until they have cleared up. Advise your client on products to use to moisturise dry areas and clear up any infections.

HEALTH AND SAFETY

If your client has piercings in the area you are working on, then ask if they can remove them. If this is not possible, take extra care with clippers and combs in this area.

HANDY HINT

If you identify an infectious condition during the consultation, you must not continue with the service. Instead give your client some advice about how to deal with the problem or suggest he visits his GP. Try to keep these conversations discreet so the client is put at ease, and explain that you will welcome him back when the infectious condition has cleared. Remember that it is not your responsibility to diagnose a skin condition and there could be legal implications for the salon if you misdiagnose.

Other factors to consider

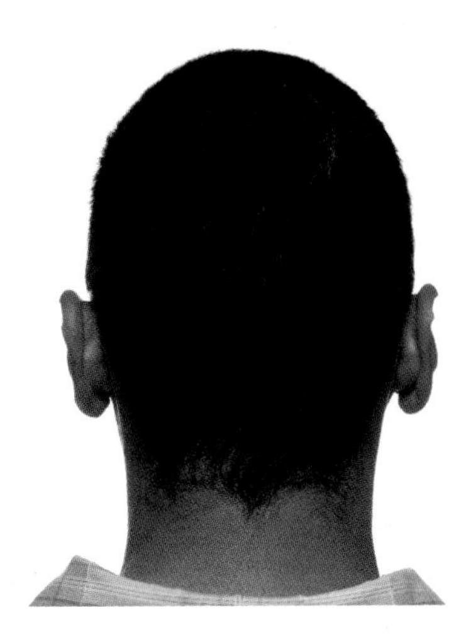

Neck shape

When considering the length of the haircut at the neck area, you should look at the shape of the client's neck. Thicker necks might suit a slightly longer cut.

Hairlines

If the hair is being cut short at the nape area, you need to consider the natural hairline shape. Along with a nape whorl, you can have hairlines that grow in different directions each side, or grow into the middle from both sides. This might affect the length you want to cut to or the shape of the end result.

Facial hair

When you are cutting the hair, you will need to consider where the head hair stops and any facial hair starts. Some clients will choose their style to look like two separate features, while others may want their head and facial hair to blend together.

ACTIVITY

Draw the different face shapes and add sketches of hairstyles that will enhance each facial shape. Alternatively, cut out images from magazines or do some internet research to create a stylebook for different face shapes.

▲ Hair is cut short and not blended into the facial hair

Factors to consider when cutting hair

Whether you cut the hair wet or dry, it will affect the technique you use and the end result. Hair should be checked while it is dry to identify the condition and fall of the hair and rechecked after shampooing to check the elasticity and natural movement in the hair. Scissors and razors are used on wet hair; clippers, scissors and thinning scissors are used on dry hair.

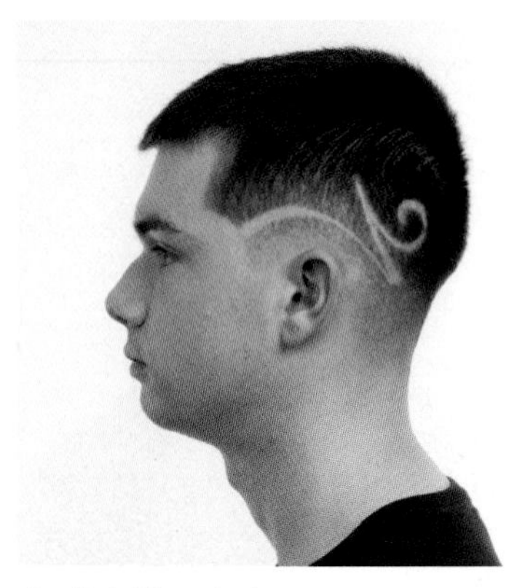

▲ Detailing designs

HANDY HINT

Hair type and classification, such as sparse hair, very curly hair, male pattern baldness and hair growth patterns, can affect the overall look and create some limitations to the design

KEY TERM

Linear – line, straight.

ACTIVITY

1. If your client has his hair cut every three months, how much has his hair grown since his last service?
2. If your client has his hair cut every four months, how much has his hair grown since his last service?

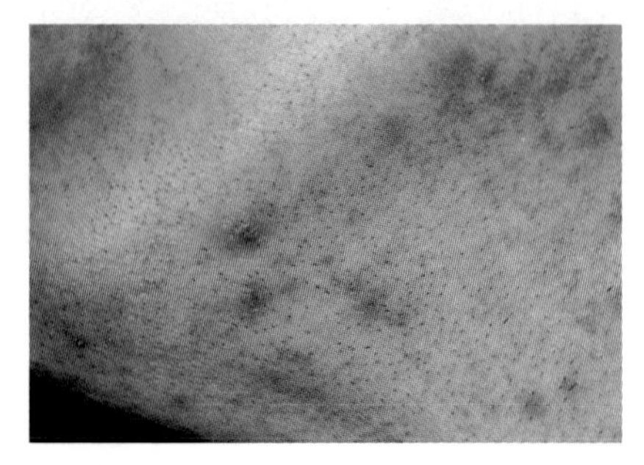

▲ Razor bumps/folliculitis

Cutting into the natural hairline

If your client has an uneven hairline, you may agree to cut into the natural shape and create a neckline to suit the style. You may also do this to avoid issues with hair growth patterns or scar tissue, moles or skin tags.

Design possibilities and limitations

You must ask your client open and closed questions to ascertain what design he would like and why. This could be for many reasons – something personal, to express his personality, religious or personal belief, or just because he likes the look of a certain design, but understanding his reason helps you to get the design right.

Ensuring a suitable foundation for detailing and outlining services

Certain patterns cannot be seen or achieved if the hair is cut too short, or if it is too long. To create **linear** patterns and shapes the ideal hair length is between 2.5 mm and 2.5 cm. If your client would like to maintain some length, then disconnecting the haircut is one way of keeping the hair longer but enabling patterns to be seen in the shorter hair. With short graduated styles you can incorporate hair designs without the overall style having to be too short.

Dealing with influencing factors

The head shape can affect the shape of the design and make straight lines appear curved if placed over prominent bones such as the occipital bone, so design placement is very important. The size of your client's head can also impact on the size and pattern of the design. If your client has a high forehead you should suggest moving the pattern away from the front hairline so you do not draw attention to the forehead height.

Average rate of hair growth

As hair only grows about 1.25 cm each month, it is important that you do not cut the hair too short. As the ideal hair length for detailing is between 2.5 mm and 2.5 cm, you can change your design every one to two months as it grows out. However, haircut styles will need a few more months' hair growth before a restyle can take place.

Effects of continual close cutting or clippering

There is a potential risk of ingrowing hairs resulting from the continual close cutting or clippering of hair. The close cutting of curly hair poses more of a risk, as the hair grows out of the follicle at an acute angle. An in-growing hair is caused where a hair curls back on itself or grows into the skin when the follicle opening is blocked by skin. This may become infected, leading to a condition called folliculitis or 'razor bumps' (pseudofolliculitis barbae), which, if left untreated, can lead to keloids. Refer to Chapter 2 for more information on keloids.

The skin can also become discoloured or calloused from continual close clippering on skin. This is caused by clippers or trimmers being too sharp, causing cuts or grazes and the new skin growing over the top looking darker in appearance and feeling dry.

Male pattern baldness

Male pattern baldness is linked to the male sex hormone testosterone as well as a person's genetics. The baldness occurs when some of the hair follicles shrink over a period of time, resulting in shorter and finer hair. Eventually, although the follicles do not completely die, they stop growing news hairs.

Typical patterns

Male pattern baldness can be identified by the key characteristics and eight scales of hair loss, often referred to as Norwood Hamilton's scale of hair loss.

The hair loss scales are:

- Scale 1–3 – hair gradually recedes over time at the temple area.
- Scale 4–6 – hair gradually thins around the crown area and the bald area gets larger over time.
- Scale 7–8 –front hairline recedes further back and the thinning of the crown area widens towards the front, until the top circular area of the head is bald.

One Two Three Four

Five Six Seven Eight

▲ Norwood Hamilton's eight scales of hair loss

HANDY HINT

Androgenic alopecia is another name for male pattern baldness. Although testosterone is a cause of male pattern baldness, a **derivative** of this hormone called dihydrotestosterone (DHT) is the main cause of shrinking hair follicles.

KEY TERM

Derivative – off shoot or by product of.

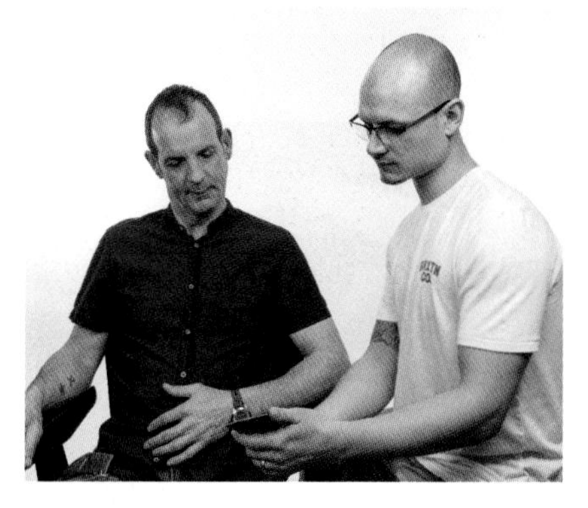

▲ Both the client and the barber have male pattern baldness, but choose different ways to wear their hair

TOOLS, EQUIPMENT AND PRODUCTS

In order to cut hair you need to understand what tools, equipment and products are available and how and when they should be used. Before you begin the cut, the hair must be prepared for the service. You must choose the correct tools and equipment to use, know the effects they achieve and how to use and maintain them. Correct techniques must be applied to cutting services to ensure the desired end result is achieved and if you encounter any problems you must know how to remedy them. At the end of the service you must provide your client with suitable aftercare advice.

▲ Hair in its natural state

▲ Hair in its blow-dried state

Prepare the hair prior to cutting

You will need to identify when to shampoo the hair – before, during or after the service. You may shampoo before the service if there are products in the hair, or if the hair condition is of mixed porosity and elasticity, to aid detangling. You may shampoo during or after the service to remove hair clippings from the hair.

When checking dry hair before the service, you are looking at a styled head of hair which might have products on, or may have been styled to change the natural fall and make the hair feel thicker. Always recheck the hair type, natural movement and fall of the hair when it has been shampooed. Consider the condition of your client's hair and detangle carefully if the hair is porous or of poor elasticity. Always detangle the hair before using clippers to avoid client discomfort.

THE HAIR PROFESSIONAL AT WORK

You may need to remove hair clippings throughout the service to ensure client comfort and maintain accuracy of the cut. This can be carried out by using a neck brush or by shampooing the hair again during the service.

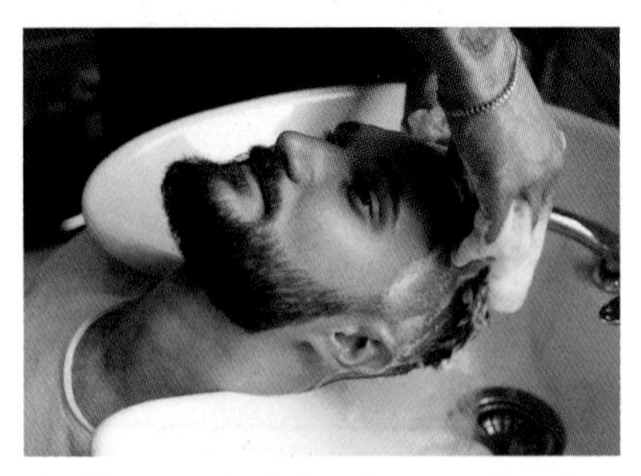

▲ Shampoo the hair prior to services to remove products from the hair

Remove hair products prior to cutting

You should always work on clean hair. If the service requires a dry hair cutting technique and the hair is oily or has products on it, then you will need to shampoo it to cleanse and remove products and then dry the hair ready for the cut.

Using barbering tools on hair that has product on it can blunt scissors and cause clipper blades to 'clog up' with hair. The clippers will become less effective at cutting the hair as well as potentially snagging hair, leading to client discomfort.

Correctly combing out the hair prior to cutting

After shampooing, hair should be combed from point to root to ensure it is tangle free and ready for cutting. Section the hair securely into sections of a manageable size.

Use of different tools, equipment and products

You will use a wide range of tools and equipment to create a variety of looks and use an assortment of products to style and finish the end result. Knowing why, when and how to use tools and equipment is vitally important and combining tools and techniques will help to master your trade.

▲ Comb through the hair to remove tangles and section it ready for cutting

The tools and equipment you are likely to use during men's hair cutting services are:

- scissors and thinning scissors
- clippers, clippers with grade attachments and trimmers
- razors
- combs.

Scissors

Scissors are held with your thumb and your ring finger – not your middle finger. Your little finger supports the scissors, often on the finger rest attached to the scissors; your first and middle fingers support the shanks. You move only your thumb when you cut the hair, as this gives you the greatest control when cutting.

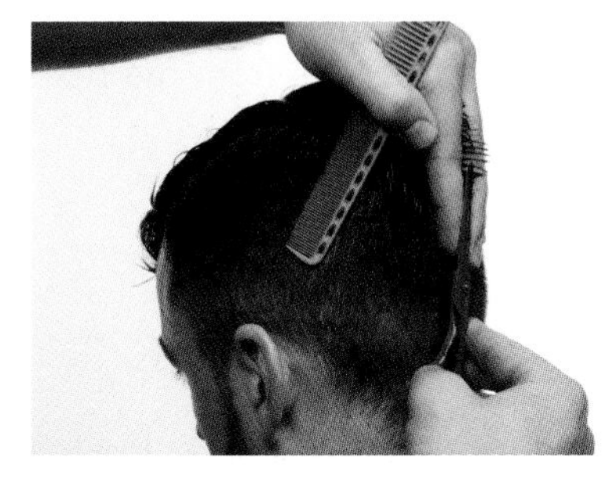

▲ Scissors being held correctly

Your scissors are likely to be the most expensive item in your tool collection. Dropping them with the blades open or pointing downwards can be very costly and affect the position of the blades. Instructions for the care of scissors are:

- use them only for their intended purpose – cutting hair
- do not carry them in the pockets of your clothes
- carry them in a safe manner and store them after use
- ensure they are fit for purpose
- use the correct type of scissors for specific styles
- clean and sterilise them after use
- remove all hair cuttings and oil them regularly
- have them professionally sharpened when required.

▲ A selection of cutting tools and equipment

For most basic cutting techniques, you will use scissors with an average blade length of 12.5–15 cm, depending on the size of your hands. However, barbers' scissors tend to be longer than those used by stylists. Choosing the right scissors for you to work with comfortably is important. As you become more experienced you are likely to want a selection of scissors for a variety of techniques, and you will probably buy more expensive scissors as your skill level increases.

Scissors are used to remove length and weight from the hair.

▲ Chipping

KEY TERM

Chipping – a texturising technique used to remove bulk from the tips of the hair.

HANDY HINT

Control your tools and use them safely to minimise damage to your client's hair and scalp, avoid accidents and maintain client comfort.

HANDY HINT

Scissors are available for left- and right-handed people. You must buy scissors to suit your cutting needs. The thumb and finger holes in scissors vary in size; try them for size before buying and ensure they are comfortable but not so loose that you could lose control over the cut.

Shorter-length scissors are good for chipping into the hair; longer-length scissors are ideal for scissor over comb techniques and are used by many barbers.

ACTIVITY

Practise holding your scissors correctly, moving only your thumb. Rest the non-moving blade on your other hand.

KEY TERM

Serrated – blades with around 30 'teeth' on one or both blades.

Thinning scissors

Thinning scissors are used to remove bulk from the hair but maintain length. The blades are either **serrated** on one or both blades and when the blades are closed together the internal bulk is cut.

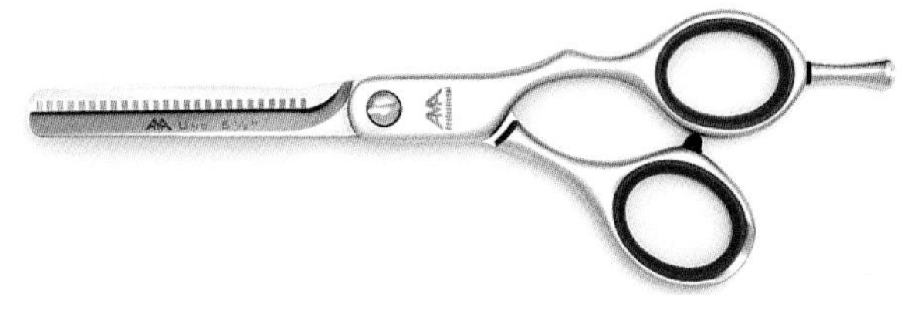

▲ Single serrated blades

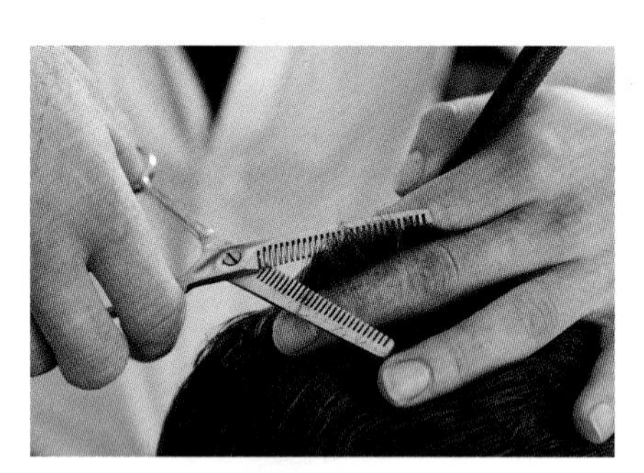

▲ Double serrated blades

Razors

Razors are generally used to add texture and thin out the hair. They can be used for close cutting against the skin – but new blades must be used for each client and extreme care must be taken.

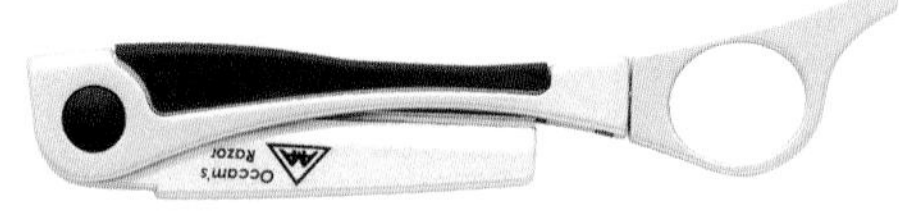

▲ Razor

Combs

Barbers can be quite particular about their combs and often have a favourite. For cutting hair, a variety of smaller combs may be used. For clipper work or scissor over comb work, the combs used are generally larger.

▲ A barber's preferred comb for cutting

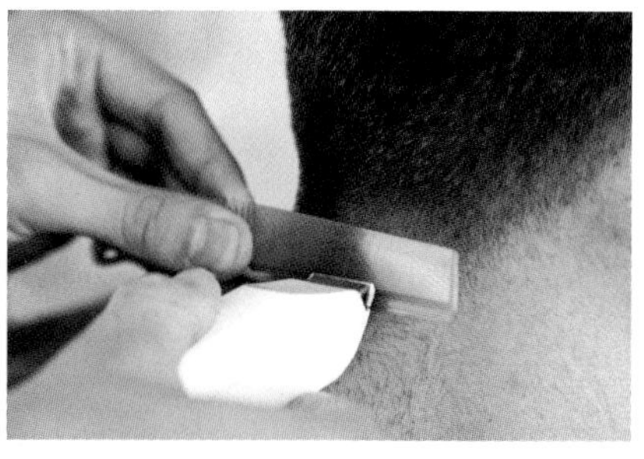

▲ A barber's preferred comb for fading

▲ A barber's preferred comb for clipper over comb

▲ A barber's preferred comb for scissor over comb

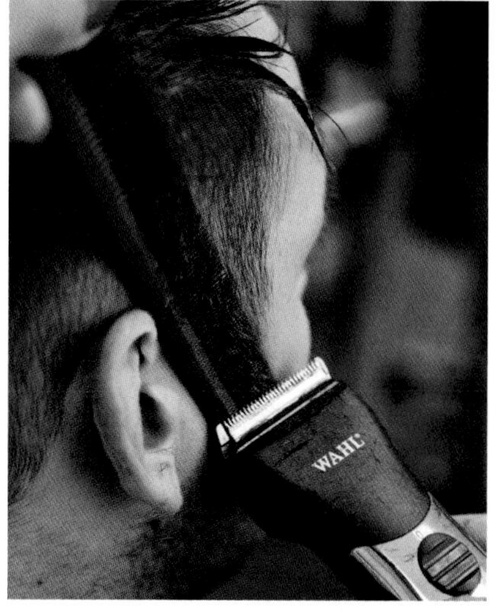

▲ A barber's preferred comb for blending in the sideburns

Types of clippers, blades and attachments

Clippers can be used with or without a clipper grade attached. If using clippers with a grade, you will need to decide the size of the grade required and this will depend on your client's requirements. Clipper grades vary in size from grade 0.5 to grade 8, gradually getting about 3 mm bigger (as a guide) with each grade:

- grade 8 – 24 mm (approximately 1 inch)
- grade 6 – 18 mm (approximately ¾ inch)
- grade 4 – 12 mm (approximately ½ inch)
- grade 2 – 6 mm (approximately ¼ inch)
- grade 1 – 3 mm
- grade 0.5 – 1.5 mm (approximately 1.8 inch)

The table below shows the various grades available and their uses.

Grade	Use
Up to grade 1	Often is used for the back and sides for fading. Also used to blend a grade 2 down into the hairline, keeping the hairline very short. Maximising how long the cut will last before it needs cutting again.
Grade 2	A common grade for the 'short back and sides'.

▲ Various clipper grades

ACTIVITY

Using the measurements given in the list above, work out the size of the following grades:

- grade 3
- grade 7.

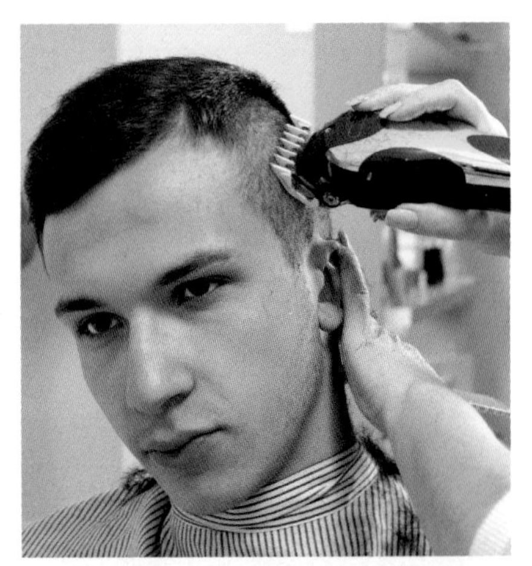
▲ Grade 8 has been used to cut the top and the back and sides are blended down to a grade 2.

Grade	Use
Grades 3 and 4	Can be used around the back and sides of a cut, but is also used to blend in the grade 2 up into the occipital area of a scissor cut.
Grades 5 to 8	Mostly used on the top and crown areas for short, layered effects. Some men have a clipper cut all over the head and any grade can be used for this, depending on the overall length required, or a variation of grades can be used so the hair gradually gets shorter towards the back and sides and hairline.

HANDY HINT

Some clippers have a lever on the side that moves the teeth of the clippers wider and creates a half grade. If you used a grade 1 attachment and widened the teeth, you could create a 1.5 grade which will be about 4.5 mm. If you used a grade 2 attachment and widened the teeth, you could create a 2.5 grade which will be about 7.5 mm.

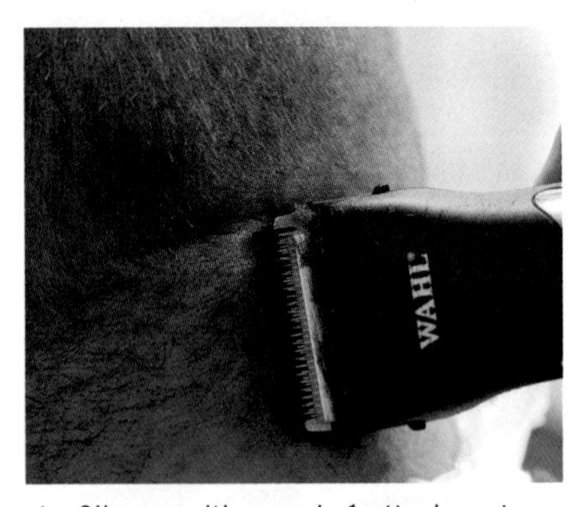

▲ Clippers with a grade 1 attachment

ACTIVITY

Using the measurements in the list of grades and in the Handy hint, work out the size of the following grades:

- Grade 4.5
- Grade 6.5
- Grade 8.5

If using the clippers all over the head, start with the largest grade and blend down to the smallest grade. If you are using just one grade size all over the head, make sure the clippers are moved across the head in different directions – front to back, side to side, etc. This is because the hair will grow in many different directions and if you follow one direction only, the hair might be cut at varying lengths.

If you are using clippers with a grade at the back and sides and a scissor cut on the top and crown, you can start with the clipper grade cut first and then blend with your layer cut. It is very likely you will need to use a clipper over comb or scissor over comb technique to fully blend these two techniques. Clippers are used on dry hair only.

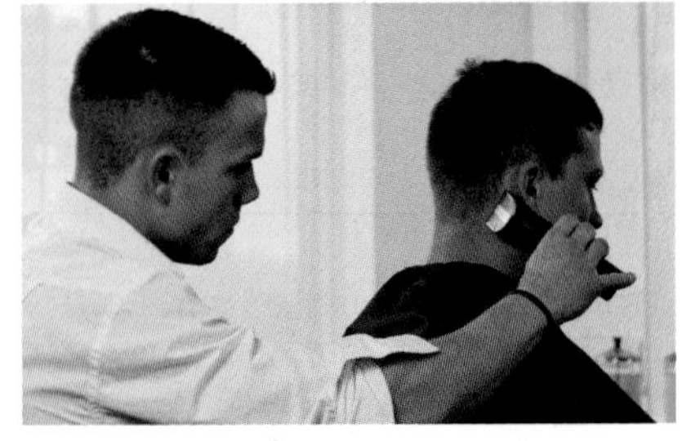
▲ Trimmers

Trimmers

Trimmers are used mostly for outlining detail, removing unwanted hair outside the shape and for close cutting work. The blades are smaller and closer cutting, making them ideal for precision work.

Correct tools for use on wet and dry hair

You will need to consider whether you are going to use a wet or dry hair cutting technique before you start the service, so you can prepare the hair accordingly. Some tools, such as scissors, can be used on both wet and dry hair, while other tools can only be used on wet hair or dry hair.

As a guide:

- scissors can be used on wet or dry hair for club cutting or texturising, and scissor over comb techniques
- thinning scissors can be used on dry hair. If used on wet hair, too much bulk could be removed
- clippers and trimmers are used on towel-dried/dry hair for clippering and clipper over comb techniques. Wet hair can cause the blades to clog up with hair, causing client discomfort and blunting of the blades. The result is cut more accurately and cleanly on dry hair, too
- razors are used on wet hair only for texturising and thinning out of the hair. Razor cutting on dry hair can snag the hair, causing damage to the cuticle layer and discomfort to the client.

▲ Razor cut wet hair

▲ Scissors used on wet hair

Products available for finishing men's hair

At the end of the hair cut you should apply products to style and finish the look created. Products to style and finish the hair may include:

- gels – generally used on wet hair for hold and texture
- wax – generally used for dry hair styling to aid movement and texture
- tonics – applied to wet hair for shine and to improve the scalp
- oils – applied to wet or dry hair for shine
- creams – applied to wet or dry hair to hold and control style
- sprays – generally applied to dry styled hair for hold
- styling powders – applied to styled hair to aid root lift, movement and hold.

▲ FAB hair tonics

▲ Clippers used on dry hair

HANDY HINT

You will use the edge of the blades on trimmers and T-liners to create simple repeated designs from lines and curves; these are demonstrated in the step-by-step section later in this chapter.

Correct use and maintenance of cutting tools and equipment

When cutting men's hair, it is important that you use your tools and equipment correctly and know how to clean, maintain and store them safely.

▲ MHFed Styling products

HEALTH AND SAFETY

Refer to the health and safety section in Chapter 1 for more in-depth information on sterilising and disinfecting.

Tool	How to use correctly and safely	Maintenance	Correct storage
Scissors (and thinning scissors)	Always carry them with the blades closed. Do not drop them as you might damage the blades.	Clean the hairs from the blades with warm soapy water. Sterilise scissors in an autoclave, sanitise in a UV light cabinet or disinfect in a Barbicide solution. Oil the blades after cleaning and sterilising.	Keep them away from young children and store them in a barber's cutting pouch or scissor case.
Clippers – mains electricity	Keep the blades well-oiled throughout use. Ensure the blades are properly aligned and adjust the blades to achieve the correct cutting length. Use on dry hair.	Remove the cut hairs from between the blades after every haircut (using a small clipper brush). Spray the blades with a chemical disinfectant and wipe the body of the clippers with chemical disinfectant wipes. Oil the blades after cleaning.	Unplug from the mains and look for any knots in the wires. Hang on a designated hook or place somewhere safe, where they cannot fall to the floor and get damaged.
Clippers, trimmers and mini clippers – rechargeable	As for mains electricity clippers.	As for mains electricity clippers.	Place the clippers back on the battery charger base to ensure they are charged and ready for the next client.

Tool	How to use correctly and safely	Maintenance	Correct storage
Razors	Always hold the razor carefully to ensure you and your client are not accidently cut with the razor blade. If you accidently drop the razor – let it go – do NOT try to catch it! You must wear gloves if you use a razor directly on your client's skin.	Remove the razor blade carefully and dispose of it in the sharps bin. Clean the body of the razor with warm soapy water and chemical disinfectant wipes.	Ideally, store your razors without the blade attached. Attach a new blade as you need it. Store the razor in a suitable scissor pouch/case.
Combs and attachments (grades)	Cutting combs are used to section the hair. Clipper grades are attached over the clipper blades and designed to create a variation of longer cutting lengths when clipper cutting.	Remove all loose hairs from the comb and grades. Wash in warm soapy water and sanitise in the UV light cabinet.	Keep all grades together and store them according to your salon policy.

HANDY HINT

Always follow your workplace, suppliers' and manufacturer's instructions to ensure the safe use of electrical equipment.

HANDY HINT

It is important to follow any stylist instructions to ensure the smooth running of the salon and to make the most effective use of your time.

THE HAIR PROFESSIONAL AT WORK

Always follow the supplier's and manufacturer's instructions for the safe use of equipment, materials and products. These instructions will tell you how to use the equipment correctly and safely, will ensure the best results for your client and maintain the life of the equipment.

How to level and test clippers

Clipper blades must be correctly **aligned** and checked before each service to ensure the blades are level and they cut evenly without pulling on the hair. After continued use, clipper blades become loose and uneven – this can be uncomfortable for your client as the blades can cause small cuts to the skin and produce an unbalanced haircut.

To test the blades are aligned and will not 'pull' on the hair, test the blades on the back of your hands. If they bite or mark the skin, the blades

KEY TERM

Aligned – brought into line and in this instance 'levelled'.

HANDY HINT

Always check your clipper blades are correctly aligned before each service. The blades must be level so that they cut evenly and do not pull on the hair.

are offset and need to be levelled. To do this, unscrew the blades and re-align them, ensuring the top blade is slightly seated back from the fixed blade, before screwing the blades together again.

APPLY CORRECT TECHNIQUES DURING BASIC BARBERING SERVICES

It is important to apply the correct techniques during barbering services to ensure you:

- establish and follow guidelines to ensure an accurate cut and create guidelines for different looks
- use different cutting techniques to create varying effects
- consider weight distribution and work with the natural growth patterns in the hair
- consider the cutting angles you use and how these impact on the overall cut
- apply the correct degree of tension when cutting
- adjust your body position and your client's to ensure accuracy
- keep the hair damp when cutting
- cross-check the haircut accurately
- create different neckline and outline shapes and cut to the natural neckline
- achieve outlines that are accurate and remove any unwanted hair outside the desired outline shape
- balance and shape the sideburns
- safely carry out an eyebrow trim
- visually check the finished cut is balanced and outlines are accurate
- leave the hair ready for the next part of the service or finish the style to meet your client's requirements.

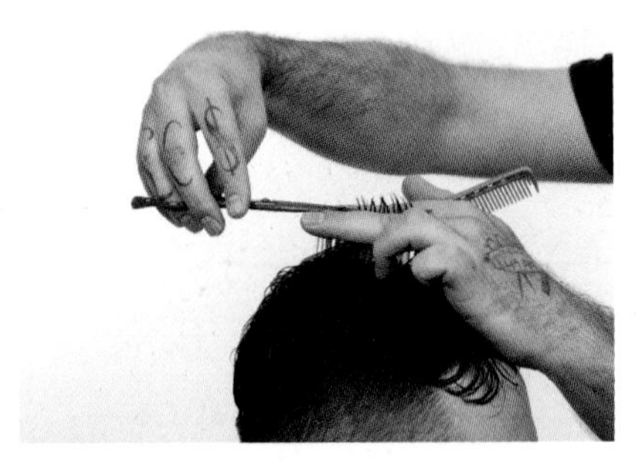

▲ You must always create a guideline to follow

Importance of guidelines

The guideline is the most important part of the haircut. If you are cutting the hair and you lose your guideline – STOP! The guideline determines the finished length of the cut and the overall shape and balance. Without a guideline you cannot work methodically through the haircut or maintain accuracy. Even the most experienced barbers will follow a guideline and use accurate sectioning.

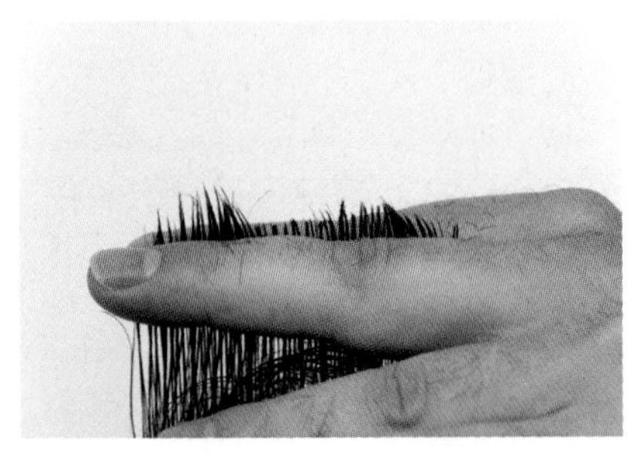

▲ Barber following the guideline when cutting

Guidelines for different cutting looks

When you have cut your guideline, every section you cut afterwards will follow this guideline to the same length, so you must hold the hair at the same angle on both sides of the head. Always ensure that your cutting sections are clean and that you take manageable-sized sections. Make sure you maintain your balance; otherwise the haircut might be uneven. The step-by-step haircuts shown later in this chapter will demonstrate in more detail the guidelines used for different looks.

HANDY HINT

If you cannot see your guideline, stop cutting, go back a few sections and find it. Or you can section the hair the opposite way to work out where you have cut up to.

Different cutting techniques and the effects achieved

When cutting men's hair, you will use a variety of techniques, each producing a different effect. Each technique used will help you to achieve the different looks required.

During this part of the chapter we will look at the techniques used:

- club cutting
- freehand
- scissor over comb
- clipper over comb
- texturising
- freehand
- razor cutting
- tapering
- graduation
- layering
- fading
- disconnecting
- eyebrow trim.

Club cutting

Club cutting is also known as blunt cutting and is the most commonly used cutting technique. It involves cutting the hair straight across, while holding the hair with tension between your fingers. This technique will reduce the length of the hair and layers but will retain the thickness of the hair. Club cutting can be carried out on wet and dry hair.

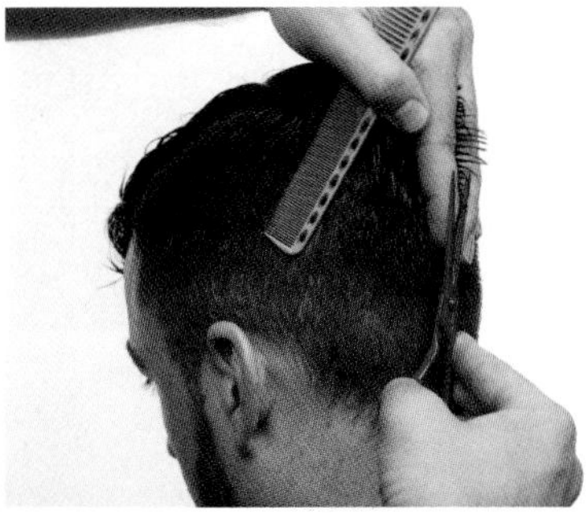

▲ Holding the hair for club cutting

Scissor over comb

When you are using the scissor over comb technique, run the comb up the hair and use it to lift and support the hair to be cut. The hair is cut with the scissors over the comb. This technique gives a graduated effect to the cut and blends short hair into the neck. This technique is most effective on dry hair.

▲ Scissor over comb technique

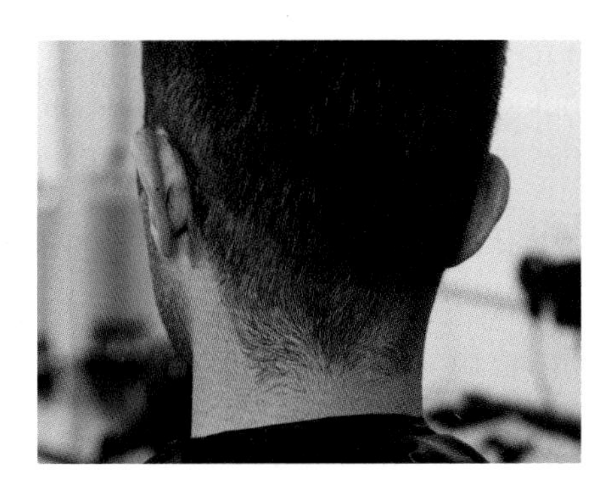

▲ Check the neckline suits your client's requirements

Clipper over comb

Clipper over comb can be used to blend in scissor or clipper cuts. This technique helps to remove any bulk or definition lines from the varying clipper grades, or where the scissor cut meets a clipper cut. It is a popular technique used on dry hair to blend and fade into the hairline.

To use this technique, follow the comb with the clippers through the back and sides, angling the comb at +45° or –45° to create longer or shorter effects.

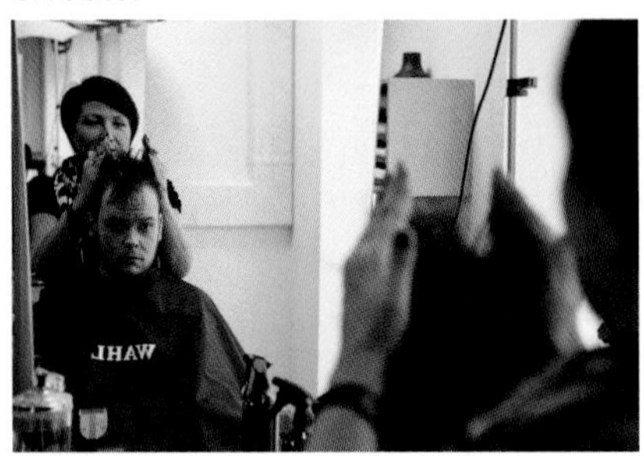

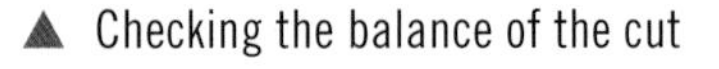

▲ Checking the balance of the cut

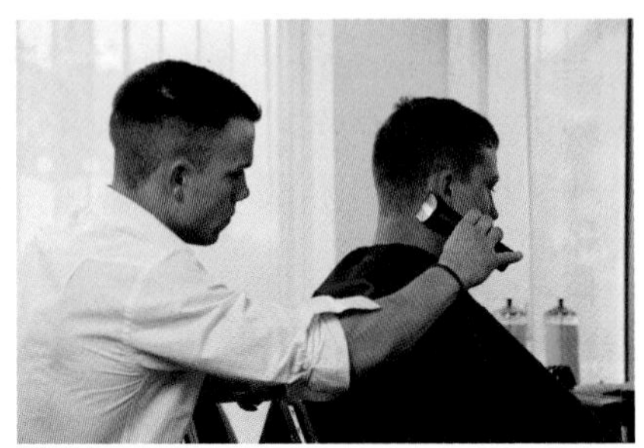

▲ Shaping the neckline

▲ Texturising – shallow point cutting

Texturising with scissors (deep point cutting)

Texturising the hair reduces the bulk at the ends of the hair; it helps to soften the shape of styles internally and externally, it can add personalisation and encourages movement throughout a longer hairstyle. A large section of wet or dry hair is taken about 5–7cm below the fingers and carefully cut inwards and slightly vertically towards the fingers. This removes bulk but maintains length (unlike club cutting where the hair is taken to the ends of your fingers and then cut straight across horizontally).

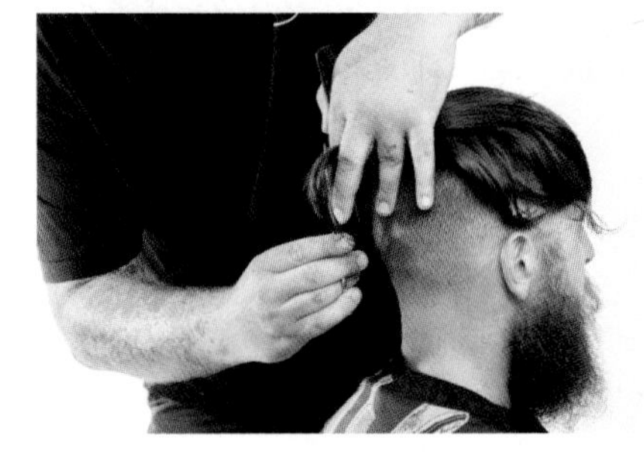

▲ Texurising – tapering

Texturising with scissors – shallow point cutting

A type of texturising which reduces lines and removes bulk on the ends of the hair. Wet or dry hair is cut in a similar way to club cutting, but the ends of the hair are removed vertically rather than horizontally.

Texturising with scissors – tapering

Wet hair is sliced vertically downwards from one point to another, blending different lengths together, producing a tapered effect. Scissor blades must not be serrated or bevelled for this technique.

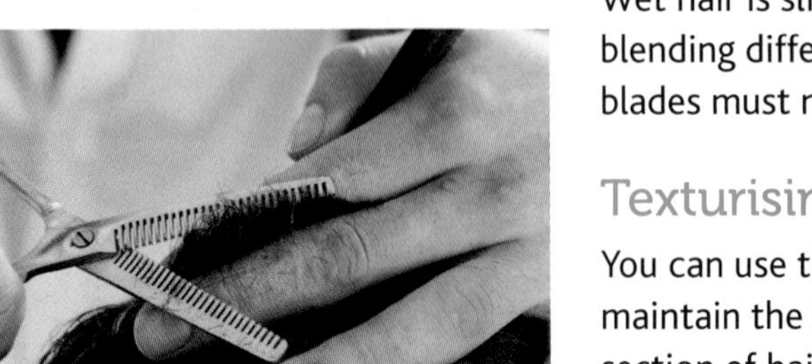

▲ Thinning out the hair

Texturising with thinning scissors

You can use thinning scissors to remove unwanted bulk from the hair but maintain the length. When using thinning scissors, you must cut into the section of hair towards the mid-lengths and ends, avoiding the root area. Thinning out the root area can cause hair to stick up and show signs that it has been thinned out. Hair should be dry while this technique is carried out; otherwise you might remove too much 'bulk'.

HANDY HINT

Remember, texturising introduces differing lengths in areas of, or throughout, the haircut to soften a hard line or to create root lift.

Freehand technique

When using the freehand technique, you must not hold the hair with any tension but instead comb the hair into position and cut. This technique can be used when you do not need any tension, such as when cutting a fringe, or allowing for the natural fall of the hair and cutting around the ears. Freehand cutting can be used on wet or dry hair but is particularly good on dry hair.

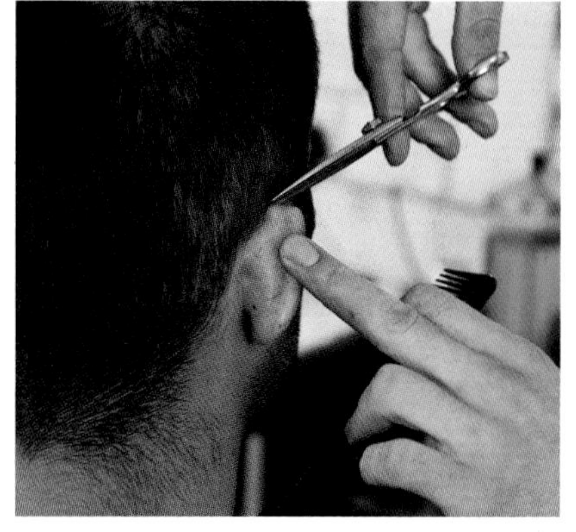

▲ Use freehand for cutting around the ears

Razor cutting – texturising

Small sections of wet hair are held outwards and the razor is used from midway to the ends, slicing through the top section of the held hair, and removing the bulk. This adds softness and accentuates texture, but should not be used on curly or fine hair.

Razor cutting

You can cut the whole hairstyle using razoring techniques rather than scissors. The angle the hair is held at is the same as for scissor cutting, but the razor is generally positioned behind your fingers holding the hair section, to ensure the tension is maintained when slicing the hair.

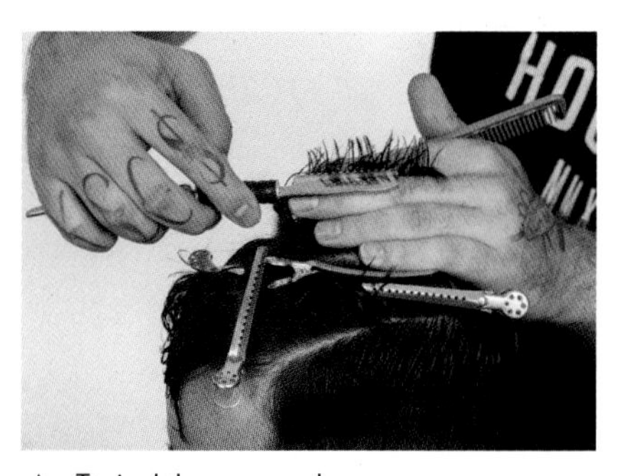

▲ Texturising – razoring

Tapering

Wet hair is sliced vertically downwards from one point to another, blending different lengths together, producing a tapered effect. Scissor blades must not be serrated or bevelled for this technique.

Graduation

Graduation is where hair gradually differs in length – hair could be gradually getting longer or shorter from one point to another. Several techniques can be used to create graduation, such as club cutting, scissor or clipper over comb, fading or tapering.

▲ Texturising – tapering

Layering

The majority of haircuts involve layering the hair; only hair that is one length is not layered. If hair is held at any angle other than 0°, then the hair will be layered thoughout.

Fading

Fading is used to blend short haircuts into the nape of the neck. If hair has been clipper cut or if scissor over comb has been used, blend the hair from the occipital bone down to blend in with the nape area and fade out to the hairline. This technique can enable the hairline shape to appear more natural looking. Fading techniques are carried out on dry hair.

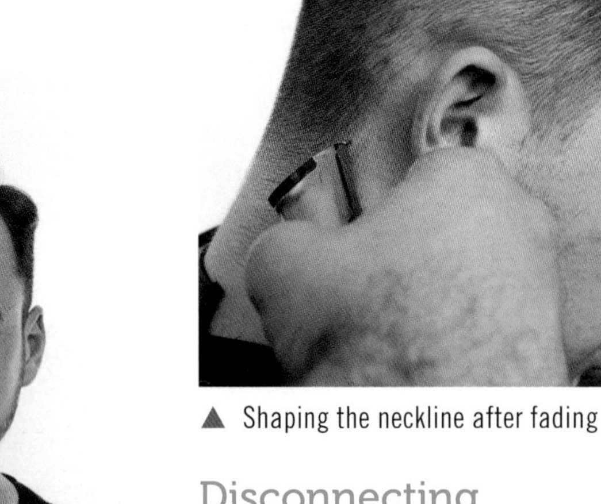

▲ Shaping the neckline after fading

▲ Bald fade

▲ Disconnection from top and sides

Disconnecting

Disconnecting involves cutting sections of the hair into style, but not blending it into the whole haircut. Varying lengths are achieved and this sometimes creates an **asymmetric** look too.

KEY TERM

Asymmetric – unbalanced, not equal, uneven, not symmetrical.

Eyebrow trim

Trimming of the eyebrows with scissors or clippers to remove length and neaten the shape.

ACTIVITY

Practise the cutting techniques described on a training head.

Different looks

You will look at how to cut men's hair using the above techniques, while following a guideline to achieve a range of different looks.

In the step-by-step part of this chapter you will learn how to use these techniques to achieve the following:

- Square layer
- Uniform layer
- Graduation
- Cut a fringe
- Work with a parting
- Cut around the ear outline
- Cut over the ear
- Create a skin fade/fade
- Flat top
- Eyebrow trim.

The step-by-step guidance will include various neckline shapes such as tapered, squared and a full neckline shape. It will also cover the following outline shapes: natural, created and tapered.

Weight distribution and natural growth patterns of the hair

The angles in which you cut hair and the degree of graduation applied will affect the overall balance of the style and the weight distribution of the haircut. It is important to work with natural growth patterns to add styling and wearability of the style – a strong hair growth pattern can affect the shape of the style and the end result. A double crown could cause a short haircut to stick up at the crown area and a widow's peak or cowlick could affect a fringe or help or hinder the shape of a quiff.

Impact of different cutting angles

The table below describes the different cutting angles and their impact on weight distribution, balance and the degree of graduation.

Look	Angle of graduation	Cutting angle	Weight distribution and balance of style
One length	The hair is pulled down at 0°.	0° 0°	The weight of this hairstyle sits at the perimeter. The balance of this style is even all around the perimeter.
Square layers	Use 0° for the baseline. For the layers at the back the hair is pulled out at 90° and the top is pulled backwards at 45° and over directed into the back sections.		The weight distribution of this haircut is towards the back and sides where the length and layers meet. The balance of this style is even throughout.

→

Look	Angle of graduation	Cutting angle	Weight distribution and balance of style
Uniform layers  	Use 0° for the baseline. For the layers the hair is pulled out at 90° throughout the entire haircut. 	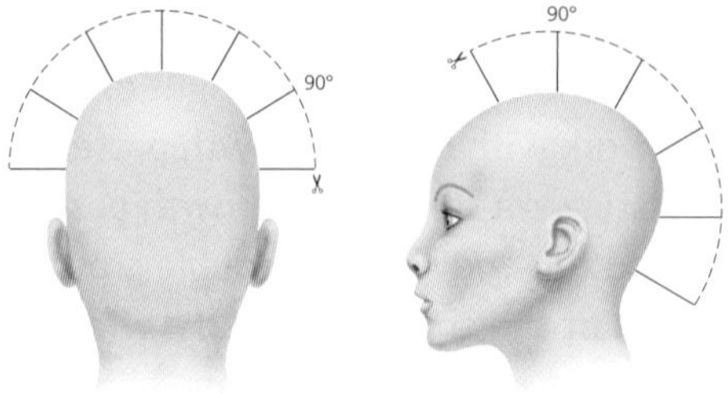 90° 90°	The weight distribution of this haircut is even throughout the style. The balance of this style is even throughout.
Graduation  	The inner layers of the hair lengths are longer than the outline shape and generally pulled out at 45°. 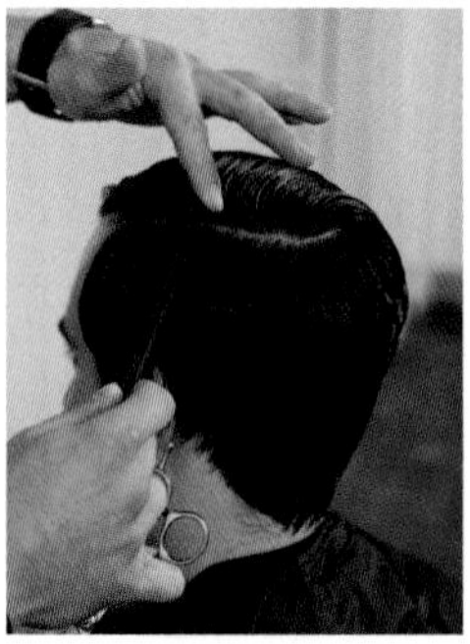	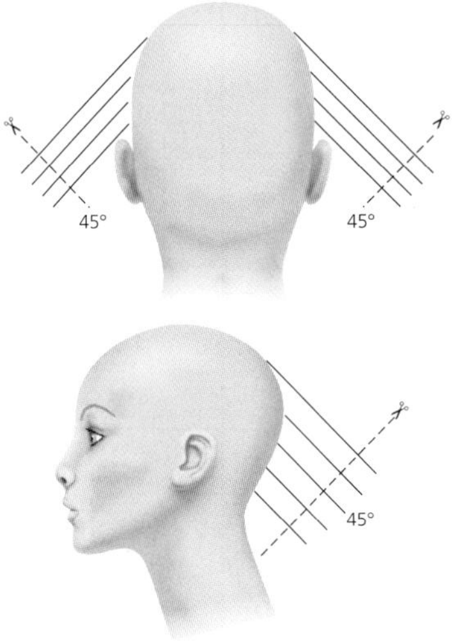 45° 45° 45°	The weight distribution of this style would be where the shape changes from 90° to 45° – around eye level at the sides and the occipital bone at the back. The balance of this style is even on both sides.
Fringes 	Often cut freehand to allow for the natural movement and fall of the hair growth patterns, but fringes can be cut under tension and pulled down to 0°. 	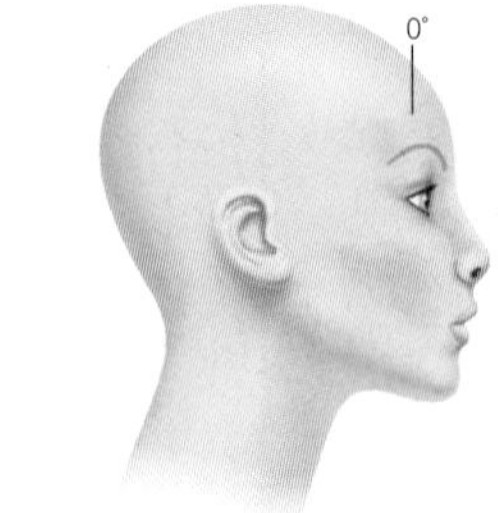 0°	Not applicable

Look	Angle of graduation	Cutting angle	Weight distribution and balance of style
Flat top	This haircut is cut squarely – the top is pulled directly up and cut straight across – mostly at 90o but towards the crown it is180°. The sides are pulled out squarely at 90° and angles to 45° at the crown. This haircut is then generally faded out.		The weight distribution of this style would be on top of the head. The balance of this style is even on both sides.

Using style magazines or the internet, research images of men's hairstyles and label the cutting angles used.

Practise sectioning and pulling the hair out at the angles described in the diagrams above.

HANDY HINT

With any cutting technique, you must always work with the natural fall of the hair, taking into account the weight distribution to ensure the expected shape can be achieved.

Apply the correct degree of tension to the hair

When you are cutting hair with tension, you must remember that wet hair stretches more than dry hair, so make sure that the end result is not shorter than you expected. You must always keep the same tension to ensure an even result. This includes keeping an even moisture balance during the cutting service, so that the hair is not of mixed porosity or elasticity. This could cause tangles, damage to the hair or uneven cutting results.

HANDY HINT

Curly hair will spring up when dry – use less tension when cutting curly hair. This can be achieved by using the wider tooth end of your comb.

Adapting position to ensure the accuracy of the cut

It is important that your client's body position is balanced and upright throughout the haircut. If your client has his legs or ankles crossed, then the balance of the baseline cut could be uneven. Equally, you must ensure that you have an even distribution of body weight. If you or your client is very tall, adjust the height of your client's chair to suit you.

▲ Keep your positioning balanced and that of your client to ensure an accurate balanced cut

HANDY HINT

It is important to keep the hair damp when cutting wet hair to ensure even elasticity and porosity. Otherwise the result could be uneven and the hair could snag and tangle when you comb through.

Regularly cross-check the haircut

Cross-checking the haircut during the service and at the end ensures an accurate finish. You can cross-check the haircut at any point during the service to check for accurate distribution of weight, balance and shape. Using the mirror will help you to check balance and shape.

Run your fingers through the hair to check it feels even throughout, especially if you have thinned the hair. Always use your mirrors and step back to look at the haircut to ensure the shape is balanced and the weight evenly distributed throughout.

▲ Keep hair damp

▲ Cross-checking horizontally

▲ Cross-checking in the mirror

▲ Ensure your client is sitting straight

▲ Poor sitting position could result in an uneven haircut

Creating different neckline and outline shapes

Neckline shapes are generally cut as either tapered, squared, a full neckline or a skin fade. Outline shapes are either natural, created or tapered outlines.

Tapered neckline

One of the more popular necklines is to blend the main haircut into the natural hairline. To create this effect, the hair is gradually cut shorter and blended into the natural shape of the hairline. You will need to consider the natural movement of the hairline, checking for any nape whorls or inward/outward nape growth patterns.

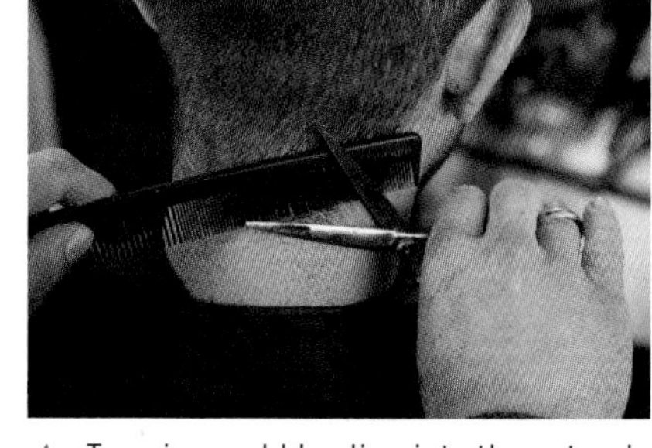

▲ Tapering and blending into the natural hairline

Square neckline

With a square neckline, the end result will be a blunt, clean finish. Use scissors or clippers to literally square off the edges of the hairline around the neck.

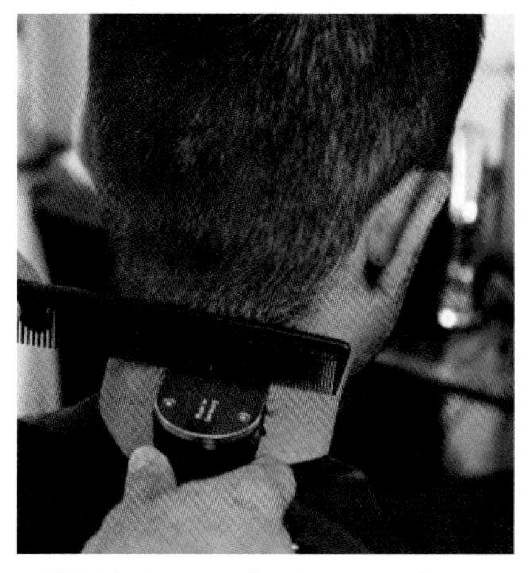

STEP 1: Clipper cut – Create a squared neckline with clippers.

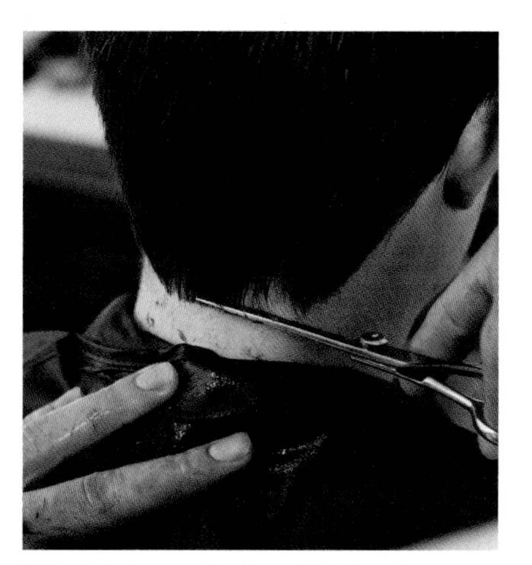

STEP 1: Scissor cut – Or cut the baseline straight across with scissors.

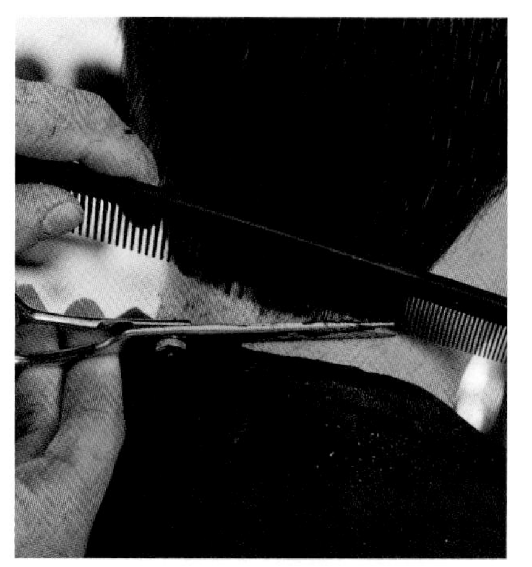

STEP 2 – Square off the edges.

Full neckline

To create a full rounded neckline, use the scissors or clippers as for the square neckline but, rather than leaving square corners, round off the edges. Although this result is not as harsh as a square neckline, it is still a blunt finish to the cut.

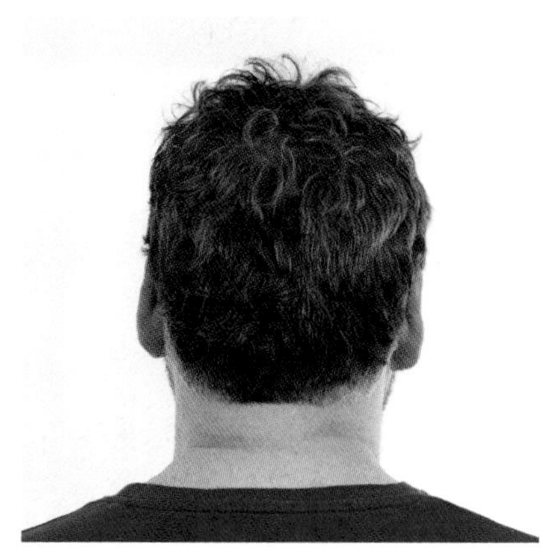

▲ Full neckline

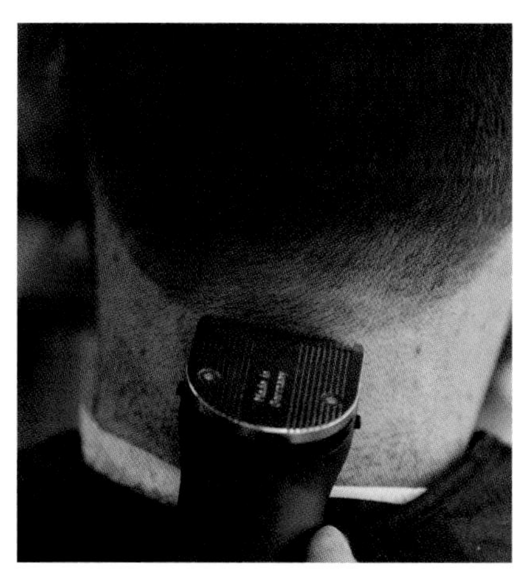

STEP 1 – Create the rounded shape at the back.

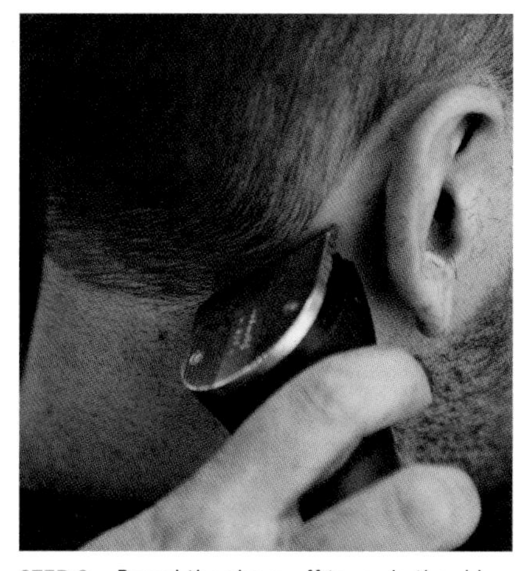

STEP 2 – Round the shape off towards the sides.

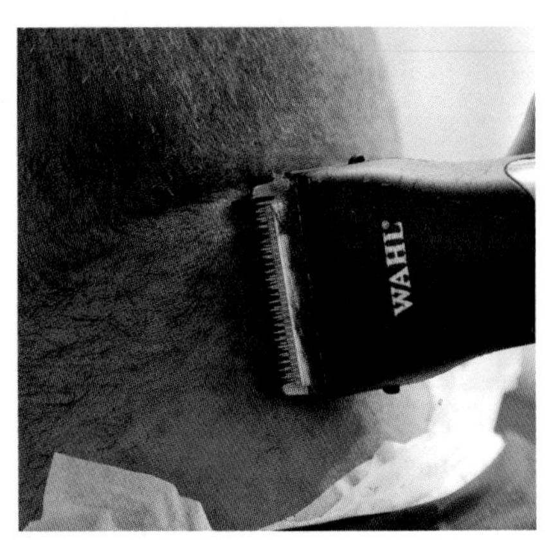

▲ Clipper cutting the hairline and hair growth direction with a grade 1 attachment

Skin fade

A faded neckline is where the hair is clipper cut and faded out using clippers without a grade attached. To create this effect, the hair is clipper cut with a grade and gradually blended into a clipper cut without a grade, into the hairline.

Outline shapes

You should agree the overall outline shape required by your client:

- Does he want a natural outline, which shows his natural hairline shape?
- Does he want a created outline, which is neatly and precisely cut with clippers or trimmers to create a bolder, definite edge and which removes unwanted hair from outside the outline shape?
- Does he want a tapered outline that is gradually faded out into the neckline?

▲ Remove unwanted hair outside the desired outline shape

Cutting to the natural neckline

When you have clipper cut or cut the hair into the neck with a scissor over comb technique, you will need to decide with your client how to fade into the neckline.

HANDY HINT

The step-by-step instructions later in this chapter show you how to achieve outlines that are accurate and remove unwanted hair outside the desired outline shape.

THE HAIR PROFESSIONAL AT WORK

It is important you balance and shape sideburns to suit the hairstyle and to meet your client's requirements. Balancing and shaping sideburns can be done by using the mirror and placing your finger where each sideburn ends, checking they are evenly placed.

▲ Cross-checking the length of the sideburns in the mirror

VISUALLY CHECK THE FINISHED CUT AND ENSURE OUTLINES ARE ACCURATE

Along with cross-checking, you must visually check the haircut to ensure outlines are accurate and the overall look is balanced. Stand behind your client and swivel the chair so your client is looking right, then you can look at the left side in the mirror and the right side by looking straight ahead and compare both sides together.

THE HAIR PROFESSIONAL AT WORK

At the end of the cutting service it is important to leave the hair ready for the next part of the service or style and finish it to meet your client's requirements. Remove all loose hair clippings by shampooing the hair again if necessary.

APPLY CORRECT TECHNIQUES DURING CREATIVE HAIR CUTTING SERVICES

Correct techniques for creative cutting include all those mentioned in basic cutting, but also:

- personalising and adapting techniques
- combining and adapting techniques to create different effects
- cross-checking the cut.

Personalising and adapting cutting techniques

As well as creating uniform and graduated looks, you may be asked to create a haircut with a parting, cut above or around the ear, disconnect part of the haircut, texturise the hair or create a fade.

Creating a parting

Some styles require you to cut the hair to a certain parting. This will create an asymmetric look, with the weight of the style distributed on one side. Always check if your client wears his parting on the left or the right side. If he does not know, check the natural fall of the hair.

Around and over the ear

Depending on the length of the haircut chosen, you will either cut the hair short around the ear or leave it longer over the ear.

When cutting hair short around the ear, you must hold the ear forward and check all lengths have been removed and the outline shape is clean and tidy. When cutting a longer style, the hair may naturally be left over the ear, but you should check the shape and fall of these lengths as the hairline is not an even shape around the ear area.

HANDY HINT

Disconnecting part of the haircut and texturising the hair are covered in the step by steps later in this chapter.

Creating a fade

Always check with your client how he would like the back and sides cut. If the hair is clippered or cut with scissor over comb and gradually gets shorter, then you should take care creating a fade to the hairline. Some clients like the hairline faded out to the skin and this is called a skin fade – you clipper or cut the hair, gradually getting shorter and eventually remove all the hair around the hairline – literally fading out the haircut. If the hair is faded out but not completely removed, then you are cutting in a hairline fade.

Effects created by combining and adapting cutting techniques

Most men's haircuts will have a combination of cutting techniques, whether this includes basic club cutting and clipper over comb, or more

HANDY HINT

Cross-checking the cut ensures it is accurate, evenly balanced and has an even weight distribution throughout.

advanced texturising, clipper work combined into a skin fade. Combining and adapting techniques is covered in more detail in the step by steps at the end of this chapter.

APPLY CORRECT TECHNIQUES WHEN CREATING BASIC OUTLINES AND DETAILING IN HAIR

Correct techniques for creating basic outlines and detailing include:

- preparing the hair prior to cutting outlines and detailing designs
- using different cutting techniques when creating designs in hair
- equipment handling techniques for achieving accurate outlines and detailing designs in hair
- visually checking outline and details of designs and the haircut.

Preparing the hair prior to cutting outlines and detailing designs

Preparing the hair for outlines and detailing normally involves cutting the hair to length and agreeing on the overall hairstyle that the design will be placed into. For outlining and detailing the hair should be between 2.5 mm and a maximum of 2.5 cm. The shorter the hair, the longer the design will last between services.

Different cutting techniques when creating designs in hair

You may need to adapt the cut to suit different head shapes and features. For example:

- The size of the pattern may need to be smaller for a small head and increased in size for a larger head.
- For a pronounced occipital bone, the protruding bone may affect the shape or design and therefore it will need adjusting.
- Avoid sharp lines pointing towards prominent features such as a pointed nose or chin.
- Avoid placing the design near the front hairline if your client has a high forehead.

Attachments

When choosing a suitable attachment for clippers, you need to consider the points below.

- Density – the thicker the hair, the short the clipper grade can be, as the design will be more pronounced. However, do not cut too short with sparse hair as the detail will be lost.

- Texture – with fine hair, the detail can be more difficult to see; care needs to be taken with coarse hair to avoid any client discomfort with the attachments getting caught in the hair.
- Length – clipper grades 1 or 2 are great for outlining and detailing; any longer and the detail can be lost and it will grow out very quickly.
- Colour – dark hair works best with the detail appearing most prominently; the fairer the hair the harder it is to see the detail of the design or sharpness of the lines created.

▲ The lighter the hair colour the thicker your lines need to be, to show the detail

Clippering

Clipper over comb can be used to blend in scissor or clipper cuts. This technique helps to remove any bulk or definition lines from the varying clipper grades, or where the scissor cut meets a clipper cut. Use clipper over comb or clippers with attachments to create a platform for your design.

HANDY HINT

Take care not to go to wide with your lines on fine or sparse hair.

Fading

Fading is used to blend out short haircuts into the nape of the neck. If hair has been clipper cut or if scissor over comb has been used, blend the hair from the occipital bone down to the nape area and fade out to the hairline. This technique can enable the hairline shape to appear more natural looking. Fading can be used to create texture in a design, give depth and perception to enhance the image and can be used for light and dark shading.

▲ Use clipper over comb to blend the hair into the scissor cut

Equipment handling techniques for achieving accurate outlines and detailing designs in hair

Select your required tools by taking into account the desired outcome and any influencing factors.

Clippers and trimmers

There are many different types of clippers and trimmers to use depending on the techniques required. You can use heavy duty, balding, fading, tapering, corded and cordless clippers. They are generally used on dry hair for removing bulk and length and for creating and fading outlines. They can be used for clipper over comb technique or used with attachments for producing varying lengths.

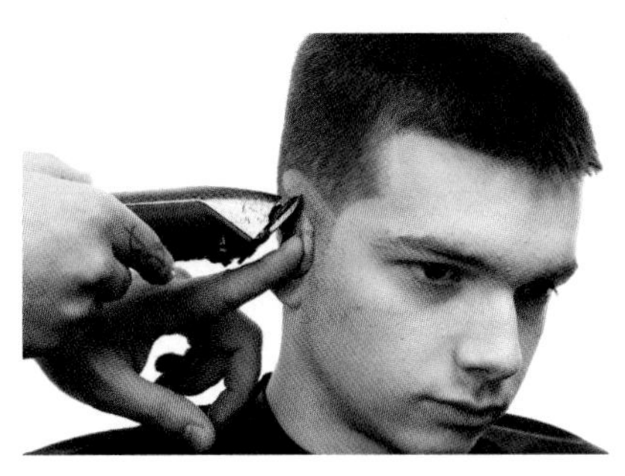

▲ Balding clippers

Avoid causing discomfort to your client and always check your blades are aligned correctly. **Callous skin** can form with continuous over use of clippers, so ensure you provide suitable advice to your client to prevent this and suggest the use of conditioning treatments to add moisture to the scalp.

KEY TERM

Callous skin – hard skin.

HEALTH AND SAFETY

Clipper blades can get hot when used for long periods of time. Take care not to burn your client's skin and allow the clippers to cool down intermittently.

HANDY HINT

It is very important to align your clippers. To do this, unscrew the blades and move the top blade a fraction to ensure the top and bottom blades are parallel to each other. Do not allow the top blade to extend over the bottom fixed blade as the skin can be caught between the blades. Once they are correctly aligned, re-tighten the screws into place.

HANDY HINT

Trimmers and T-liners are used to define the outlines and details within the design. T-liners look similar to trimmers but the blades are 'T' shaped which allows the edges to be used for more intricate detailing work. Both are maintained in the same way and need to be oiled regularly.

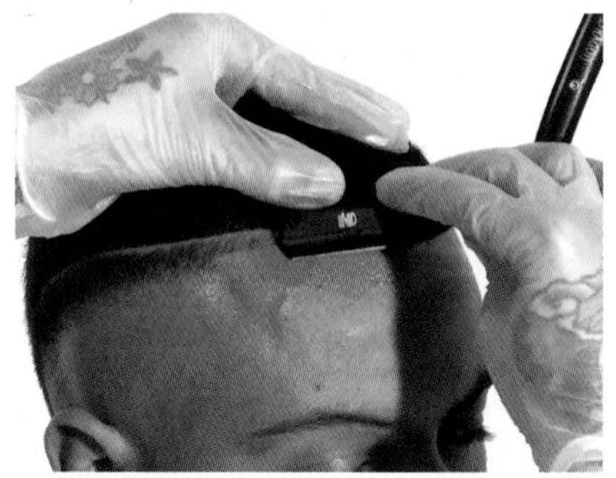

▲ Razoring

KEY TERM

Complex – intricate.

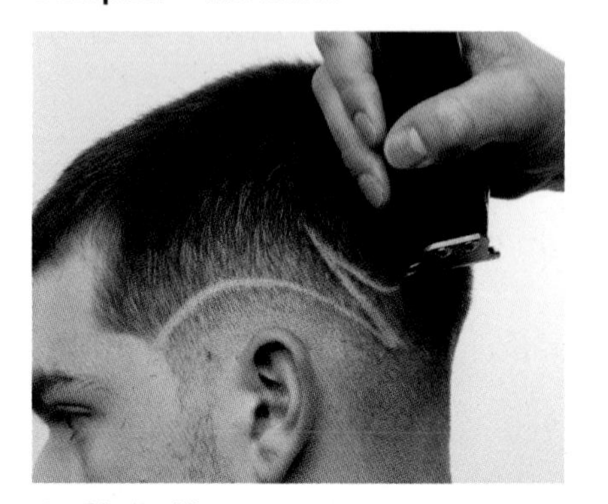

▲ Channelling

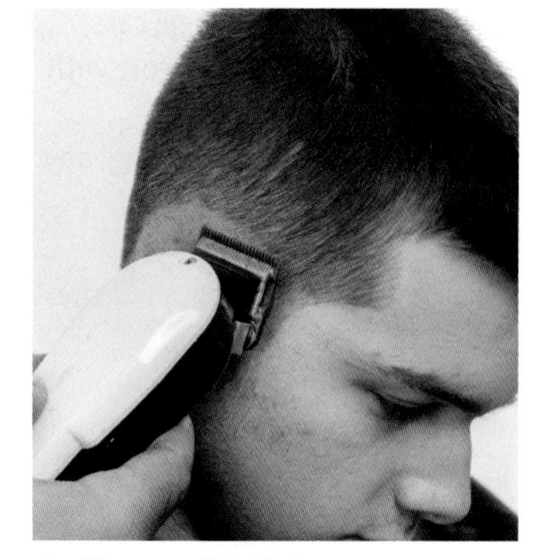

▲ Clippers – thin blade

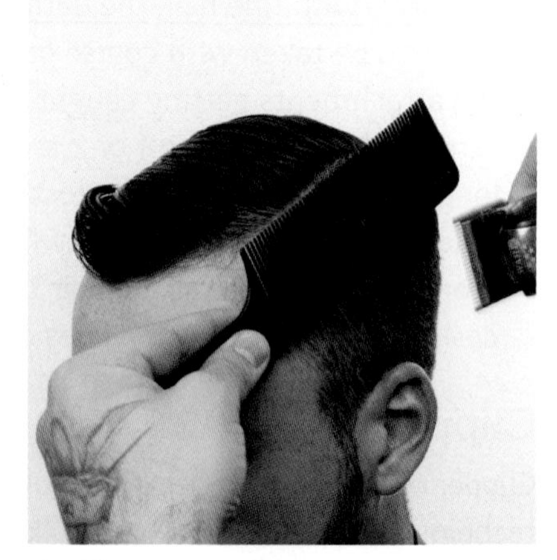

▲ Clippers – cordless

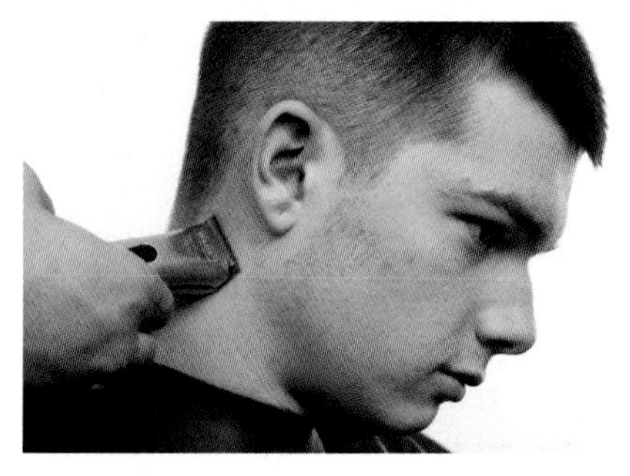

▲ Trimmers in use

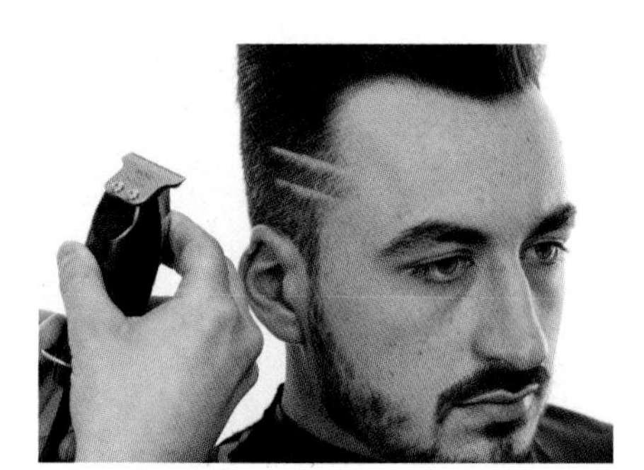

▲ T-liners

HEALTH AND SAFETY

Test the clippers on your arm or hand before placing onto the client's skin, in case the clippers 'bite' or catch the skin. Visually check the alignment of the blades before commencing the service.

HEALTH AND SAFETY

Razors can be used to create and define outlines and to fade outlines.

Make sure you hold razors correctly with your thumb and third finger when cutting, as they are extremely sharp. Ensure you always keep the blades closed when not in use.

Scissors

Scissors can be used to cut the main style of the hair prior to the patterns and detailing being added.

Channelling

A technique used to create **complex** lines, by placing the edge of the blades on the scalp and 'drawing' your design. You would use T-liners or balding clippers to remove the hair and create clean narrow lines that can be curved or straight.

Straight lines – tramlining

This technique is used when the simplest lines are being created – a form of channelling, but which is generally basic and linear. You would use clippers or T-liners to create tramlines.

HANDY HINT

For most detailing and outlining you would use the freehand technique as you cut without tension to create your design, and to define the edges of the pattern.

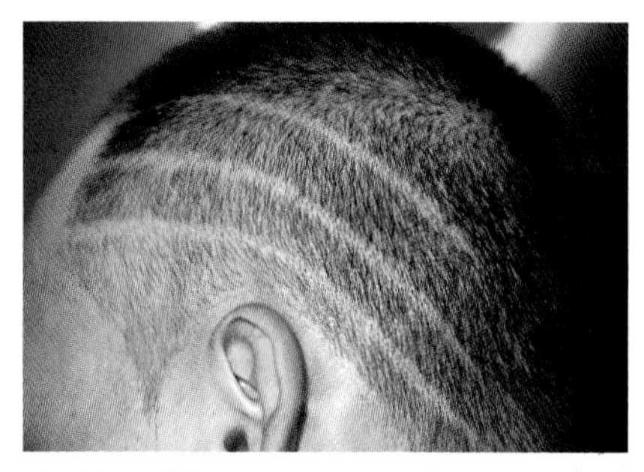

▲ Straight lines

KEY TERM

Linear – straight, direct lines.

Visually checking outline, detailing designs and cut

Before you begin the cut, double check if you need to adapt any part of the design to suit the client's head shape and size. Throughout the haircut make sure the design is meeting the client's requirements and explain what you are doing every step of the way to reassure him. Adapt your body position when required to maintain a good posture, and adapt the sitting or head position of your client to ensure an accurate result can be achieved.

Throughout the creation of the detailing and at the end of the haircut you must look for any unevenness in the design and adapt as required. Use your mirrors and check all around the head for balance and symmetry in the design.

Problems that may occur during services

As with any service, sometimes things do not go to plan. The main causes of problems with the detailing and outline service are generally lack of concentration or poor planning and running out of room for your design. To prevent this from happening ensure you sketch out your design and ideally create a stencil to work from.

Other problems and resolutions are shown in the table below.

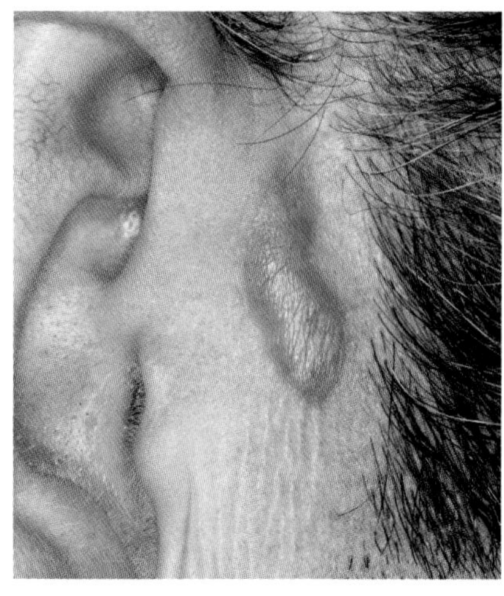

▲ Keloid scarring

Problem	Cause	Resolution
Attachments come off during the clipper with attachment cut.	Poor concentration.	Amend the design to suit the 'bald spot' created when the grade came off.
Lines are too wide or too long.	Poor planning.	Re-evaluate and amend the design and fade out if necessary.
Too much hair is removed.	Poor planning, poor consultation or a lack of concentration.	Re-evaluate the design and adapt the look: make the lines into curves or make the lines wider to incorporate removed hair; adapt techniques and fade out if necessary.

Problem	Cause	Resolution
Incorrect use of fading.	Poor skill or lack of concentration.	Adapt the design.
Dark/red patches appear on the skin.	Failure to consult and diagnose contra-indications and by continual close cutting of the skin which can become sensitive.	Stop future services until the condition improves and advise on products to use, such as those containing aloe vera.
In-growing hairs	Failure to consult and diagnose contra-indications and by blocked follicles that can then become infected which can lead to keloid scarring.	Stop future services until the condition improves. Advise on how to exfoliate and what products to use, such as those containing aloe vera
Cuts to the skin.	Lack of concentration and damaged/unaligned tools.	Clean the cut and apply a plaster if necessary. Re-align tools.

PROVIDE CLIENTS WITH ADVICE AND RECOMMENDATIONS

Before you commence the service, you should provide advice and recommendations on the range of traditional and current men's hair shapes. You should guide your client on where to find sources of information and design ideas and explain how to access these.

Range of traditional and current men's hair shapes

There are many basic patterns and designs for your client to choose from:

- Linear patterns – straight lines that can be used on their own or linked within a design. Linear patterns work well when outlining around the hairline.
- Curves – curvatures in the head, twists, turns, bends and arches can be linked with linear designs and are great for detailing.

In your design artwork you may incorporate shapes such as:

- triangles (three-sided shapes)
- square, rectangle, kite shapes (four-sided shapes)
- pentagon (five-sided shapes)
- pentagram (five-pointed star)
- pentacle (symbol of a star encased in a circle).

ACTIVITY

Shapes such as squares, stars, crosses and diamonds are more challenging to do than straight lines or curves. These are shapes you can create and learn as you increase your skills. As your confidence grows, why not try creating shapes on a training head?

ACTIVITY

Research the meaning of the following shapes:

- ellipses
- obtuse
- polygon
- polyhedron.

ACTIVITY

Designs can be one-dimensional (1D) or 2D or 3D:

- points – a barber may use points to create dots or small round spots within a design; they have no dimension, only a dot or position
- one line – a barber would use these for linear designs as they are one-dimensional (1D)
- flat shapes may be used to create designs that are two-dimensional (2D) such as square, round, oval or star
- cubes or picture designs are three-dimensional (3D) and you will learn and develop these with your level 3 skills.

As your confidence and skill increases, why not try creating these shapes on a training head?

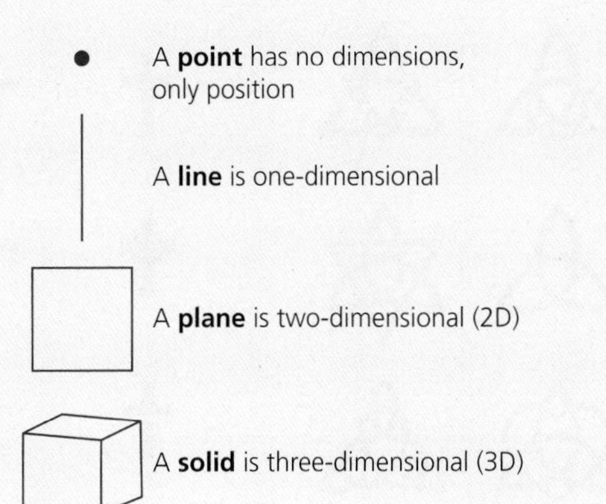

HANDY HINT

The pentagram and pentacle can be linked to witchcraft, magic or even religion.

A pentagram is often linked to 'man' – the top point of the triangle being the head and the other 4 points representing the limbs.

A pentacle is often more symbolic, and is commonly seen within witchcraft and paganism. This is a five-pointed star encased in a circle, with one point always pointing upwards. The upward point is representative of the spirit and the other four points represent an element – earth, air, fire and water – all things that contribute towards life.

▲ Pentagram

▲ Pentacle

HANDY HINT

To draw a pentagram, first draw a polygon and then extend the edges.

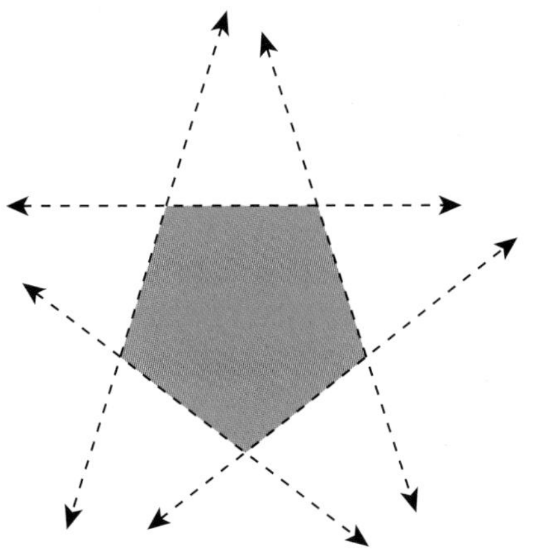

ACTIVITY

Identify other potential sources where you could find hair designs to show your clients.

Agreement of placement

If you or your client have found an internet image of men's hair designs, then the size and placement of that design is likely to be similar for your

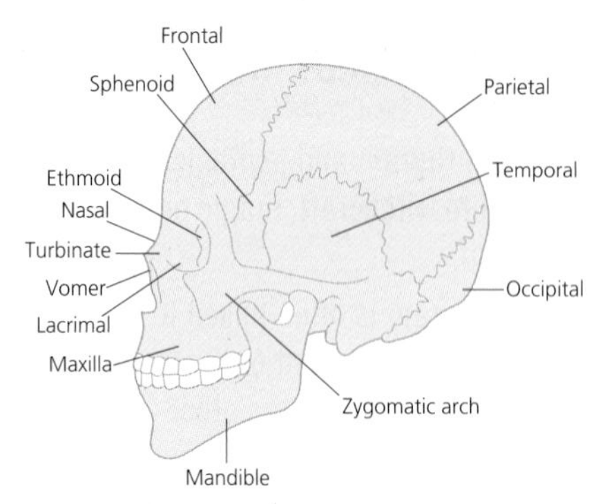

▲ Bones of the skull

▲ Celtic cross

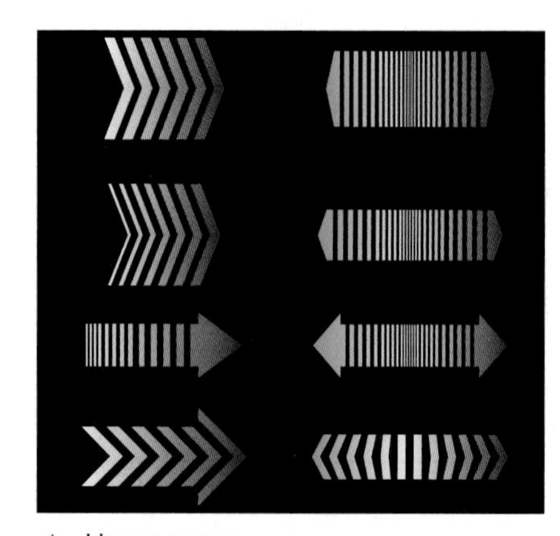
▲ Linear arrows

HANDY HINT

Practise your design pattern on paper before you start your creation. Think about how you will apply the pattern on your client's head.

HANDY HINT

Once you have agreed your design and know the service requirements, you should advise your client on likely duration of the service and the costs involved.

client. However, sometimes a client will show you a design pattern that is not from someone's head, but perhaps from tribal or Celtic artwork. Judging how to adapt the size of the pattern to suit your client's head can be challenging. When you are deciding on the size of design it is important to consider the scale of the image you have seen and the size and shape of your client's head.

The most popular areas of the head for design placement are:

- temporal bone area (temple/side hairline area) for the start of most detailing and linear designs
- from the frontal bone area (front hairline area) for outlining
- occipital bone and towards the nape for more intricate designs and detailing with patterns.

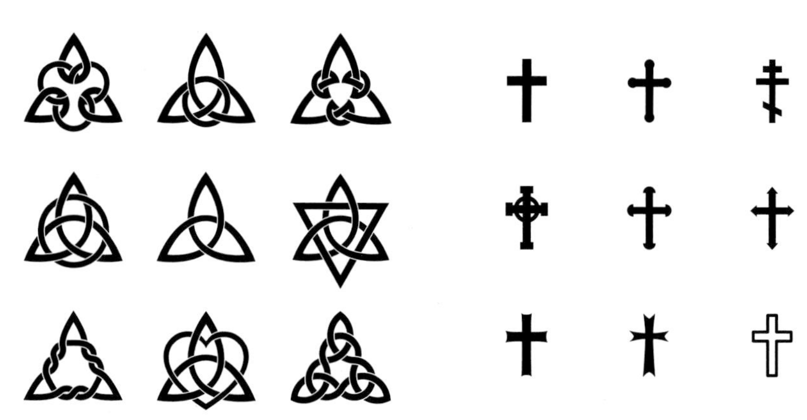
▲ Celtic knots – curved designs

▲ Crosses/icons

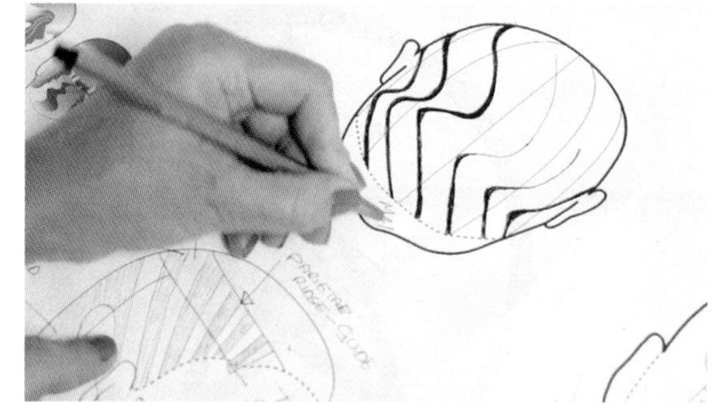
▲ Draw your design on paper to practise

Principles of creating designs

Some designs can be extremely difficult to create and require the advanced skills of an experienced barber. You may need to adapt the design or the haircut to suit the head shape of your client, or the texture and density of the hair.

Design possibilities and limitations

There will always be some limitations on the design possibilities; this may be down to the skill of the barber, while hair density, classification, length, texture and even the hair colour of the client can prevent the desired result from being achieved.

Intricate outlining cannot be carried out if the hair is sparse as any mistakes will be harder to correct or disguise. For dense/abundant hair, your lines will need to be wider to show shape, curve or line detail clearly.

Hair growth patterns, such as a nape whorl, may make the hair look bald and affect the design. Depending on the growth pattern you can try to incorporate it into the design or you may need to change the detail of the design completely to suit.

Sources of design ideas

If your client does not know the design he would like, you should explore possible options by showing your client different images. Your salon may offer a consultation service prior to the actual appointment date/time to discuss and explore design options. This may incur an extra charge or be provided as part of the service, but you should always agree the cost of the service with your client before you start, so that he does not receive any financial surprises at the end of the service.

If using the internet and multimedia to search for inspiration try the following:

- internet search engines – key in words like 'hair pattern design', look in 'images' and choose an option from the results
- Pinterest – you will find lots of photos of design ideas which you can save and 'pin' to your own board for future use
- Instagram – try searching using #hairpatterns or #hairtattoodesign.

> **THE HAIR PROFESSIONAL AT WORK**
>
> Always present information and recommendations on patterns clearly to your client, so he feels confident to begin the service, understands the process involved and for how long he will have to commit to the design.

Provide advice and recommendations on salon products and services

It is essential that you provide suitable aftercare advice to your client on maintaining the look you have created, whether that is a haircut, a creative cut or outlining and detailing services. You should advise on products and how to use them, what equipment would best enable him to recreate the look and when to return for his next haircut. You could even suggest colouring services that might enhance the style.

▲ Ask your client if he would like to buy any products or equipment

Styling and finishing products to maintain the look

If your client has had a full cut-and-blow-dry service, you should have talked about the products that you used during the styling service and explained why and how you used them. If the service was a wet cut, discuss how your client should finish the look himself.

Advise your client on which styling and finishing products would enhance and support his finished look. Explain how particular styling products will aid the drying and styling process, help control the hair and provide longevity to the finished result. You should advise him on how much product to use and how to apply it. If the product could cause a build-up on the hair, advise your client on how to remove the product effectively.

Once a design has been created, it is important to advise your client on how to maintain his new look. Wax is a good product to use to flatten down the style and make the hair look denser. A little hair spray or shine spray can be added at the end to finish the look.

You should suggest to your client to buy the retail products you have used and also encourage him to use massage products containing aloe vera or tea tree to close the pores and prevent any irritation from occurring.

You could suggest the following products to help your client style his hair in between salon visits.

Product	Use
Wax	Use on dry hair to finish; adds pliable hold. Wax works well on detailing and outlining details too.
Grooming cream	Use on wet or dry hair; gives a firm hold with a matt finish.
Clay	Use on wet or dry hair to support the shape and offer a medium shine.
Pomade	Use on dry hair; this is a wax-free substance offering a flexible hold and creating a wet look.

Product	Use
Fiber	Use on dry hair for a firm hold that leaves hair pliable.
Gel	Use on wet or dry hair to create a textured 'gloss' look.

Tools and equipment to maintain the look

Throughout the styling service, you should advise your client on which tools to use at home to recreate his look, and during the blow-dry service demonstrate what you are doing and why. This gives your client a thorough understanding of what he will need to do when he is styling his hair at home. Talk to him about how to create body or movement if required, or how to prevent it. Remember to discuss the health and safety side of styling and the use of electrically-heated styling equipment, such as straightening irons and how these could cause damage to the hair.

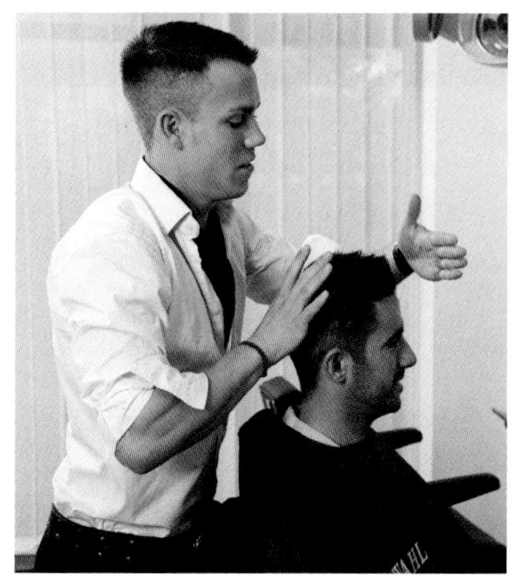

▲ Show your client how to add texture to the style

Time interval between services

You should advise your client on when to book his next hair cutting service. To help guide him, explain that it depends on how quickly his hair grows. You should suggest that he returns to the salon when the style grows out of shape and when he has trouble maintaining the style, as this might indicate it is ready for a cut.

For detailing and outlining intervals, it is better for the barber if the appointments are more regular as it prevents having to redesign the image when it grows out; this can be more cost effective for the client too. The time interval will vary between clients as it will depend on the average growth rate and how intricate the design is.

HANDY HINT

The average rate of hair growth is 1.25 cm per month

Present and future services

Having discussed the cutting service with your client, you may wish to recommend colouring services to enhance the image created. Adding colour and highlights to a haircut helps to add texture and definition to

HANDY HINT

Temporary colour using hair chalks or hair pencils can be added to the artwork and design. You literally colour the hair or scalp with the chalks or pencils to enhance the detail or design.

the shape. Without doubt, colour enhances and complements every style you create.

After detailing and outlining, your client may benefit from a scalp treatment to add moisture to the scalp and to prevent callouses occurring. Alternatively, you could offer a colour service to enhance the patterns and details created.

Advise your client about any special offers that may encourage him to try new services.

▲ You could recommend enhancing a haircut with subtle colours to add depth, tone and shine

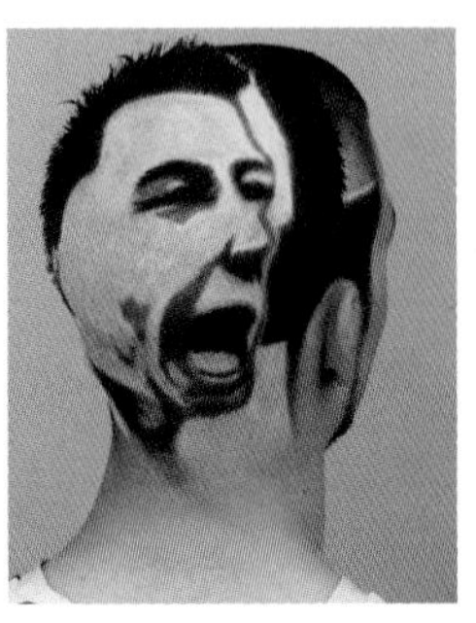

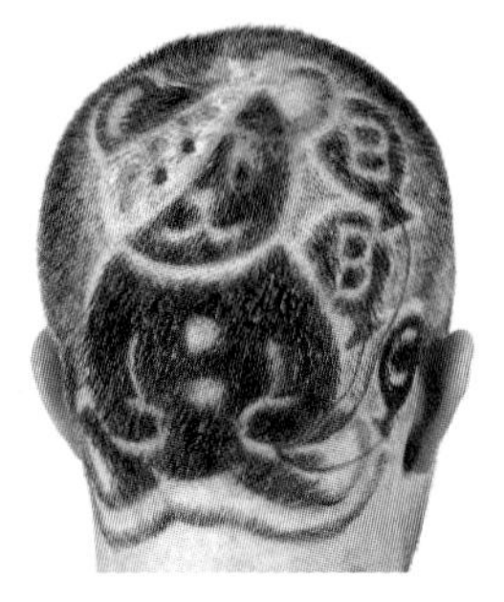

▲ Temporary hair colours

ACTIVITY

Read the advert below and then find the information from the text and answer the questions.

Beau's Barber Shop Special Promotion Day – Introducing Lexi Andrea Adams
13th January

At Beau's barbers we specialise in men's grooming and for one day only we are offering discounted services to introduce our amazing new barber, Lexi.

Lexi's promotional men's grooming services include:

Service	Usual Price	Promotional Price	Saving
Wet cut	£22.00	£14.75	33%
Cut and blow-dry	£28.00	£18.75	33%
Beard trim	£12.00	£8.00	33%
Fashion colour	£30.00	£15.00	50%

There are loads more offers in store. Come down and have a look for yourself – get here early to avoid the queues!

You'll find us at 148 Old Victoria Lane, Heath Park.

1 When is the promotional day being held?
2 Where is Beau's Barber Shop?
3 List one service that has a 33% discount.
4 If the fashion colour was discounted at 33%, what would the cost be?
5 If all services were discounted at 25%, what would the cost be on the promotional day?

WHAT YOU MUST DO

For your practical assessments you must:

- apply safe working practices when cutting hair
- cut hair using basic barbering techniques
- creatively restyle hair
- create basic outlines and detailing designs in hair.

Apply safe working practices

Safe working practices include:

- prepare for cutting services
- selecting suitable products, tools and equipment
- applying safe and hygienic methods of working throughout services.

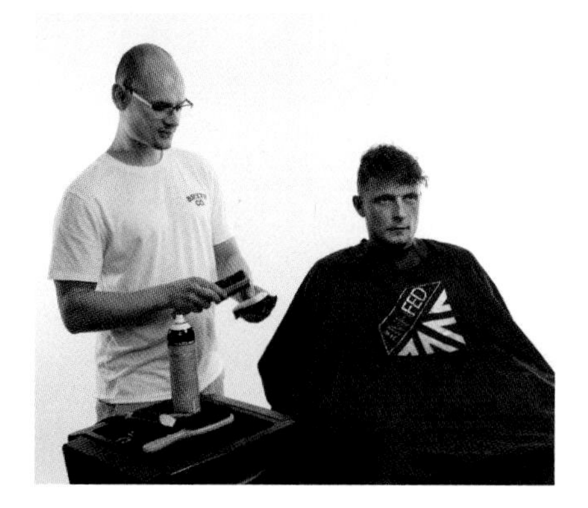

Prepare for cutting services

You must prepare for cutting services by:

- preparing your client to meet the salon's requirements
- protecting your client's clothing throughout the service
- replenishing low levels of resources, when required, to minimise disruption to your own work and to clients
- ideally using a neoprene cutting collar to keep the hair clippings from entering the neck area.

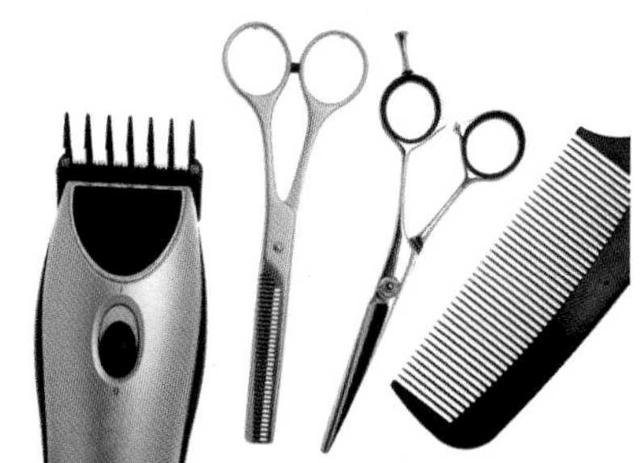

▲ Tools and equipment prepared for the service

Select suitable products, tools and equipment

Before commencing with the service you must:

- select suitable products to work with and to aid finishing the look
- choose suitable tools and equipment to achieve the look required, such as clippers, trimmers, scissors and thinning scissors.

Apply safe and hygienic methods of working throughout services

Throughout the service you must:

- maintain your responsibilities for health and safety
- keep your client's skin free of excess hair cuttings
- position your client to meet the needs of the service without causing them discomfort and adjust the height of the barber chair to suit you
- ensure your own posture and position minimise fatigue and the risk of injury
- ensure your work area is clean and tidy by using working methods that:

- minimise the risk of cross-infection
- make effective use of your working time
- ensure the use of clean resources
- minimise the risk of harm or injury to yourself and others
- promote environmental and sustainable working practices.

Ensure your personal hygiene, protection and presentation meet accepted industry and organisational requirements and you wear personal protective equipment when required. Always follow workplace, suppliers' and manufacturer's instructions for the safe use of equipment, materials and products, and when required, follow the instructions of any senior barbers throughout the service.

Cut hair using basic barbering techniques

You must:

- consult with clients to confirm the desired look
- cut the client's hair
- provide aftercare advice and recommendations on the service provided.

Consult with clients to confirm the desired look

It is important to carry out an in-depth consultation prior to the service and throughout the cutting process to ensure you and your client agree the requirements and to reassure him that you have listened to his request. Follow the cutting process shown in the diagram.

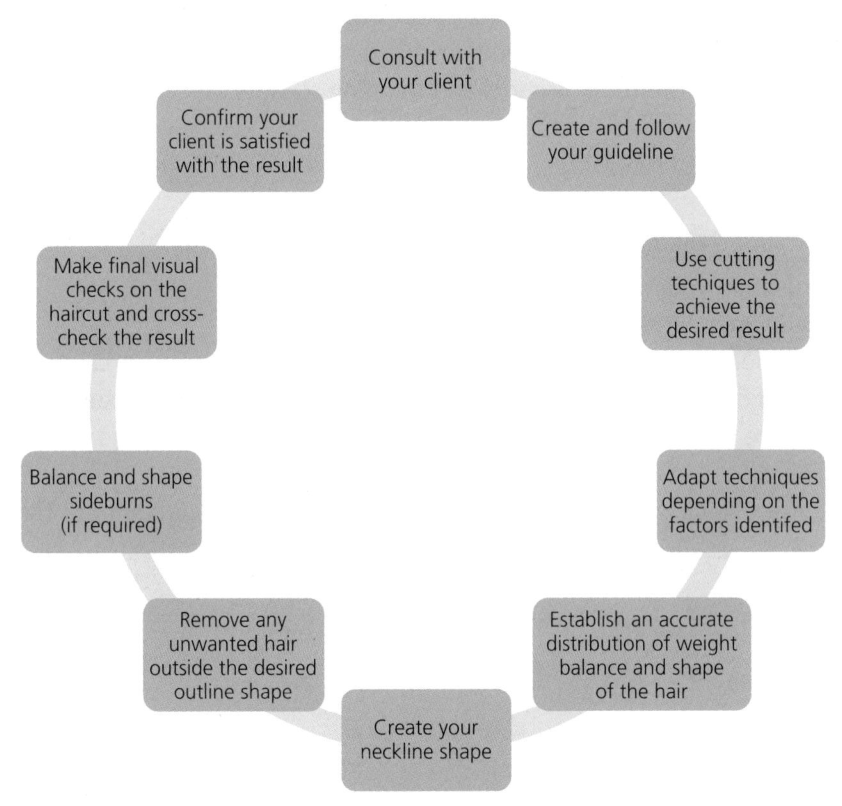

▲ Always follow the cutting process and consult with your client throughout

You must always carry out a thorough consultation with your client to identify the service objective, your client's needs and whether you are able to carry out his request. During the consultation you should tell him how long the service should take and how he can maintain the look between salon visits. The consultation process should continue throughout the cutting service, as you should update your client on the progress of the haircut and check you are cutting to the agreed lengths

▲ Always consult with your client about the service requirements

HANDY HINT

Ask your client where he wears his parting, but always check visually for the natural fall of the hair.

▲ Check the natural fall of your client's hair

Cut hair to achieve a variety of looks

To create a look you must:

- prepare your client's hair prior to cutting,
- create and follow the cutting guideline(s) to achieve the required look
- use cutting techniques that suit your client's hair type and achieve the desired look
- adapt cutting techniques to take account of factors likely to influence the service
- change your own position and that of your client to help ensure the accuracy of the cut and to establish accurate distribution of weight balance and shape of the hair
- towards the end of the haircut, create neckline shapes, taking account of the natural hairline and ensure the outline's shape is accurate, removing any unwanted hair outside the desired outline shape
- check the balance and shape of the sideburns to suit the hairstyle and to meet your client's requirements
- make final visual checks to ensure that the finished cut and outlines are accurate
- leave the hair ready for the next part of the service or finish the style to meet your client's requirements and confirm your client's satisfaction with the finished cut.

Provide clients with advice and recommendations on the service(s) provided

Throughout the service and at the end, ensure you give your client advice and recommendations on the service provided. This should include how to maintain the look, time intervals between services and advice on recommended products and additional services.

▲ Aftercare

STEP BY STEP

In this part of the chapter you will look at how to:

- create a square layered cut
- create a uniform layered cut

- create graduation
- create a flat top
- cut a fringe
- work with a parting
- cut around the ear outline
- cut over the ear
- fade into the hairline
- trim eyebrows.

Creating a square layer look

When cutting the hair to create a square layer look, you will need to make a guideline section for the length of the hair and one for the internal layers of the hair. The hair is cut at 90° at the back and the top is angled at 45° and over and directed towards the back and side sections.

Men's cut – square layer

STEP 1 – Carry out consultation and check hair and scalp.

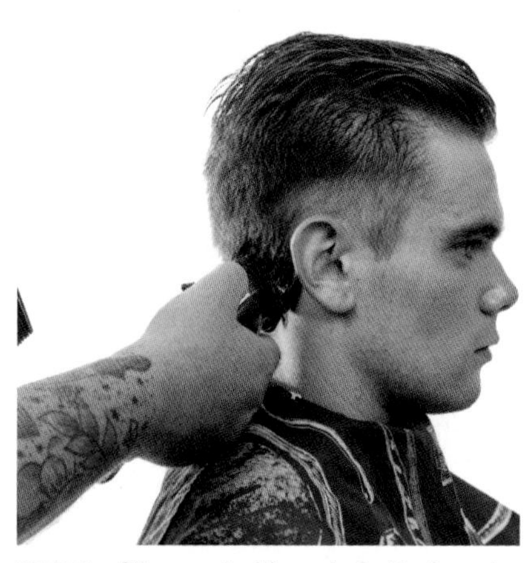
STEP 2 – Clipper cut with grade 2 attachment the back and sides to occipital bone area.

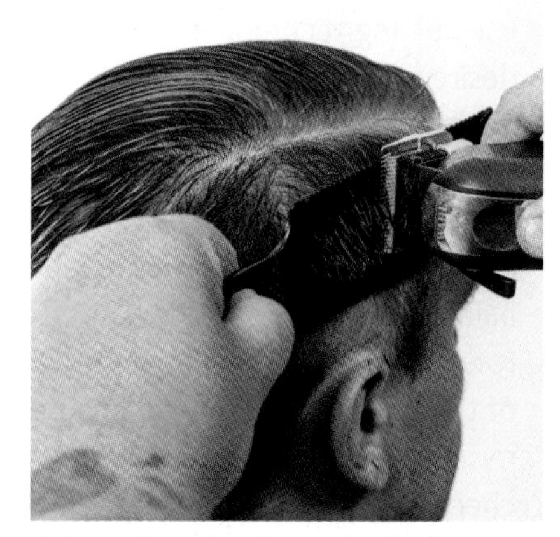
STEP 3 – Blend the clipper cut with clipper over comb technique to create graduation

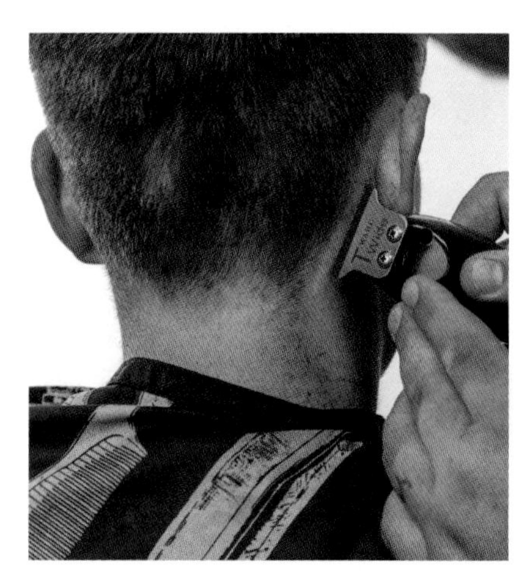
STEP 4 – Remove and tidy the unwanted hair outside of the clipper cut area using T-liners or trimmers.

STEP 5 – Wearing gloves, razor cut the hair closely against the skin so the shape and cut is maintained for longer.

STEP 6 – Cut the top with square layers, taking each section directly upwards and cutting vertically at 90° and complete the whole top area to the same level.

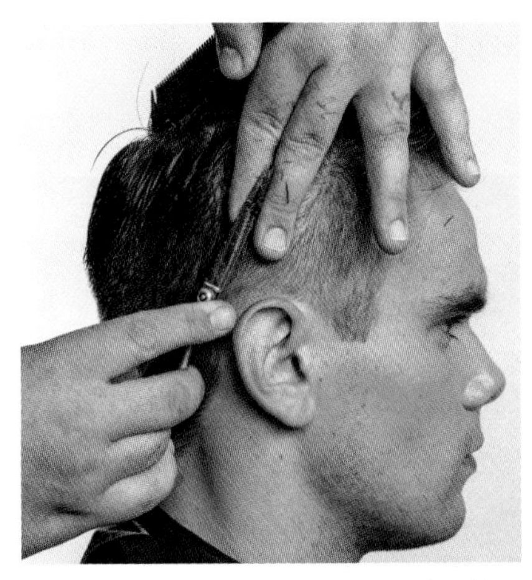

STEP 7 – Blend the square shape into the sides by removing the length as the hair is pulled directly out at 90°.

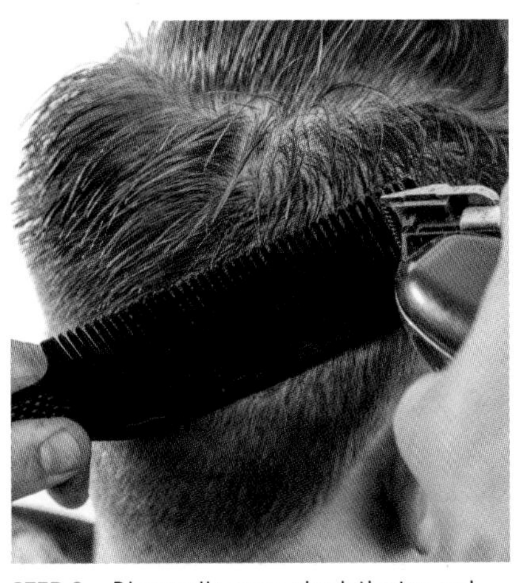

STEP 8 – Diagonally cross-check the top and sides with clipper over comb technique to eliminate ridges or lines.

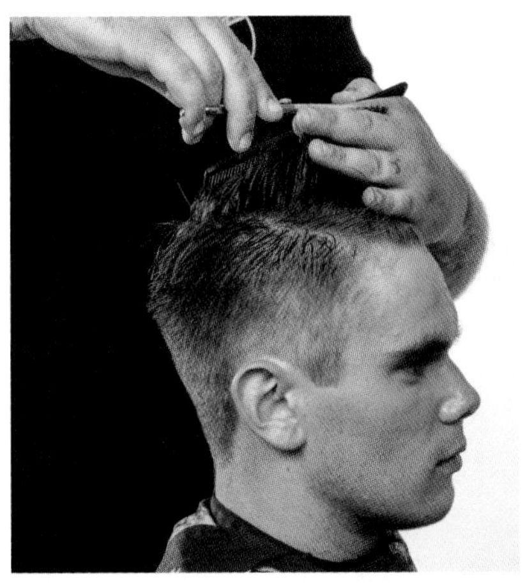

STEP 9 – Cross-check the top for balance and shape.

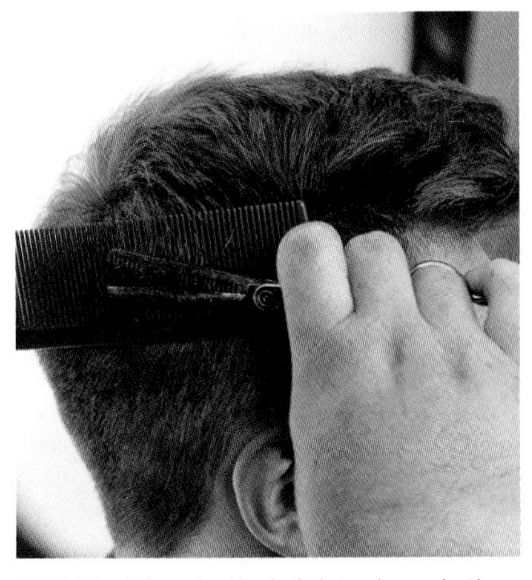

STEP 10 – Blow-dry the hair into shape, in the direction the hair grows and texturise the side edges with thinning scissors over comb.

STEP 11 – Texturise the back section to ensure the cut is blended through.

STEP 12 – Add styling products and finish the look.

Creating a uniform layer look

When cutting the hair to create a uniform layer look, you will need to make a guideline section for the length of the hair and one for the internal layers of the hair. The hair is cut at 90° all over.

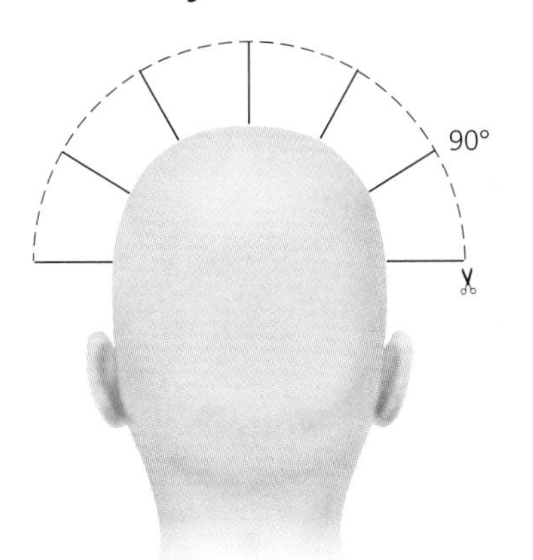

90°

▲ Uniform layer angles

ACTIVITY

Practise a square layered hair cut on a training head.

ACTIVITY

Create a mood board of varying square layer looks and write up how to achieve one of the images.

Uniform layers with thinning to create a textured look

STEP 1 – Section hair using the recession and upper occipital bone as guidelines, to create horseshoe sections.

STEP 2 – Take a vertical section from the centre of the occipital bone at 90° to create the first guideline.

STEP 3 – Using the initial guideline, take radial sections throughout the back of the head.

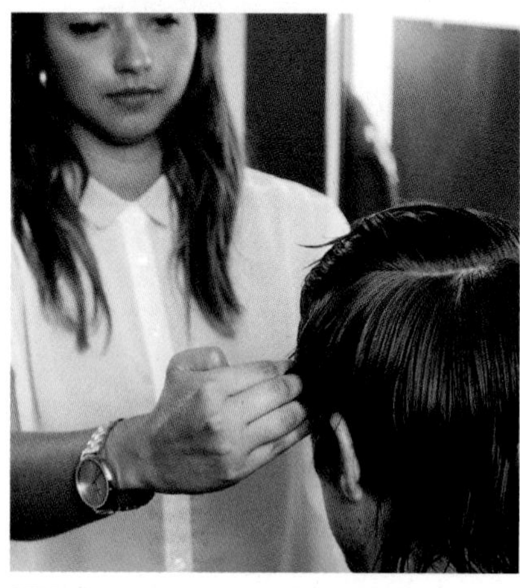

STEP 4 – Cross-check your cut and check the weight and balance of the hair.

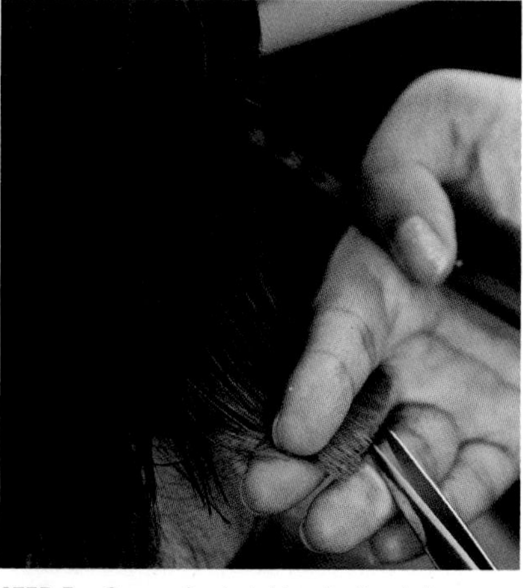

STEP 5 – Cross-check, taking horizontal sections.

STEP 6 – Using your initial guideline section, cut a guideline for the crown.

STEP 7 – Follow the crown guideline and cut your profile line through the top of the head.

STEP 8 – Use the profile guideline to cut square layers through the top sections.

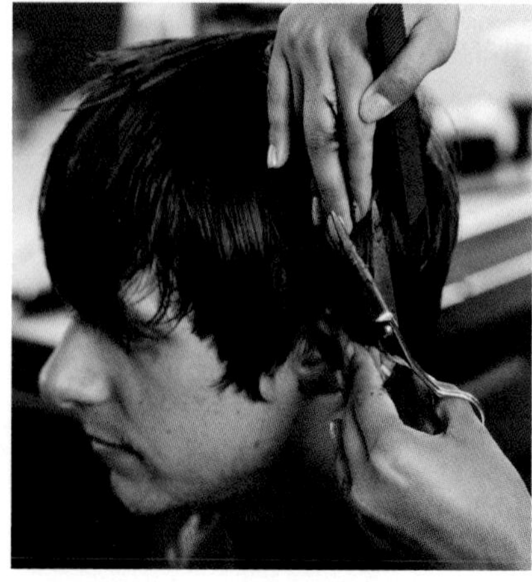

STEP 9 – Connect the top to the sides, removing the corners, connecting both guidelines.

STEP 10 – Dry the hair and refine the perimeter using a freehand technique.

STEP 11 – Connect the fringe to the rest of the hair, removing any corners.

STEP 12 – Finish the look by texturising, following your initial cutting pattern using a deep point cutting technique.

ACTIVITY

Create a mood board of varying uniform layer looks and write up how to achieve one of the images.

ACTIVITY

Practise a uniform layered haircut on a training head.

Creating a graduated layer look

When you create a short graduated haircut, the hair must gradually get shorter towards the nape and neck area. The top can be cut in a similar way to the uniform layers and held out at 90°, but the sides and back of this style must be cut at 45°.

Graduated look with clippering techniques

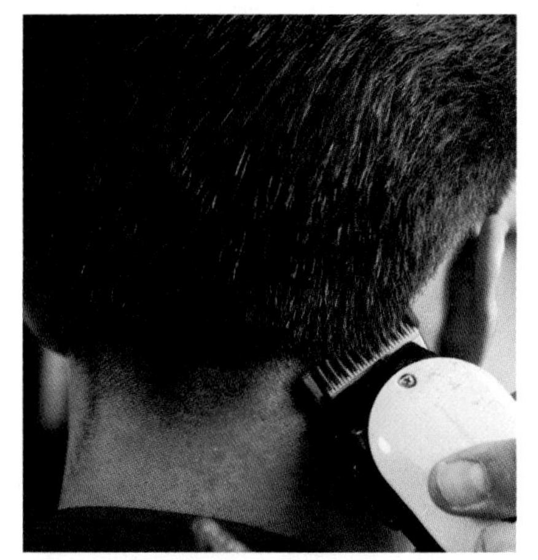

STEP 1 – Starting at the nape area using a clipper grade 1, pull away to create graduation from the nape.

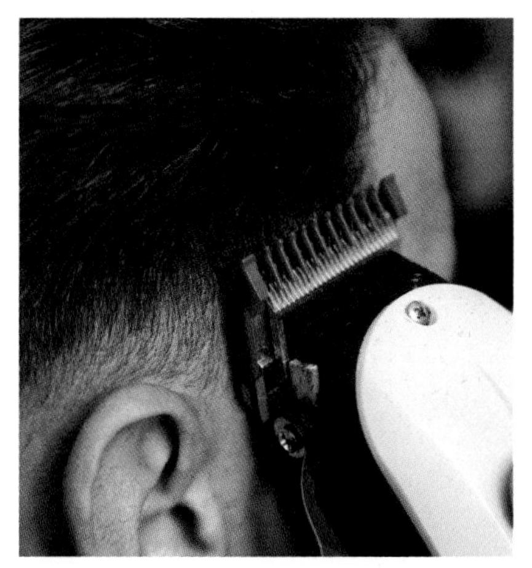

STEP 2 – Follow the previous technique around the sides, not going higher than temples.

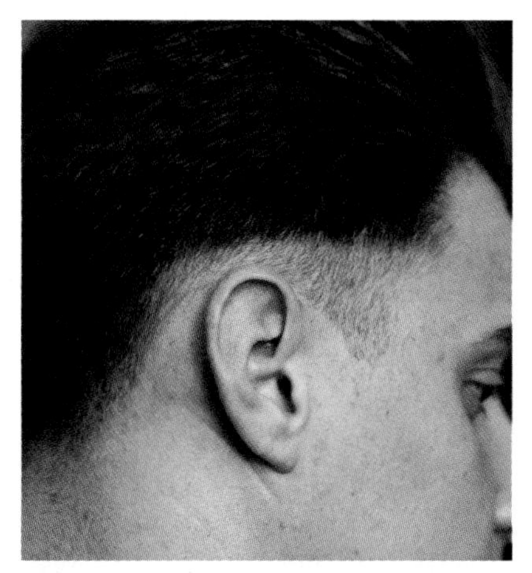

STEP 3 – This is the shape created.

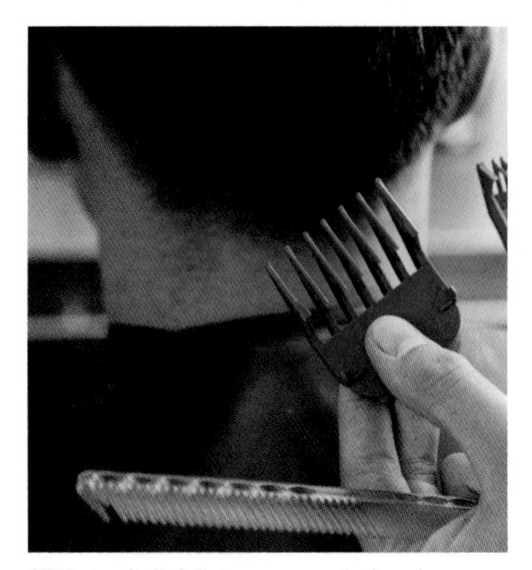

STEP 4 – Switch between a grade 1 and a grade 2. Using the grade 2, remove the weight line around nape and temple area.

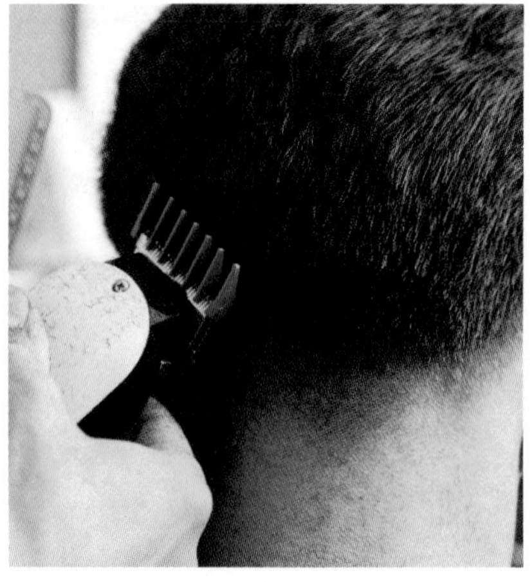

STEP 5 – Check the balance of the shape created in the mirror.

STEP 6 – Starting from the crown working forward, club cut through the top.

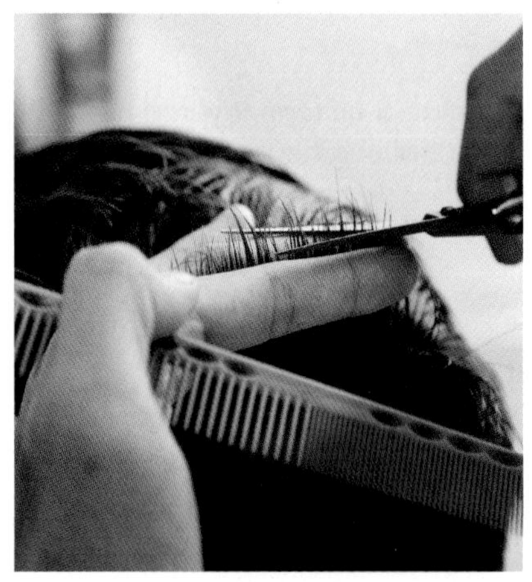

STEP 7 – When you get to the front, slightly angle towards the crown to create graduation and more length around the front.

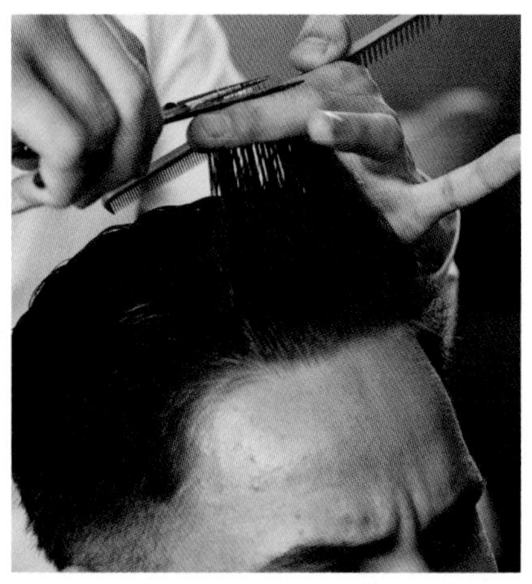

STEP 8 – Working from the side panel to the lower occipital bone, blend using scissor over comb to remove the weight line.

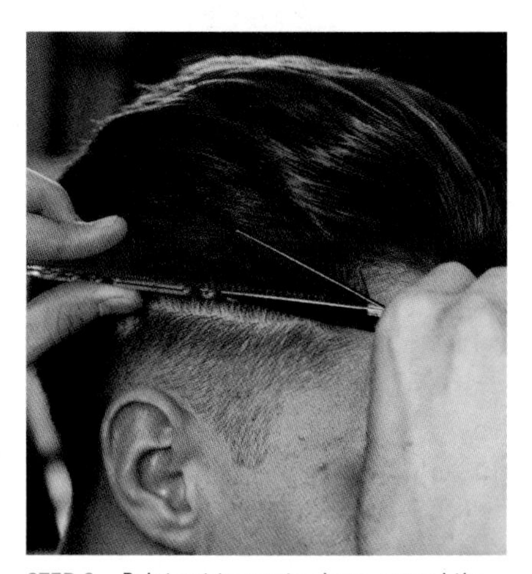

STEP 9 – Point cut to create shape around the ear.

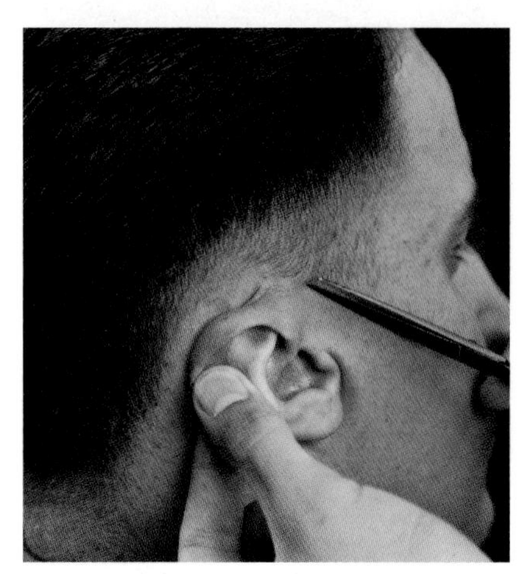

STEP 10 – Taper the neckline, angling the comb to create graduation.

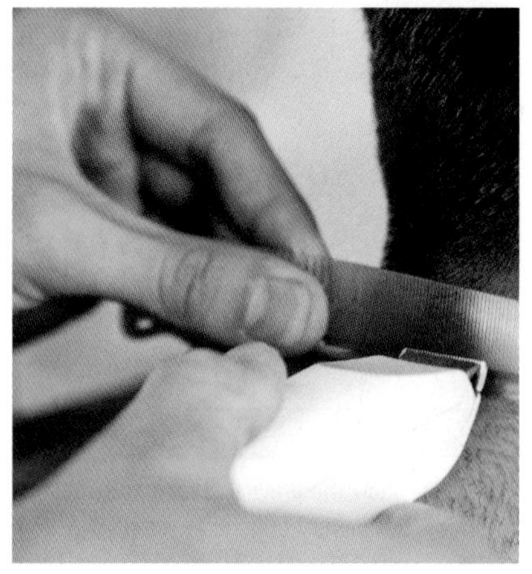

STEP 11 – Adjust the clipper lever to grade 0 to create skin fade around the edges.

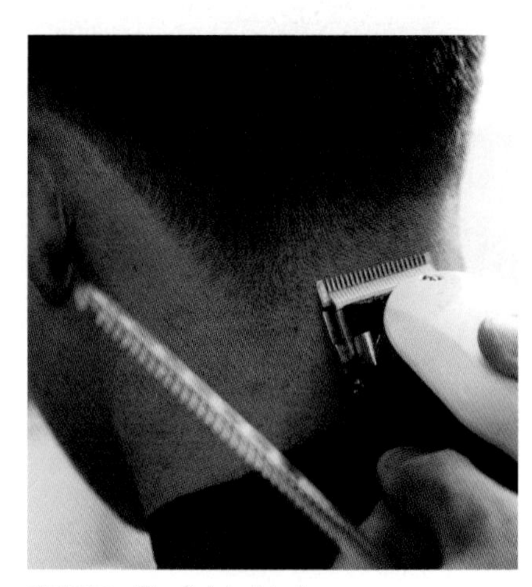

STEP 12 – The finished look.

ACTIVITY

Draw the correct cutting angles used to create a graduated layer look.

ACTIVITY

Create a mood board of varying graduated layer looks and write up how to achieve one of the images.

ACTIVITY

Practise a graduated layer haircut on a training head.

Cutting graduation – creating a fade

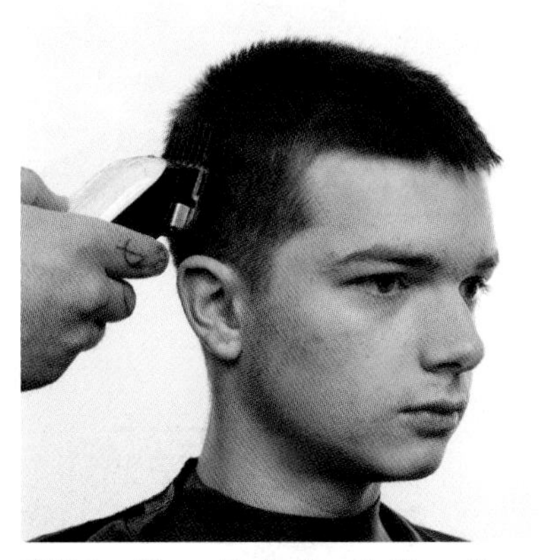

STEP 1 – Clipper the back and sides with a closed blade grade 2 attachment, stopping at the curvature of the head.

STEP 2 – Open the clipper blades with the tapering arm to grade 2.5.

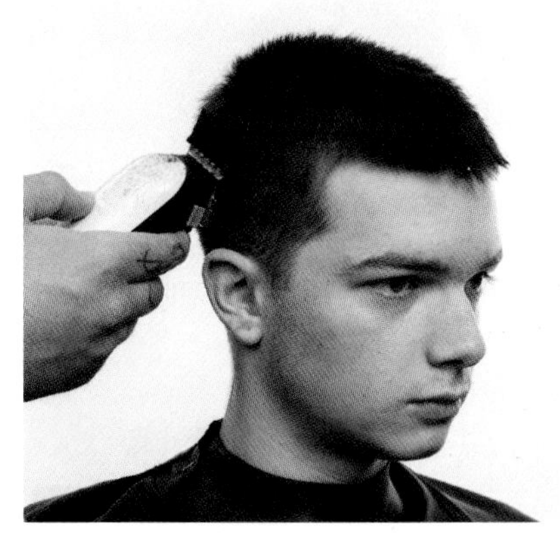

STEP 3 – Blend in the grade 2, with the grade 2.5 to remove weight line.

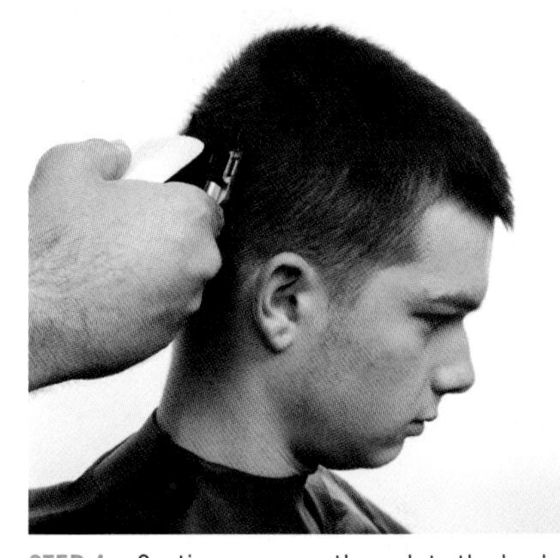

STEP 4 – Continue process through to the back.

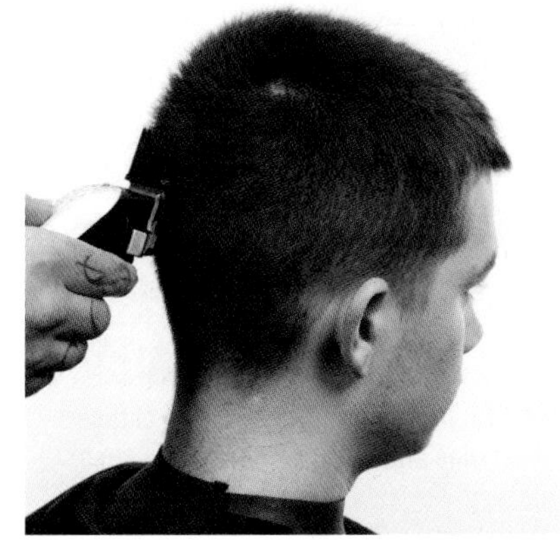

STEP 5 – Change attachment to grade 3 with open blades (3.5) and repeat process to blend in weight line further if required.

STEP 6 – Continue on through back and sides.

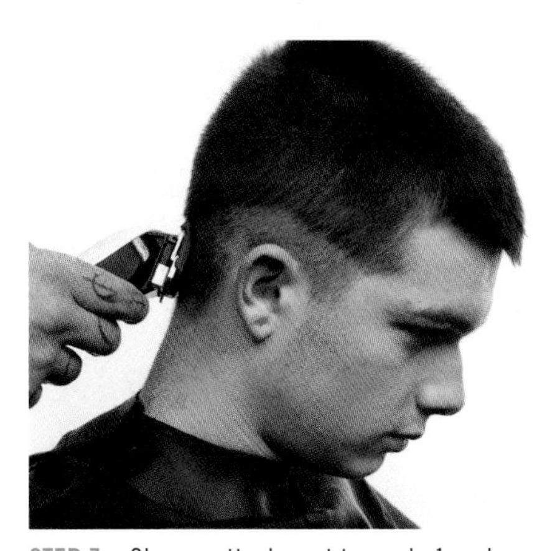

STEP 7 – Change attachment to grade 1 and clipper up to temple line through the front and the occipital bone towards the back.

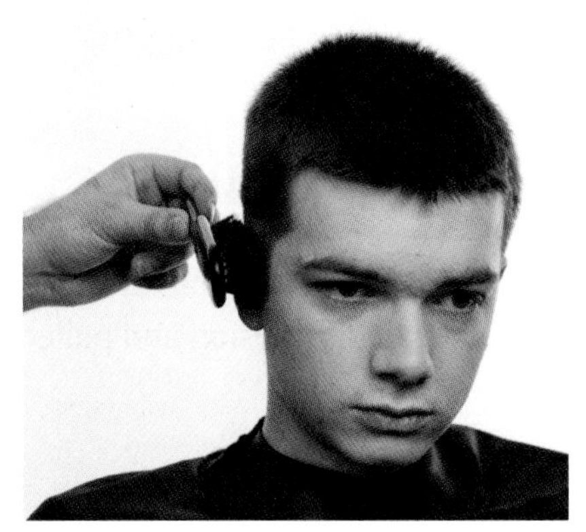

STEP 8 – Use a fade brush to remove loose hairs.

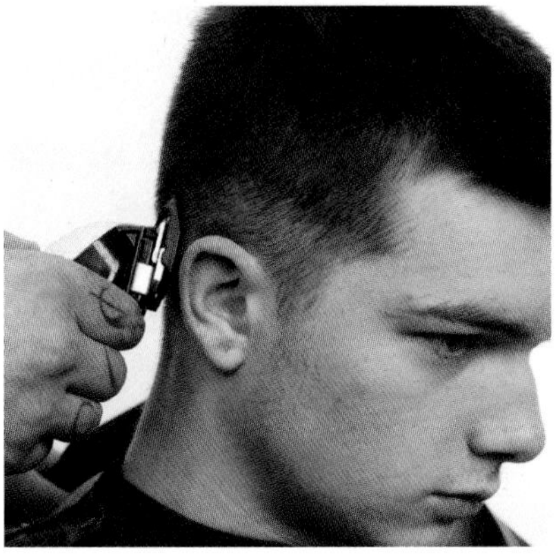

STEP 9 – Blend the line with a grade 1 with open blades (grade 1.5), removing loose hairs with the brush as you cut.

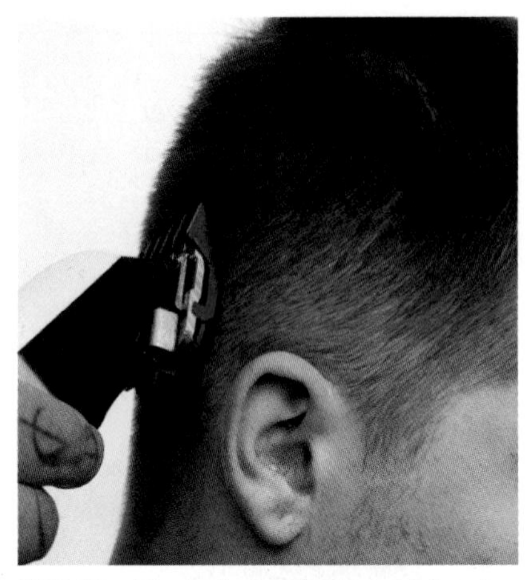

STEP 10 – Attach clipper attachment 1.5 and blend with open blades to remove fine hairs and blend.

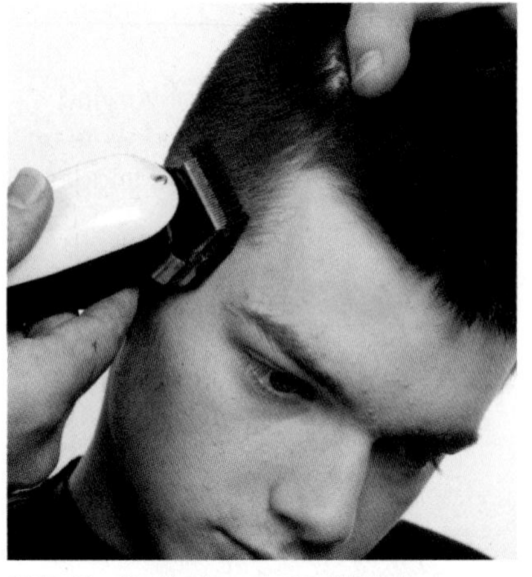

STEP 11 – Reattach grade 1 with blades open. Holding scalp with tension, refine and blend the final areas for a flawless finish (keeping your brush to hand to remove loose hairs). Go over the back and sides, blending and refining.

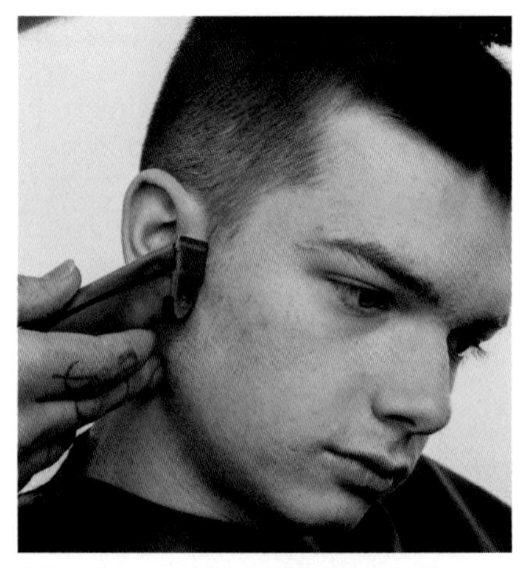

STEP 12 – Use mini trimmers to create the outline.

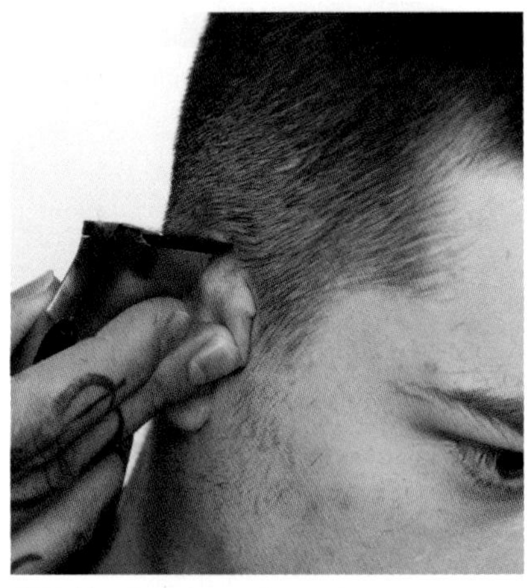

STEP 13 – Hold the ear forward to cut the hair behind the ears with the mini trimmers.

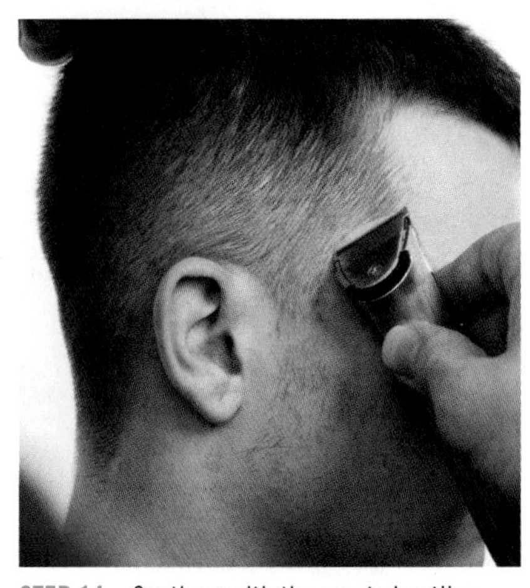

STEP 14 – Continue with the created outline and neckline and tidy the front hairline area.

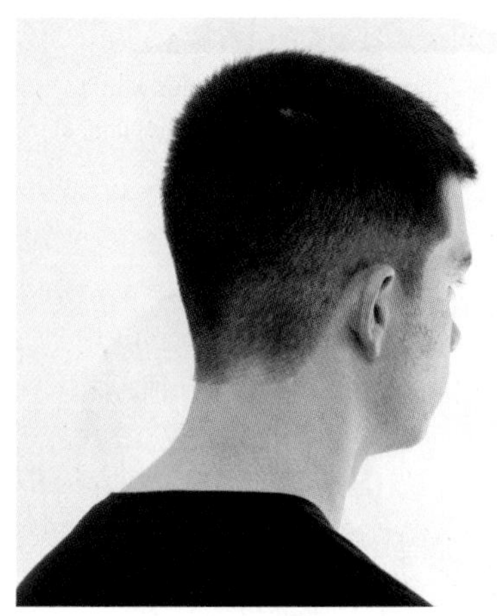

STEP 15 – The finished look.

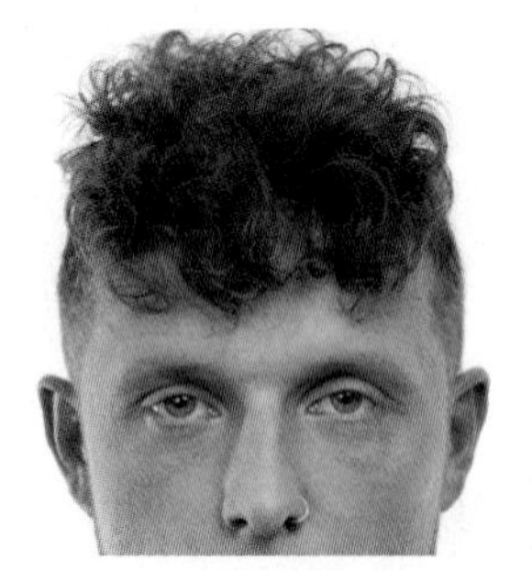

▲ Remember that curly hair will make a fringe look shorter once it has dried

ACTIVITY

Practise cutting a fringe on a training head.

ACTIVITY

Research on the internet or in style magazines for styles with fringes.

Cutting a fringe

Fringes are generally cut with freehand techniques to allow for the natural movement and fall of the hair growth patterns. However, fringes can be cut under tension and pulled down to 0°.

Cutting with a parting

Clients, who wear their hair with a parting may choose to have a connected or disconnected parting. Alternatively, they may have a 'hard-part', where the parting line is clippered and extra defined.

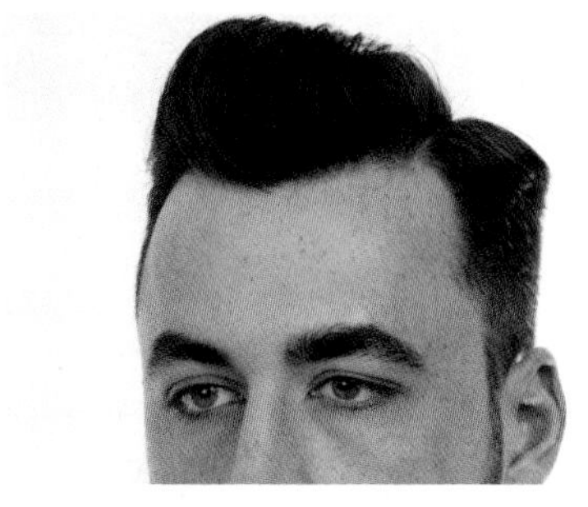

▲ Disconnected parting

▲ Blended parting

▲ Hard-part – a clippered parting for extra definition

Cutting around the ear outline

When you are cutting a style above the ear, you need to cut the hair cleanly around the ear area. If the hair is left too long around the ear, then it might appear as if it needs cutting again just a week or two later. To help achieve a clean cut around the ears, hold/gently fold your client's ear forward towards the face (or ask your client to hold their ear if you prefer). While the ear is held gently forward you can freehand cut around the shape of the ear. Sometimes clippers are used without a grade, to carefully follow the hairline around the ear area and create a neat finish.

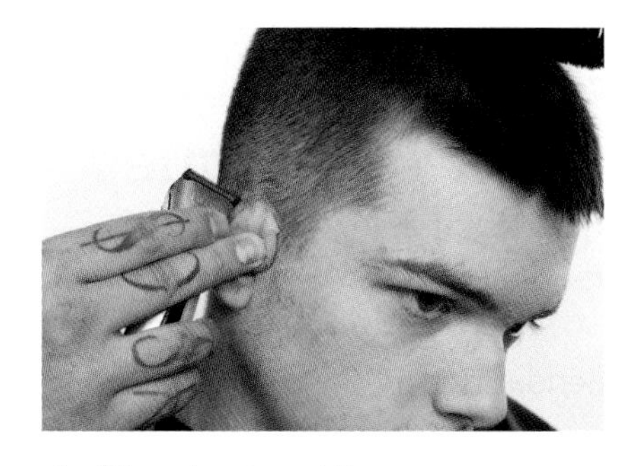

▲ Clippering around the ear

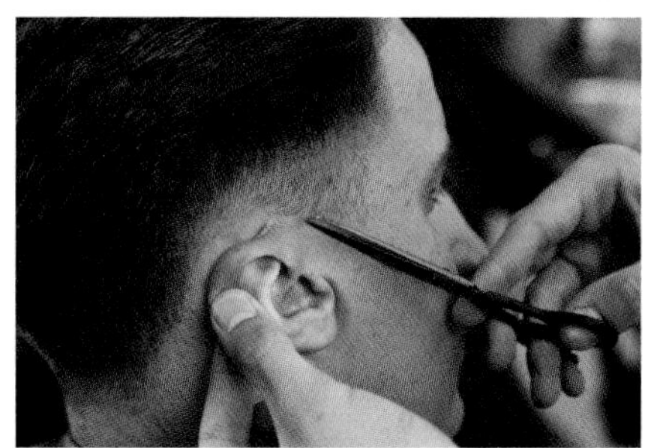

▲ Cutting around the ear

ACTIVITY

Practise cutting over the ear on a training head.

Cutting over the ear

Hair that is cut over the ear is left a little longer and therefore covers at least the top of the ear.

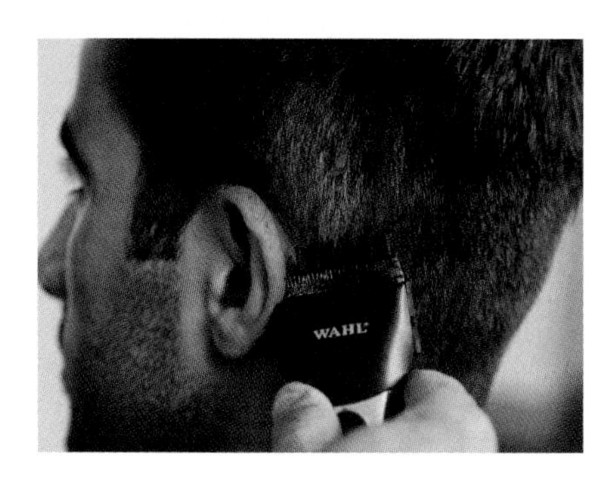

Neckline and outline shapes

Always check with your client the neckline and outline shape required. Some clients prefer a natural finish, allowing the natural hairline shape to show through. Other clients may prefer a created shape or one that gradually tapers out.

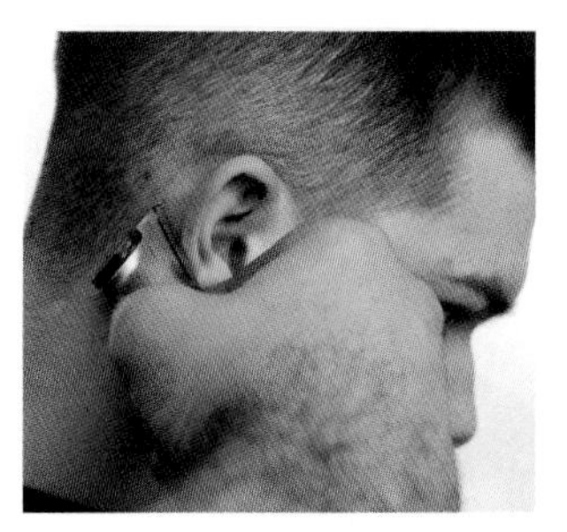
▲ Tapered neckline

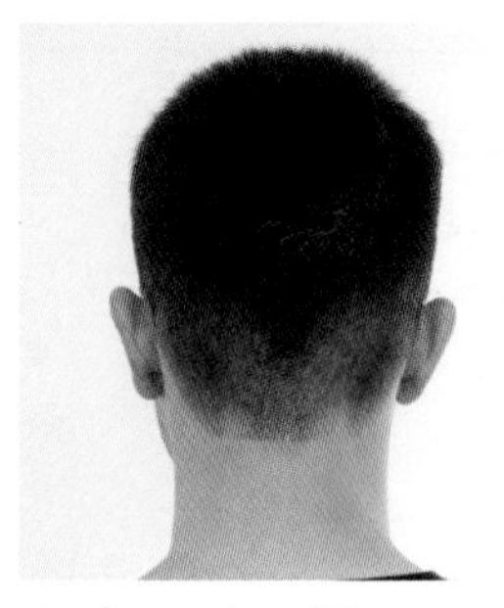
▲ Squared neckline

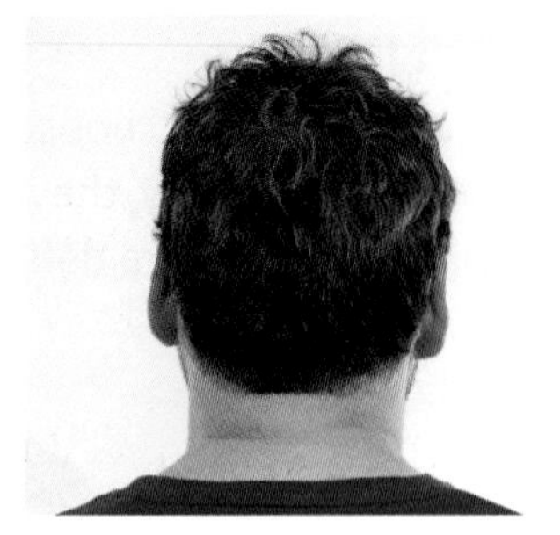
▲ Full neckline

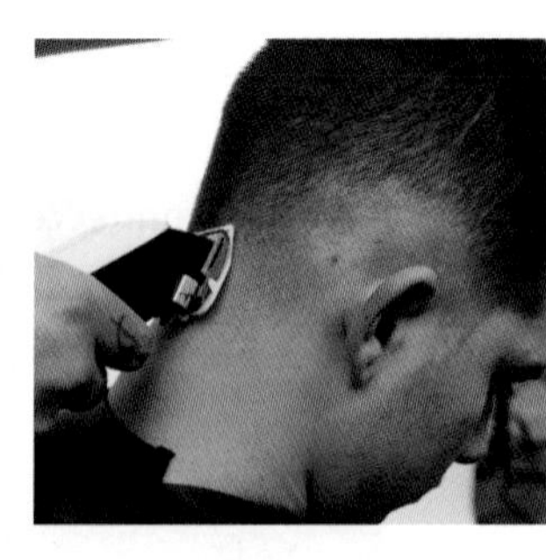
▲ Skin fade

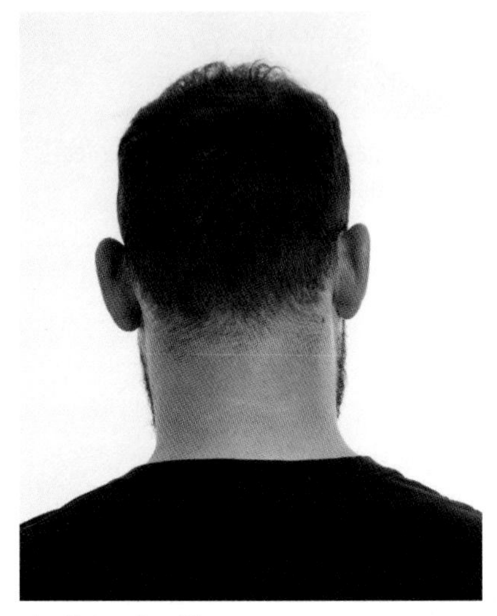
▲ Natural outline

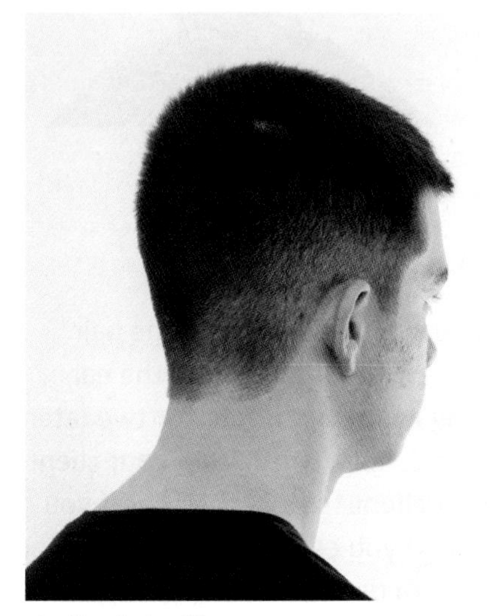
▲ Created outline

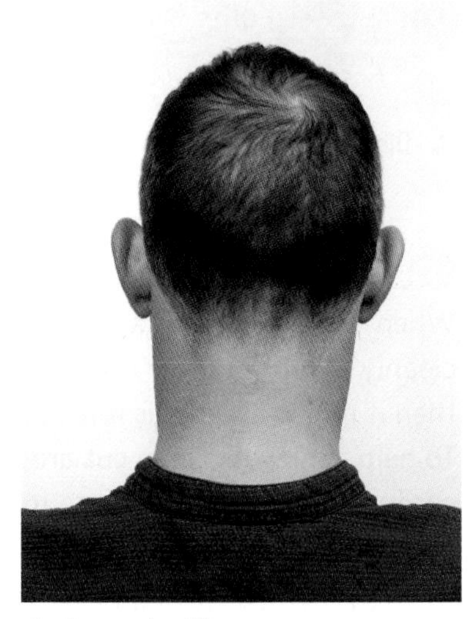
▲ Tapered outline

Creatively cut hair using a combination of barbering techniques

You must:

- consult with clients to confirm the desired look
- cut the client's hair
- provide aftercare advice and recommendations on the service provided.

Consult with clients to confirm the desired look

During the consultation you must:

- establish factors that may influence the service prior to cutting
- explore the variety of looks with your client using relevant visual aids
- ask your client if he wants his head hair blended into his facial hair (if he wears facial hair), if he wears side burns and if he wants a clean neckline or has it faded out for a more natural finish
- recommend a look that is suitable for your client, basing your recommendations on an accurate evaluation of your client's hair and its potential to achieve the look
- confirm with your client the look agreed at consultation before commencing the cut and continue to consult during the cutting service to confirm the desired look.

Creatively restyle hair to achieve a variety of looks

You should:

- aim to complete the cutting service within a commercially viable time
- once you begin, establish and follow suitable cutting guideline(s) and personalise your cutting techniques and effects to take account of factors that will influence the desired look
- as you work, change your own position and that of your client to help you ensure the accuracy of the cut
- combine and adapt your cutting techniques and effects in an innovative way to achieve the desired look and establish accurate distribution of weight, balance and shape by cross-checking the cut
- create outline shapes that are accurate and remove any unwanted hair outside the desired outline shape
- restate neckline shapes which are accurate and take account of the natural hair line and balance and shape sideburns to meet the client's requirements
- take action to resolve any problems arising during the cutting service
- make a final visual check to ensure the finished cut and outlines are accurate
- towards the end of the cut, use creative finishing techniques that complement the cut and ensure you blend the client's own hair with any added hair, when required
- ensure the finished restyled look complements the client's features and enhances their personal image and that of the salon
- confirm your client's satisfaction with the finished look.

Provide clients with advice and recommendations on the service(s) provided

Throughout the service and at the end, ensure you give your client advice and recommendations on the service provided. This should include how to maintain the look, time intervals between services and advice on recommended products and additional services.

STEP BY STEP

Creatively cutting hair incorporates all the techniques and looks covered so far, but also includes skin fading, razoring cutting and disconnection.

Creating a skin fade

To create a skin fade, carry out steps 1 to 12 of 'Cutting graduation – creating a fade' (above) and then:

STEP 13 – To create the skin fade, use 000 bulk clipper (balding clippers) and follow the guide from below the temple, round the ear, removing hairs as you go.

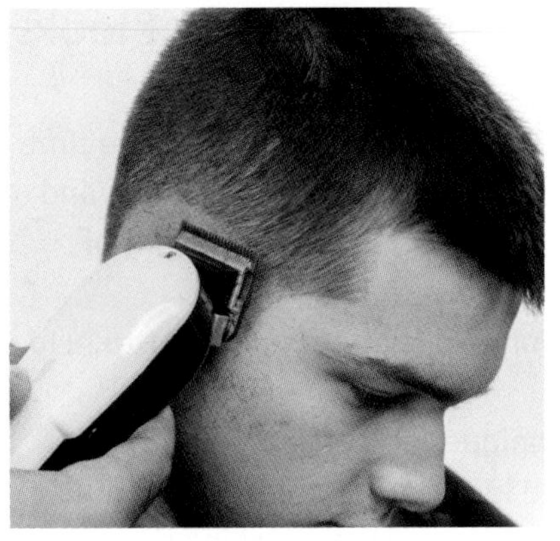

STEP 14 – Continue with thin bladed clippers using the fade blade to blend.

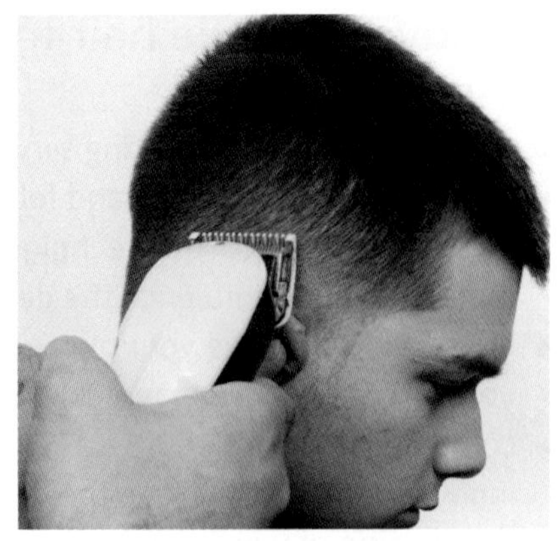

STEP 15 – Add a '0' attachment and blend and refine, continuing to brush away loose hairs for clear view points.

STEP 16 – Hold scalp with tension and repeat, refine and blend with a grade 1 attachment by adjusting the tapering arm to refine the transition.

STEP 17 – Repeat again with grade 1.5 (open).

STEP 18 – Complete the outline shape to achieve the finished look.

Creating a disconnected look with razoring techniques

STEP 1 – Gown, prepare and cut back and sides with a clipper grade 1.5 – just above temples and occipital to the curvature of the head.

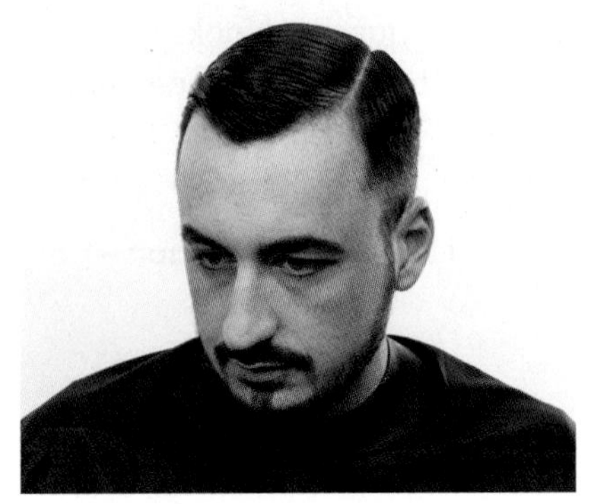

STEP 2 – Section the hair to the natural parting, in readiness for the disconnection.

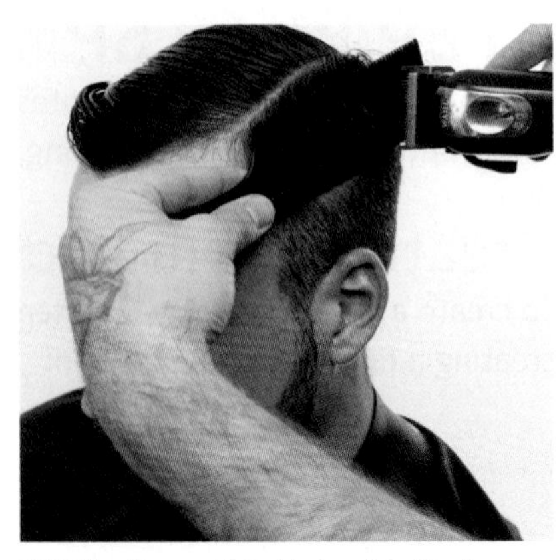

STEP 3 – Remove the side length with clipper over comb technique.

STEP 4 – Visually check the balance of the straight parting disconnected area.

STEP 5 – Cut the other side, maintaining the top lengths.

STEP 6 – Cut the crown to above occipital bone, taking vertical sections and blending into the clipper cut.

STEP 7 – On the top, cut in your profile guideline from forehead to crown.

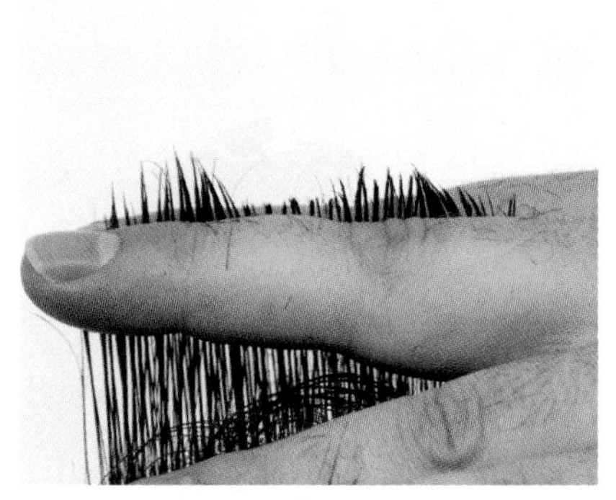

STEP 8 – Cut top to length following the guide.

STEP 9 – Over direct the top fringe area to maintain length.

STEP 10 – Cross-check in the opposite direction.

STEP 11 – Razor cut the top and left hand side to remove bulk and add texture to the style (avoid razoring near the parting area, as it will affect the style).

STEP 12 – Dry hair, apply styling product and complete the finished look.

◀ Alternatively this haircut could be completed with a skin fade.

Creating a quiff disconnection cut

STEP 1 – Carry out consultation and check hair and scalp.

STEP 2 – Section the top cleanly and securely out of the way.

STEP 3 – Clipper cut the back using a grade 1 attachment and slightly over-directing the clippers at the disconnection point (the sectioned-off hair), to give a squarer shape.

STEP 4 – Use clipper over comb to ensure the shape blends out the final clipper cut.

STEP 5 – Remove loose hairs with a bristle brush and check evenness of cut.

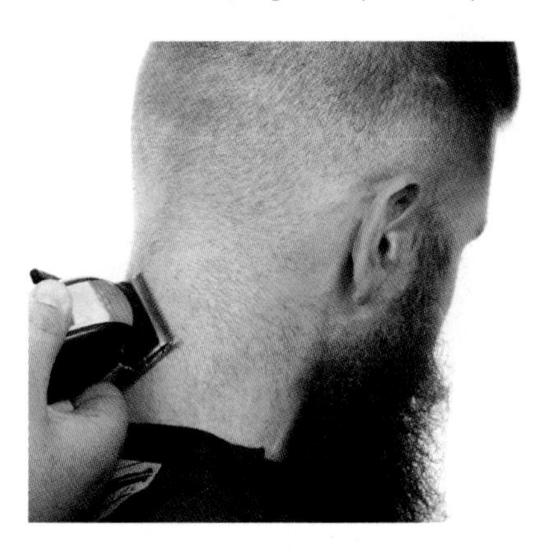

STEP 6 – Blend 0.5 into the 1 and taper out the neck hairline to grade 0. Clean up the hairline edges with a razor (while wearing gloves).

STEP 7 – Remove agreed lengths using club cutting techniques to create a square layer on top.

STEP 8 – Cut the remaining top area into a uniform layer.

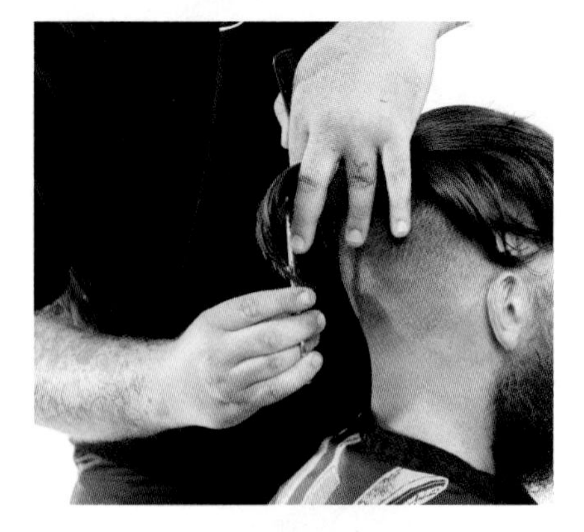

STEP 9 – Create a short graduated layer through the sides and back.

STEP 10 – Diagonal cross-check through the haircut.

STEP 11 – Point cut and texturise the top for shape and movement.

STEP 12 – Finish with a volume blow-dry styled into a pompadour shape.

Eyebrow grooming

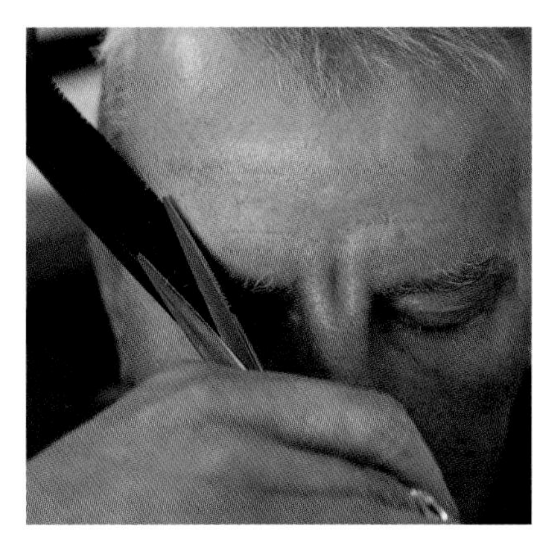

STEP 1 – Using either clipper or scissor over comb techniques, remove excess length.

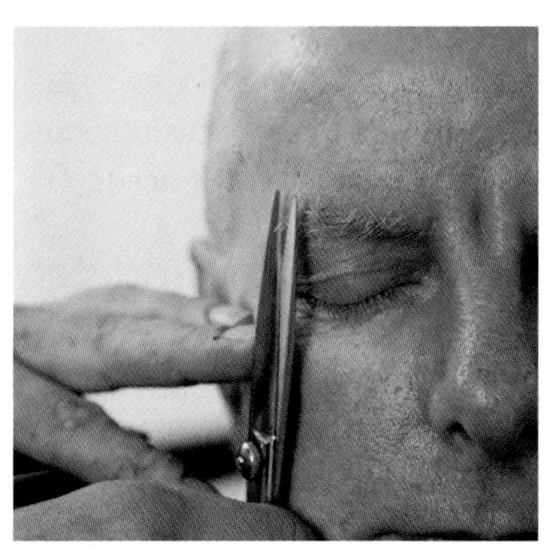

STEP 2 – Using freehand, remove any stray long eyebrow hairs.

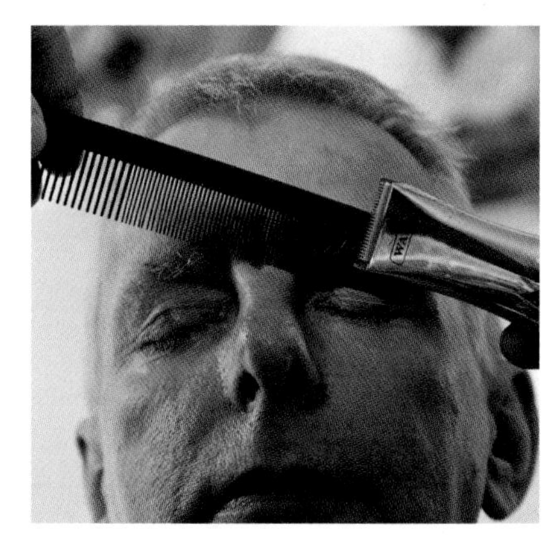

STEP 3 – Comb up and down the eyebrow to cut any stray long eyebrow hairs.

HANDY HINT

To ensure client comfort when removing eyebrow hair, make sure you protect your client's eyes by asking him to keep his eyes closed throughout the eyebrow trim.

ACTIVITY

State ways you can protect the environment when cutting men's hair.

Create basic outlines and detailing design in hair

You will use and adapt different techniques to create designs and detailing to achieve a variety of looks; these may include straight lines, repeated lines, curves and hairline outlines.

To maximise the design's potential, when positioning the design you must consider:

- the **contour** of your client's head
- any growth patterns
- any scarring or scar tissue
- the hair's density.

KEY TERM

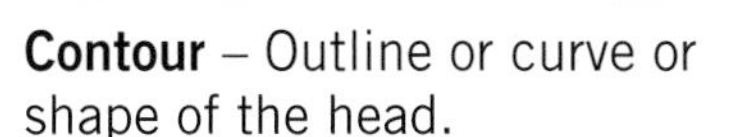

Contour – Outline or curve or shape of the head.

▲ Agree the image design to created

HANDY HINT

Having discussed with your client his requirements and identified any factors that may affect the desired result you are ready to agree and finalise the design.

HANDY HINT

When you are agreeing your design artwork you can work freehand, but it is best to create and use a stencil.

KEY TERMS

Commercially viable – to make a profit and remain competitive within the industry.

▲ Aftercare

Plan and agree hair outlines and detailing design with your client

At the start of this service you must:

- research a portfolio of outlines and detailing designs suitable for use with your client. Explore these outlines and detailing designs with your client using relevant visual aids
- ensure you give your client time and encouragement to put forward their own ideas on design and the image they wish to create
- ensure your client is aware of what the agreed service will entail and its likely duration
- double check and confirm your understanding of your client's requirements and base your recommendations on an accurate evaluation of their hair and its potential to achieve the outline and detailing design
- recommend a look that is suitable for your client's perceived image and agree the design with your client, taking into account factors influencing the service
- make sure the service outcomes and likely costs are acceptable to your client and meet their needs.

Create outlines and detailing design in hair

You should:

- aim to complete the service within a **commercially viable** time.
- brush or comb your client's hair in the direction of the natural growth before you begin the design, and regularly do this throughout the service
- position the outline and detailing design to meet the agreed design plan and adapt the size of the outline and detailing design to suit your client's head size, shape and existing haircut
- use suitable cutting techniques to achieve the definition, shape and depth of outline and detailing design required
- make sure you change your own position and that of your client during the service to help you to ensure the accuracy of the cut
- continue to consult with your client during the cutting process to confirm the desired outline and detailing design and overall effect being created. If problems during the design process occur, take suitable action to resolve them and ensure the finished look meets the design agreed with your client. Confirm your client's satisfaction with the finished look.

Provide clients with advice and recommendations on the service(s) provided

Throughout the service and at the end, make sure you give your client advice and recommendations on the service provided. This should include how to maintain the look and the time intervals between services.

STEP BY STEP

Now that you understand the theory and have carried out the consultation and client hair and skin checks, you are ready to learn the different haircuts and start designing!

Outlines and detailing design

You need to cover straight lines, curved lines, repeated lines and hairline designs.

Creating straight and repeated line

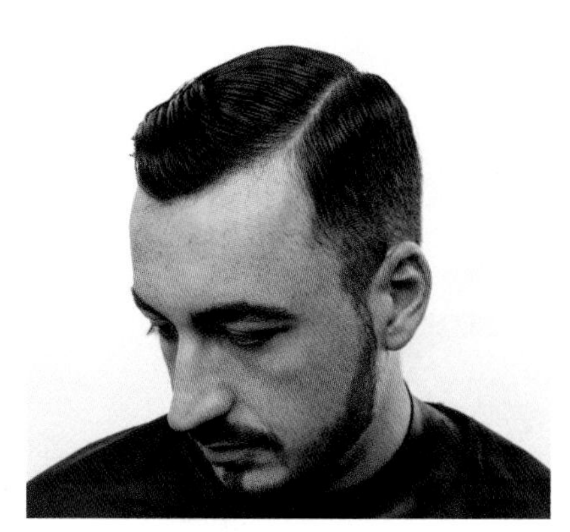

STEP 1 – Gown and protect the client. Prepare the hair with a completed cut to create a canvas for design and then dry the hair.

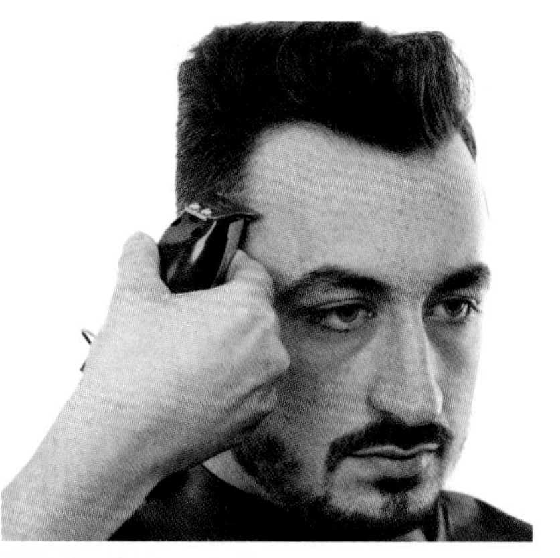

STEP 2 – Holding the T-liners, rest your fingers on the head for support.

STEP 3 – Position the client's head correctly, then starting around the temple area, cut your first line.

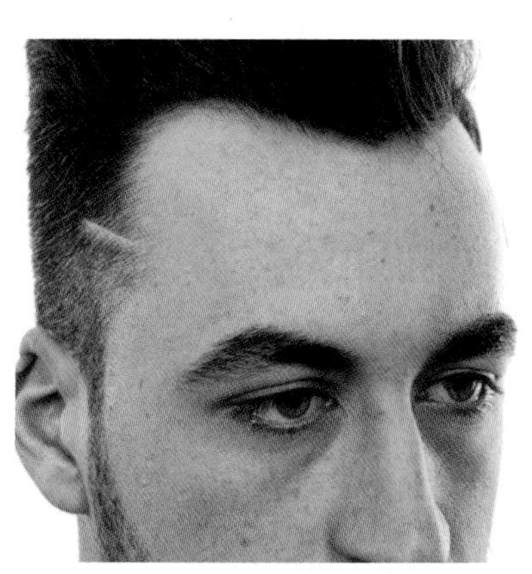

STEP 4 – Go over the cut design line several times to ensure all hairs have been cut and the line is accurate.

STEP 5 – Continue with the design line to increase the length to the width of two clipper lengths.

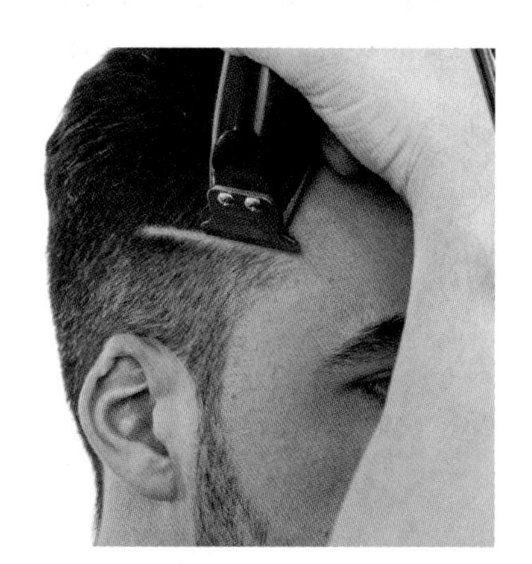

STEP 6 – Turn the T-liners upside down and re-cut to ensure both sides of the line are cut cleanly and sharply.

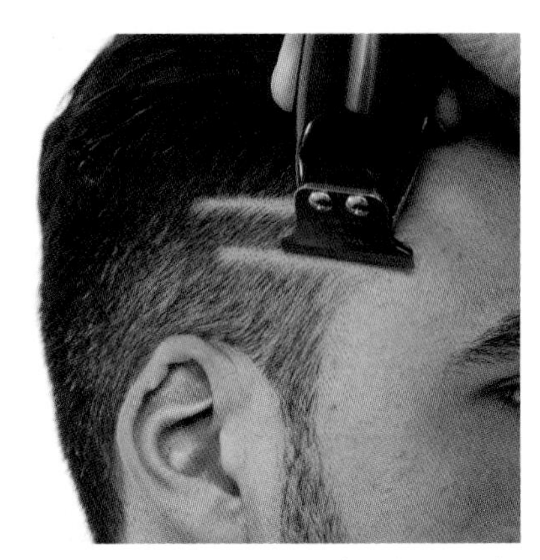

STEP 7 – Repeat a second line 1 cm lower and cut the length.

STEP 8 – Continue the line to the length of one-and-a-half clipper lengths, so the second line is shorter. Repeat with an upside T-liner cut to sharpen the line design and tidy any edges around the hairline.

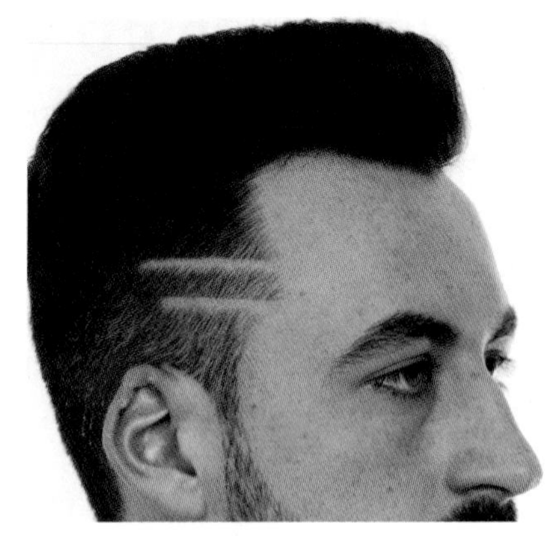

STEP 9 – Apply finishing products and finish.

Creating straight and curved lines

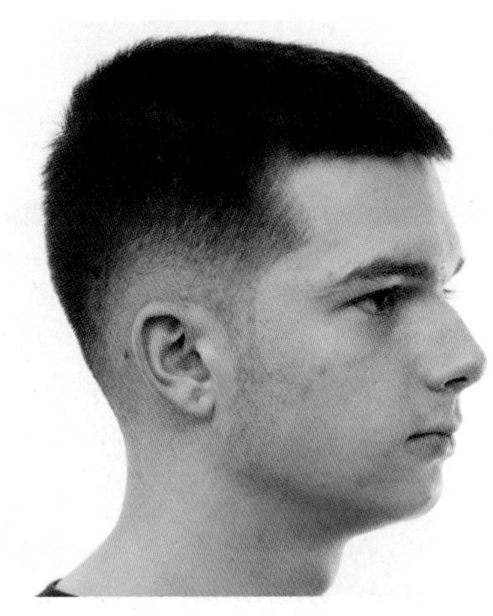

STEP 1 – Gown and protect the client and cut the hair into a style to create a canvas.

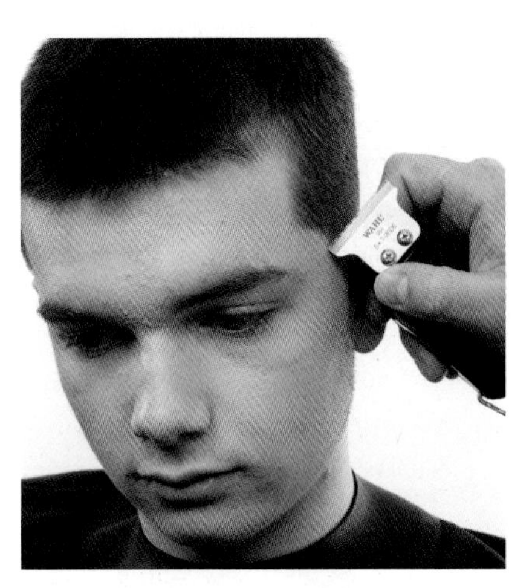

STEP 2 – Use the edge of the T-liner against the head to start the curve design.

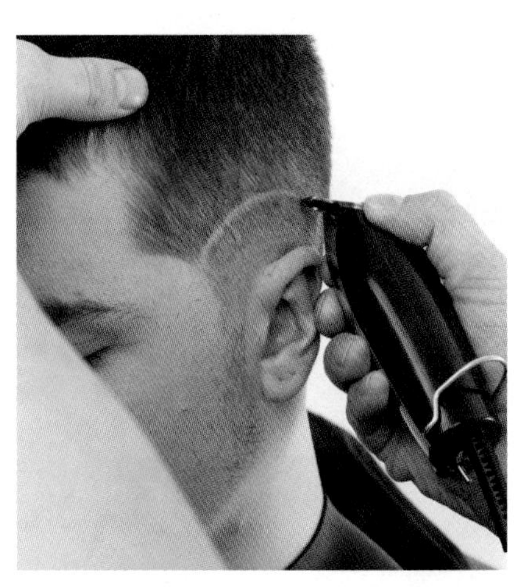

STEP 3 – Create a curved arch over the top of the ear using the edge of the T-liner at all times.

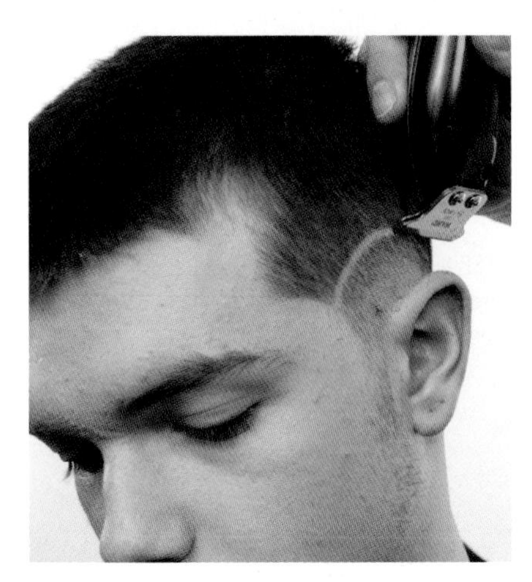

STEP 4 – Repeat the line by turning the T-liners upside down.

STEP 5 – Using the T-liners flat against the head, create an adjoining straight line.

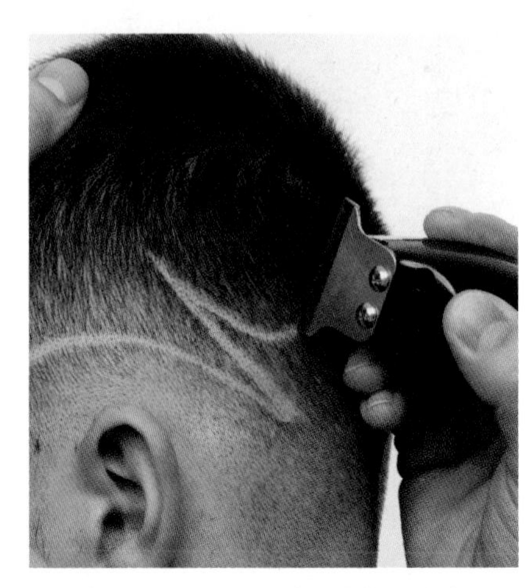

STEP 6 – Using the edge of the T-liner blade, create a curve coming off of the straight line.

STEP 7 – Continue the design with a spiral curve, turning the blades upside down to crisp the edges.

STEP 8 – Sharpen the lines by adjusting the thickness of some of the lines to accentuate the design lines and curves.

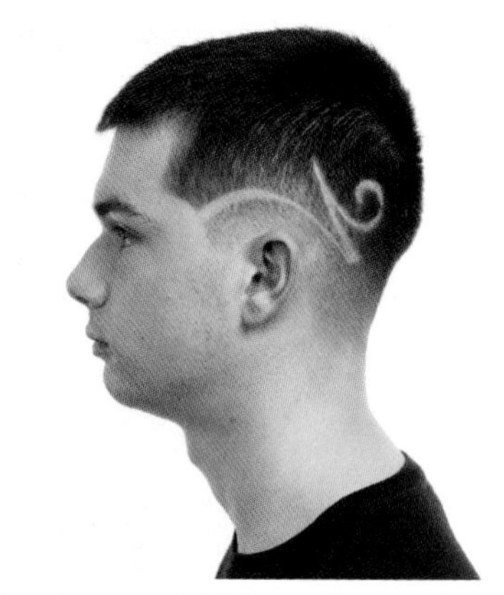

STEP 9 – Apply finishing products such as wax or shine spray to complete the look.

Outlining the hairline

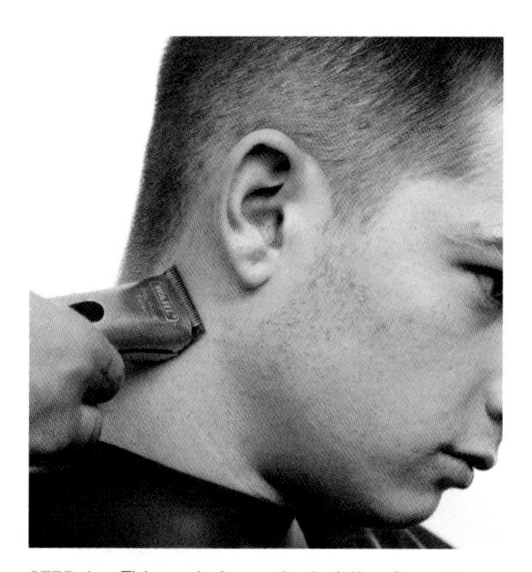

STEP 1 – Tidy and shape the hairline from the neck to the ear.

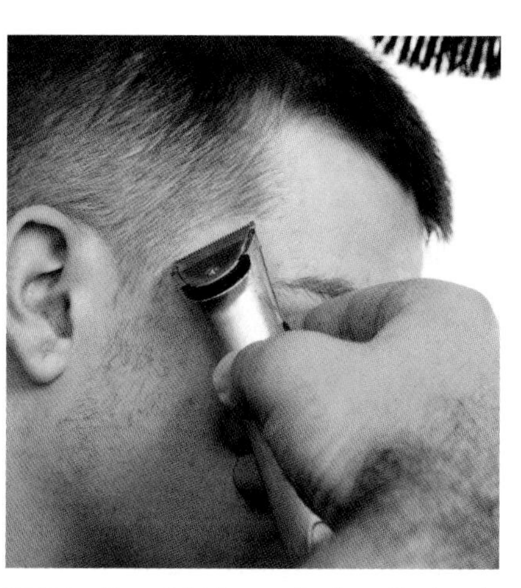

STEP 2 – Use mini trimmers to shape the temple area and tidy the hairline shape.

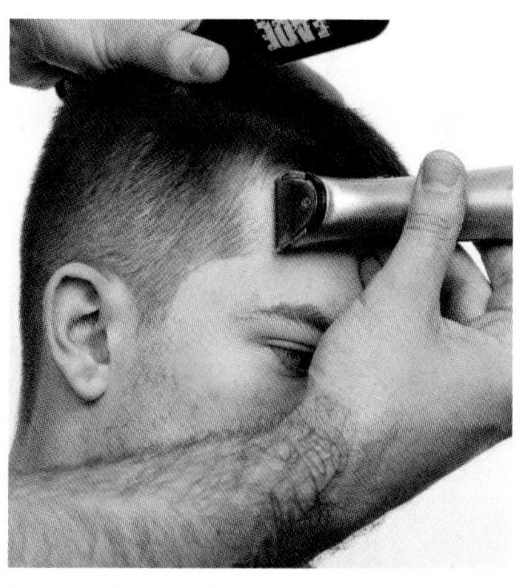

STEP 3 – Create a line or shape to suit the client and style requirements.

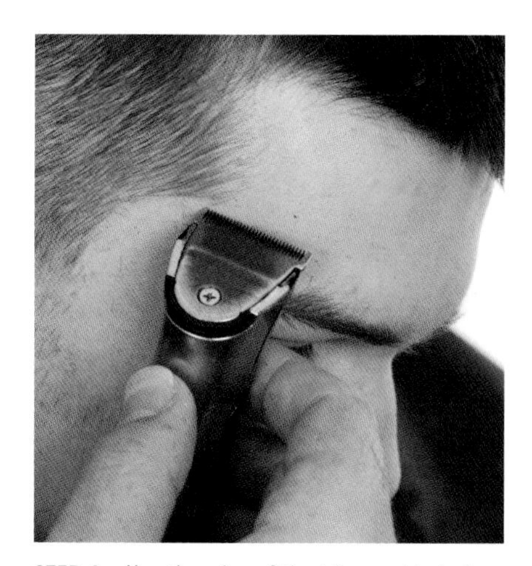

STEP 4 – Use the edge of the trimmer blade for finer details.

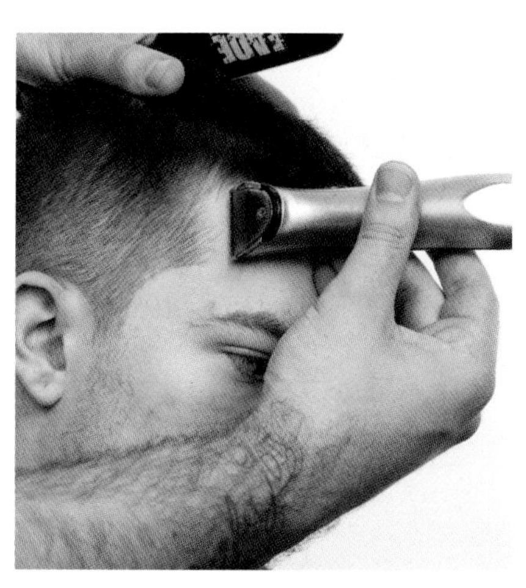

STEP 5 – Continue above the hairline and shape (including the front hairline if required).

STEP 6 – The finished look.

Outlining the hard-parting

STEP 1 – Gown and protect the client and complete a haircut in readiness for outlining the parting. Find the parting to work to and apply grooming wax to hold either side of the parting in place for the cut.

STEP 2 – Start at the front hairline using T-liners directly onto the scalp and supporting with your finger for balance, create your first line.

STEP 3 – Use the first cut as your guide for the next cut.

STEP 4 – Continue with the line, cutting back towards the crown area.

STEP 5 – Refine the edges to sharpen the line.

STEP 6 – The finished look.

Test your knowledge

Question 1

Describe three contra-indications that will prevent the cutting service from being carried out.

Question 2

Describe the characteristics of male pattern baldness.

Question 3

Describe the main cause of male hair loss.

Question 4

You have identified an infectious condition as you start to cut your client's hair. What action should now be taken?

Question 5

What hair growth patterns need to be considered when cutting the back and sides short?

Question 6

Describe how to cross-check your haircut for balance and accuracy.

Question 7

Describe how growth patterns may affect the service.

Multiple choice questions

8 Which of the following is the best way to position a client to achieve a balanced hairstyle?
- a With the neck supported by a neck rest
- b With the legs supported by a footstool
- c With the legs crossed and back firmly supported by the chair
- d With the legs uncrossed and back firmly supported by the chair

9 Which of the following factors can affect the length of the finished style when cutting hair?
- a Elasticity
- b Porosity
- c Density
- d Texture

10 Which of the following should be avoided when a client has a widow's peak?
- a Short nape
- b Clipper cut
- c Fringe
- d Razoring

11 A common clipper grade used for short back and sides is number 2. Which one of the following hair lengths is achieved by using a number 2?
- a 24 mm
- b 18 mm
- c 12 mm
- d 6 mm

12 Which of the following techniques is the best to use when working with the natural fall of the hair?
- a Club cutting
- b Clipper over comb
- c Scissor over comb
- d Freehand

13 Which of the following best describes the technique of fading?
- a Cutting outline shapes in the hairline
- b Blending short layers in the nape area
- c Blending long layers at the crown with short layers at the nape
- d Using freehand around the ears and around the hair growth patterns

14 Which of the following describes a disconnected cut?
- a Joining long and short layers together
- b Long layers with reduced bulk
- c Varying lengths within the cut
- d A softer shape around the sides

15 Which of the following best describe the effects of a thinning technique?

a Reduces bulk while retaining length

b Blends shorter hair into the neckline

c Creates straight lines and retains thickness

d Creates unblended lengths

16 Which of the following can be caused by regularly cutting close to the skin during detailing services?

a Impetigo and hair damage

b Calluses and in–growing hairs

c Pediculosis capitis and alopecia

d Male pattern baldness and tinea capitis

17 Which of the following is the main cause of male pattern baldness?

a Stress

b Tension on the follicles

c Heredity

d Psoriasis

CHAPTER 6

STYLE AND FINISH HAIR USING A RANGE OF TECHNIQUES TO ACHIEVE A VARIETY OF LOOKS

Hannah Stoneham – Strangeways Hair Salon

Being an Apprentice is great, not only are you earning, you are building a career by learning a trade. I have grown so much by taking every opportunity given to me and soaking up as much education as I can.

Starting at Strangeways salon while still at school, I went on to achieve both Level 2 and Level 3 NVQ Apprenticeships. I then completed my salon's vardering programme and graduated to the floor. I have also qualified as a Tutor and Assessor, so can now pass on my knowledge and experience.

To get the most from your Apprenticeship, I would advise you to plan – planning, knowing what you need and how to get there is key! By showing that you are hungry for it, you will fly and, though you'll make mistakes, it's fine as it's how you correct them that defines you. I really hit a wall when I got to my Level 3, as I was just itching to become a stylist on the salon floor. They say good things come to those who wait and that is so true – I wouldn't be as confident as I am now doing restyles and colour changes if I hadn't stuck it out. Hairdressing is a thriving industry and it takes skill and determination but it is also one of the most rewarding. Doing a Hairdressing Apprenticeship opens so many doors from teaching and assessing, cruise ship work, session work and travelling. As they say, the world is your oyster!

I love teaching and moulding the next generation. No two days or clients are ever the same and this is what I love so much about my job. You never get bored in this industry.

I've had so many highs during my career – I won the Junior of the Year British Hairdressing Business Awards, 1st place in the Jet Goes Live Hair Competition, and I've been nominated for Stylist of the Year at the British Business Awards 2017. I've also assisted in a photoshoot for Fudge and judged local competitions.

Gaining your Apprenticeship is all about taking the opportunities made available to you. Remember when you are in the salon, watch as much as you can – you'll pick up tips and tricks from just watching senior members of the team doing clients' hair. A smile goes a long way, nobody wants a grumpy hairdresser! I would say that one of the biggest things within our industry is not only your skill but how you present yourself. You will meet all sorts of different clients along the way – some that just want to zone out and relax to some that want to off-load and tell you everything. Above all, being approachable and friendly goes a long way!

This chapter maps to:

- Unit 4 Style and finish hair using a range of techniques to create a variety of looks (Level 2 Diploma for Hair Professionals – Hairdressing)

INTRODUCTION

The styling and finishing of men and women's hair usually completes and complements the overall service. If the hair has just been cut or coloured, the styling and finishing procedure presents the cut and colour to the client in the best way.

Creatively setting and dressing hair can be very exciting and rewarding. It gives you the chance to be imaginative and produce a variety of different looks. Current setting techniques are at the forefront of fashion; setting long hair can create a base for hair up styles or produce the end look of soft curls as well as catwalk styles. Creative setting gives you the chance to have fun, show off your artistic flair and your dressing skills!

It is essential that the overall finish is satisfactory to your client and they are advised on how to maintain their style between salon visits.

You will use a variety of products and tools to create the looks while combining techniques such as styling/finger drying and finishing, setting, dressing, plaiting/braiding and twisting as well as using additional hair.

After reading this chapter you will:

- understand how health and safety policies and procedures affect styling and finishing services
- know how to blow-dry and finger dry hair into shape
- be able to creatively set and dress hair
- be able to work with temporary added hair
- know how to finish hair.

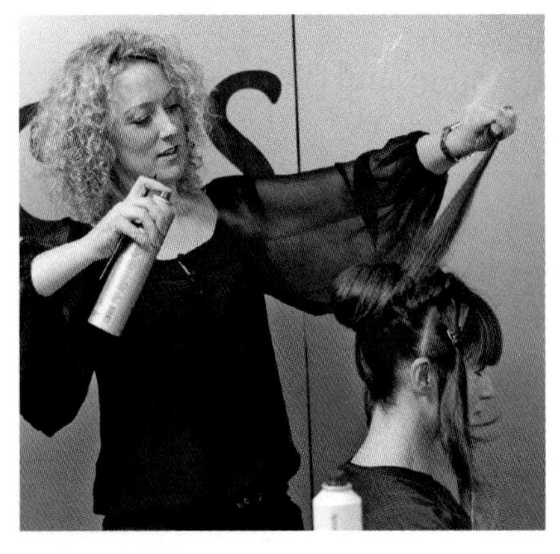

▲ Stylist applies hairspray to provide a lasting finish to a style

HEALTH AND SAFETY POLICIES AND PROCEDURES

As with all services, health and safety policies and procedures affect styling and finishing services. It is important that your clients and salon visitors are kept safe at all times.

The main Acts covered during styling and finishing services include:

- Health and Safety at Work Act – maintain health and safety before, during and throughout the service; gown and protect your clients and take care with setting and styling equipment
- Control of Substances Hazardous to Health Regulations (COSHH) – follow the manufacturer's instructions when using and handling styling and finishing products, wear gloves, and store and dispose of products correctly

- Electricity at Work Regulations – use electricity safely and check electrical appliances before use; ensure hairdryer vents are cleaned and hair free, and heated styling equipment (such as straightening irons) are free from products which will burn when switched on
- Environmental Protection Act – avoid wasting energy and switch off dryers and heated appliances when not in use. Do not waste products, use sparingly and dispose of waste correctly, recycling where possible.

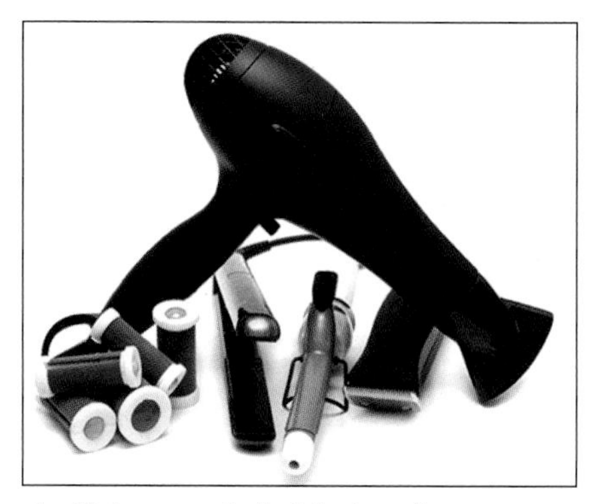

▲ Make sure all electrical appliances are safe to use

HEALTH AND SAFETY

Refer to Chapter 1 for a recap on the health and safety legislation you must follow when styling and finishing hair.

Prepare your client for styling and finishing services

During the styling, setting and dressing services make sure that you maintain a good posture and keep your back straight with your legs slightly apart for an even balance. A good posture will help to prevent back injuries and stylist fatigue. Keep your trolley to the correct side of you – right-hand side if you are right-handed and left-hand side if you are left-handed. This will help you work safely, effectively and methodically, as it prevents you having to stretch over for tools and equipment.

Shampooing and conditioning the hair prior to starting styling or wet setting prepares the hair in readiness for the service. Styling or setting products are then applied to towel-dried hair. Remove any excess moisture from the hair prior to styling or setting to prevent discomfort to your client and to ensure the service is carried out in a timely manner.

To ensure your client's comfort, make sure their feet are supported on a footstep, if the stylist chair is raised, or flat on the floor. Sit them upright with their back against the chair. It is important that your client is comfortable throughout the service and evenly balanced, so you can produce a balanced hairstyle.

Importance of personal hygiene and presentation

It is important that your appearance and hygiene meet the requirements of your salon and industry standards. When styling hair and using the hairdryer, you will get hot and you may perspire, so make sure your personal hygiene is of a high standard and wear loose fitting clothing.

THE HAIR PROFESSIONAL AT WORK

Your salon image is invaluable, so always look your best. Poor standards of hygiene, health or image can cause offence to others, cross-contaminate and present a poor salon reputation.

HANDY HINT

For more information on appearance, personal hygiene and behaviour, refer to Chapter 1.

Describe hazards and risks

There are many hazards and risks in the salon which can pose a potential risk to you and your clients and affect services, as shown in the table below.

Hazards which exist in your workplace	Potential risks	Safe working practices which you must follow
Use of substances – styling and finishing products	Damage to hair if used incorrectly Dermatitis Allergic reactions	Follow instructions and use substances correctly. Wear gloves to protect your hands. If gloves are not worn ensure you rinse styling products from your hands, so they are not dried into your skin throughout the working day. Ask your clients about any allergies they may have.
Use of electricity	Damage to hair/skin Electric shock	Know how to use electrical appliances. Follow the MFIs and visually check equipment before use. Check the heat setting is suitable for the hair type and condition of hair. Use with dry hands only. Do not overload sockets.
Slippery surfaces	Risk of injury from slipping over	Check floor areas for spillages and mop up if required. Styling products are often oily and cause slippery surfaces, so clean the floor area if you identify a slippery surface. Display a warning sign.
Trip hazards	Risk of injury from falling over	Remove any trip hazards such as wires from dryers and heated styling equipment (tongs/irons) from around your workstation.

HANDY HINT

Remember dermatitis can be recognised by inflamed skin, which may be red and sore, and the skin can weep and split.

Promote environmental and sustainable working practices

Throughout the service you should promote environmental and sustainable working practices by reducing and managing waste. Dispose of waste correctly, particularly empty hairspray cans as these are pressurised containers and could explode. Use products cost effectively and use the correct amounts; recycle or refill where possible. Reduce energy wastage and turn off electricity when appliances are not in use. Use your time effectively and avoid time wasting because time is money!

▲ Contact dermatitis

Waste disposal methods

You should recycle styling and finishing products where possible. Some products may be refillable, reducing the amount going into landfill. You must dispose of empty containers in the correct manner. Look at the back of the container for any written instructions or follow the symbols shown below.

Green Dot

The Green Dot (sometimes black and white or colourless) symbol does not necessarily indicate that the packaging can be recycled. It is a European symbol used on packaging to signify that the manufacturer has made a contribution towards the recycling of packaging.

Litter bin symbol

This symbol reminds us to be a good citizen and dispose of the container in the correct manner and not to litter the environment.

Mobius Loop

The Mobius Loop recycling symbol is one of the most widespread recycling symbols used and indicates that the container is recyclable. Although your local recycling facility may not recycle it, it can be recycled where such facilities exist. Your salon should check with your local authority if they can handle that material. Sometimes you will see a percentage figure in the middle of the loop which indicates how much of the packaging contains recycled material.

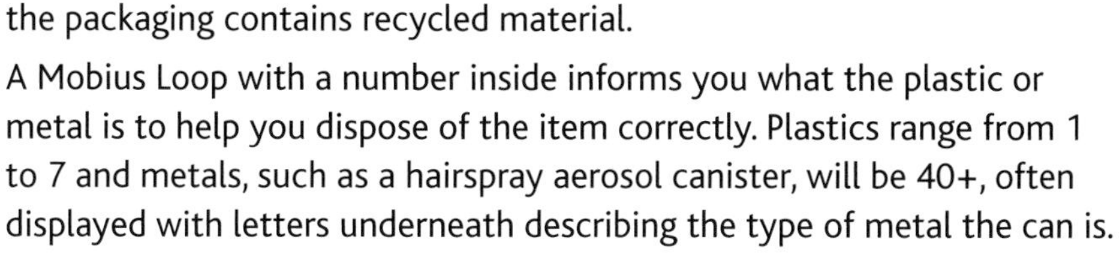

A Mobius Loop with a number inside informs you what the plastic or metal is to help you dispose of the item correctly. Plastics range from 1 to 7 and metals, such as a hairspray aerosol canister, will be 40+, often displayed with letters underneath describing the type of metal the can is.

plastic symbols explained

The chart below will help you identify different types of plastics to make recycling a little easier!

Symbol	Polymer type	Examples	Recyclable?
1 PETE	PET Polyethylene Terepthalate	Fizzy drinks Mineral water bottles Squashes Cooking oils	✓ Recycling points are located throughout the UK
2 HDPE	HDPE High Density Polyethylene	Milk bottles Juice bottles Washing up liquid Bath & shower bottles	✓ Recycling points are located throughout the UK
3 V	PVC Polyvinyl Chloride	Usually in bottle form however not that common these days	✓ Some Recycling points in the UK
4 LDPE	LDPE Low Density Polyethylene	Many types of packaging are made from these materials, for example, plastic formed around meats and vegetables.	Due to the mixture of compounds these plastic types are hard to recycle and not generally recycled in the UK
5 PP	PP Polypropylene		
6 PS	PS Polystyrene		
7 OTHER	OTHER All other resins and multi-materials		

For information about where to recycle different types of materials please check out the bank locator on recycle-more.co.uk.

www.recycle-more.co.uk please recycle me after use

ACTIVITY

Look at your salon range of products. Using the internet, do some research into which plastics and metals can be recycled by your local authority. Do not forget an aerosol canister often has a plastic lid, which will be recyclable too.

HEALTH AND SAFETY

Do not throw away an aerosol can that is not empty as it can be very dangerous. Aerosol cans are pressurised and they could explode if they are exposed to high heat or flattened. This could happen in the waste truck, which could cause injuries.

Importance of a clean and tidy work area

You must keep your work area clean and tidy at all times. Working safely, cleanly and tidily minimises risk of harm and injury to yourself and others and prevents cross-contamination. It also gives the client an image of professionalism while their hair is being styled.

Make sure that your trolley and work station are prepared for the required styling or setting service and that you are ready for the client to arrive. The salon should be prepared with a supply of clean gowns and towels for the services ahead.

HANDY HINT

Always keep an eye on your surrounding areas as well as your client. Check the area is safe to work in and does not put you or your client at risk of harm.

HANDY HINT

Cross-infection and cross-infestation are caused by poor hygiene and cross-contamination. The spread of germs from one person or surface to another will spread infections, while tools that have not been sterilised correctly could lead to cross-infestation.

HEALTH AND SAFETY

Cross-infection and cross-infestation will upset clients, create a bad reputation for the salon and could lead to a loss of business.

▲ Use a steriliser spray to keep work surfaces infection free

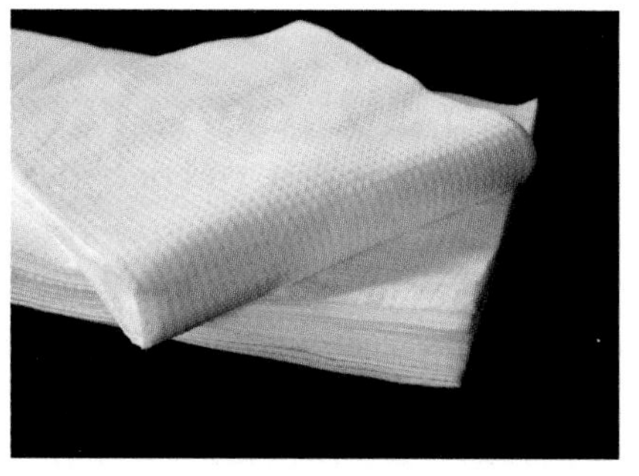

▲ Always use a clean gown and towels

HEALTH AND SAFETY

Refer back to Chapter 1 for more information on sterilisation.

Importance of consulting with clients

You must always complete a thorough consultation with your client to identify their requirements, decide on the most suitable tools and equipment to use, and ensure you achieve the desired result.

Ask questions such as:

- How do they want they hair styled?
- Do they want height, lift, body, curls or a smooth style?
- Do they have a parting and, if so, which side?
- How often do they style their hair at home?
- What products and tools do they use at home?
- What is the reason for having their hair styled – a special occasion or work function?

When questioning your clients you can find out if they have any concerns. Always check the hair and scalp for any potentially contagious **ailments**.

▲ Consult with your client

KEY TERM

Ailment – condition/disease/illness.

BLOW-DRY AND FINGER DRY HAIR INTO SHAPE

Your clients may have their hair styled for a special occasion or at the end of a hairdressing service to complete the look.

You will need to be able to blow-dry hair on a variety of hair types and lengths, including very curly, curly, wavy and straight hair, above- and below-shoulder lengths, and layered or one-length looks.

Finger drying

You will also need to be able to finger dry hair, which can create movement, volume and/or curls.

When finger drying hair, you must ensure you achieve the required amount of volume, movement and/or curl. You should massage the root area in the direction in which the lift and volume are required. Applying products at the root area will support the style.

▲ Finger dried hair

▲ Diffuser drying hair

Short hair can be styled using a hand-held hairdryer and using your hands and fingers as the tools. This works particularly well for hair with movement and texture, requiring a finished look that is modern and funky. Your choice of styling products will influence the end result, as support from the product is required.

Using attachments – diffuser drying

Hair with movement, curl or body can be scrunch-dried with a diffuser attachment. This technique works particularly well with medium to longer hair lengths. You should use curl-activating products to enhance curls and movement, and to support the style.

Physical effects of setting on the hair structure

To understand the physical effects that blow-drying, finger drying and heated styling processes have on the hair structure, you first have to understand the basic science of hair.

Hair is mostly composed of a hardened fibrous protein called keratin. Keratin is made up of amino acids and peptide bonds which originate in the hair follicle. These many amino acids and peptide bonds form the **polypeptide** chains (coils). The polypeptide chains are held together by permanent and temporary bonds inside the cortex layer of the hair.

KEY TERM

Polypeptide – this word is derived from poly (many) and peptos (broken down).

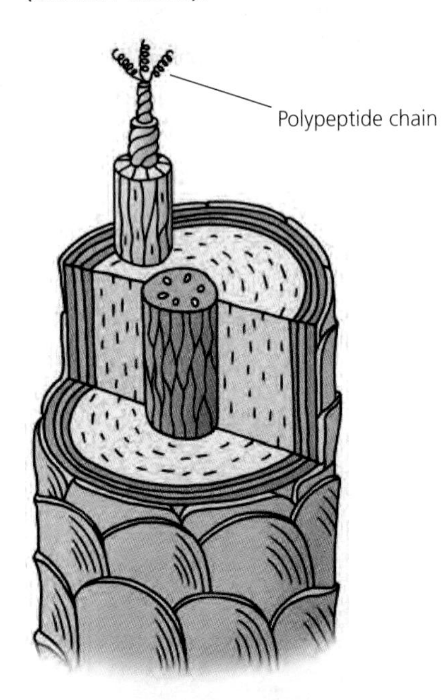

▲ Polypeptide chains inside the cortex of the hair

Bonds in the hair

Hair can be naturally curly, wavy or straight. It is held in its natural state by the permanent and temporary bonds. The permanent bonds are called disulphide bonds and the temporary bonds are called hydrogen or salt bonds.

Permanent bonds

These bonds are broken by chemicals, such as perm solution, and can be changed from naturally straight to chemically curly. The permanent disulphide bonds are shown in the hydrogen diagram as S–S.

Temporary bonds

The temporary bonds are weakened and softened by the styling of hair and they temporarily change the natural state from straight to curly, or wavy to straight.

The temporary hydrogen bonds are shown as H–O and the salt bonds are shown as – and +.

The flow chart below shows the make-up of the hair.

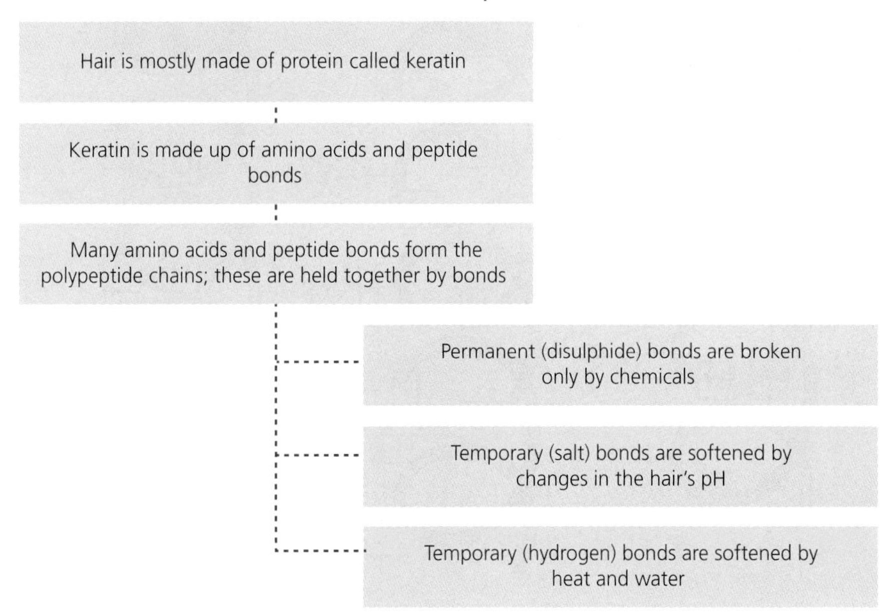

Salt bonds

The salt bonds are weak bonds that are temporarily softened by changes in pH by the use of weak acids or alkalis. They are reformed by normalising the pH.

Hydrogen bonds

The main bonds that are broken when styling the hair are the hydrogen bonds. These are broken by heat or water and hardened by drying or cooling the hair. Hydrogen bonds give the hair its strength and its flexibility to move freely; it is what makes the hair elastic. Well-conditioned hair with a strong cortex can stretch up to a further half of its original length when wet; this is due to the temporary breaking of the hydrogen bonds.

Alpha and beta keratin

Hair in its natural state of curly, wavy or straight is described as being in an alpha keratin state. When hair has been wetted, stretched and dried into a new shape it is described as being in a beta keratin state.

Heat from styling equipment, such as tongs and straightening irons, can also change the state from alpha keratin to beta keratin when the hair has cooled into its new shape. The temporary bonds that are changed during the heat styling process are hydrogen bonds (shown as H–O) and salt bonds (shown as – and +).

The permanent bonds that are changed during a perming or relaxing process are called disulphide bonds and are shown in the diagram below as S–S.

The following diagram shows the polypeptide chains and how the permanent and weak temporary bonds hold the hair together. When styling or setting the hair, the hydrogen (H–O) bonds are broken and reformed.

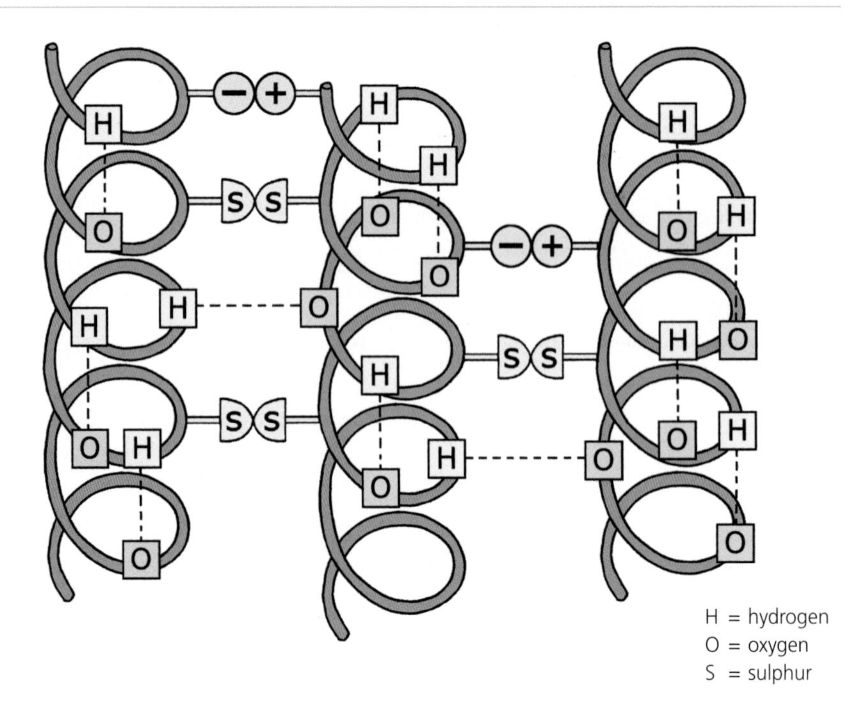

▲ Hydrogen (H–O), disulphide (S–S) and salt (+ and –) bonds

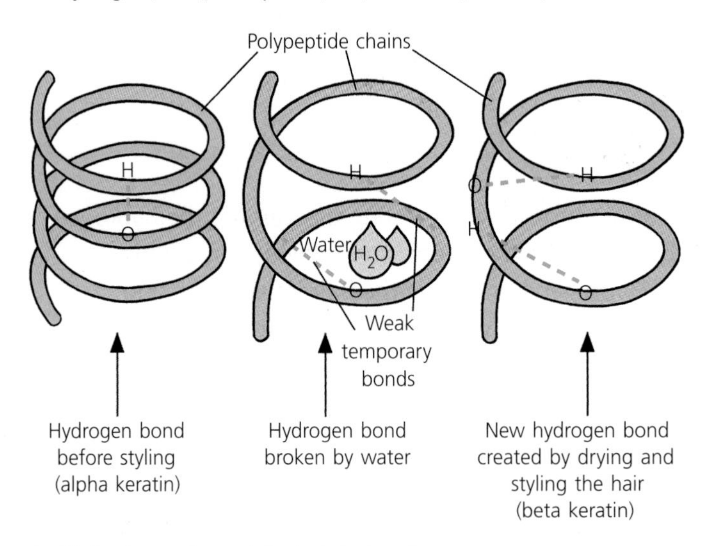

▲ State change from alpha to beta keratin

HANDY HINT

The weak temporary hydrogen bonds are softened by water and heat, and hardened by drying and cooling of the hair.

HANDY HINT

Remember hair in its natural state is in an alpha keratin state; when wetted, stretched and dried, its new state is beta keratin.

Effects of humidity on hair

Hair is **hygroscopic**, which means it can absorb moisture from the atmosphere. The finished hairstyle is therefore affected by the humidity and moisture present in the air. The hair absorbs the moisture from the air and the beta keratin state changes back to alpha keratin, because the moisture softens the temporary hydrogen bonds and the hair reverts back to its original state.

KEY TERM

Hygroscopic – absorbs moisture

HANDY HINT

Humidity returns the hair to the alpha keratin state by adding moisture from the air.

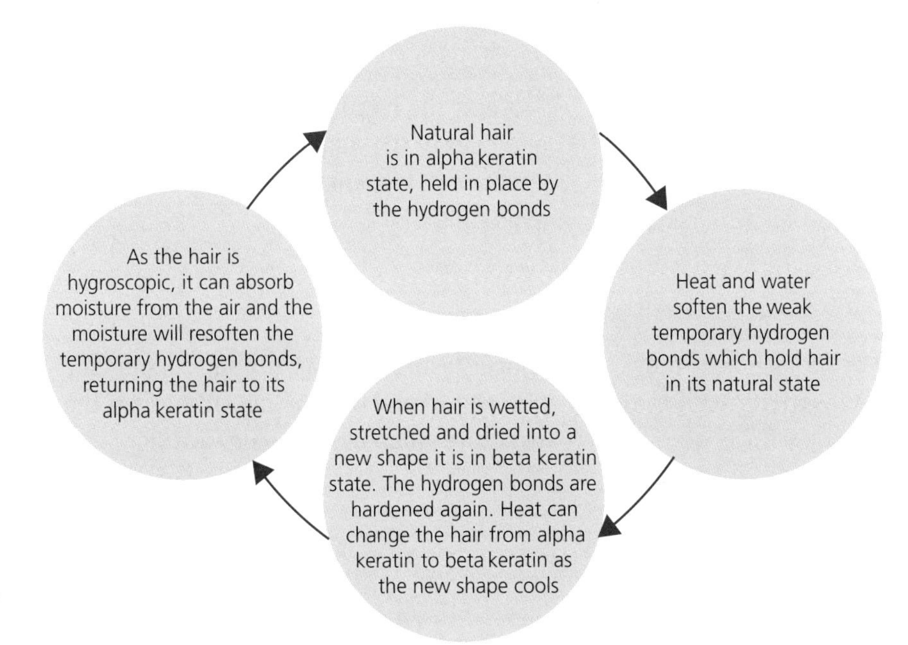

▲ The alpha to beta keratin process

Keep hair damp during the drying process

Each client's hair will dry out at a different rate, and, as wet hair stretches allowing a new shape to form, an even moisture balance is required. If areas of the hair have started to dry during the styling process, then hair will lose its elasticity and the ability to stretch sufficiently, so the result may be uneven. You must mist the hair sections lightly with a water spray if you notice an uneven elasticity when drying the hair, to allow the bonds to be reformed evenly into their new position.

Products used for styling and finishing hair

There are hundreds of different styling and finishing products available on the market to help the stylist and client maintain great-looking hair. They are all marketed differently to attract various client groups to their designs. The instructions on the product advise you and the client how to use the product effectively and how much of the product should be used. Always read the manufacturer's instructions (MFIs) to ensure you use the correct amount to achieve the best result, to prevent overloading the hair and to protect the environment.

Styling (and wet setting) products

You are likely to use different products for styling and setting the hair. Some products are designed to be used only on wet hair, some only on dry hair, and some are suitable for both wet and dry hair.

The following table shows which products should be used to achieve the most effective result for styling *wet* hair.

HANDY HINT

Keeping the hair misted and with even moisture balance helps you to produce a smooth, even effect when blow-drying the hair.

HANDY HINT

Sectioning and securing hair out of the way prevents the hair from drying too quickly and disturbing the areas that you are working on.

HANDY HINT

Refer to Chapter 1 for more information on the importance of adhering to instructions.

HANDY HINT

The products you use for wet styling are exactly the same for wet setting techniques.

Product	How to use	Effect achieved and benefit to the client
Heat protector	Spray evenly through towel-dried hair, or prior to using heated styling equipment.	Protects the hair from the drying effects and heat of the hairdryer and heated appliances. Prevents frizz and gives an even finish.
Blow-dry/setting lotion Blow-dry lotion Setting lotion	Spray or sprinkle near the root area and work through to the ends.	Longer-lasting volume, lift and support for fine hair of any length. Can strengthen the structure when blow-drying/setting.
Mousse/activators	Apply a golf-ball-sized amount to towel-dried hair and comb through evenly.	Enhances curls and offers support and hold to hair blow-dried with a radial brush, or set with rollers.
Cream	Rub a liberal amount between your palms and distribute evenly throughout the hair.	Provides flexible body and pliable style support. Adds definition, control and texture to shorter hair lengths, eliminates frizz and maintains moisture.
Gel	Use on damp hair and distribute evenly through the hair before blow-drying, finger drying or setting.	Provides volume and texture for all hair lengths and hair types.
Serum	After shampooing, rub two to five drops of serum into your palms and apply to wet hair, distributing evenly.	Ultra-shine finish for all styles and hair types. Enhances coloured hair and provides an anti-frizz effect by coating the hair with a smoothing liquid which forms a barrier to moisture.
Anti-frizz lotion/moisturiser	Distribute evenly through damp hair, dry and style as required.	Achieves a smoother, straighter appearance by taming frizz and curls. It coats the hair and forms a barrier to prevent moisture from humidity affecting the finished look. Ideal for any hair length.

Finishing (and dressing) products

Finishing/dressing products are applied to *dried* hair and are designed to support the finished look and give the style **longevity**.

The table shows which finishing products are recommended to achieve longer-lasting effects. (Note: this information is the same for dressing techniques, which are covered later in this chapter.)

KEY TERM

Longevity – long-lasting effects, durable.

Finishing or dressing product	How to use	Effect achieved and benefit to the client
Heat protector	Spray onto clean, dry hair before using heated appliances.	Provides a protective shield or film over the outside of the cuticle scales and protects the hair from the heat of the appliance. Ideal for all hair lengths.
Hairspray	Shake well and spray on the hair from about 20 cm away.	Finishes the style with a shine and long-lasting shape, leaving the hair touchable and without stiffness. The spray forms a barrier to prevent absorption of moisture. Ideal for medium to longer hair lengths.
Cream/paste	Apply using your fingertips, moving from root to point to create texture and movement.	Adds definition and texture to shorter hair lengths and supports, lifts and adds shine and body to medium or longer hair.
Gel	Massage a small amount into your palms and work evenly into the hair, shaping and moulding into shape with your fingers.	For stronger-hold looks. Gel can provide an elastic effect, causing the hair to bounce back into style.
Serum	Rub two to five drops of serum into your palms and apply to dry hair, distributing evenly before straightening.	To calm frizzy hair and flyaway ends, and protect hair from heated appliances by coating the hair to form a protective barrier.

Finishing or dressing product	How to use	Effect achieved and benefit to the client
Wax	Apply with your hands and fingertips through the hair, avoiding the root area. For funky, messy looks, apply using your palms and target the ends of the hair.	For soft, supple hold and great shine. Ideal for short hair.
Gloss	After drying, lightly mist the hair or apply cream gloss with your fingertips, avoiding the root area.	Optimal shine, texture and condition – ideal for medium to longer hair lengths.

HANDY HINT

Using too much product is wasteful and the salon will lose profit; excessive use of products can also overload the hair, affecting the end result.

ACTIVITY

In pairs, identify your salon's product range for styling hair and list the benefits to the client. Describe how each product should be used.

HANDY HINT

Use the correct quantity of product to avoid overloading the hair and choose the correct product to achieve the best result.

HANDY HINT

Always replenish stock without causing a disruption to the client's service and report shortages to the relevant person.

ACTIVITY

Wella Curl Craft wax mousse comes in a 200 ml container.

1 If you waste 8 ml of this product on every client and use this on 12 clients per week, how much product would you waste every week?
2 How many full containers of Curl Craft Wax would you waste in a three-month period?
3 If the product costs the salon £6.20 + VAT, how much money has been wasted?

Choose suitable styling and finishing products

You must confirm the finished look your client requires so that you can choose the most suitable products, tools and equipment to achieve the best result.

Make sure you use suitable styling products for wet or dry styling/setting. When you are using heated appliances you must use products that protect the hair from heat and prevent damage. Always follow manufacturer's instructions when using styling and finishing products.

HANDY HINT

Ask a stylist in your salon what finishing products they are using when styling, dressing and finishing the hair and why they have chosen these products. This will help you to understand your salon's range of products.

Directions: Spray 10-12 inches from dry hair to finish the look.
Layer more spray for stronger control.
Instantly brush it away to shape and reshape.

Caution: This product is flammable.

▲ Always follow MFIs

Equipment used for styling and finishing hair

When styling and finishing hair you will use a variety of tools and equipment, such as brushes and combs, hand-held hairdryers, straightening irons or curling tongs.

Always ensure your equipment is in good working order and fit for use. Use equipment correctly, following the MFIs to minimise damage to the tools and prevent any risk of injury to you and your clients. Maintain the condition of your tools and prevent a reduction in their performance by cleaning them regularly and keeping them free from product build-up and hair. Before plugging in and switching on your hairdryer, check that it is safe to use and the air vent filter is attached and clean.

The table below shows the tools and equipment available for use.

Tools and equipment	Use
Wide-toothed comb	To detangle the hair before styling/ setting – comb through from point to root.
Cutting comb	To cleanly section the hair when styling.
Denman brush (flat)	To create a smooth, straight finish, such as a 'bob' style – brush the hair from roots to point.
Vent brush (flat)	To create a textured straight finish – brush the hair from roots to point. To remove roller marks from the set – brush through the dry set to break up the roller pattern.
Small radial brush (round)	To create root lift, volume and small curls in layered hair when styling – hair is wound from points to root.
Medium radial brush (round)	To create root lift and medium curls in short- to medium-layered hair, and waves in longer hair when styling – hair is wound from points to root.

Tools and equipment	Use
Large radial brush (round)	To smooth and straighten, and create soft waves in longer hair when styling – hair is smoothed and straightened as the brush is moved through the roots to points under tension.
Rake attachment	To blow-dry African type/very curly hair straight – rake is used to lift the tightly curled hair into place as the hair is dried.
Hand-held hairdryer	To dry the hair during blow-drying.
Diffuser attachment	To aid finger drying and encourage curls and lift in curly or wavy hair – the diffuser aids heat but limits the blast of hair flow, allowing the heat to dry the curls more naturally and the hands to position the curls into place.
Nozzle attachment	To direct the airflow and heat from the hairdryer – the airflow is directed from roots to points to smooth the cuticle layers and promote shine.
Straightening irons	To smooth and straighten dried hair – hair is moved through the irons from roots to point. To create soft curls on dry hair – hair is curled/twisted through the irons and gently pulled through them from root to point.
Tongs	To create curls and body – hair is wound point to root and curled.
Wands	To create soft curls on long hair – hair is wrapped around the wand from root to point.

Current techniques for blow-drying, finger drying and finishing hair

Current techniques for blow-drying, finger drying and finishing hair are:

- smoothing and straightening the hair – using large radial brushes or flat brushes depending on the texture of the hair
- creating volume – using a large radial brush for root lift and back-combing/brushing techniques
- creating movement – using a radial brush for root lift and movement
- creating curls – using radial brushes and heated appliances such as tongs and wands. Hair can also be placed in a large barrel curl after drying to set the curl in place
- finger-drying – hair is **manipulated** into shape with the hands and dried using a hand-held dryer.

Step-by-step instructions on how to carry out these looks are given at the end of this chapter.

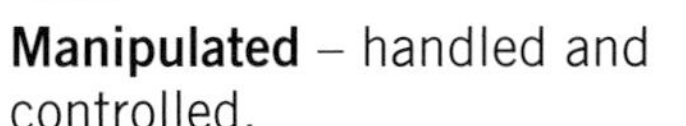

KEY TERM

Manipulated – handled and controlled.

▲ Blow-dried hair

How different factors affect the styling process and the finished look

You must always thoroughly analyse your client's hair and scalp, completing visual checks and relevant hair tests. Feel the hair and carry out a porosity and elasticity test to identify if the hair is porous/non-porous or has strong/weak elasticity.

HANDY HINT

You must carry out a porosity test to identify if the cuticle scales are open, and the hair is therefore porous, and an elasticity test to test the strength of the cortex.

HANDY HINT

For a recap on how to carry out a porosity and elasticity test on the hair, refer to Chapter 1.

THE HAIR PROFESSIONAL AT WORK

Listen to the stylists in your salon consulting with their clients to help you master these valuable skills.

HANDY HINT

Refer back to Chapter 1 for more information on maintaining customer care, personal and professional ethics, identifying and confirming the client's expectations and keeping the client informed and reassured.

Factors that need to be considered when styling, setting and dressing are shown in the diagram.

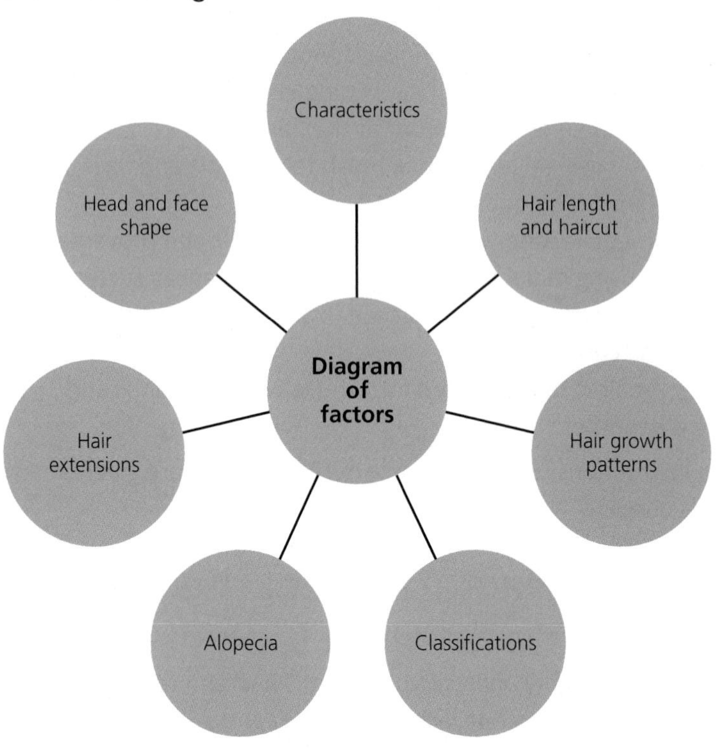

Hair characteristics

Factor	Effect on the styling/setting process and the finished look
Texture – fine Fine hair	You need to consider the length of fine hair, as longer lengths can look thinner and may require gentle back-combing for more support. Fine hair will need less quantity of product. Use products that support the style and give the hair body and volume – even for smooth straight styles. Fine hair will need brushes/rollers to give root lift and support the style. Finger drying with a diffuser may work well if the hair has natural body and movement, or a brush blow-dry for lift. Tonging may help give longevity to curls but take care with the heat settings on fine hair. You may need to use more rollers and smaller sections to give the illusion of thicker hair. When using heated appliances, lower the heat settings.
Texture – coarse Coarse hair	Coarse hair can have a tendency to look rough and dry and may need taming and controlling to ensure the style looks its best. Smoother styles may be difficult for the client to maintain between salon visits. Coarse hair will need more products that smooth the hair and give it shine, such as a serum. Coarse hair will need a bristle brush to smooth the hair, but will not require much root lift. Coarse hair will benefit from smoothing and blow-drying, rather than finger drying. Straighteners can be used to smooth the coarse look of the hair. When using heated appliances, increase the heat setting to help smooth and tame coarse hair.

Density – sparse  Sparse hair	**Sparse** hair should be treated in the same way as fine hair when styling; however, it will dry quicker. Back-combing may be required to aid support within some styles. For sparse hair less product is required and take care not to overload it. Take care with tools and pins on sparse hair and avoid causing your client any discomfort. Avoid excessive heat on sparse hair.
Density – abundant  Abundant hair	**Abundant** hair will take longer to dry and may make the style look big, so an appropriate style needs to be considered. If styling hair into a **chignon**, avoid too much back-combing or back-brushing as this will promote more volume. Abundant hair will need more products – use those that do not provide any volume or lift but help to smooth the hair. Thoroughly dry the root area and take smaller sections of hair; blow-dry towards the ends. Avoid brushes that promote volume and root lift. Avoid root movement that promotes volume and makes hair look thicker. Rollers with pins may help you to control the hair. Extra pins and grips may be required when putting hair up. Always rough-dry abundant hair before sectioning and blow-drying/setting to make effective use of your time and reduce the excess moisture. Use straightening irons to help flatten thick hair if a smooth style is required.
Porosity  Porous hair can tangle and break easily	If the hair is porous it may have a 'fluffy' appearance on the ends and will tangle easily; take care not to catch the hair in the equipment. Avoid 'sticky' products that offer strong hold as the hair will tangle easily. Suggest smoothing products, such as serums. Use heat protectors with heated appliances. You should avoid non-bristle brushes and Velcro rollers as these may cause the hair to snag and break. Use smoothing brushes and wide-toothed combs. Suggest minimal use of heated appliances, as these will cause further worsening of porosity. Nozzles may be suitable, attached to the dryer to encourage the airflow down the hair to help smooth the cuticles. Avoid too much direct heat.
Elasticity 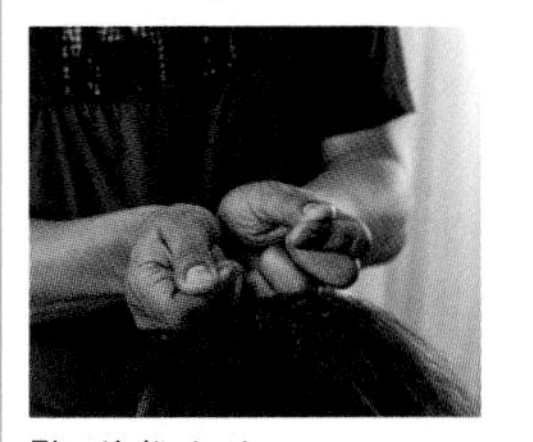 Elasticity test	Weak hair has lost its elasticity and should not be stretched. As above, avoid longer styles and suggest shorter lengths and/or conditioning treatments to improve the condition of the hair's cortex. Follow instructions as for porous hair.
Condition 	Hair that is in bad condition will either have poor porosity or poor elasticity and possibly both – the style may look lacklustre in appearance and be hard to manage. Back-combing or back-brushing may need to be avoided. Follow instructions as for porous hair.

KEY TERMS

Sparse – thinly scattered.
Abundant – great in amount or number.
Chignon – roll of hair, worn at the back of the head.

Hair cut

Factor	Effect on the styling/setting process and the finished look
Hair length 	Longer hair requires more maintenance and can make styling/setting difficult. Longer layers will need to be supported with suitable products and styling tools. More blow-drying is likely to be required on longer hairstyles, and possibly the use of straightening irons or tongs to give long-lasting effects. Ensure the hair is long enough to be put up and meet the client's requirements. More supporting products, such as hairsprays and root lift products, may be required. You must use heat protectors with any heated appliance. Use serums on the ends of the hair. Use less product for shorter hair lengths. More product will be required for longer hair. A variety of brushes may be required to obtain root lift. Large round radial brushes/rollers will help to obtain lift and smooth the hair. Small rollers may get caught in long hair. A good, professional hairdryer would be beneficial to you to speed the drying process time. Nozzles may help when blow-drying to smooth the hair and help direct the heat where it is needed. Straightening irons/tongs or heated rollers can be used, but wet setting techniques will have a longer-lasting effect on the style.
Haircut 	The haircut is very important, as this is how the hair has been cut for the style; you must work with it, not against it. Identify if you are blow-drying or finger drying the hair to achieve the best finished result. If you are setting the hair for a special occasion, check the layer lengths are long enough for the setting roller chosen and the desired look. You should suggest and use products to support the style. Identify if you need root lift, curls and/or volume. Use products to suit the length and condition of hair. Use a radial brush for lift and volume, or a flat brush to smooth and avoid lift. When setting, identify if you will need lift and volume to help decide on roller size and **on-base** or **off-base** setting techniques. Does the result require a set or brush and hairdryer blow-dry, or can you use a diffuser and finger dry? Would a nozzle help you to smooth the hair? Would the style benefit from straightening or tonging for longevity? If using heated appliances, again decide on the most suitable appliance – tongs or heated rollers for curls and lift, straightening irons for straight looks and flat curls.

KEY TERMS

On-base – brush or roller sits directly on top of the section/meche of hair.
Off base – brush or roller is dragged below the section/meche of hair.

Hair growth patterns

Factor	Effect on the styling/setting process and the finished look
Cowlick 	When styling fringes, identify potential problems with cowlicks and widow's peaks. Consider winding techniques to overcome some hair growth patterns. A cowlick affects the fringe area; you may need to advise the client of a more suitable style. When working with a cowlick, use a stronger styling product on the fringe area and a hairspray to hold. Use a brush/roller to smooth and control the cowlick, or work with it when finger drying the hair. Use a nozzle when blow-drying to aim the airflow in the direction you want the cowlick to go. Try using straighteners to hold the cowlick in place, taking care with the heat near the skin. Consider the setting wind direction to aid working with a cowlick.
Nape whorl 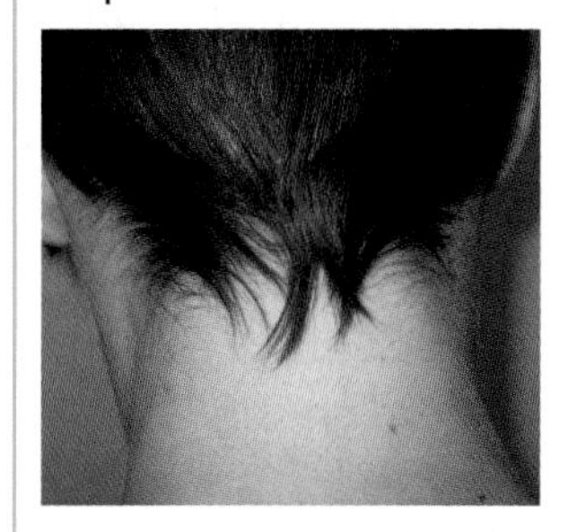	Nape whorls do not cause a problem to longer styles. Consider style direction when dealing with nape whorls on shorter styles, and avoid lift. Use a strong finishing product on a nape whorl if it tries to defeat you. A little hairspray may help too. Use a flat brush and dry into the neck to avoid root lift near the nape whorl. Use a nozzle on the hairdryer to aim the airflow downwards and dry the nape whorl flat. Straighteners will not help you if the hair is short – you will burn the client's neck.
Double crown 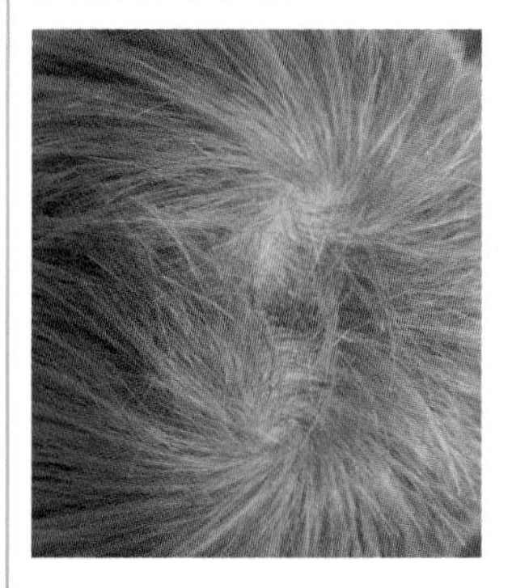	Try to work with double crowns, as they can cause the hair to stick up. Play with the hair and see in which direction it settles the best; use this to recommend to your client the best direction for the style. Use a strong-hold styling product around the crown area and hairspray to hold the finished look. Use a radial brush and direct the airflow to the root, bending the hair into the desired direction. Adjust the roller size if need be on the double crown. Use off-base rolling where needed to avoid additional lift. Use a nozzle with the hairdryer to aim the airflow in the desired direction. If aiming for a funky, messy image, work with the double crown and use it in a finger dry.
Widow's peak 	With a widow's peak, you should avoid fringes and aim for styles where the front section is styled backwards or slightly to one side. Use products to hold and support the hair over or to one side. Use a radial brush/roller to direct the root area over or to one side. Use a nozzle on the hairdryer to aid the direction of the airflow. Diffusers can be used to finger dry and manipulate the hair into the desired direction. Straighteners and irons can also be used – take care near the skin and forehead.

HANDY HINT

Maintaining even porosity when styling the hair is really important, as it will help to avoid tangles and causing discomfort to your client.

HANDY HINT

Always record on a record card the outcome of any tests and your client's verbal responses to any questions asked, in case you need to refer back to the information in the future. This is particularly important if there are any problems and you need evidence of the client's comments.

ACTIVITY

Always write clearly, checking your spellings and accuracy when completing record cards.

Hair classifications

Factor	Effect on the styling/setting process and the finished look
Type 1 Straight hair – fine/thin	Hair tends to be very soft, shiny and oily; it can be difficult to hold a curl. Use products that will aid body and hold. Avoid oily products and do not overload the hair. Use tools that will grip the hair and hold it in place while styling, as it will resist curling. May benefit from using heated styling equipment such as tongs if curl and body is required. Hair will benefit from wet setting prior to dressing the hair.
Type 1 Straight hair – medium	Hair can have lots of volume and body and can be wonderful to work with. Use products to suit style. Use tools to suit style. Use equipment to suit style.
Type 1 Straight hair – coarse	Hair can be extremely straight and difficult to curl. Use curl- or body-enhancing products that will aid body and hold. Use tools that will grip the hair and hold it in place while styling, as it will resist curling. May benefit from using heated styling equipment such as tongs if curl and body are required.
Type 2 Wavy hair – fine/thin	Hair can normally be styled easily and has a definite 'S' pattern. Use products to suit style. Use tools to suit style. Use equipment to suit style.

Factor	Effect on the styling/setting process and the finished look
Type 2 Wavy hair – medium 	Hair tends to be frizzy and a little resistant to styling. Use styling products to smooth frizz and also give hold and movement to the hair. Use tools that will grip the hair and hold it in place, as it will resist styling. May benefit from using heated styling equipment such as tongs or straightening irons to provide longevity to the style.
Type 2 Wavy hair – coarse 	Hair tends to be very resistant to styling and normally very frizzy. The waves are often quite thick. Use products to smooth frizz and control the waves, while providing hold. Use tools that will smooth the frizz and grip the hair, holding it in place, as it will resist styling. May benefit from using heated styling equipment such as tongs or straightening irons to provide longevity to the style.
Type 3 Curly hair – loose curls 	Hair tends to have a combination texture – it can be thick with lots of body, but can sometimes be frizzy. Use products to smooth frizz. If working with the curls use curl-enhancing products or smoothing products if a sleeker style is required. If working with the curls, use a diffuser and control the curl with a finger dry. If aiming for a smoother look, use a medium to large radial brush to smooth the curls. If curling, tongs may help even out the curls. If smoothing, straightening irons will provide longevity to the smoother style. Wet setting will help produce a more even curl that will be smoother in appearance than if you use heated rollers.
Type 3 Curly hair – tight curls 	This hair can also have a combination texture. Hair tends to have a medium amount of curls. Use products that will work with the curls and even out the textures – serums, heat protectors, creams and wax work well. If working with the curls, use a diffuser and control the curl with a finger dry. If aiming for a smoother look, use a large radial brush to smooth the curls. As hair can be frizzy it will tangle easier. Take care with combs and hard brushes. Take care with all tools, avoid pulling on the hair and work with the curls wherever possible. If smoothing the hair, straightening irons will provide longevity to the smoother style – but ideally work with the curls and not against them, as continued straightening of curly hair will cause damage.

→

Factor	Effect on the styling/setting process and the finished look
Type 4 Very curly hair – soft	Hair tends to be fragile, tightly coiled and has a defined curly pattern. Use products that will protect the hair from heat and further damage, but also help to control the curls. Take care with tools, avoid pulling on the hair and work with the curls wherever possible. Use diffusers to style the hair. As the hair is fragile, avoid wherever possible the use of heated styling equipment.
Type 4 Very curly hair – wiry African hair	Hair tends to be very fragile and tightly coiled and has more of a 'Z' pattern shape. Use products that will protect the hair from heat and further damage, but also help to control the curls. Take care with tools, avoid pulling on the hair and work with the curls wherever possible. Use diffusers to style the hair. As the hair is fragile, avoid wherever possible the use of heated styling equipment.

Alopecia

If you are working on a client with alopecia you will need to consider the hairstyle and finish if the client wishes to try to disguise and cover up the area of hair loss. Discuss and advise your client on the best options, explaining how products can help to hold the hair in position and a few well-placed hair grips could help too.

Hair extensions

You will need to take extra care if your client has hair extensions or has recently had them removed. If there are hair extensions in the hair, then you need to consider the tools you use and how the finished result will look.

If hair extensions have recently been removed you will need to consider the condition the hair may be in and use less tension when styling or setting. If you think the hair is in poor condition, carry out a 'pull test' to evaluate if hair loss is likely. To do this, gently pull a small section of hair at the root area. If 12 or more hairs are lost from the root area then there is evidence of excessive or abnormal hair loss

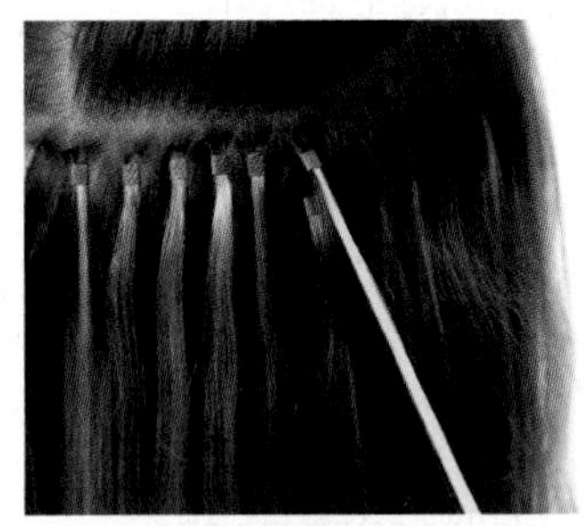

▲ If your client has hair extensions, take care when styling and dressing the hair.

Head and face shapes

Always try to enhance the face shape and create an oval look finish. Avoid additional width and height on round faces. For square face shapes soften the jawlines.

Head and face shape	Effect on the style/set
Oval 	Oval is known as the ideal face shape. You can be creative and confident with your style when you are working with this face shape.
Round 	Suggest a style that gives an illusion of an oval face shape. Avoid width at the sides and too much height.
Square 	Suggest a style that gives an illusion of an oval face shape. Aim for styles that soften the jawline and are swept on the face slightly.
Oblong 	Suggest a style that gives an illusion of an oval face shape. Avoid height but add width. Avoid hair length finishing just below the jaw. Fringes can visually help reduce the length of the face.
Heart 	Suggest a style that gives an illusion of an oval face shape. Avoid width at the temple area, which exaggerates the heart shape. Add balance near the jawline. If the client has pointed features, such as nose or chin, avoid a centre parting which brings unwanted attention to the areas – opt for side partings instead.

It is important to consider your client's features – faces with sharp noses should not be styled with centre partings; if ears protrude you should avoid styles that expose the entire ear.

▲ Sharp nose

▲ Protruding ears

It is not just hair and skin colour that varies across ethnicities, facial characteristics vary enormously too:

- face and skull shape
- width of the cheeks
- nose shape – nasal openings and the bridge of the nose
- eye shape
- lip shape and fullness/thickness.

ACTIVITY

As the shape of the skull, face, nose and eyes varies so much, discuss in pairs how techniques and styles may need to be adapted to ensure the desired chosen style would suit a diverse range of clients (think about ethnicity, age, etc.).

Manage different hair lengths when styling hair

Pulling the hair with tension as you dry it will make the style last longer, particularly if the hair is long or one length. Curly and layered hair being blow dried straight will need a lot more tension than straight or wavy hair. A large radial brush will help you to smooth and straighten curls, but still create volume and movement. Ensure the tension is firm but avoid causing discomfort to your client.

Effects of blow-drying on the finished result

If the tension is not maintained correctly when styling the hair, then styled curls may drop out, a smooth straightened style may become frizzy and wavy, and the longevity of the style will be lost.

KEY TERM

Meche – size of section.

When styling hair always ensure that the size of hair **meche** and the size of the brush are suitable for the style being created and the density of hair:

- Meche too large will cause curls to be different sizes and/or hair to be dried unevenly, affecting the balanced look.
- Brush too small – curls too small.
- Brush too large – not enough curl/body.

The angle in which you direct the brush and airflow through the hair will aid you in achieving root lift and volume where required.

▲ Airflow directed away from scalp, following direction of cuticle scales root to point

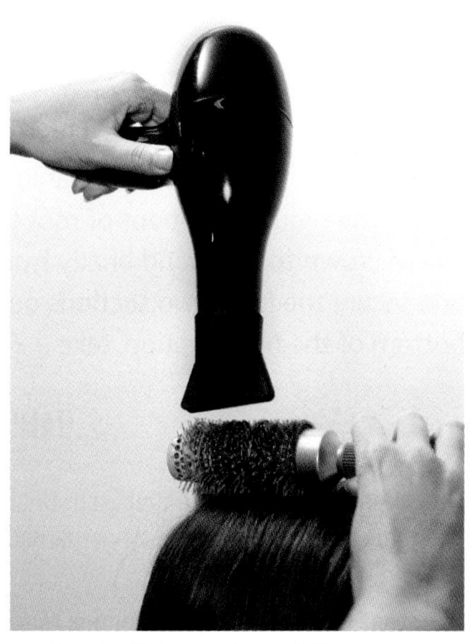

▲ Brush sitting on-base at the root area for lift and volume

HANDY HINT

Remember, hair must always be kept damp throughout the service to ensure an even curl result and to enable you to control the curl and movement.

THE HAIR PROFESSIONAL AT WORK

A professional stylist will always allow the hair to cool before removing the hair meche from the brush, or the curl will not hold and the style may drop.

Importance of direction of air flow

You must always ensure you direct the airflow away from the client's scalp to prevent burning them and causing discomfort. Always keep the airflow moving, as keeping it in one area could cause damage to the hair and scalp.

You should direct the airflow in the direction of the style to ensure root lift where required. Follow the cuticle direction, aiming downwards from root to point to follow and smooth the cuticle scales, avoiding disturbing the hair you have already dried.

Controlling and sectioning hair for styling

Whether you are finger-drying or blow-drying short or long hair you must have control. Curly hair can be challenging, even for the most able stylist, but using suitable products and tools helps control the hair. Your brush choice and size will vary, depending on the client's hair length, the desired look, degree of curl, and the movement and volume required. Refer to the previous charts to choose the most suitable products and tools for styling the hair.

ACTIVITY

Watch a stylist blow-dry the hair and observe how they hold the hairdryer in the direction of the cuticle layer.

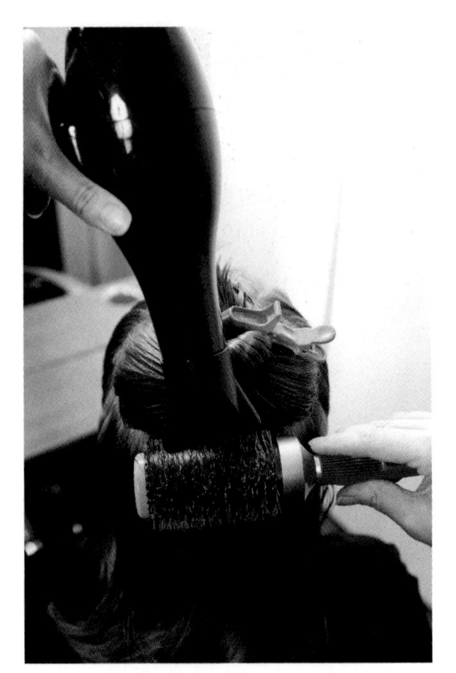

▲ Brush at root area, smoothing hair and achieving volume

▲ Cleanly sectioned hair

A methodical working pattern with clean sections is also very important. When you are working on medium to long hair you must section it cleanly, and secure the hair you are not currently working on out of the way. This will prevent it from drying too quickly and disturbing the areas that you are working on.

Influence of section size and drying angle on volume and direction

Take manageable sections to enable you to dry each part thoroughly and obtain the required amount of root lift. Part the hair and section it from ear to ear, crown to nape, and finally from the crown to the front hairline. Clip and secure the front two sections out of the way, and, starting from the bottom of the nape section, take a 2 cm thick section, securing the rest.

HANDY HINT

Keep your section sizes about 2 cm thick, depending on the density of the hair and the brush size chosen. Work methodically, ensuring each section is dry before moving on to the next.

For your front sectioning technique (ear-to-ear and crown-to-front hairline), work with the natural parting of the hair.

Effects of curling on- and off-base

You should keep the brush on the base of the section if you require lift (on-base) and drag the hair back away from the section (off-base) if you require a flatter look.

Using heated appliances to finish hair

When using heated appliances to finish the hair, you must always use a heat protector and check that the temperature setting is suitable for the hair condition, type and density. You should use a bristle brush to smooth and detangle the hair before straightening, and cleanly section the hair into manageable sections. Allow the hair to cool in its new state prior to finishing the style.

Adapt temperature of equipment to suit different hair types

Heat alone can also change the keratin state, for example using heated styling equipment, such as heated rollers, tongs and straightening irons. However, because of the lack of excess moisture in the hair, the result will not last as long.

Avoid using too much heat on African-type hair, as this will dry out the moisture from the hair. African-type hair is naturally low in moisture (1 per cent moisture, 99 per cent protein) due to the natural curl pattern and slightly open cuticle. Excessive use of heat will make hair that already lacks moisture feel and appear drier. As with all hair types, African-type/

type 4 hair is moisturised from the sebaceous gland. However, due to the curl pattern it takes longer for the sebum produced by the sebaceous gland to wind its way down the length of the hair. This is why it is important to add moisturising products to constantly rebalance the moisture level in the hair.

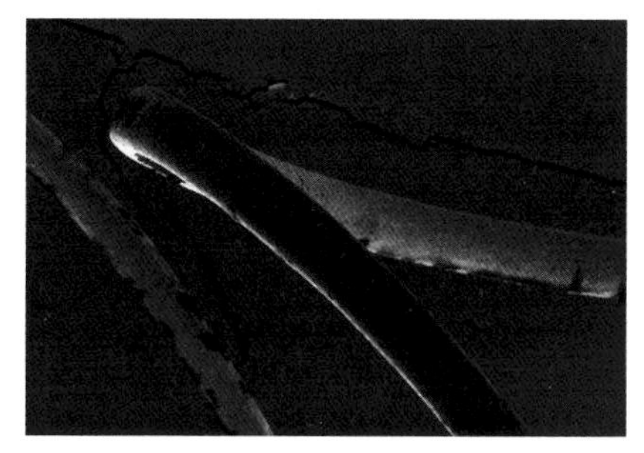

▲ Microscopic view: curl and porosity of African-type/type 4 hair

Effect of incorrect application of heat

Before using hairdryers or heated appliances, always protect the hair with a heat protector to prevent damage and to prolong the style. You must take into consideration the texture and density of the hair, as fine, sparse hair will need considerably lower temperature settings to prevent damage to the cuticle scales and cortex. Always avoid contact with the skin when sectioning the hair and using the appliance. Check all appliances for safety before using.

HANDY HINT

The incorrect application of heat can cause damage to the hair and the scalp. If the cuticles are damaged then the hair will increase in porosity and the hair may lose some of its elasticity. The hair may also be discoloured if damaged by heat.

▲ Heat diffuser

Allow hair to cool prior to finishing

After blow-drying or when using heated appliances, always allow the hair to cool, or use the cool setting button on the hairdryer for a minute or so at the end. Once the hair has cooled the hydrogen bonds are hardened in their new shape of beta keratin and the result will be longer lasting.

HANDY HINT

Remember, always allow the hair to cool, which allows the hydrogen bonds to harden in their new shape and prolong the style.

When and how to apply different techniques to achieve the desired look

Fine hair or styles requiring volume and lift may need back-combing or back-brushing to keep the style and volume in place. Back-combing or back-brushing is carried out by taking a section of hair and holding it with tension. The brush/comb is inserted into the root area, pushing the new hair growth back towards the root. This causes a gentle, controlled tangle of hair at the root area, providing lift and padding.

When the style is finished you should apply your chosen finishing products and visually check the end result for balance and shape.

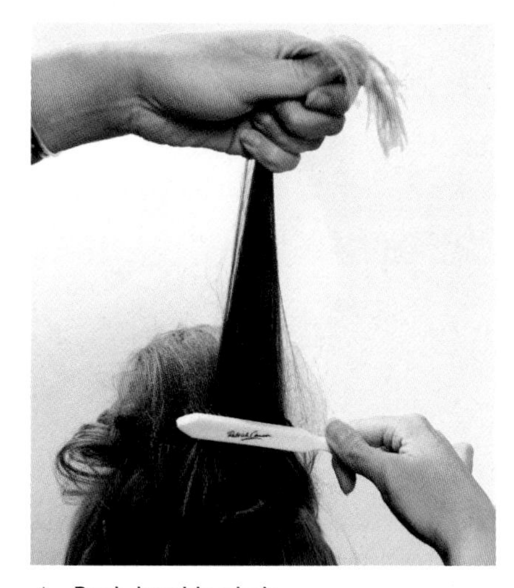

▲ Back-brushing hair

Importance of providing clients with advice and recommendations

During and after the service, it is important that you provide aftercare advice and give your client instructions on maintaining the style and condition of the hair. During your consultation you will have identified what the client does on a day-to-day basis and how much time they have to spend on styling or setting their hair.

You should provide advice on how to maintain their look, different products and their use, and when to return for future or additional services.

Together with advising on the best products and equipment for maintaining the style at home, you should give advice on which tools to use. Recommend brushes that will help the client to recreate the look, explain how to use them and show them how to follow the direction of the cuticle. You should explain how to section the hair and demonstrate how to clip hair out of the way to help them control their hair and methodically style it, enhancing the end result and using their time effectively.

HANDY HINT

When styling or setting your client's hair, consider the weather outside! Is it misty or humid? You may need to adapt the products you use to suit humid/damp weather. You may need to consider firmer holding styles/sets to combat this.

Time intervals between services

Advise your client when to return to the salon for either a weekly style and finish service, or a haircut when the style becomes difficult to manage themselves. You should explain to your client how long the style is likely to last. You may also have discussed any additional services that your client may benefit from, such as colour, body perms or treatments. Suggest to your client a date and time when these services could be carried out.

▲ Suggest new products to suit the style

Present and future products and services

Advise your client on the products you used to create their initial style and ask them about the products they already use at home. This will enable you to identify if they would benefit from buying new products to maintain their look or to recreate it at home. Always advise your client on how to use the products and how to remove them from the hair to prevent build-up. If you are recommending back-combing or back-brushing techniques, your client will also benefit from conditioning treatments.

▲ Recommend styling products to enhance and support the style

THE HAIR PROFESSIONAL AT WORK

When providing aftercare advice you should identify opportunities to sell retail. Show your clients the products you have used and let your client smell and feel the texture of the products and let them hold the equipment too. Demonstrate the equipment you have used and explain how it would benefit your client to use it at home in between salon visits.

HANDY HINT

When providing advice ensure you follow the legal requirements and always be honest about what products and equipment can do.

ACTIVITY

1. List the types of question you would ask your client if they wanted their hair put up for a day at the races.
2. Highlight which of your questions are open and which are closed questions.

HANDY HINT

Listen to the stylists in your salon consult with their clients and note the open and closed questions they use.

HOW TO SET AND DRESS HAIR

You need to know how to set and dress a variety of looks and be able to use and adapt different setting techniques. These looks and techniques are:

- rollering/setting – using various sized rollers depending on the length of the hair and style required and winding point to root
- spiral curling – using rollers, tongs or wands and curling from root to point
- wrap setting – smoothing the hair straight and flat around the head in a clockwise or anti-clockwise direction
- pin curling – winding from point to root to give volume or flat movement, depending on the on-base or off-base technique used
- hair up – set hair is pinned into place to create a style
- plaiting/braiding, twisting and knots – strands of hair are twisted, plaited or knotted to create a style
- added hair to enhance a style – additional hair is secured temporarily to a style to add length, density or interest to the end result.

Identify the tools, equipment and products available and the effects they achieve

Although the products used for setting will be very similar to those used for styling, the tools can be quite different.

When setting and dressing the hair you will use a variety of products, such as mousse, setting lotion, hairspray, serum, creams, heat protectors and wax.

You will use a variety of tools and equipment, such as setting/bendy rollers, heated rollers, brushes and combs, hood dryers, straightening irons, wands and curling tongs.

ACTIVITY

In pairs, identify your salon's product range for styling, setting and dressing hair and list the benefits to the client. Describe how each product should be used.

Use different tools and equipment for setting and dressing

Always ensure your equipment is clean, in good working order and fit for use. Use equipment correctly, following the MFIs to minimise damage to the tools and prevent any risk of injury to you and your clients.

Tools and equipment	Use and effects achieved
Tail/pintail comb	Cleanly sectioned hair when setting.
Dressing-out comb	Back-combing, teasing and dressing out the finished result – use the teeth of the comb at the root area and push the hair towards the roots several times to create a mass of hair for volume and support. Use the metal teasing prongs to lift and separate hair and spray into place.
Section clips	Securing hair in place.
Flat brush-Vent or paddle brush	Smoothing hair in readiness for sectioning or to put hair up. Removing roller marks from the set – brush through the dry set to break up the roller pattern.
Flat brush - dressing-out brush	Dressing a set and removing roller marks from the set – brush through the dry set to break up the roller pattern.
Straightening irons	Smoothing and straightening dried hair – hair is moved through the irons from roots to point. Creating soft curls on dry hair – hair is curled/twisted through the irons and gently pulled through them root to point.
Tongs	Creating curls and body – hair is wound point to root and curled.
Wands	Creating soft curls on long hair – hair is wrapped around the wand root to point.

Tools and equipment	Use and effects achieved
Velcro rollers	Creating curls on dry hair – setting to create curls – hair is dampened with setting lotion and dried under a dryer.
Setting rollers	Setting the hair – wound point to root.
Bendy roller	Spiral curling/setting, creating a tight or loose spiral curl.
Pin curl clips	Holding pin curls in place – clipped in at the root area to hold the coil in place.
Hood dryer	Drying wet sets.

Tools and equipment	Use and effects achieved
Grips and pins	Securing and holding chignons, rolls and hair up – hair is gripped or pinned into place securely at the root area.
 Back-combing brush	Back-brushing the hair for volume and support – the brush is placed at the root area while holding the hair under tension and the hair is pushed towards the roots to create a 'nest' of hair creating volume.
 Heated rollers	Setting dry hair – hair is wound around heated rollers point to root and left to cool, before dressing out.

ACTIVITY

Calculate how long it will take for you to set up the trolley, set the hair, allow for it to cool and then dress it out. What is your estimation? How would this time vary between clients with long or short hair?

▲ Heated styling equipment – use it safely

ACTIVITY

Prepare a trolley and work area with all the tools you would need for a hair up style on long hair to be set using heated rollers. What products could you use to set and dress this style?

HANDY HINT

There are so many products to choose from and a vast amount of tools you could use to create your clients' looks. You need to consider all the factors to choose the right products and tools for your clients and to achieve the desired look. Consider the products and tools you would use if your client wanted a soft curly hair up look for her day out at the races.

During styling and setting services you will be working with electrical equipment on wet and dry hair and using substances that could be hazardous to your health if inhaled, ingested or absorbed.

Take care when using electrical items and products. Always follow the instructions of the manufacturer, the supplier and your salon.

Heated styling equipment

When using electrical equipment, be aware of potential hazards and follow the Electricity at Work Regulations. Always ensure your equipment is in good working order and fit for use to prevent harm to you and others. Use equipment correctly, following the MFIs.

To use heated styling equipment correctly:

- never use electrical appliances with wet hands
- know how to use the appliance
- visually check the body and plug of the appliance
- check the wires and remove kinks and knots
- follow the Electricity at Work Regulations
- follow MFIs to ensure you use the appliance correctly and achieve the best results
- use the appliance for the correct purpose.

Heated appliances can damage the hair and burn you and the client, so it is essential that you use the equipment correctly and safely. The table below shows how to use and maintain heated styling equipment.

HEALTH AND SAFETY

When using electrical equipment, be aware of potential hazards and follow the Electricity at Work Regulations. You must visually check your appliances for cracks in the main body or plug and kinks in the wires. Always label, remove and report faulty electrical equipment.

Equipment	How to use	Safety considerations and maintenance
Heated rollers	Heat the appliance. Use a flat brush to detangle the hair. Section the hair cleanly – no bigger than the rollers' width or depth. Take a heated roller carefully in your fingers. Protect the ends of the hair with an end paper. Roll the hair section from point to root, either on-base or off-base depending on the style, and secure with the pin. Complete the full head using the chosen winding technique. Leave to cool and then remove the rollers. Dress the finished result.	Check the appliance is safe to use. Check the appliance is fit for purpose. Visually check the body and plugs for cracks. Check the wires for kinks and knots. Check the temperature before use. Avoid contact of heated rollers with the skin. Ensure pins are not touching the skin and scalp. Use heat-protecting products. Clean and sterilise rollers after use.
Straighteners	Heat the appliance. Use a flat brush to detangle the hair. Section the hair cleanly. Comb the section of hair to be straightened. Run straighteners down the hair section from root to point. Complete the whole head in a methodical manner. Leave to cool. Dress the finished result.	Check the appliance is safe to use. Check the appliance is fit for purpose. Visually check the body and plugs for cracks. Check the wires for kinks and knots. Check the temperature before use. Avoid contact of straighteners with the skin and scalp. Use heat-protecting products. Clean the heating plates once cooled and ensure they are free of products.

Equipment	How to use	Safety considerations and maintenance
Tongs and wands	Heat the appliance. Use a flat brush to detangle the hair. Cleanly section the hair. Comb the section of hair to be curled. Curl the hair section from root to point (wand) or point to root (tongs). Complete the whole head in a methodical manner. Leave to cool. Dress the finished result.	Check the appliance is safe to use. Check the appliance is fit for purpose. Visually check the body and plugs for cracks. Check the wires for kinks and knots. Check the temperature before use. Avoid contact of tongs/wand with the skin and scalp. Use heat-protecting products. Clean the body of the tongs or wand once cooled and ensure they are free of products.
Hood dryer	Place the client comfortably under the dryer. Set the timer for the suitable time frame considering the density and length of the hair. Check that the hair is dry. Allow to cool once dried.	Check the appliance is fit for use and safe. Check the temperature setting with your client. Ensure the metal pins are not touching the skin or scalp. Wipe over the hood of the dryer with a sterile wipe or disinfecting spray and cloth.

THE HAIR PROFESSIONAL AT WORK

Always use tools that are in good condition – maintain their condition by ensuring they are cleaned effectively and free from oil, product build-up and hair.

ACTIVITY

How long will the following services take?

- A client for a wet set on long hair, left under a hood dryer to dry and then combed out.
- A client for a dry set, cool down and hair up.
- A client for wet set and pin curls, dried and dressed out.

ACTIVITY

1 List the tools and equipment you would need to:
   - dry set and put hair up
   - wet set loose curly/frizzy, medium-length hair smooth but with body.

2 Which products would you use for these styles?

ACTIVITY

1 Choose one setting product and one dressing product that a client may purchase and calculate the costs.

2 What would your 10% commission be?

HANDY HINT

Poorly maintained tools and equipment can lead to issues of health and safety, a risk of cross-infection and infestation and a negative salon image.

Use of specific setting and dressing products in your salon

Refer back to the styling section in this chapter for a full list of available products used for styling and setting hair. You must be able to explain the manufacturer's instructions on the use of the specific setting and dressing products in your salon.

ACTIVITY

Identify your salon's product range for styling and finishing and list their benefits to the client.

ACTIVITY

Look at your fellow stylists and identify what products you would use on their current hairstyles.

Effect of different factors on the setting and dressing processes and the finished look

Refer back to the styling section in this chapter for a full description on the factors that affect styling and setting services.

HANDY HINT

Hair classifications are very diverse, as are your clients. For example, setting type 1 straight coarse Asian hair will be very different to setting type 4 African-type tight curly hair.

HANDY HINT

When styling or setting your client's hair you must always consider how the different factors affect your client's choice of style, as well as the products you choose and the tools and equipment you use. Your consultation is extremely important and is your chance to find out as much about your client's hair as possible.

Apply correct techniques during setting and dressing services

It is important you apply the correct technique during setting and dressing to ensure you achieve the desired end result. The table describes the different setting techniques and the effects achieved.

Rollering, curling, wrap setting and pin curling

Setting technique	Use and method
Rollering	To create curls, body and volume. Hair is wound around a roller from points to root.
Spiral curling	You can achieve spiral curls with tongs, rollers or 'bendy rods'. The technique used is the same as with conventional setting or tonging, except the hair is wound along the length of the roller or tong (instead of the hair being wound back over itself). Starting from the points and working towards the roots, wind the hair along the tong or roller, in a spiral wind allowing for the direction of the root movement required. This technique gives soft or tight curls, depending on roller size, which fall in a similar way to natural curls.
Wrap setting	Wrap setting is where you section, comb and then wrap the wet hair around the head in a clockwise or anticlockwise direction. The hair is dried under a hood dryer for up to 90 minutes and then dressed out into a straight smooth style. This setting method is popular on African-type hair and very curly hair, and the use of styling products such as Africare Foam Wrap Setting Lotion is very important in order to achieve the end result.

→

Setting technique	Use and method
Pin curling to give volume	Pin curling involves a setting technique of winding without the aid of a roller. Great skill and hand dexterity are required, and once this craft is mastered it is a skill in its own right. You may not need to set without the aid of rollers often, but imagine going to a photo shoot or visiting a bride's home to style their hair, only to find you do not have enough rollers, or worse, you have forgotten them! The ability to pin curl gives great curl results and the hair dries much faster than when it is tightly wrapped around a roller. Using pin curls to set dry hair after a round brush blow-dry provides longevity and hold to the styled hair. Pin curls are created by a wet setting technique. The section patterns and winding techniques can be the same as for winding with a roller, and the hair is wound from point to root. Pin curls can be used on very straight African-type hair or on woven hairstyles. Hair that is texturised or curly may not be suitable for this hairstyle, as the hair may be too frizzy when dry and the finished curl will not be structured enough. To create pin curls with root lift and volume, you can use 'stand-up' pin curls, sometimes called barrel curls. Use a suitable product and comb the wet hair upwards, at about 90° to the head. Roll the hair downwards from point to root, without a roller. Secure the hair on-base with a pin curl clip. This technique produces soft curls or waves and volume.
Pin curling to give flat movement	After you have applied a suitable styling product, comb the wet hair downwards at about 45° and feed the hair through your fingers to create a flat, open-coiled curl. Secure the hair off-base with a pin curl clip. This technique produces flat movement and waves throughout the hair. To create movement through the hair but without root lift and volume, you can use 'lie-down' pin curls, sometimes called a flat barrel curl.
Clock-spring pin curls for flat movement	For 'clock-spring' pin curls, follow the technique described above for pin curls for flat movement, but feed the hair through your fingers and create a closed-in coiled curl that is smaller in the centre and gradually gets larger towards the outside of the coil. Clock-spring pin curls create flat movement that has tighter curls and body at the ends of the hair, where the coil was at its tightest, and gradually loosens towards the root.

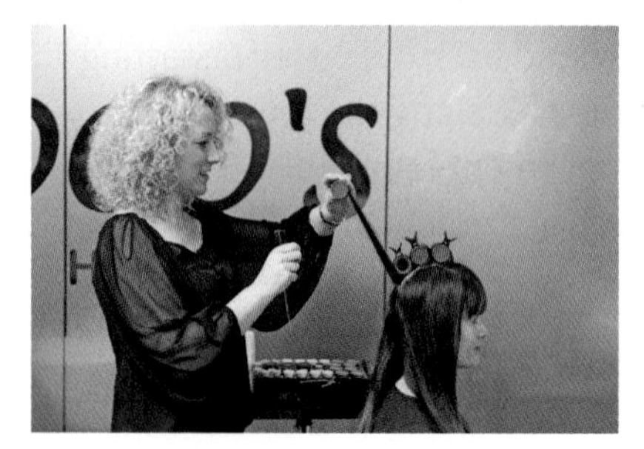

▲ Sectioned long hair while setting

Sectioning and winding techniques

You must always section the hair cleanly – use either a pintail or tail comb, depending on your personal preference. When you are working on long hair, always secure the hair you are not working on out of the way.

You must always ensure you take manageable size sections (meches), which are no larger or wider than your roller choice. Small rollers give tighter curls, and medium to large rollers give looser curls, so choose your roller size to suit the required style, taking into consideration the hair's length and density.

When setting the hair you will need to consider whether volume, lift and curl are required. Hair can be rolled to sit on-base or off-base, and the wind can be directed to suit the style, or a brick wind can be used to avoid roller and section marks. Hair can also be wound from root to point – such as when using a wand or curling with straightening irons, or from point to root when winding hair around a roller or pin-curling.

The wide choice of winding techniques helps you to create lift and curl, with varied root movement and direction. Changing your roller size enables you to achieve tighter or looser curls.

Sectioning and winding techniques	Use and method
Point to root	Hair is wound from the points of the hair up to the roots around a roller or straightening irons.
Root to point	Hair is wound from the roots to the points of the hair down a bendy roller or a wand.
On-base	Ensure your section meche is combed directly upwards for on-base winds, at 90° to create lift and volume.
Off-base	Ensure your section meche is combed slightly backwards for off-base winds at 45°, with the root dragged to create flatter curls.
Directional	Setting the hair in the direction in which it is to be styled ensures the root movement falls in line with the desired style result. This method enables you to work with partings – style the hair to one side, creating the look of the style, in the same way you would blow-dry.
Brick	If the style requires a more blended look that is free from partings and section patterns, then the ideal technique is brick winding. This involves setting the hair in horizontal rows across the head, ensuring that the following row is offset, so it looks like brickwork.

Wrap-set hair to achieve the desired look

Wrapping of the hair around the head means that the contours of the head form the finished shape of the hair. The hair must be combed regularly in the same direction during the wrapping process, to ensure it lays flat and smooth against the scalp.

Dressing techniques

Now that you have learnt the art of setting the hair, it is time to have fun dressing it out and putting it up. By setting the hair first, you have a solid foundation to build on. Most hair up styles require some body or curl to be added to support the up-do. For chignons and bouffant styles, the hair may need to be straightened to obtain a smooth finish.

The dressing techniques you may use are curls, rolls, smoothing and back-brushing and back-combing. These are described in detail in the step by steps at the end of the chapter.

Adapting the size of your rollers and estimating the size of sections and amount of rollers required will require you to use your maths skills. The angles in which you roll the hair will also involve you using and applying maths.

Estimate how many rollers you would use to create a brick wind set and a spiral set. Carry out these services on a training head and compare your estimates to actual requirements.

Dressing techniques	Use and method
Hair up/rolls	After setting the hair, it can be dressed and put up to create a variety of different looks from classic rolls and chignons to contemporary soft flowing styles.
Curls	After setting the hair, it can be dressed into soft natural-looking large curls.
Back-combing and back-brushing	Hair can be back-combed or back-brushed to provide volume, lift and support to hair up styles or hair that is left down but needs extra staying power.
Twists/knots	Hair can be knotted and twisted to create current looks.
Plaits/braids	Hair can be plaited or braided in many ways – traditional French plait, Dutch braids, corn rows, etc. Plaits can use on-scalp or off-scalp techniques to create a variety of looks.
Adding hair	Hair can be added to enhance a style and add bulk, length, colour, curl and texture. Hair can be added with freehand techniques and secured with grips and pins, clipped in, added as individual strands or as clipped in hairpieces such as a fringe.

▲ Securing dressed hair with spray

Influence of the angle of winding

The angle of winding influences the volume and direction of the hair. The more volume that is required, the more root lift that is needed, and this situation requires on-base winding.

When winding the hair to sit on-base you must:

1. Take the section of hair to be rolled and comb it upwards, straight from the head.
2. Hold the section at 90° from the head.
3. Wind the hair downwards from point to root around the roller, ensuring that the completed roll sits on the base of its own section, at the root area.
4. Ensure that you wind the hair considering the root direction required, so as to give maximum support to the style.

▲ On-base

▲ On-base winding – curls with volume and lift

If the style you are creating needs less root lift and a flatter look, you should direct your wind off-base. This involves dragging the root back, slightly away from the roller base and section. At 45°, complete the wind with the roller almost sitting on the root of the section below. The roots then dry or cool without creating lift.

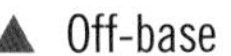

▲ Off-base

▲ Off-base winding – flat curls

HANDY HINT

If your roller size is unsuitable and too large, your curl result will be unsatisfactory and may loosen with time. If too small, the resulting curl may be too tight and the hair length may also appear shorter than expected.

Brush out set hair sections

When dressing out a wet set, brush the hair thoroughly to ensure you break up all the roller marks and remove all partings to blend the hair. This will also help to reduce the stiffness of the dried setting product and create a softer appearance.

Methods of handling, controlling and securing hair

Long hair can tangle easily and get caught in a roller, so take care when winding the hair around the roller: control the wind and make sure you have all the required sectioned hair neatly wrapped around the roller. When you are happy that the roller has been wound effectively, secure it in place with a hairpin.

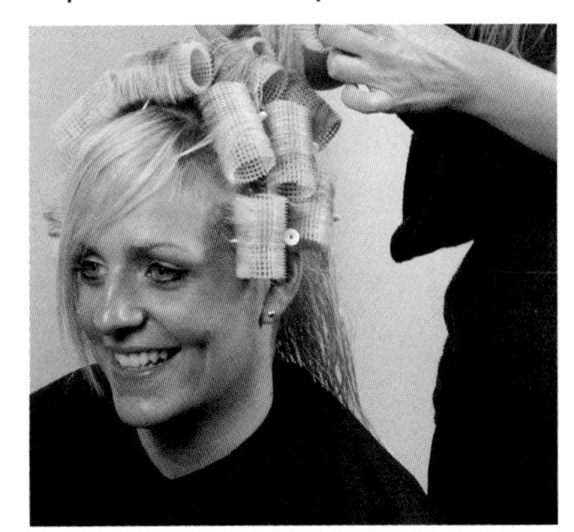

▲ Neatly winding the hair

▲ Badly rolled hair – hair not sectioned cleanly and not held with tension

HANDY HINT

Always ensure that the hair section is a suitable size for your chosen roller. If sections are too large the curls will be softer and less root lift will be achieved.

ACTIVITY

You are using your maths skills when you estimate the size of the section to take, and when working on-base at 90° or off-base with varying angles of winding.

Maintain the correct tension

Pulling the hair with tension as you wind will make the set last longer and the hair stretch into its new position.

Effects of incorrect application of heat

Incorrect application of heat can cause damage to the hair and a loss of elasticity, damage to the cuticle scales and an increase in porosity. You could also discolour the hair, or cause client discomfort.

Heat protectors

Heat protectors will protect the hair from heat by creating a barrier over the cuticle layer, preventing a degree of damage and providing a sleeker finish.

Taking down the hairstyle

Care must always be taken when removing rollers from the hair. If you have cleanly wound the hair around the roller with even tension, then rollers should be easily removed from the hair. Once the hair is dried (or cooled) you should remove the pin and gently unwind the roller, maintaining even tension throughout to avoid catching the hair and causing discomfort.

Equally, when removing heated tongs or wands from the hair after winding, be careful not to burn you or the client and leave the hair to cool and set in place before any dressing takes place.

If your client has had their hair put up, you will need to advise them on how to remove the grips and pins and take the hair down. At the end of the service advise your client of where the last pins were inserted, so they know roughly where to start when taking out the pins and grips. Advise the client on how to remove the pins and grips so they do not cause themselves any discomfort. Explain how they should brush their hair once all the pins have been removed. Advise the client on what brush to use when removing back-combing or back-brushing from the hair, to avoid damaging the hair and discomfort being caused.

THE HAIR PROFESSIONAL AT WORK

Provide effective aftercare to your client for back-combing and back-brushing removal at home. Advise your client to take small sections and use a soft bristle brush to gently brush through the hair, starting at the points and working up towards the roots.

▲ Back-brushed hair

Physical effects of setting on the hair structure

Hair is flexible and elastic when wet and can be stretched into a new shape. When hair is set from wet to dry or heat to cool, the temporary bonds are broken and re-fixed into a new position.

Refer back to the styling part of this chapter for more information on the physical effects of styling and setting.

Effects of humidity on hair

As the hair is hygroscopic, humidity will cause curls to drop and volume and movement in styles to be lost. Use heat protectors and hair spray to protect the hair against humidity and to delay the hair's return to alpha keratin, prolonging the longevity of the beta keratin style.

▲ Apply setting and dressing products to protect the hair from humidity

Keep hair damp during setting

Make sure that you keep the hair damp throughout the winding process to maintain an even elasticity and to allow the hydrogen bonds to set in their new stretched position, setting the hair in a beta keratin state.

Importance of questioning clients

Prior to the start of the service it is important that you confirm the style requirement. Throughout the service you should check you are meeting your client's expectations and that she is happy with the process. Checking your client is happy throughout the process will enable you to make changes to the style if she is not happy with the look being created.

Provide clients with advice and recommendations

As part of the service and for your client to make the most of their set and dressed hair, you must provide them with aftercare advice.

Providing your client with advice on maintaining an everyday style will be a little more straightforward than the aftercare required for hair up styles and dressed looks. For all options you should advise your client on which products, tools and equipment work best and how to maintain the look. You could offer some tips for recreating the style themselves, but it is fair to say that the look they will achieve is unlikely to be of a professional standard. After all, the client came to you, the expert, to obtain the required look.

▲ Suggest new products to suit the style

Time intervals between services

You should explain to your client how long the style is likely to last. If it is hair up, then the client is likely to take the style down at the end of the evening, but a set to create curls may last for a few days.

▲ Products that may benefit the style

Advice on products and services

Always advise your client on how to use the products and how to remove them from the hair to prevent build-up. If you are recommending back-combing or back-brushing techniques, your client will also benefit from conditioning treatments.

Retail opportunities

When providing aftercare advice you should identify opportunities to sell retail. Show your clients the products you have used and let your client smell and feel the texture of the products; let them hold the equipment too. Suggest styling products, such as serums for conditioning and protecting the hair, and lotions or mousse that will aid styling wet hair. Suggest finishing products that protect against moisture or heat, or spray to hold the style in place for longer. Demonstrate the equipment you have used and explain how it would benefit your client to use it at home in between salon visits.

THE HAIR PROFESSIONAL AT WORK

When providing advice make sure you follow the legal requirements and be honest about what products and equipment can do.

WORK WITH TEMPORARY ADDED HAIR

Prepare the hair

Before you attach additional hair to a style you should check the hair and scalp condition. If you are adding length and density to a style, you will also be adding weight to the hair, so the strength of the natural hair needs to be considered. Carry out visual checks, as well as elasticity, porosity and pull tests to check the strength and condition of the hair.

Prepare the hair by brushing it through (where possible and appropriate) to remove tangles, section the hair in readiness for the hair placement and prepare the hair to be added.

Attach, maintain and remove hair attachments

There are several ways in which hair can be added for a short-term non-commitment style. Most of these can be easily removed by the client in their own home when the style is being removed.

▲ Clip in hair extension

Apply temporary hair attachment systems

Temporary hair can be added using freehand techniques, where strands are clipped in with pins and grips, or plaited and weaved into a style. There are lots of clip-in wefts available for clients to use at home. In between visits, these work very well for hair up styles and to create length, colour or texture to enhance a style. You can even add a temporary fringe that is discreetly clipped into the front hairline.

Choice and placement of temporary hair attachment systems

Once you know the type of look required and the techniques you will use to set the hair you can decide which method of temporary hair systems is best. The style choice is very important and must be decided upon before the type of temporary hair can be chosen; otherwise the look may not be achieved effectively. With the final look in mind, you can confirm the length, colour, thickness, texture and reason for the added hair to ensure the right one is chosen and placed securely where required.

The advantages and disadvantages of temporary hair systems are shown in the table.

Temporary hair systems	Advantage	Disadvantage
Clip on and grip in Clip on hair extension	Quick and easy to attach. Can add variety of lengths, colours and textures.	Can weigh the style down. Limited looks are achievable. Clips can be noticeable in fine hair and in some styles.
Plaited Plaited hair extension	More flexible with movement. Extended range of looks achievable. Can look natural. Increases density of hair.	Can cause traction alopecia. Reduces the hair's natural moisture levels. The finished result is not very adaptable. Client cannot remove these as easily at home.

Provide clients with advice and recommendations

If your client has had added hair put into the style you must advise them of how to remove the hair and when to do so. If a client is tempted to leave a plaited or clipped in extension in for a longer time frame they will put extra tension on the hair and scalp. It is important that you advise them how to comb or brush their hair after removing the added hair as well as how to recondition the hair.

HOW TO FINISH HAIR

After setting the hair and creating a fantastic look it is important that you finish the hair to a high standard.

HANDY HINT

Most added hair will be artificial hair and therefore will not tolerate high heat or the use of heated styling equipment.

Adapt temperature of equipment to suit different hair types

The temperature of heated appliances must be adapted for the different hair types due to the moisture levels within the hair. Fine hair to very curly (type 4) hair will be more susceptible to damage and breakage caused by high heats, than dense wavy hair.

Effects of incorrect application of heat

If hair is exposed to high temperatures or heat is left on the hair for too long, then damage to the cuticle layer will occur. This will cause the porosity levels to increase in the hair. The hair and scalp could also be burnt, causing discomfort and client anxiety.

Allow hair to cool prior to finishing

Hair needs to be allowed to cool before finishing in order to allow the temporary bonds to set in their new position and provide longevity to the style.

Apply back-combing and back-brushing techniques to achieve the desired look

Back-combing and back-brushing techniques should be applied when height, volume or support is required to enhance the style. See the step-by-step guides on how to carry out these techniques.

WHAT YOU MUST DO

Apply safe working practices

Prior to starting the styling or setting service you must prepare your client and work area to meet salon requirements:

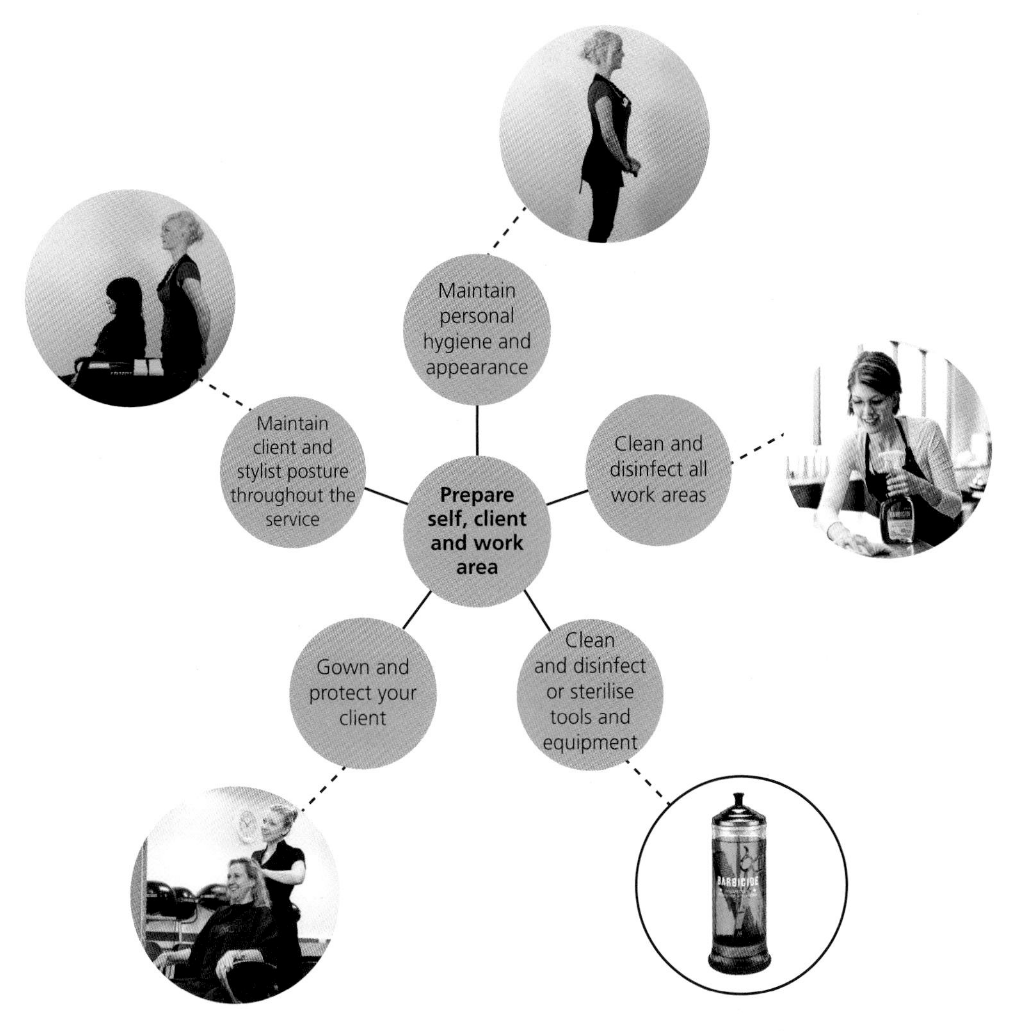

Apply safe and hygienic methods of working throughout services by:

- maintaining your responsibilities for health and safety
- protecting your client's clothing and positioning them to meet the needs of the service without causing discomfort
- ensuring your own posture and position while working minimises fatigue and the risk of injury and your personal hygiene, protection and appearance meets accepted industry and organisational requirements
- following workplace and suppliers' or manufacturer's instructions for the safe use of equipment, materials and products and applying and using suitable products.

HANDY HINT

Promote environmental and sustainable working practices throughout the service by reducing waste and energy, and managing waste (recycle, re-use, safe disposal).

▲ Hygienic methods of working throughout service

Carry out styling and finishing services

When carrying out your client services you must work to commercially viable times to ensure the salon runs smoothly and to time.

As a guide you should aim to work towards the following time frames:

ACTIVITY

Compare the above time frames to your salon target times and identify any variations. Remember, it is important that you aim to work to your own salon timings and meet their requirements

Service	Guide time
Short hair blow-dry	30 minutes
Finger dry	15–30 minutes
Long hair round brush curly blow-dry	45–60 minutes
Short hair wet set	20 minutes to wind and 10 minutes to dress out after drying
Long hair wet set	30–40 minutes to wind and 10–15 minutes to dress out after drying
Long hair dry set	30–45 minutes including dressing out
Plait and twisting	From 30 minutes
Hair up	From 30 minutes
Hair up with added hair	From 45 minutes

HANDY HINT

When carrying out the services shown in the table, you must apply suitable products and follow the manufacturer's instructions.

STEP BY STEP

Style and finish hair

For your assessments you will have to blow-dry and finger dry a variety of styles. It is important you identify your client's requirements and asking open and closed questions will help you to do so.

Consult with clients to confirm the desired look

Before blow-drying or finger drying the hair you must confirm the desired look with your client. You will need to ask your client the following questions:

- What is their vision for the finished look?
- What products do they generally use on their hair and why?
- What lifestyle factors affect the time they spend on their hair between salon visits?
- Have they been happy with their previous style and do they wish to change or alter anything?
- Have they had any specific problems maintaining their style?
- What equipment do they use at home?
- Do they have any allergies?

You will need to visually check and feel the hair to identify:

- the condition of the hair and scalp
- the length, style, type, texture and density of the hair
- any growth patterns
- the client's head and face shape
- any scalp problems
- how long the service will take.

Once you have this information from your client you will be able to provide them with advice and recommendations on what products to use to maintain the look, or suggest any additional services that may benefit the client.

Blow-dry hair into shape

When blow-drying hair you must:

- apply suitable products, following manufacturer's instructions
- control your styling tools to minimise the risk of damage to the hair length, client discomfort and to achieve the desired look
- take sections of hair which suit the size of the styling tools
- maintain an even tension throughout the blow-drying process
- keep the hair damp throughout the blow-drying process
- test the temperature of heated styling equipment throughout the service
- control the hair length during the blow-drying process, taking account of factors influencing the service
- use tools and equipment in a way that achieves the desired blow-dry finish.

ACTIVITY

Using your English skills, think of any other questions that you could ask your client about their hair or their requirements.

During this process, write notes about any allergies and the condition of the hair on a record card in case you need to refer back to the information in the future, or if there are any problems and you need evidence of the client's comments. You must write clearly and ensure all spelling and details are correct.

ACTIVITY

During the consultation you will need to use your communication skills to ask your client questions to identify their needs, and to identify any factors that may affect the service. Remember to speak clearly and use jargon-free language.

Round brush blow-dry to create movement and curl

STEP 1 – After shampooing and conditioning the hair, prepare the hair with products such as smoothing oil, salt spray or serum, depending on the hair type/texture, and remove excess moisture,

STEP 2 – Section the hair from crown to nape and divide into three sections (left, middle and right).

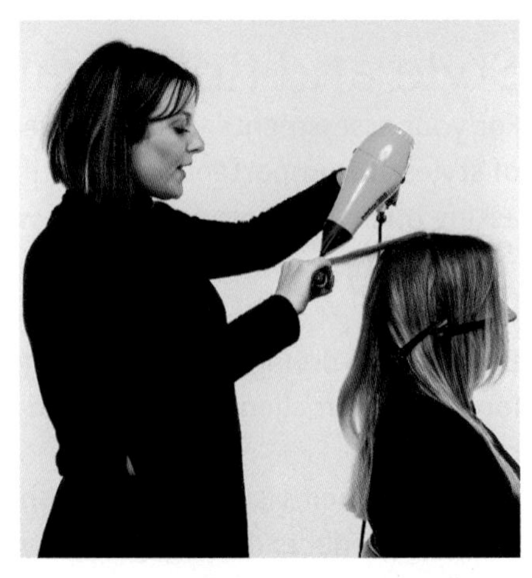

STEP 3 – Dry the middle crown section with a medium radial brush.

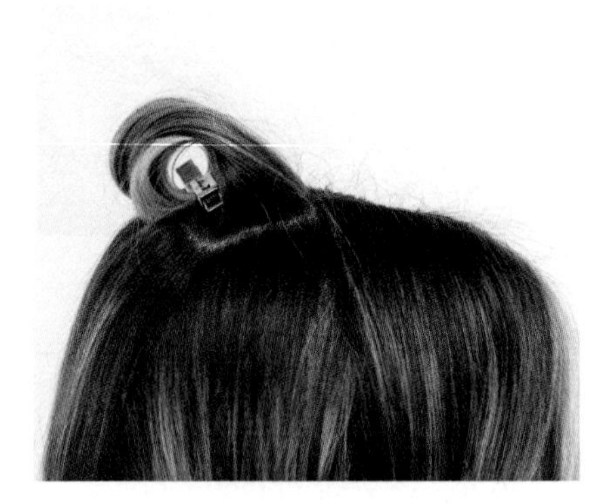

STEP 4 – Clip the dried hair into a large barrel curl to set.

STEP 5 – Complete the middle section.

STEP 6 – Continue the process with the left and right back sections.

STEP 7 – Complete both sides and the top and allow the dried hair to cool.

STEP 8 – Dress the curls, back brushing where required.

STEP 9 – The finished look

Short layered above-shoulders hair blow-dried with a small to medium radial brush to create volume.

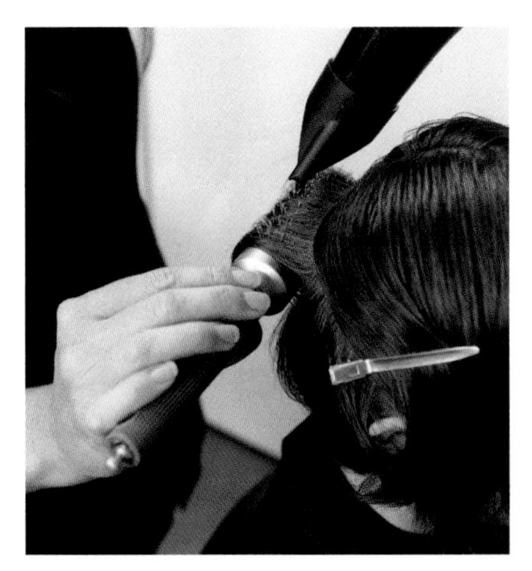

STEP 1 – Apply styling product and section the hair, blow-dry from root to point.

STEP 2 – Continue to blow-dry, lifting the hair for root lift and support.

STEP 3 – Keep the brush on-base for volume at the roots.

STEP 4 – Check the balance and ensure the client is happy with the end result.

Finger dry hair into shape

When finger drying hair you must:

- apply suitable products, following manufacturer's instructions
- keep the hair damp throughout the styling process
- control the hair during the styling process, taking account of factors influencing the service
- ensure that finger drying achieves the direction, volume and balance for the desired look.

Finger dry short hair

Finger dry short hair to create movement and texture.

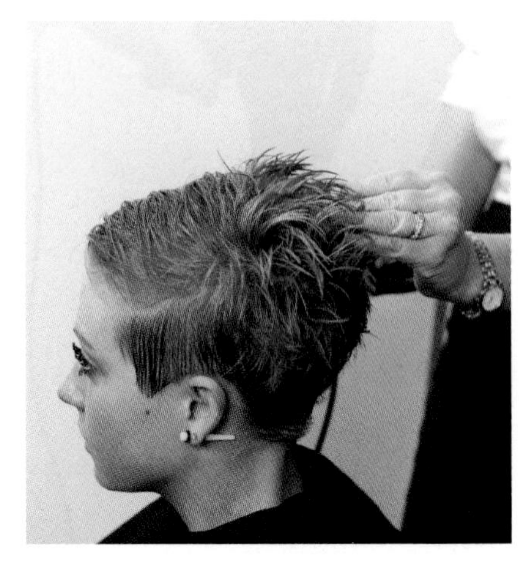

STEP 1 – Apply the product, removing any excess moisture by 'rough' drying.

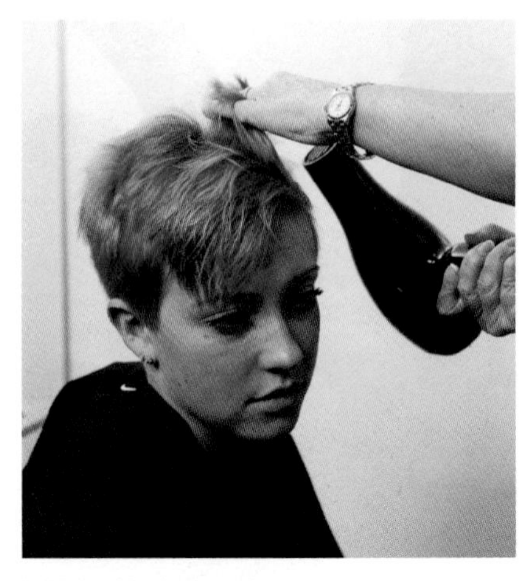

STEP 2 – Manipulate the root area to create body and movement.

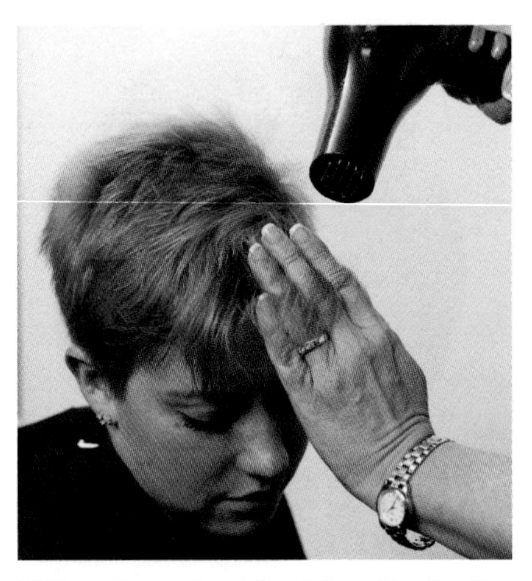

STEP 3 – Ensure the airflow follows the direction of the hairstyle.

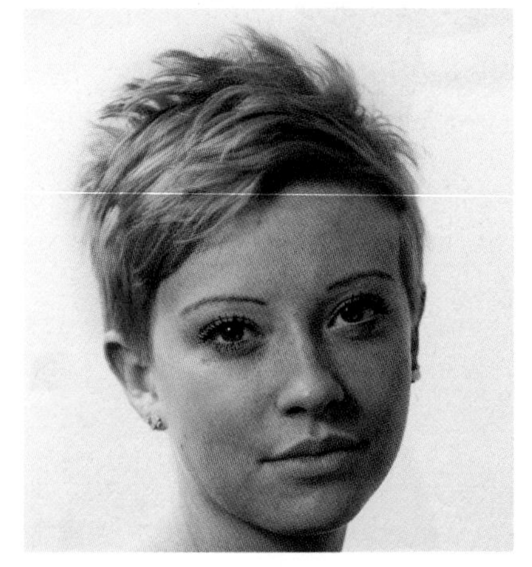

STEP 4 – Check the balance and ensure the client is happy with the end result.

Diffuser drying curly long hair

Hair with movement, curl or body can be scrunch-dried with a diffuser attachment. This technique works particularly well with medium to longer hair lengths. You should use curl-activating products to enhance curls and movement, and to support the style. However, use minimal handling of the hair.

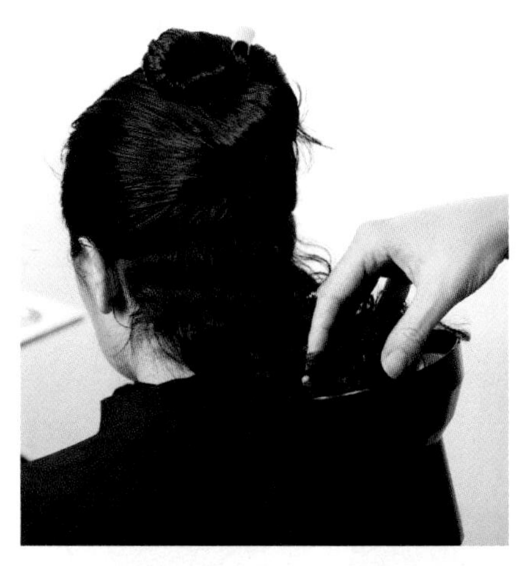

STEP 1 – Apply the styling product and section the hair; place the hair into the diffuser.

STEP 2 – Continue to finger dry, gently manipulating the hair at the root area for lift.

STEP 3 – Avoid 'overplaying' with the curls: let the diffuser curl the hair where possible.

STEP 4 – Check the balance and ensure the client is happy with the end result.

Finish hair

When finishing the hairstyle you must:

- use heated styling equipment, when necessary, that is at the correct temperature for your client's hair and the desired look
- control your use of heated styling equipment (when used) to minimise the risk of damage to the hair and scalp, client discomfort and to achieve the desired look
- take sections of hair which suit the size of the heated styling equipment (when used)
- use back-combing and back-brushing techniques, when required, to achieve the desired look
- apply and use suitable products, when required, to meet manufacturer's instructions
- ensure the finished look takes into account relevant styling factors influencing the service
- ensure the finished look meets the intended shape, direction, balance and volume agreed with your client.

Using straightening irons to smooth and straighten the hair

STEP 1 – Section the hair and apply a heat protector.

STEP 2 – Heat the straightening irons to the desired temperature and slowly move them from root to point.

STEP 3 – Continue around to the side section, taking small sections at a time

STEP 4 – Check the balance and ensure the client is happy with the end result.

HANDY HINT

See Chapter 7 for step-by-step instructions for blow-drying and styling of men's hair.

Provide clients with advice and recommendations on the service provided

You must provide your client with suitable aftercare advice and recommendations on the service provided; this should include the advice shown in the diagram.

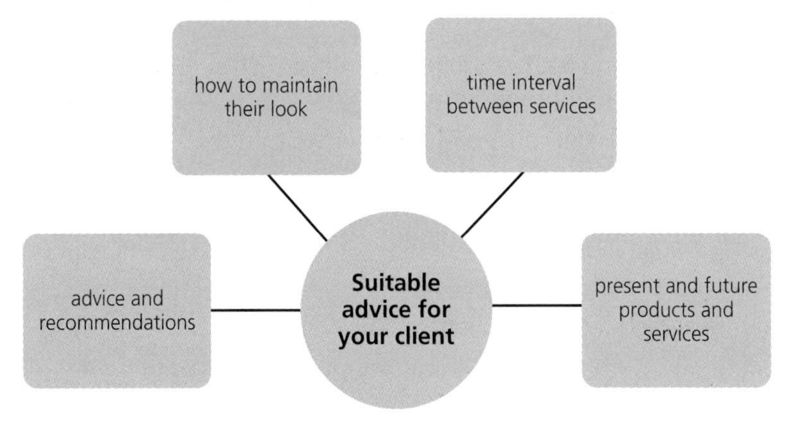

Creatively set and dress hair

You will need to demonstrate different styles for a variety of occasions. During your hairdressing career you will have the opportunity to set and dress hair for clients going to a ball, a wedding, the races, nightclubbing and, of course, for everyday styles, suitable for work or a day at the beach!

Consult with clients to confirm the desired look

Ask open and closed questions to help you identify your client's requirements, such as the reason for their set and dress. Is the client attending a special event or occasion? Will your client be inside or outside, as you will need to consider the weather? Is the event during the day or evening? Will your client be dancing – the style will need to be secured in place for an active day.

Set hair

When setting hair you must:

- confirm and agree with your client the setting techniques and look required
- control your tools and equipment to minimise the risk of damage to the hair and scalp, client discomfort and to achieve the desired look
- apply and use suitable products, following manufacturer's instructions
- control your client's hair throughout the setting process, taking account of factors influencing the service and the occasion for which the style is required
- take sections of hair which suit the size of the tools and equipment
- keep the hair damp (when necessary) throughout the setting process
- section and wind the hair cleanly and evenly to achieve the desired look
- ensure all wound rollers, when used, are secure and sit on-or off-base to meet the style requirements
- maintain the correct tension throughout the setting process
- remove any items used for setting, avoiding discomfort to your client
- ensure your setting techniques achieve the desired look.

ACTIVITY

Use your English skills to find out as much information from your client as you can. Open questions, which require the client to give a more in-depth answer, start with 'what', 'why', 'how' and 'when'. Closed questions help to confirm and define details, as they are answered with 'yes' or 'no'.

THE HAIR PROFESSIONAL AT WORK

When preparing a client's hair for a specific occasion, the longevity of the style needs to be considered – does the client want a style for day wear, evening wear or a special event? A special hair up-do may last only for a day or evening; a curly set may last a few days. Depending on the style, choose products, tools and equipment to support and create the desired look.

Dress hair

When dressing hair you must:

- leave your client's hair free of all section marks as necessary
- use heated equipment, as necessary, at the correct temperature for your client's hair and the desired look
- control your tools and equipment to minimise the risk of damage to the hair and scalp, client discomfort and to achieve the desired look
- apply and use suitable products, following manufacturer's instructions
- ensure the finished look takes into account relevant factors influencing the service
- ensure your dressing techniques and effects achieve the intended shape, direction and volume agreed with your client
- confirm your client's satisfaction with the finished look.

Set and dress hair to create curls

Traditional wet set wound in a brick wind pattern.

ACTIVITY

Practise these set and dress to create curls techniques and time yourself.

HANDY HINT

When dressing out a wet set, brush the hair thoroughly to remove all the roller marks and remove all the partings to blend the hair. This will also help to reduce the stiffness of dried setting products and create a softer appearance.

STEP 1 – Prepare your client for the service and apply styling products. Wind the rollers from point to root in a brick wind formation.

STEP 2 – Complete the whole head wind and dry the hair with a hood dryer or similar.

▲ Remove roller marks

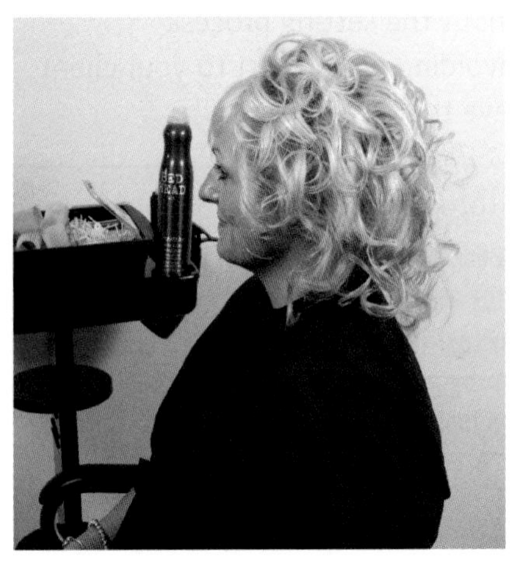

STEP 3 – Allow to cool and remove the rollers. Using a dressing-out brush, remove the roller marks.

STEP 4 – Dress the hair into the desired style and apply your finishing products. Check the balance and ensure the client is happy with the end result.

Dry setting directional wind technique using heated rollers

STEP 1 – Wind the hair from points to roots in a directional manner. Roll the hair on-base to maintain root lift and volume.

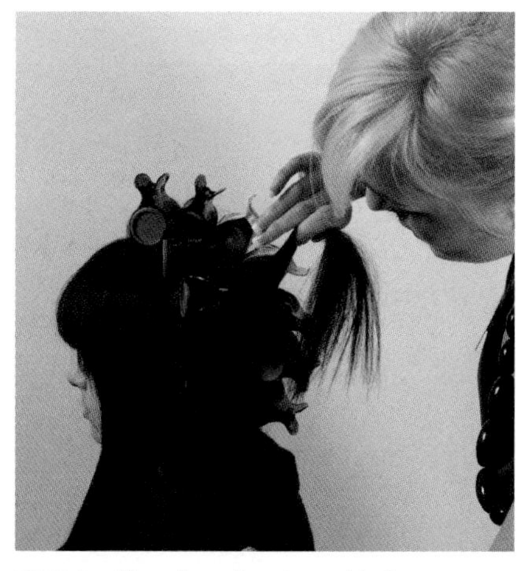

STEP 2 – Allow the rollers to cool before you remove them.

STEP 3 – Use your hands or a brush to remove roller marks. Dress and back-comb the hair into the desired style. Apply your chosen finishing products. Check the balance and ensure the client is happy with the end result.

Dry setting directional wind techniques using Velcro rollers

Long, layered hair is dry set on larger Velcro rollers and combed out to produce a curly style with body and root lift.

STEP 1 – Apply your products to your client's dry hair and wind from point to root.

STEP 2 – Wind all the hair into your chosen wind.

STEP 3 – Dry the hair, remove rollers and run your fingers through the hair or brush through to remove roller marks, then apply finishing products. Check the balance and ensure the client is happy with the end result.

Pin curls to create volume

Stand up pin curls (barrel curls) styled on wet hair that is medium to long in length.

STEP 1 – After gowning and preparing your client, apply styling product and section the hair. Roll the hair from point to root around your fingers into the direction of the style. Secure the curl with a pin curl clip.

STEP 2 – Repeat as required. Ensure the pin curl sits on-base for maximum root lift. Dry the hair and leave it to cool.

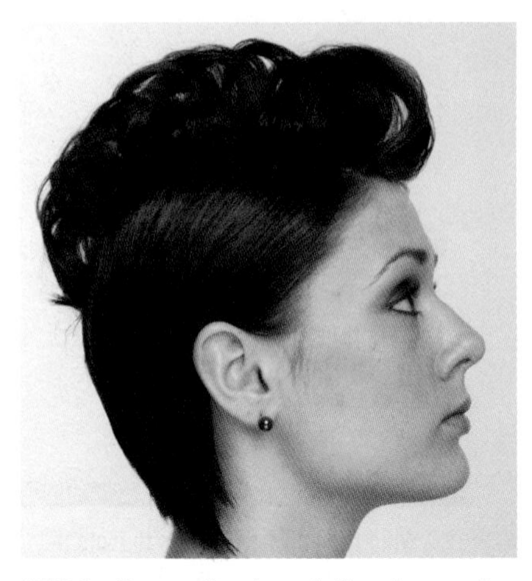

STEP 3 – Remove the pin curl clips, dress and tease the hair into the desired style and apply finishing products. Check the balance and ensure the client is happy with the end result.

Pin curls to create flat movement

STEP 1 – Create a side parting and take a small section of hair (6–12 mm in width). Comb the section of the hair from ends to roots. The section should be 6–12 mm in width. Place an end paper on the ends. Curl the hair in a flat circle between your fingers in an anticlockwise direction

STEP 2 – Secure the hair, following the root direction of the hair. Continue using a brick wind and place clockwise pin curls from the right side of the head around to the left of the head.

STEP 3 – In the following row, place the pin curls in the reverse order using a row of anticlockwise pin curls, working left to right. Continue using this reverse pin curling technique of anticlockwise and clockwise pin curls until you have completed the whole head.

STEP 4 – Leave the hair to dry for 45 minutes to one hour (depending on the length). Comb the hair out into ringlets and soft curls. Apply serum, oil sheen spray and holding spray if required. Check the balance and ensure the client is happy with the end result.

Using a wand or tongs to create waves and movement – tongs for flat movement

STEP 1 – Prepare the trolley and your client's hair by applying heat protector and hairspray.

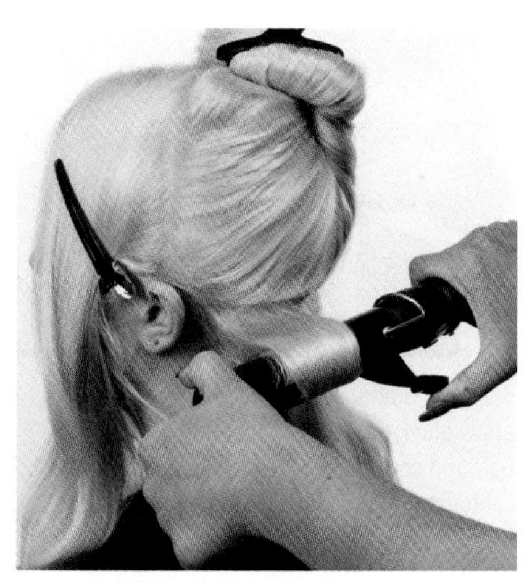

STEP 2 – Cross section the hair and, starting at the nape area, secure the remaining hair out of the way. Take large sections of hair and wind the tongs from point to root.

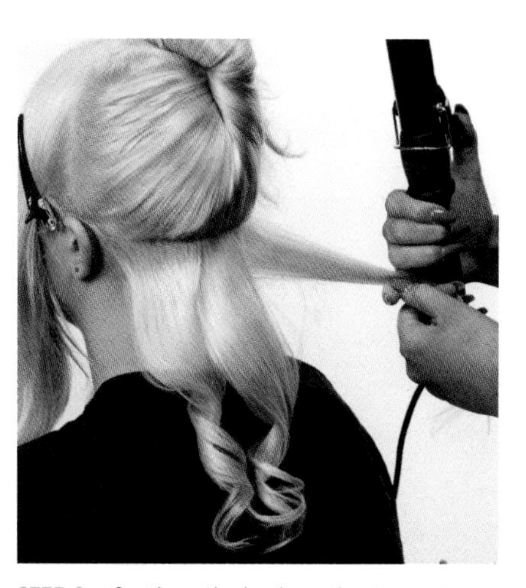

STEP 3 – Continue the back section to create soft curls.

STEP 4 – Continue with your sections through the back and sides, curling the hair without any root lift, winding from point to root.

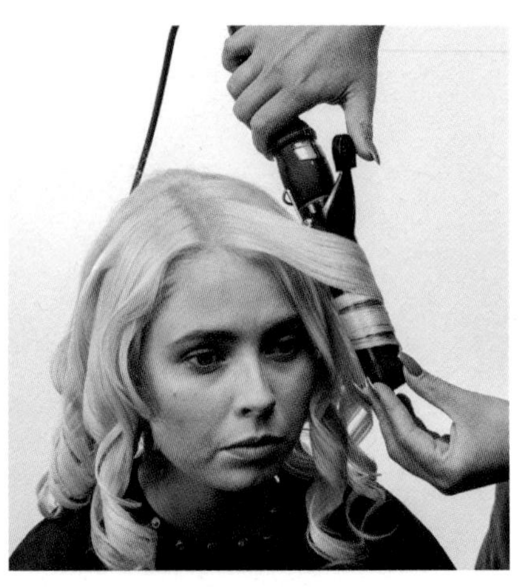

STEP 5 – Through the top section, avoiding root lift, work with the direction of the parting to suit the style.

STEP 6 – Apply serum, brush the hair and dress the soft curls into place, securing with a medium hold spray to create a soft wave final look.

Set and dress hair smooth – wrap setting

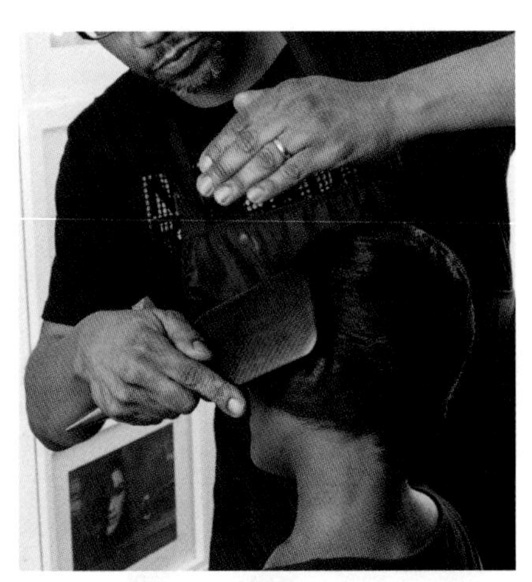

STEP 1 – Shampoo and condition the hair and apply plenty of smoothing cream. Section the hair and comb it smooth, wrapping it around the contours of the head.

STEP 2 – Continue this process around the head, smoothing the hair and adding more product if required. Secure the hair in place with either hair clips or a hair scarf/wrap.

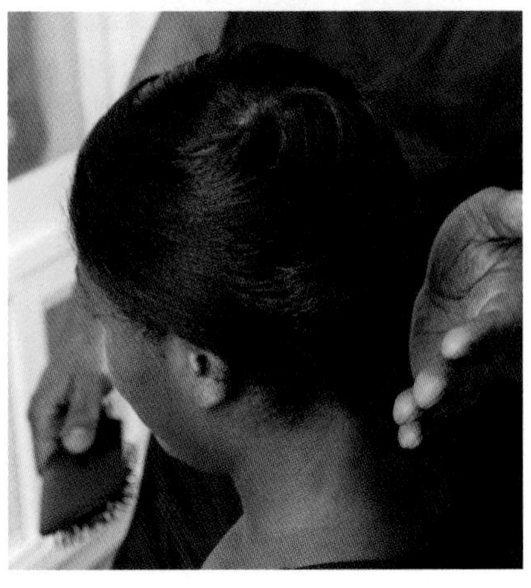

STEP 3 – Dry the hair under a hood dryer for up to 90 minutes and check it is dry before dressing out. Dress the hair into style and add finishing products to add shine and hold.

STEP 4 – The finished look.

Hair up style

Creating a bouffant roll

This bouffant style uses a 'beehive' attachment for extra root lift.

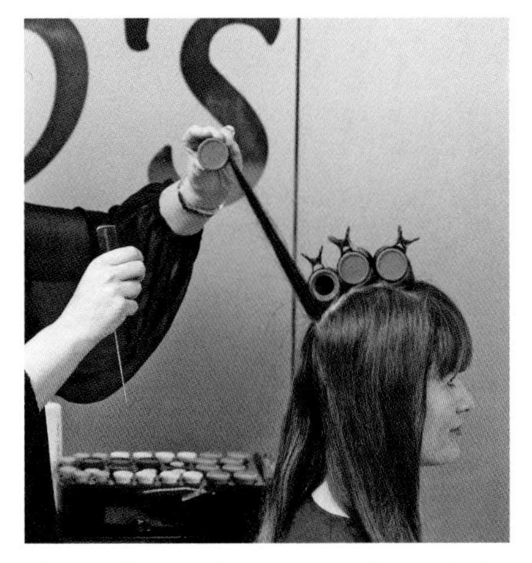

STEP 1 – Gown and prepare your client and set the hair with heated rollers. After removing the rollers, apply hairspray to the sections of hair and secure the back section into a bun.

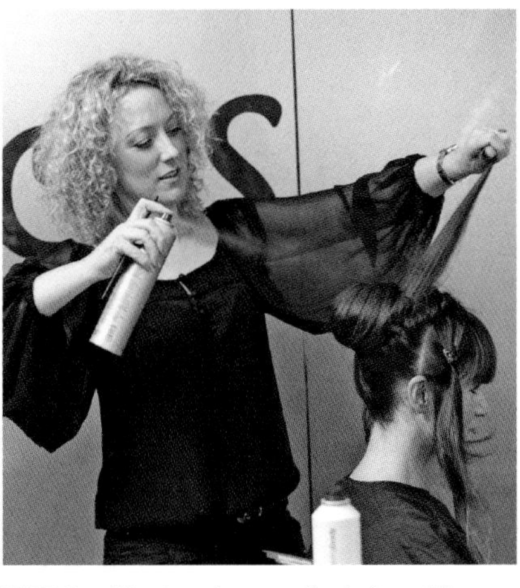

STEP 2 – Attach and secure the hair padding on top of the bun.

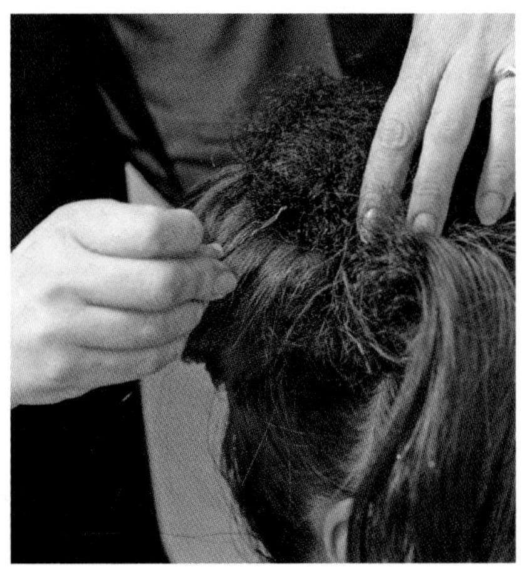

STEP 3 – Back comb each section of hair.

STEP 4 – Dress the hair over the hair padding into a bouffant, and secure with grips and pins. Tease the hair into place and apply finishing products.

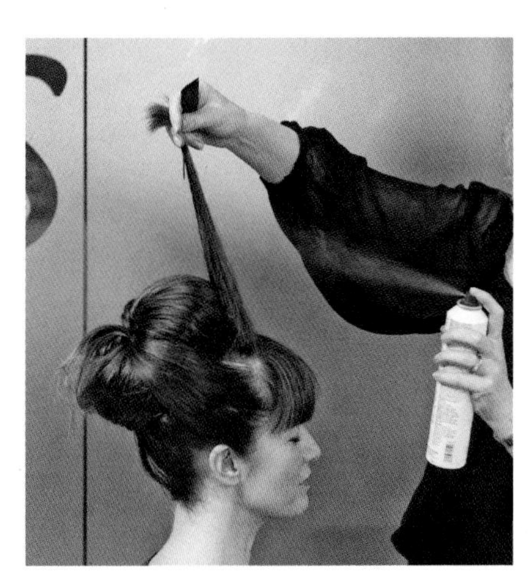

STEP 5 – Smooth any stray hairs with a comb or dressing-out brush and add more spray.

STEP 6 – Check the balance and ensure your client is happy with the end result.

HANDY HINT

Always ensure you handle and control the hair effectively when dressing it, setting the hair first. Using back-combing or back-brushing helps you to manipulate the hair into place. To help secure the hair, use grips, pins and hairspray.

Creating a vertical roll

STEP 1 – Gown and prepare your client and set the hair.

STEP 2 – Apply styling products to dry hair and back-comb the roots.

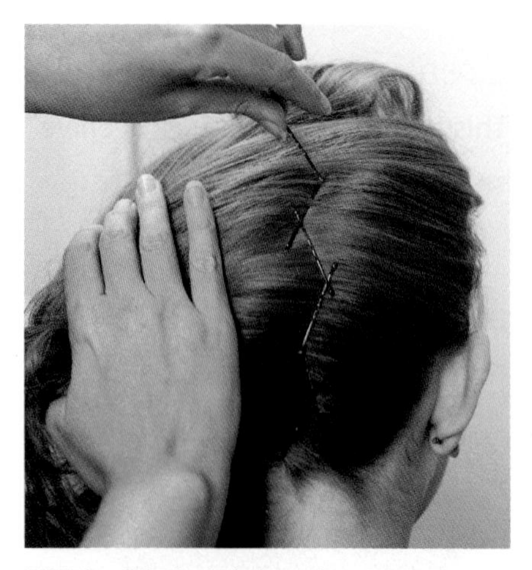

STEP 3 – Grip the hair down the centre, criss-crossing the grips.

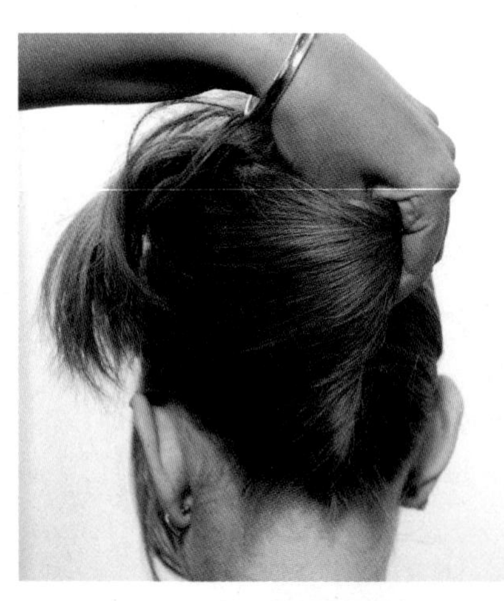

STEP 4 – Fold the hair, and slightly twist it over the grips, securing the hair with pins.

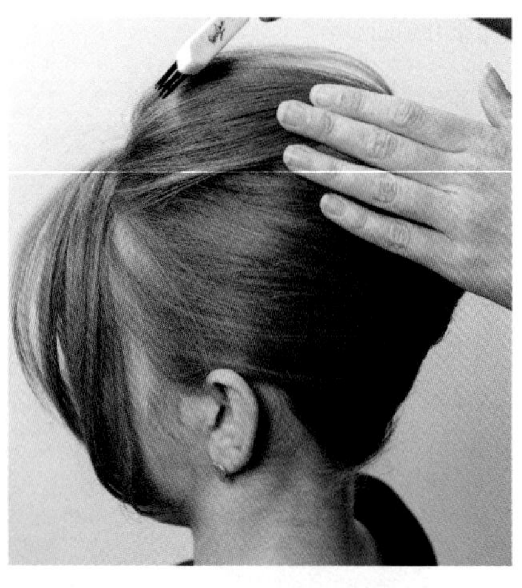

STEP 5 – Tuck the ends under the roll, smooth over the top section and apply finishing products.

STEP 6 – Check the balance and ensure your client is happy with the finished result.

Creating a hair up style incorporating a variety of techniques – plaits, knots and curls

STEP 1 – Prepare the hair by applying hairspray, heat defence and create curls with large tongs.

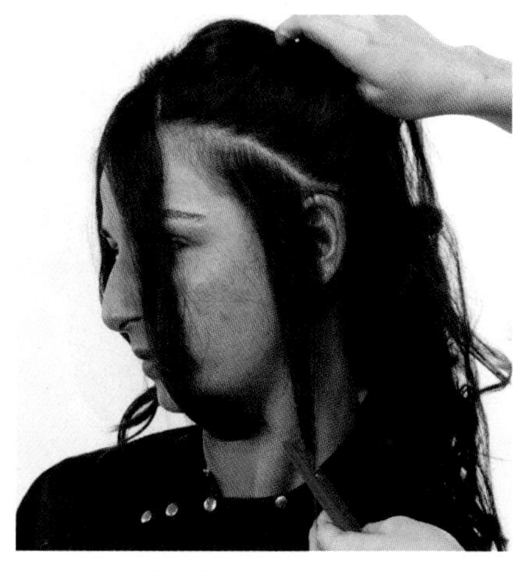

STEP 2 – Section the hair to put up, leaving out the hair which will remain left down and curly.

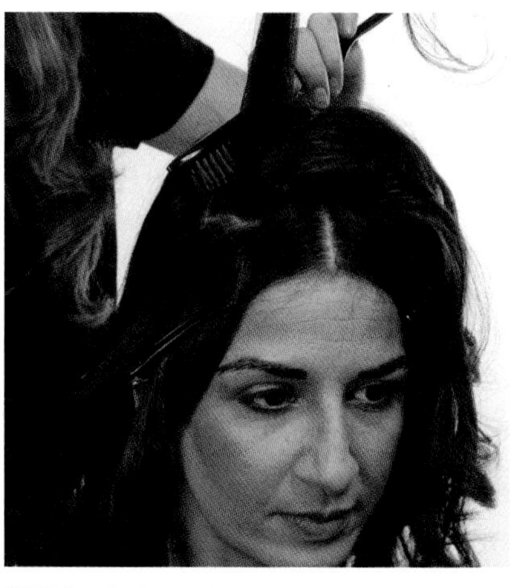

STEP 3 – Back-comb or back-brush the hair for height.

STEP 4 – Check the balance of the height created.

STEP 5 – Secure the hair in place by criss-crossing two grips.

STEP 6 – Plait the first side and secure the hair with a grip.

STEP 7 – Plait the other side and secure some of the hair back into a small ponytail using a band.

STEP 8 – Roll and pin the curls into place.

STEP 9 – Continue to roll and pin the ponytail to create curls and knots.

STEP 10 – Complete the curls and knots, leave some curls loose and check for balance and style security.

STEP 11 – Ensure the hair up is balanced and blended into the remaining loose curls.

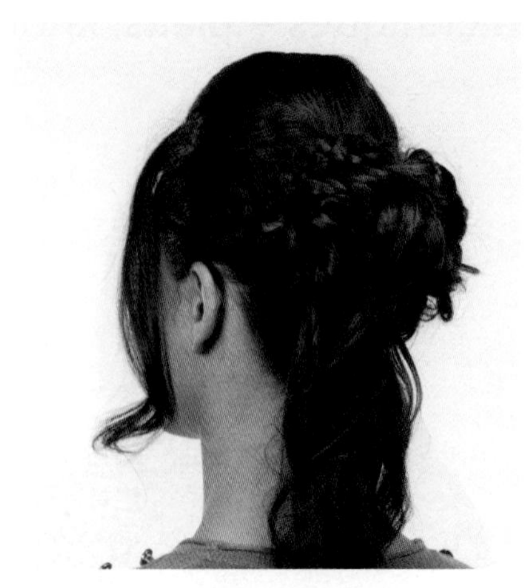

STEP 12 – The finished look.

Plait and twist hair

STEP 1 – Model before.

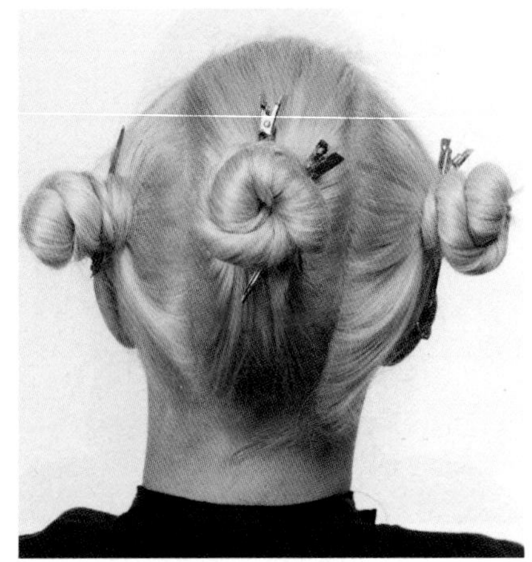

STEP 2 – Section the hair into three sections, from the middle of each eyebrow to the nape area, and secure in place.

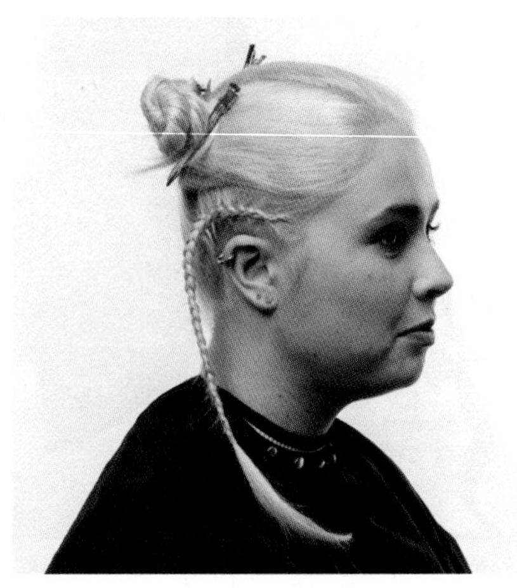

STEP 3 – On one-third of your front right section, plait the hair from temple to behind the ear.

STEP 4 – On the second third of your front right section, above the first plait, add a two-strand twist.

STEP 5 – Complete this side with another plait and then do the other side.

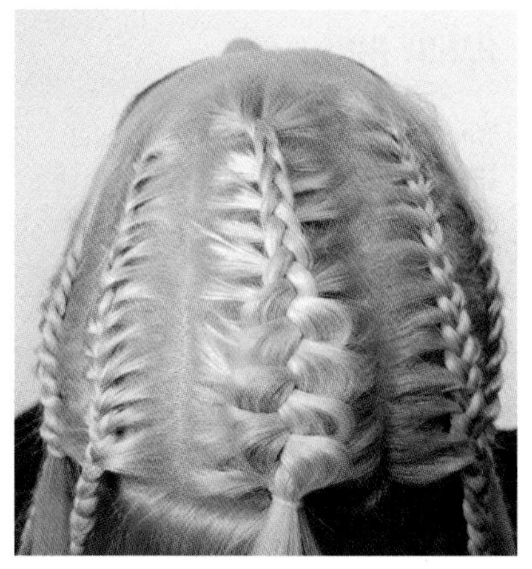

STEP 6 – Dutch plait the hair on top, from the front to the crown area and pull out the sections to create a looser loop.

STEP 7 – Continue to pull out loops through the top section/Dutch plait.

STEP 8 – Curl the back section with tongs and secure the ends of each plait and twist.

STEP 9 – The finished look.

Work with temporary added hair

When adding temporary hair you must:

- select and use added hair which is of a suitable:
  - texture
  - colour
  - length
  - width
- prepare the added hair according to the manufacturer's instructions, when required
- prepare your client's hair in a way suitable for the technique to be used
- confirm with your client the look agreed
- part the sections cleanly and evenly to meet the requirements of the temporary attachment systems to be used
- section the hair in a way that will allow the added hair to lie in the direction required

HANDY HINT

When consulting with clients about the hair to be added you must confirm the look agreed prior to starting the service.

- add hair in a way that takes into account the factors influencing the service and avoids potential damage to your client's hair
- check the comfort of your client at regular intervals throughout the service.

Finish hair

When finishing the style of added temporary hair you must:

- use heated styling equipment, when necessary, that is at the correct temperature for your client's hair and the desired look
- control your use of heated styling equipment (when used), to minimise the risk of damage to the hair and scalp, client discomfort and to achieve the desired look
- take sections of hair which suit the size of the heated styling equipment (when used)
- use back-combing and back-brushing techniques, when required, to achieve the desired look
- apply and use suitable products, when required, to meet manufacturer's instructions
- ensure the finished look takes into account relevant styling factors influencing the service
- ensure the finished look meets the intended shape, direction, balance and volume agreed with your client.

Add hair to enhance a style

STEP 1 – Colour the hair to the desired base shade. Back of the head – create a zigzag section using 27–29 bonds, tracking and alternating the colours throughout the application.

STEP 2 – Back of the head – create another zigzag section about a hand-width over the previous section using 30–32 bonds.

STEP 3 – Right side – continue from the first zigzag section on the back of the head, using 21–23 bonds.

STEP 4 – Right side – continue from the second zigzag section on the back of the head, using 21–23 bonds.

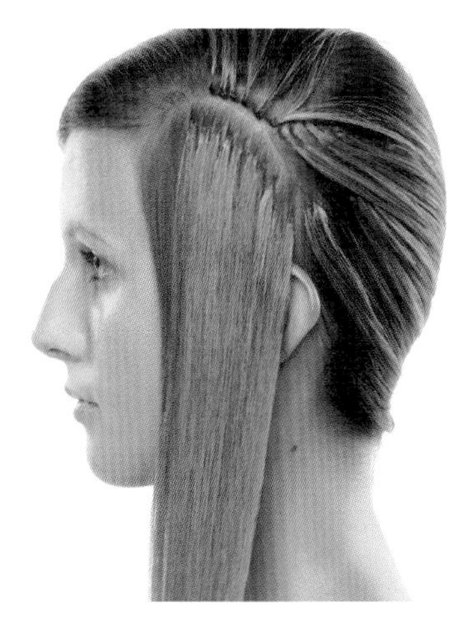

STEP 5 – Left side – make a diagonal line upwards as a continuation of the first zigzag section on the back of the head, using 9–11 bonds.

STEP 6 – Left side – continue from the second zigzag section on the back of the head, using 7–9 bonds.

STEP 7– The finished look.

You can use short-term extensions in various forms to add a creative and innovative design into the hair.

Bonded wefts – bonded techniques

In bonded techniques, wefts of hair are cut to size. Glue is applied to the root area of the natural hair and the wefts are secured in place by the glue.

STEP 1 – Section the hair and prepare the weft to be attached.

STEP 2 – Remove the sticky back from the strip of glue.

STEP 3 – Attach the weft to the glued area.

STEP 4 – Continue to add the wefts until the desired results are achieved.

STEP 5 – The finished look.

Provide clients with advice and recommendations on the service(s) provided

Remember to provide advice and recommendations on:

- how to maintain their look
- time interval between services
- present and future products and services.

Test your knowledge questions

Question 1

State the advice you would give to your client if it is hot and humid outside or damp and foggy.

Question 2

Agostina just had a chignon style – what aftercare advice would you provide to her for maintaining the style and removing it from her hair later?

Question 3

Describe how you would protect fine hair when using straightening irons.

Question 4

Jayne has straight, type 1 fine hair that is mid-length and slightly damaged. How would you create a curly round brush blow-dry look and what products and tools would you use to achieve longevity to Jayne's hairstyle?

Question 5

Ariane has dense long hair with poor elasticity. Explain how would you ensure her comfort and maintain even porosity while styling her hair?

Question 6

How would you control mid-length, type 4, wiry hair during a wrap set?

Question 7

Why should hair always be allowed to cool before removing the hair meche from the brush?

Multiple choice questions

8 Are the following statements true or false?
Statement 1: Hair is hygroscopic – it has the ability to absorb moisture.
Statement 2: Alpha keratin is hair in its natural state.

a True, true
b True, false
c False, true
d False, false

9 Repeated tension on the hair will result in:

a Fragilitis crinium
b Alopecia areata
c Traction alopecia

10 Hair set on-base will give:

a soft curls
b maximum volume
c maximum curls
d minimal root lift

11 Wefts and added hair can be used to:

a shorten a style
b add length
c hold ornamentation in place
d give a historical look

12 Are the following statements true or false?
Statement 1: Using too much product will hold the hair in style.
Statement 2: Using less product will protect the hair.

a True, true
b True, false
c False, true
d False, false

13 Which one of the following is the best method of controlling the hair when plaiting?

a Ask the client to hold the sections not being plaited
b Use oil-based products and apply heat
c Work methodically and apply tension
d Hold the hair close to the scalp

14 African-type hair lacks moisture and is:

a elastic and delicate
b coarse and dense
c fine and brittle
d dry and fragile

15 Which one of the following describes the effect of using a vent brush when drying hair?

a Textured straight finish
b Volume and root lift
c Waves in longer hair
d Curls in shorter hair

IGNAS DILYS – TONI&GUY, ALTRINCHAM

I moved from Lithuania to England in September 2015 specifically to get a qualification with Toni&Guy as I knew the brand was very high profile and the training programme offered is one of the best you can get in Europe.

With my mother being a hairdresser, I was close to the industry from a young age. Once I started to look into hairdressing across the world I realised how much of an opportunity it was for me to gain a skill, especially by doing an Apprenticeship with industry-leading companies like Toni&Guy, Vidal Sassoon, Wella and L'Oréal. It was at this point that I decided to leave my home country and family to come to England to pursue my career as a hairdresser.

I chose to work with Toni&Guy because I like the style of the company, the funkiness of the brand's aesthetic and the collections they launch every year. The possibilities are limitless after you qualify with the company and your skill is recognised across the globe.

In less than two years, I feel that I have achieved more than I ever imagined – I have done my NVQ Level 2 and vardered in such a short period of time that I couldn't be even close to doing hairdressing back in Lithuania. I feel very motivated with the opportunities to go forward within the company.

My aspirations in the future are to become an Educator at the Toni&Guy Academy, qualify as an Art Director, work in London Fashion Week and represent the brand as a member of the Art Team. I feel like I have the ambition and skill to do that in less than five years' time.

This chapter maps to:

- Unit 10, Style and finish men's hair (Level 2 Diploma for Hair Professionals – Barbering).

INTRODUCTION

From finger drying short, textured hairstyles to blow-drying the pompadour, drying and finishing men's hair is becoming an integral service in the current barbering market. A professional barber should demonstrate good dexterity skills to be able to manipulate and shape different hair lengths and densities, to suit the needs of every client.

After reading this chapter you will:

- understand how health and safety policies and procedures affect drying and finishing services
- know how to dry and finish hair
- dry and finish hair.

HEALTH AND SAFETY POLICIES AND PROCEDURES

It is important that you and your work area are prepared before your client arrives to promote a professional image. Men's cutting and styling services generally have a quick **turnover** of clients, many offering a no-appointment necessary service. Being prepared for the service will help keep the barber salon running smoothly.

KEY TERM

Turnover – trade.

Throughout the service you must follow the health and safety requirements of the service and within your job role. For a recap on your responsibilities and how these relate to a men's drying service, refer back to Chapter 1.

▲ Barber salon prepared ready for the service

HANDY HINT

Refer to Chapter 1 for more information on appearance, personal hygiene and behaviour.

Personal hygiene

Ensure you start your day with a shower, fresh breath and clean clothes. Apply deodorant and a splash of aftershave/perfume so you smell good too. Make sure your own hair is clean and presentable, in line with your salon image.

Prepare and protect your client

It is rare for a male client to visit the barbers for a shampoo and drying service only. It is much more likely you will need to prepare the client for a cut and dry service. Always make sure you use a clean gown and towel to protect your client's clothes from products as well as any hair cuttings.

Some salons shampoo the hair again after a cutting service to remove the hair clippings and then style and finish the look. Once the hair has been shampooed, you should apply any products to the hair, ideally wearing gloves to protect your hands from dermatitis.

Potential hazards and risks

As with all services there are potential risks to people's health if hazards are not identified and the risks of injury are not prevented.

Safe and hygienic working methods and practices

During the styling service make sure that you maintain good posture and keep your back straight with your legs slightly apart for an even balance. A good posture will help to prevent back injuries and fatigue.

For the comfort of your client make sure they have their feet supported on a footstep, if the barber chair is raised, or have their feet flat on the floor. Sit them upright with their back against the chair. It is important that your client is comfortable throughout the service and evenly balanced, so you can produce a balanced look.

▲ Safe and hygienic working methods and practices

Preventing contact dermatitis

After shampooing your client's hair and applying their styling products, wash and dry your hands to prevent the development of contact dermatitis when carrying out drying and finishing services.

Preventing cross-infection and cross-infestation

You must keep your work area clean and tidy at all times. Make sure that your trolley and workstation are prepared for the required service and that you are ready for the client to arrive. Clean and sterilise or disinfect

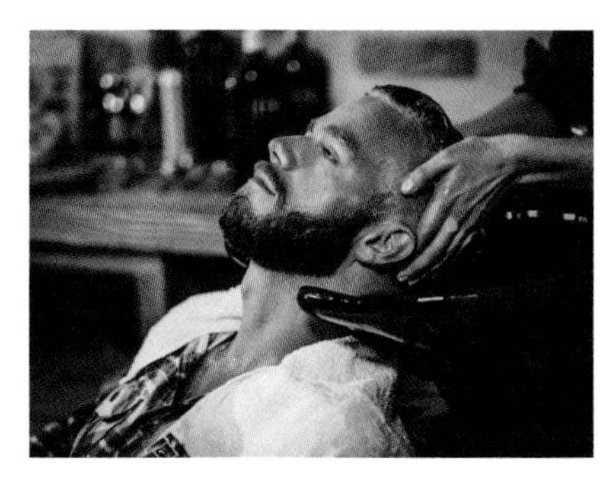

▲ Shampoo the client

ACTIVITY

Describe the potential hazards and risks which exist in your workplace and the safe working practices which you must follow.

▲ Client prepared for service

HEALTH AND SAFETY

Dispose of any products correctly ensuring that you maintain sustainable practices and recycle where possible.

ACTIVITY

Describe different types of working methods that promote environmental and sustainable working practices.

HANDY HINT

Dermatitis can be recognised by inflamed skin, which may be red and sore, and the skin can weep and split.

▲ Clean and sterile tools

HANDY HINT

Poor standards of health and hygiene can cause offence to others, cross-contaminate and present a poor salon image.

ACTIVITY

Describe the methods of cleaning, disinfecting and or sterilisation used in the salon for drying services.

▲ Check the hair and scalp prior to the service

your tools and equipment to ensure they are hygienic and ready for use. Clean your workstation and surfaces with detergent and water before spraying with disinfectant.

Working safely, cleanly and tidily minimises risk of harm and injury to yourself and others, prevents cross-contamination and gives the client an image of professionalism.

DRY AND FINISH HAIR

You must always complete a thorough consultation to identify your client's requirements, before you can decide on the most suitable tools and equipment to use, and ensure you achieve the desired result.

Before the hair is shampooed and prepared for the service you should carry out a porosity test on the hair to see if it's porous or non-porous. Porous hair will hold onto the water and may tangle or snag on combs or hairbrushes; so extra care needs to be taken when drying, as the cuticles are raised and damaged. Non-porous hair has smooth, closed cuticles and should be less prone to tangles and easier to work with.

Once the hair has been shampooed, you must carry out an elasticity test to ascertain how the hair stretches when wet and to decide on the strength of the cortex. If the hair has weak elasticity and the cortex is damaged you should be careful not to over-stretch the hair as it may break. If the hair springs back to its original length, then its elasticity is strong and the cortex is in good condition.

Over-drying porous hair and over-stretching weak hair could cause further damage to the hair and may lead to breakage, so always ensure you test the hair and use brushes and tools suitable for the hair's condition.

You will need to visually check and feel the hair to identify:

- the condition of the hair and scalp
- the hair length, style, type, texture and density of the hair
- any growth patterns
- the client's head and face shape
- any scalp problems.

Consult with clients

You must ask questions and check the hair and scalp to identify if there are any factors that may limit or prohibit the service.

It is important to confirm with your client the look agreed at consultation to ensure both parties agree with the style you are working towards. Remember to question your client during the service to check he is still happy with the style planned.

Questions could include:

- How do you like to wear your hair?
- Do you have a parting?
- What products do you use to style your hair?

- What styling tools do you use?
- Do you spend much time drying and styling your hair?
- Do you wear your hair differently for work or going out?
- Do you like a style that has body and movement or flatter styles?
- Is there anything about your hair your do not like or struggle to manage?
- Do you want to try anything different with your hair today?
- What would you like me to do to your hair today?

ACTIVITY

Use your English skills to obtain as much information from your client as you can. Open questions require the client to give a more in-depth answer and begin with 'what', 'why', 'how' and 'when'. Closed questions help to confirm and define details and are answered 'yes' or 'no'.

ACTIVITY

How many of the following questions are open questions?

1. Do you normally use products on your hair?
2. How busy is your lifestyle?
3. What type of work do you do?
4. How often do you shampoo your hair?
5. What products do you use on your hair?
6. Do you blow-dry your hair at home?

Factors that may influence the service

As you are likely to be carrying out a cutting and drying service you will need to ask open and closed questions to help you to identify your client's requirements, such as:

- How do they want their hair to look?
- What products do they generally use on their hair and why?
- What life factors may affect their hairstyle? For example, daily swimming or going to the gym, working on a building site in dusty conditions, riding a motorcycle.
- Have they been happy with their previous style and do they wish to change or alter anything?

▲ A client who exercises regularly may prefer a low-maintenance hairstyle

Haircut

When you have found out the above information you will know the type of haircut to be carried out and you can make sure that the hair is styled to suit the cut. When you know the style requirements, you will be able to choose your tools and products to suit the style and the hair's characteristics.

Hair characteristics

Factors	Effect on the style	Effect on products	Effect on tools
Texture – fine	You need to consider the length of fine hair, as longer lengths can look thinner. More supportive, stronghold products will be required.	Fine hair will need less product applied. Use products that support the style and give the hair body and volume – even for smooth straight styles.	Fine hair will need to be blow-dried with a brush to give root lift and support the style.
Texture – coarse	Coarse hair can have a tendency to look rough and dry and may need taming and controlling to ensure the style looks its best. Smoother styles may be difficult for the client to maintain between salon visits.	Coarse hair will need more products to be applied and you will need to use products that smooth the cuticle and give it shine, such as a serum.	Coarse hair will need a bristle brush to smooth the hair.
Density – sparse	Sparse hair should be treated in the same way as fine hair when styling; however, it will dry quicker.	For sparse hair less product is required. Take care not to overload it.	Take care with tools on sparse hair and avoid causing your client any discomfort.
Density – abundant	Abundant hair will take longer to dry and may make the style look big, so it is important to select the correct style to suit this hair type.	Abundant hair will need more products; use those that do not provide any volume or lift but help to smooth the hair.	Avoid brushes and creating root movement that promotes volume and root lift and makes the hair look thicker.

Hair classifications

Factors	Effect on the style	Effect on products and tools	Effect on equipment
Type 1 hair Straight hair – fine/thin	Hair tends to be very soft, shiny and oily, it can be difficult to hold curl/ body.	Use products that will aid body and hold. Avoid oily products and do not overload the hair. Use tools that will grip the hair and hold it in place while styling, as it will resist curling/ movement.	Using heated styling equipment such as straightening irons to bend the hair and create movement may assist styling.

Factors	Effect on the style	Effect on products and tools	Effect on equipment
Type 1 hair Straight hair – medium	Hair can have lots of volume and body and can be easy to work with.	Use products to suit style. Use tools to suit style.	Use equipment to suit style.
Type 1 hair Straight hair – coarse	Hair can be extremely straight and difficult to create body.	Use products that will aid body and hold or movement-enhancing products. Use tools that will grip the hair and hold it in place while styling, as it will resist movement.	Using heated styling equipment such as straightening irons to bend the hair and create movement may assist styling.
Type 2 hair Wavy hair – fine/thin	Hair can normally be styled easily and has a definite 'S' pattern.	Use products to suit style. Use tools to suit style.	Use equipment to suit style.
Type 2 hair Wavy hair – medium	Hair tends to be frizzy and a little resistant to styling.	Use styling products to smooth frizz and also give hold and movement to the hair. Use tools that will grip the hair and hold it in place, as it will resist styling, or finger dry the hair for a more rugged look.	Using heated styling equipment such as straightening irons to provide longevity to the style may help.
Type 2 hair Wavy hair – coarse	Hair tends to be very resistant to styling and normally very frizzy. The waves are often quite thick.	Use products to smooth frizz and control the waves, while providing hold. Use tools that will smooth the frizz and grip the hair holding it in place, as it will resist styling, or finger dry the hair for a more rugged look.	May benefit from using heated styling equipment such as straightening irons to provide longevity to the style.

Factors	Effect on the style	Effect on products and tools	Effect on equipment
Type 3 hair Curly hair – loose curls	Hair tends to have a combination texture – it can be thick with lots of body, but can sometimes be frizzy.	Use products to smooth and prevent frizz. If working with the curls, use curl-enhancing products or a smoothing product if a sleeker style is required. For low maintenance styles and when working with the curls, use a diffuser and control the curl with a finger dry. If aiming for a smoother look, use a medium to large radial brush to smooth the curls.	If smoothing, straightening irons will provide longevity to the smoother style.
Type 3 hair Curly hair – tight curls	This hair can also have a combination texture. Hair tends to have a medium amount of curls.	Use products that will work with the curls and even out the textures – serums, heat protectors, creams and wax would work well. For low maintenance styles and when working with curls, use a diffuser and control the curl with a finger dry. If aiming for a smoother look, use a large radial brush to smooth the curls. As hair can be frizzy it will tangle easier. Take care with combs and hard brushes. Take care with all tools, avoid pulling on the hair and work with the curls wherever possible.	If smoothing the hair, straightening irons will provide longevity to the smoother style – but ideally work with the curls and not against them, as continued straightening of curly hair will cause damage.
Type 4 hair Very curly hair – soft	Hair tends to be fragile, tightly coiled and has a defined curly pattern.	Use products that will protect the hair from heat and further damage, but also help to control the curls. Take care with tools, avoid pulling on the hair and work with the curls wherever possible. Use diffusers to style the hair.	As the hair is fragile, avoid wherever possible the use of heated styling equipment.

Factors	Effect on the style	Effect on products and tools	Effect on equipment
Type 4 hair Very curly hair – wiry: African-Type hair	Hair tends to be very fragile and tightly coiled and has more of a 'Z' pattern shape.	Use products that will protect the hair from heat and further damage, but also help to control the curls. Take care with tools, avoid pulling on the hair and work with the curls wherever possible. Use diffusers to style the hair and a hair rake to maintain the curl.	As the hair is fragile, avoid wherever possible the use of heated styling equipment.

HANDY HINT

Hair classifications are very diverse, as are your clients. Styling straight, coarse Asian hair will be very different to styling tight, curly African-type hair. It is not just hair and skin colour that varies across ethnicities, facial characteristics vary enormously too:

- face and skull shapes
- width of the cheeks
- nose shapes – nasal openings and the bridge of the nose
- eye shape
- lip shape and fullness/thickness.

Hair growth patterns

Factors	Effect on the style	Effect on products and tools	Factors
Hair growth patterns – cowlick Widow's peak	When styling fringes, identify potential problems with cowlicks and widow's peaks. You may need to advise a more suitable style, or suggest ways to work the cowlick or widow's peak into the style. With a widow's peak, you should avoid fringes and aim for styles where the front section is styled backwards or slightly to one side.	When working with a cowlick, use a stronger styling product on the fringe area and a hairspray to hold. Use products to hold and support the hair over or to one side when styling hair with a widow's peak. Use a brush to smooth and control the cowlick, or work with it when finger drying the hair. For a widow's peak use a radial brush to direct the root area over or to one side.	Use a nozzle on the hairdryer to aid the direction of the airflow. Diffusers can be used to finger dry and **manipulate** the hair into the desired direction. Straighteners can also be used – take care near the skin and forehead.

Factors	Effect on the style	Effect on products and tools	Factors
Hair growth patterns – nape whorl	Consider the nape line and shape direction when dealing with nape whorls on shorter styles.	Use a strong, heavy finishing product on a nape whorl if it tries to defeat you. Wax can work well, but be careful not to make the nape area look oily. A little hairspray may help too. Use a flat brush and dry into the neck to avoid root lift near the nape whorl.	Use a nozzle on the hairdryer to aim the airflow downwards and dry the nape whorl flat. Do not try to use straighteners – they will not help and you will burn the client's neck.
Hair growth patterns – double crown	Try to work with double crowns and create texture to the style, but avoid causing the hair to stick up. Play with the hair and see in which direction it settles the best; use this to recommend to your client the best direction for the style.	Use a stronghold styling product around the crown area and hairspray to hold the finished look. Use a radial brush and direct the airflow to the root, bending the hair into the desired direction. Dry the hair **off-base** where needed to avoid additional lift.	Use a nozzle with the hairdryer to aim the airflow in the desired direction. If aiming for a funky, messy image, work with the double crown and use it in a finger dry.

Male pattern baldness

Some clients with male pattern baldness will want their style to cover the hair loss area where possible. Often this involves keeping the top section a little longer and styling the hair back and slightly to one side. If the hair loss is great, hairspray will be required to help keep the hairstyle in place.

▲ Man with male pattern baldness wearing his hair forward and longer on top

▲ Man with early signs of male pattern baldness and front hairline recession

KEY TERM

Manipulate – control.

HANDY HINT

Off-base means dragging the root back, slightly away from the brush base and away from the section.

On-base means winding the brush from point to root onto the section base.

HANDY HINT

Refer to Chapter 5 for more information on male pattern baldness.

HANDY HINT

Male pattern baldness is often referred to as Hamilton's pattern of male pattern baldness or Hamilton-Norwood scale of male pattern baldness.

Head and face shape

Head and face shape	Effect on the style
Head and face shape – oval 	Oval is known as the ideal face shape. Be creative and confident with your style, knowing you are working with this face shape.
Head and face shape – round 	Avoid width at the sides and too much height on top as the face will look fuller and rounder.
Head and face shape – square 	Some male clients will like the masculine face shape and you can encourage the squareness and enhance it with square hairstyles/ shapes, or round off the shape to take the harshness away.
Head and face shape – oblong 	Avoid adding height (and therefore adding length to the face shape). Suggest a fringe to visually help reduce the length of the face if your client prefers to take the attention away from his long face.

▲ Male pattern baldness

HANDY HINT

Consider your client's features – faces with sharp noses should not be styled with centre partings; if ears protrude you could suggest styles that do not expose the entire ear.

▲ Client with a high forehead wearing his hair off his face

KEY TERMS

Humidity – moisture/dampness (in the air).

Hygroscopic – absorbs water.

HANDY HINT

Humidity returns the hair to the alpha keratin state by adding moisture from the air.

HANDY HINT

To learn about these bonds in more detail, refer to Chapter 6.

HANDY HINT

The weak temporary hydrogen bonds are softened by water and heat, and hardened by drying and cooling of the hair.

HANDY HINT

Remember: hair in its natural state is in an alpha keratin state; when wetted, stretched and dried, its new state is beta keratin.

Effects of humidity on the hair

When you style hair, you need to understand how **humidity** may affect the style. Hair is **hygroscopic**, which means it can absorb moisture from the atmosphere. The finished hairstyle is therefore affected by the humidity and moisture present in the air. The hair absorbs the moisture from the air and the beta keratin state changes back to alpha keratin, because the moisture softens the temporary hydrogen bonds and the hair reverts back to its original state.

Effects of heated styling equipment

Hair can be naturally curly, wavy or straight. It is held in its natural state by permanent and temporary bonds in the polypeptide chains. Permanent bonds need to be broken by chemicals, but when styling hair you soften the weak temporary bonds and temporarily change the hair's natural state.

The temporary bonds are hydrogen and salt bonds and can be broken, allowing the hair to change from straight to curly, or curly to straight.

Hydrogen bonds give the hair its strength and flexibility to move freely; it is what makes the hair elastic. Well-conditioned hair with a strong cortex can stretch up to a further half of its original length when wet; this is due to the temporary breaking of the hydrogen bonds.

Alpha and beta keratin

Hair in its natural state of curly, wavy or straight is described as being in an alpha keratin state. When hair has been wetted, stretched and dried into a new shape it is described as being in a beta keratin state.

Effect of heat on the hair structure

The main bonds that are broken when styling the hair are hydrogen bonds. These are broken by water or heat and hardened by drying or cooling the hair.

Heat alone can also change the keratin state; for example using straightening irons will change the state from alpha keratin and when the hair has cooled into its new shape it becomes beta keratin. However, due to the lack of excess moisture in the hair, this change will not last very long.

Keep hair damp throughout the drying process

Each client's hair will dry out at a different rate, and, because wet hair stretches allowing a new shape to form, an even moisture balance must be maintained. If areas of the hair have started to dry during the styling process, then hair will lose its elasticity and the ability to stretch sufficiently, so the result may be uneven. You must mist the hair sections lightly with a water spray if you notice an uneven elasticity when drying the hair, to allow the bonds to be reformed evenly into their new position.

▲ Mist hair with water to ensure an even porosity when styling hair

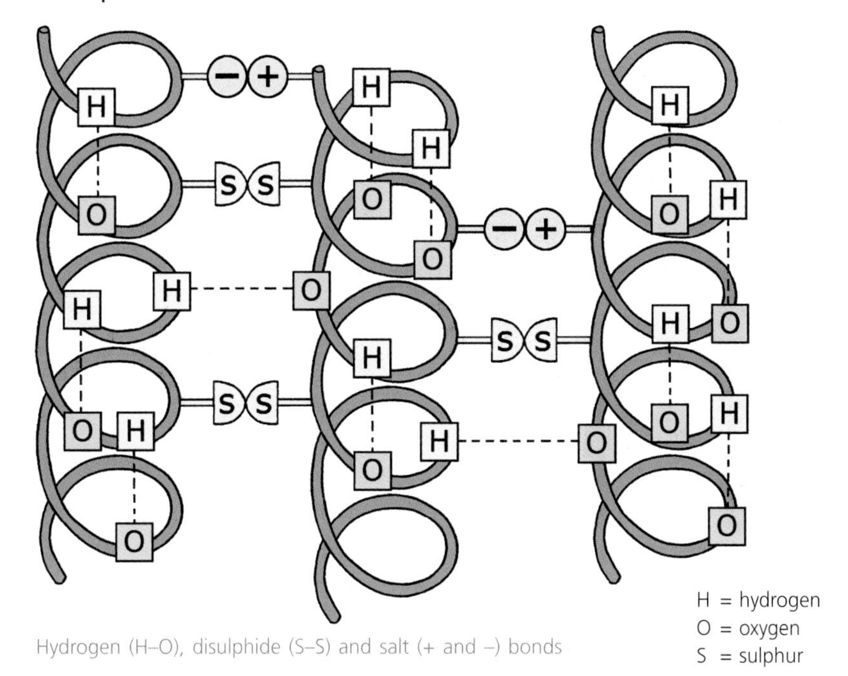

▲ Stage change from alpha to beta keratin

Using heat protectors

When hair is exposed to heat above 110°C, the following problems occur:

- damage to the cuticles, leaving the hair feeling rough to the touch
- damage and potential breakage to the hair structure as the keratin in the cortex is weakened
- colour fade.

Using a heat protector places a barrier between the hair shaft and the heat source.

▲ Heat protector spray

Tools, equipment and products available

When styling men's hair you may use a variety of electrical equipment and round or flat brushes to create the style required. Products should be chosen to suit the style worn and the hair type.

Select tools and equipment for styling

When using electrical equipment always follow the manufacturer's instructions to ensure you achieve the best result.

Tool	When and why you use it
Round brush	Used when blow-drying to style, smooth, straighten, add volume/root lift and create curl/movement.
Flat brush	Used when blow-drying to create a smooth, straight finish or to add texture to straight hair.
Rake attachment	Used when blow-drying African-type/very curly hair.
Hair dryer	Used to dry the hair when blow-drying or finger drying.
Straightening irons	Used to smooth and straighten dried hair.

ACTIVITY

List the tools and equipment you would need to:

- blow-dry short hair into a quiff
- finger dry short, curly hair.

Which products would you use for these styles?

Select products for styling

There is quite a range of men's styling products to choose from. It can be confusing deciding on the best product to use to achieve the desired results, so always read the instructions provided to identify how and when to use them.

Product	Why and how you use it
Spray	Some sprays can be used on wet hair to support the root area. Most are used on dry styled hair to provide extra hold, provide shine and lock-in the style.
Mousse Redken Guts10	Used on towel-dried hair to provide support when blow-drying. Gives the hair a boost with flexible fullness and volume. Lifts the roots and provides a foundation for styling.
Grooming cream Lock Stock and Barrel Pucka Grooming Creme	A weightless grooming cream, usually used on dry hair. Provides versatile styling control for short and long styles. It gives a medium pliable hold with a natural sheen that washes out easily in water.
Gel	Used on wet or dry hair to create a textured 'gloss' look – the ultimate in holding power, it helps hair look thicker with added shine. It provides a very strong hold with a high shine, prevents flaking, avoids drying the hair and scalp and allows for easier distribution through hair.
Wax NaCreo – Aqua Wax Blond	Used on dry hair to finish; adds pliable hold. It conditions the hair, providing an incredible shine and creates style and texture without weighing hair down. Some wax products add colour, masking the white hairs in a natural way.

Product	Why and how you use it
Tonic Fab Hair Tonic	Used on wet hair to tame it and make it more manageable, providing shine and a refreshing feeling.
Oil Morgan's Luxury Hair Oil	Used on wet hair to provide frizz and humidity control and to protect against the elements. A non-greasy formula that absorbs easily without residue. Used on dry hair to achieve ultimate shine. Restores and hydrates dry hair while enhancing shine and manageability.
Serum	Used on wet hair to strengthen and protect it from the damage done by overexposure to the sun. Helps stop fizziness and tangling. Used on dry hair to nourish and provide a more natural look. Smooths and softens the hair, providing a long-lasting shine.
Styling powder Fudge Professional Big Hair Elevate Styling Powder	Used on dry hair for an instant root boost. A fine, dry powder with no stickiness, providing long-lasting style with a matte finish. Sprinkle onto roots of dry hair and rub with fingertips to elevate the style.

HANDY HINT

Some products such as wax and cream are described as fibre, putty or pomade.

ACTIVITY

Identify your salon's product range for styling hair and list the benefits to the client. Describe how each product should be used.

Make sure you use suitable products for styling hair wet or dry. When using heated appliances, you must use products that protect the hair from heat and prevent damage.

To use products effectively:

- always follow MFIs
- follow COSHH Regulations

- wash your hands after application and ideally wear gloves to apply products
- dry hands after washing and moisturise regularly to avoid dermatitis
- use the correct quantity of product – avoid overloading the hair
- avoid product waste
- choose the correct product to achieve the best result.

HEALTH AND SAFETY

When using styling and finishing products you must do so safely and economically. Always ensure you follow COSHH.

ACTIVITY

Look at your salon's product range for styling hair and identify the benefits to the client.

Describe how each product should be used.

Choose a retail product for wet styling and one for dry hair styling and calculate the costs.

What would your 10% commission be?

▲ Display your products in view of your client so he can see what you are using on his hair

Follow salon/barbershop and manufacturer's instructions

It is important that you follow the manufacturer's instructions for the use of the specific styling and finishing products in your salon, as well as any instructions issued by your salon/barbershop. This will ensure you achieve the best possible result and avoid damage to the hair, or overloading the hair with products.

Applying correct techniques during services

You will need to be able to style hair on a variety of hair types and lengths, such as very curly, curly, wavy and straight hair and above- and below-shoulder lengths.

Current techniques for drying and finishing hair

The different brush drying techniques you may use are described below.

- Smoothing and straightening the hair – using large radial brushes or flat brushes depending on the texture and movement within the hair; you may use straightening irons too. The hair is dried off-base and the brush is angled flat towards the scalp and pulled through from root to point to keep the hair straight throughout. Apply products before styling that smooth the cuticle, such as oils and serums, and prevent moisture from penetrating the hair and finish with hairspray.
- Creating volume – using a large radial brush for root lift. The brush is angled on-base to create body, lift and volume. Apply products before styling that add volume or body, like a mousse, and finish with a cream, wax or gel depending on the style created.
- Creating movement – using various sizes of radial brushes for root lift and movement within the hairstyle. The brush should be angled

on-base for movement with volume and off-base for flatter roots and movement through the mid-lengths and ends. Apply products before styling that encourage movement or enhance curls, like a mousse or styling cream, and finish with a cream, wax or gel depending on the style created.

Another drying and finishing technique you may use is to create texture using finger dry techniques to work with the haircut, but create a certain 'roughness' or naturalness to the style.

You can see the step-by-step instructions for how to carry out these looks towards the end of this chapter.

▲ Style hair with a radial brush for root lift and volume

▲ Finger dry hair for movement and texture

Finger drying

You will need to be able to finger dry hair, which can create movement, volume, texture and curls.

When finger drying the hair, you must ensure you achieve the required amount of volume, movement and texture by elevating the roots to allow the heat from the dryer to access the roots of the hair. You should massage the root area in the direction in which the lift and volume are required and elevate the hair as you dry it. Applying products at the root area will support the style.

Short hair can be styled using a hand-held hairdryer and using your hands and fingers as the tools. This works particularly well for hair with movement and texture, requiring a finished look that is modern and funky. Your choice of styling products will influence the end result, as support from the product is required.

If you are working with curly hair you can use a diffuser on the end of the hairdryer. This will take the blast out of the airflow, but still supply the warm air required to dry the hair, enabling the curls to remain intact and not look fluffy in appearance.

ACTIVITY

Watch a barber blow-dry or finger dry the hair and observe how they hold the hairdryer in the direction of the cuticle layer.

Effects of products and tools

Whether you are finger drying or blow-drying short or medium-length hair, you must have control. Curly hair can be challenging to the most able barber, but using suitable products and tools such as a diffuser when finger drying and a nozzle when blow-drying helps you to control the hair. Your brush choice and size will vary, depending on the client's hair length, the desired look, degree of movement and volume required. A methodical working pattern is very important.

▲ Various sized round brushes

Direction of the air flow

The angle at which you direct the brush and airflow through the hair will aid you in achieving root lift and volume where required.

You should keep the brush on the base of the section if you require lift (on-base) and drag the hair back away from the section (off-base) if you require a flatter look.

HANDY HINT

It is importance to use a nozzle when carrying out drying techniques to direct the heat along the hair shaft following the direction of the cuticle. This will help you to avoid burning the scalp and causing discomfort to the client.

▲ Brush off-base

Section sizes and drying angle

When styling hair you must adapt the size of the hair section to suit the style and the density of your client's hair. Dense hair needs smaller sections to ensure the hair dries evenly. Styling hair with root lift will also benefit from smaller sections and dried on-base to create more lift. Angle the hair to suit the level of lift or flatness required. At the back and side, hair should be angled downwards and not elevated if lift is not required; equally hair should be lifted and angled upwards (above 90°) for volume and movement.

▲ Use a nozzle when carrying out drying techniques

Controlling hair and maintaining tension

Pulling the hair with tension as you dry it will make the style last longer, particularly if the hair is a little longer. Curly and layered hair being blow-dried straight will need a lot more tension than straight or wavy hair. Ensure the tension is firm but without causing discomfort to your client.

Effect of incorrect application of heat

For coarse or thick hair, you can use a high heat setting on the hairdryer, but on finer hair or porous hair adjust the temperature so it is cooler and does not cause damage to weaker hair. Always ensure your client is happy with the hairdryer temperature and check you are not causing discomfort or burning him.

Adapt equipment temperature

Avoid using too much heat on type 4 hair, as this will dry out the moisture from the hair. Type 4 hair and African-type hair are naturally low in moisture (1 per cent moisture, 99 per cent protein) due to the natural curl pattern and slightly open cuticle. Excessive use of heat will make hair which already lacks moisture, feel and appear drier. As with all hair types, African-type hair is moisturised from the sebaceous gland. However, due to the curl pattern it takes longer for the sebum produced by the sebaceous gland to wind its way down the length of the hair. This is why we have to add moisturising products to constantly rebalance the moisture level in the hair.

▲ Take extreme care with heat on type 4 very curly hair

HANDY HINT

Remember: incorrect application of heat can cause damage to the hair and a loss of elasticity, damage to the cuticle scales and an increase in porosity. You could also discolour the hair, or cause client discomfort.

▲ Check the balance of the style

Allow hair to cool prior to finishing

After blow-drying, or when using heated appliances, always allow the hair to cool, or use the cool setting button on the hairdryer for a minute or so at the end. Once the hair has cooled the hydrogen bonds are hardened in their new shape of beta keratin and the result will be longer lasting.

Once the hair is dry, allow the hair to cool and visually check the balance of the style. Check it is dry throughout and to your client's satisfaction. Apply finishing products to either add texture, or support the finished look.

HANDY HINT

Remember to allow the hair to cool, as this hardens the hydrogen bonds and sets the new shape to prolong the style.

Providing clients with advice and recommendations

To ensure your client is satisfied with the end result, it is important to achieve a finished look which meets the intended shape, direction and volume agreed.

During and after the service you should recommend aftercare and give your client advice on how to maintain their look, products and their use, and when to return for future or additional services.

Retail and maintaining the style

Together with advising on the best products and equipment for maintaining the style at home, you should give advice on which tools to use. Recommend brushes that will help the client to recreate the look, explain how to use them and show them how to follow the direction of the cuticle. Show your client the products you have used on his hair and recommend which ones he purchases for home use.

When providing advice always follow the legal requirements and always be honest about what products and equipment can do.

Time intervals between services

Advise your client when to return to the salon for a repeat service or a new service. Explain that if they struggle to style their hair, it has probably grown out of shape and they should return for a cut and blow-dry service. Suggest they book in every four to six weeks (four weeks for short clipper cut/shaved services and six weeks for styles that are worn a little longer, and particularly styles worn over the ear). Their average rate of hair growth will also influence service intervals.

▲ Recommend products you have used and show them to your client

Present and future products and services

You should advise your clients on the products you used to create their initial style, asking them about the products they already have, and suggesting which new products they would benefit from purchasing and using. Always advise your client on how to use the products and how to remove them from the hair to prevent build-up.

WHAT YOU MUST DO

For your practical assessments you must:

- Apply safe working practices when drying and finishing men's hair
- Dry and finish hair.

Apply safe working practices when drying and finishing men's hair

During your assessments, you must:

- prepare for drying and finishing services and ensure you protect your client to meet your salon's requirements
- apply safe and hygienic methods of working throughout services by maintaining your responsibilities for health and safety and protecting your client's clothes throughout the service. Adapt the position of you and your client to meet the needs of the service without causing them discomfort and ensure your own posture and position while working minimise fatigue and the risk of injury. Keep your work area clean and tidy throughout the service and use working methods that:
  - minimise wastage of styling and finishing products
  - minimise the risk of damage to tools
  - minimise the risk of cross-infection
  - make effective use of your working time
  - ensure the use of clean resources
  - minimise the risk of harm or injury to yourself and others
  - promote environmental and sustainable working practice.
- Ensure your personal hygiene, protection and appearance meet accepted industry and organisational requirements and that you follow workplace and suppliers' or manufacturer's instructions for the safe use of equipment, materials and products. Always ensure you dispose of waste materials correctly.
- Select suitable products, tools and equipment for the chosen service after confirming with your client the look agreed at consultation and during the service.
- Carry out the drying and finishing services completing the service within a commercially viable time.

ACTIVITY

Check with your salon manager the expected drying and styling services times that you should be working to.

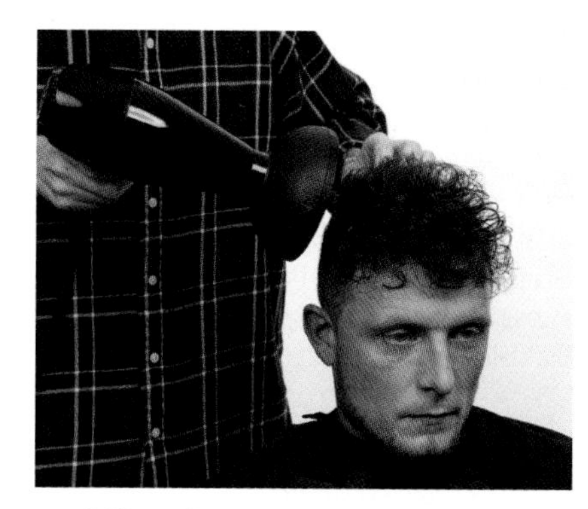

▲ Diffuser/finger-drying service

Dry and finish hair

When carrying out drying and finishing services you must consult with your clients to confirm the desired look and confirm the look agreed at consultation and during the service.

Throughout drying and finishing services, you must control your styling tools and equipment to minimise the risk of damage to the hair and scalp, client discomfort and to achieve the desired look. Styling and finishing products, when used, must be suitable to achieve the desired result and you must follow manufacturer's instructions at all times.

When styling, control your client's hair while taking into account all factors that may influence the service. Ensure you use and adapt your drying techniques to achieve the desired look and check the temperature of heated styling equipment throughout the service. The finished look must take into account the relevant factors and achieve the finished look which meets the intended shape, direction and volume agreed with your client.

At the end of the service confirm your client's satisfaction with the finished look and provide clients with advice and recommendations on the service(s) provided.

STEP BY STEP

Finger dry – creating movement and texture

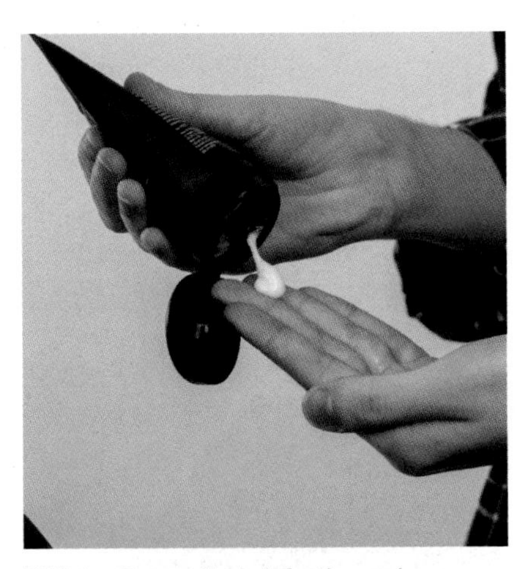

STEP 1 – Prepare the hair for the service – shampoo and condition the hair and remove excess moisture. Apply styling cream to support the style and provide strength.

STEP 2 – Work styling cream into the hair.

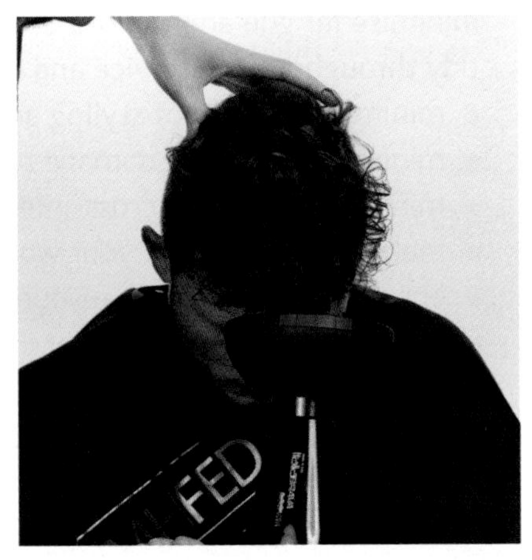

STEP 3 – Tip the head forward to manipulate the root area and dry the hair in the direction of the style using a hand held hairdryer.

STEP 4 – Ensure the roots are dried and the style is balanced.

STEP 5 – Apply styling powder to add matify, add texture and medium support and use a wide-toothed comb/streaker comb to separate curls.

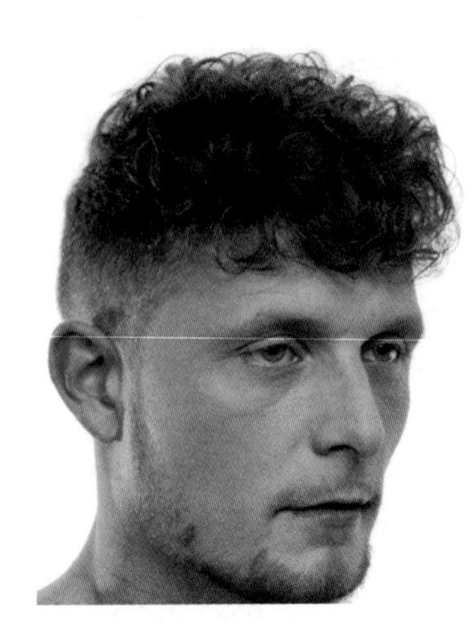

STEP 6 – The finished look.

Blow-dry hair – creating volume and movement

Pompadour quiff style

STEP 1 – Prepare hair for service and apply styling cream to strengthen the style and provide volume.

STEP 2 – Using a flat brush, blow-dry the sides back.

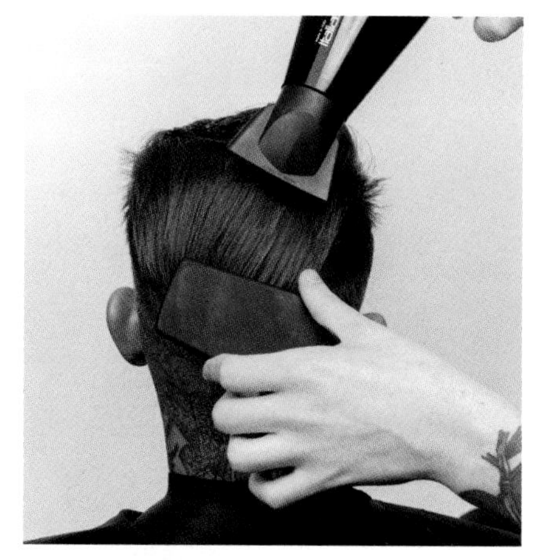

STEP 3 – Continue using the flat brush at the lower crown and back areas.

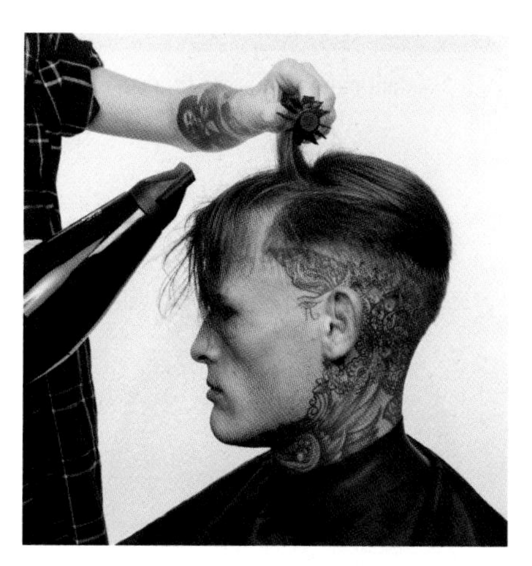

STEP 4 – Use a round brush from the top crown forward to create lift and volume at the root area.

STEP 5 – Use a larger round brush at the fringe for extra height and direct the root area upwards on-base for maximum volume.

STEP 6 – Apply product wax or clay through the sides to flatten and to add shine and a smooth finish.

STEP 7 – Using your fingers and a comb, smooth the shorter hairs down and into style.

STEP 8 – Apply styling powder at the roots on top for extra hold and height and finish with spray.

STEP 9 – The finished result.

Blow-dry hair – smoothing and straightening

Hair is dried using a flat brush such as a vent brush or Denman. For a straighter look you may use straightening irons too. The hair is dried off-base and the brush angled flat towards the scalp and pulled through from root to point to keep the hair straight throughout.

STEP 1 – Prepare the hair for the service, gown and protect the client, add serum oil to the hair to help smooth the hair and heat protector. Remove excess moisture before blow-drying.

STEP 2 – Section and secure the hair for methodical working. Using a flat brush, smooth and straighten the hair, working through the back.

STEP 3 – Continue this process through each side.

STEP 4 – Dry the top sections to partings.

STEP 5 – Use straighteners to smooth and straighten the hair and create a flatter look.

STEP 6 – Straighten the fringe, apply finishing cream and hairspray to create the finished look.

Test your knowledge

Question 1

Describe the effects of using a hairdryer nozzle.

Question 2

Why should hair always be allowed to cool before removing the hair from the brush?

Question 3

Describe suitable products to use on hair with coarse texture to give it shine.

Question 4

Explain the characteristics of type 4 very curly wiry hair.

Question 5

Describe the effects on the temporary bonds when styling hair from wet to dry.

Multiple choice questions

6 Are the following statements true or false?
Statement 1: Hair is hygroscopic – it has the ability to absorb moisture.
Statement 2: Beta keratin is hair in its natural state.

a True, true

b True, false

c False, true

d False, false

7 Hair dried on-base will give:

a loose curls

b maximum root lift

c tight curls

d minimal root lift

8 Too much heat on the hair will result in:

a fragilitis crinium

b alopecia areata

c ringworm

d traction alopecia

9 Are the following statements true or false?
Statement 1: Using too much product will hold the hair in style.
Statement 2: Using less product will protect the hair.

a True, true

b True, false

c False, true

d False, false

CHAPTER 8

COLOUR AND LIGHTEN HAIR USING A RANGE OF TECHNIQUES

OMOLADE ADEYIGA – TONI&GUY GLOUCESTER ROAD

My name is Omolade Adeyiga and I am an apprentice at Toni&Guy, Gloucester Road. I haven't always been a hair stylist – I first decided to pursue an academic path going to university, getting a degree and a job in banking. But I'd always had a passion for hairdressing, and had even worked at a hair salon while studying. Eventually, I recognised that I was unhappy with the career direction I had taken in banking, simply because I wasn't doing what I was passionate about.

So, I decided to pursue hairdressing. When I began as an Apprentice, it was challenging feeling like I was starting again at the beginning when I was 25 years old and my fellow Apprentices were 16/17 years old. It was important for me to adapt and allow myself to be able to relate to them. I also keep asking 'why' questions to my tutors, always wanting to learn and develop my skills. I definitely think I'm proof that you can absolutely chase your passions, no matter how difficult or long your path might seem.

Since starting my Apprenticeship, I found that blow-drying clients' hair in the salon gives me the chance to work on clients and get a feel of what it will be like once I'm qualified. Helping stylists in the salon create different looks on their clients allows me to learn different techniques. I also had the opportunity to take part in the Toni&Guy Assistant Competition which allowed me to express my creativity and skills.

My advice to anyone who wants to take a career path in hairdressing will be to have an end goal as well as short-term goals, and be patient. These goals are what will keep you going on days when you feel like giving up. You need to be ambitious in wanting to learn and practise as much as you can, plus always ask questions because the Apprenticeship is the time to make mistakes and learn.

This chapter maps to:

- Unit 5 Colour and lighten hair using a range of techniques (Level 2 Diploma for Hair Professionals – Hairdressing)

INTRODUCTION

Colouring is one of the most exciting, creative and profitable services in hairdressing, but it can also be the most challenging. It is one of the most popular services offered in salons as colouring the hair adds texture, style and creativity to individualise a look. The service you offer and the skills you develop in colouring will be among the most important you learn. The theory you learn in colouring will be useful throughout your hairdressing career, so maximise your potential by mastering these colouring skills.

After reading this chapter you will:

- be able to apply safe working practices when colouring and lightening
- know how health and safety policies and procedures affect colouring and lightening services
- know how to prepare for colouring and lightening
- be able to colour and lighten hair
- know how to resolve basic colouring problems.

HEALTH AND SAFETY POLICIES AND PROCEDURES

You have already looked at health and safety, and your professional and salon/stylist image in Chapter 1, but you will now revisit these areas specifically in relation to the colouring service.

KEY TERM

Hydrogen peroxide – the solution that activates the colouring product to allow the colouring process to take place.

When colouring or lightening hair you may be using permanent colours, lighteners and **hydrogen peroxide** in various strengths, so health and safety is very important. Always ensure you mix colours and lighteners in the designated area of your salon and that your working environment is well ventilated.

Always carry out a thorough consultation with your client, checking the hair and scalp condition and carrying out all relevant tests. You must follow the manufacturer's instructions and protect both your client and yourself.

Personal responsibilities for health and safety

You must always adhere to all the health and safety Acts, but during a colour service you must pay particular attention to the Control of Substances Hazardous to Health (COSHH) Regulations 2002.

When mixing, using and applying colours, make sure you follow:

- the manufacturer's instructions (MFIs)
- local by-laws
- your salon's policies and procedures.

This includes wearing personal protective equipment (PPE) and SHUD:

- **S**toring chemicals and substances correctly
- **H**andling chemicals and substances correctly
- **U**sing chemicals and substances correctly
- **D**isposing of chemicals and substances correctly

SHUD derives from the rules of COSHH.

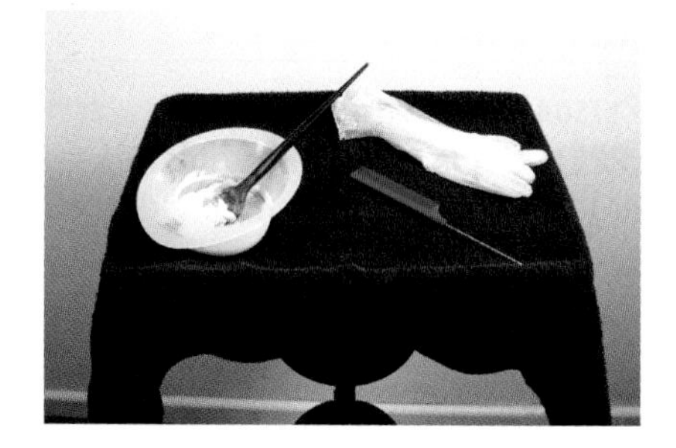

▲ Wear gloves when mixing chemicals

HANDY HINT

SHUD – what you **SHOULD** do when using chemicals.

Select colour and products

When using chemical products you must consider the effects they have on the environment. Always follow the requirements of your local council and local by-laws by disposing of your colouring waste in an environmentally friendly manner.

HEALTH AND SAFETY

Refer to Chapter 1 for more information on the health and safety Acts you must follow.

Protective clothing

Protective clothing is used to protect your client's clothing and to protect your clothes and hands. You must suitably protect your client for the service required. Always use:

- a fresh clean towel
- a fresh clean gown
- a plastic/disposable cape or another fresh clean towel (this may vary according to your salon requirements).

A client must wear a gown during a chemical service to protect their clothes. Some salons apply barrier cream around the client's hairline and ears before applying dark shades of colour directly onto the scalp to prevent skin staining.

HEALTH AND SAFETY

Refer to Chapter 1 for more information on health and safety and environmental and sustainable working practices.

HEALTH AND SAFETY

Disposable capes are waterproof and prevent colour and moisture from seeping onto the clients' clothing; they also prevent staining and damage to the salon's gowns and towels. They are designed for single use and should be disposed of in the bin after the service.

▲ Gowned client

Personal protective equipment

Personal protective equipment (PPE) for the stylist and the assistant includes:

- gloves to protect your hands from chemicals and staining
- aprons to protect your clothes from chemical damage.

If you suffer with asthma or allergies, you should:

- wear a particle mask when mixing or using colours and lightening powders to prevent inhaling substances
- wear eye protection when mixing colours and lightening powders to prevent chemicals from entering the eyes.

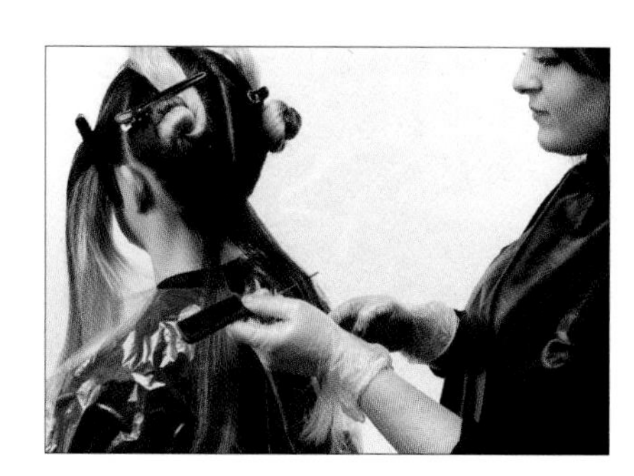

▲ Wearing gloves and apron

KEY TERM

Personal protective equipment (PPE) – your personal protective equipment, not your client's!

▲ Avoid spreading germs

ACTIVITY

List four ways to maintain your personal hygiene. List five things about your appearance that are important. Discuss your answers with your supervisor or tutor.

For professional use only.

Always read the safety instructions and follow the directions for use carefully.

IMPORTANT: This product is not intended for use on persons under the age of 16.

▲ MFIs with age restrictions

▲ Mix colours correctly and safely at all times

Always wear your PPE. It is important to protect your hands from contact dermatitis and to protect your clothes from damage when colouring. Remember to clean any products off of your skin immediately. Dry your hands and apply a moisturiser or barrier cream to your hands for extra protection against dermatitis.

Personal hygiene and presentation

Always make sure you are healthy for work and well presented, wearing suitable clothing and limited jewellery to enable safe working. Your own hairstyle and colour should be an advertisement and selling point for the salon. You should always have clean, styled hair and represent your salon's image.

Make sure all areas of the salon are hygienic and ready for the client. Poor standards of health and hygiene can offend your clients, spread germs and cause cross-contamination. Always seek guidance from your manager before going to work if you have a potentially infectious condition.

Age restrictions for colouring and lightening services

In November 2012 a new European Union (EU) directive came into force prohibiting certain colours and chemicals being used on any person below the age of 16 years.

The two restricted chemicals used in hair colours are:

- HC Orange No2
- 2-hydroxyethylamino-5-nitroanisole.

Manufacturers using products containing these chemicals are required to ensure their labelling includes the phrase, 'This product is not intended for use on persons under the age of 16'.

Colours that are mixed with hydrogen peroxide are also not permitted for use for clients below the age of 16 years.

ACTIVITY

Research your salon's product range to identify which products have manufacturer's instructions that state, 'This product is not intended for use on persons under the age of 16'.

HANDY HINT

Always note previous treatments, known allergies, skin disorders, medical instructions or advice and evident hair damage on the client's record card.

Hazards and risks

Almost anything can be a hazard in the salon and it is your responsibility, along with your employer, to prevent these hazards becoming risks to the safety of yourself and others. Maintaining a clean and tidy salon, following instructions and wearing PPE helps to reduce hazards and risks.

A hazard is something with the potential to cause harm. A risk is the likelihood of the hazard's potential being realised. Chemicals are a hazard! If chemicals are not stored, handled and used correctly then they pose a risk to you and those around you.

ACTIVITY

Watch and observe a colour service, then list all the potential hazards as you see them.

Dangers of inhalation of powder lighteners

Inhaling the fine powders from lightening products can cause **respiratory problems**, particularly if you suffer from asthma or other lung-related health problems. To prevent any health issues, you should wear a particle mask and always mix the product in a well-ventilated area.

KEY TERMS

Inhaling – breathing in.

Respiratory problems – breathing problems.

Safe and hygienic working methods and practices

Safe working practices include:

HEALTH AND SAFETY

Refer to Chapter 1 for more information on hazards and risks and safe working practices.

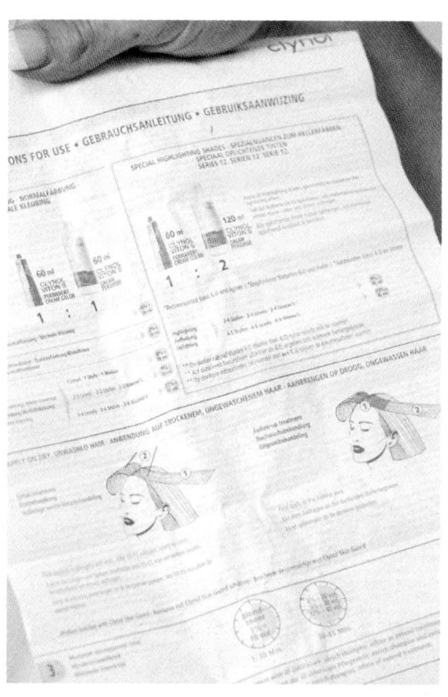

▲ Always read and follow the MFIs

HANDY HINT

When mixing chemicals and products, always wear your PPE and mix in a well-ventilated area. Remember to follow COSHH and SHUD, and safely measure your peroxide and other liquids at eye level to ensure accurate measurements.

A clean, well-prepared workstation will help you to sustain a hazard-free working environment and prevent cross-contamination. Always work efficiently and maintain a professional image. Report any problems with tools and equipment to a senior member of staff, and inform the relevant person of any products which need re-ordering.

To prevent cross-infection and infestation you should maintain a clean and tidy work area, work safely and hygienically, and clean, disinfect and sterilise your tools, equipment and work area after every client.

Client preparation

When your client arrives, sit them comfortably at your workstation, gown and protect their clothes and skin, and carry out a thorough consultation.

Prepare your client's hair by brushing it through to detangle it and section the hair ready for the service to ensure it is manageable. Protect the skin with barrier cream to prevent staining prior to a scalp application service, if required.

▲ Trolley on right-hand side, stylist and client positioned appropriately

Position of your client and yourself

You could be standing for long periods of time when colouring hair, so to ensure you are comfortable throughout you must stand correctly. Your client may be sitting in one position for a couple of hours so always check that they are comfortable too.

Keep an even balance through your body and avoid favouring one leg when you stand for long periods of time. Ensure your trolley is prepared in advance of the service and, if right handed, position your trolley to your right-hand side and vice versa if you are left handed.

HANDY HINT

When you are ready to start the colour service, check that your client is sitting in a balanced and comfortable position. Ensure your client's feet can either reach the floor or a footrest and that their back is supported against the back of the chair.

Minimise the risk of product contact on client's skin, clothes and surrounding area

When you apply colouring products you must work cleanly and methodically. Do not overload your tint brush with products as it may drip onto your client's clothing or skin. Section the hair neatly to assist you with a precise application and keep your sections clean as you progress, to avoid spreading products to around your client's hairline, surrounding areas and clothing.

HEALTH AND SAFETY

Always take precautions when using powder and other lighteners. Mix in a well-ventilated area and wear your particle mask if you have a respiratory disorder, such as asthma.

HANDY HINT

Bad news always travels more quickly than good news! Look after your clients when colouring their hair and respect their skin, clothing and belongings.

Promote environmental and sustainable working practices

Wasting products costs your salon money and in the long run this may cost you money too, since the more money the salon makes, the bigger likelihood of a pay rise for you. Waste products also affect the environment.

Always mix your colours and lightening products following the instructions; remember to consider the service you are carrying out and the density and length of the client's hair.

HEALTH AND SAFETY

Refer back to Chapter 1 for more information on environmental and sustainable working practices.

▲ Mix the correct amount of product to suit the hair length and density of the client

Waste disposal methods

At the end of the service, immediately remove waste products and dispose of them in the dedicated salon waste bin. Many salons rinse any unused chemicals down the sink with plenty of water. However, you should follow local by-laws and MFIs which say that chemicals should be disposed of in a chemical waste bin and collected by the local council.

ACTIVITY

If a stylist mixed up 10 ml more peroxide than they needed for each colour client, over 25 clients 250 ml of peroxide has been wasted (10 x 20 = 250 ml, a ¼ of a litre bottle).

1. If over one week, six salon stylists all wasted 10 ml of peroxide, and carried out a total of 120 colour services – how many mls of peroxide have been wasted?
2. If one litre of peroxide costs £9+VAT, how much money has been wasted?

HANDY HINT

Always mix the correct amount of product to suit the service, and the hair length and density of the client.

Contact dermatitis

When using colouring and lightening chemicals you are more at risk of developing dermatitis. Always protect your skin and wear gloves when:

- mixing chemicals
- rinsing tint bowls and brushes
- using colouring products
- removing colouring products from your client's hair
- mopping up spillages.

HEALTH AND SAFETY

Be safe – look after your hands and protect yourself from dermatitis. You should rinse, dry and moisturise your hands after every service.

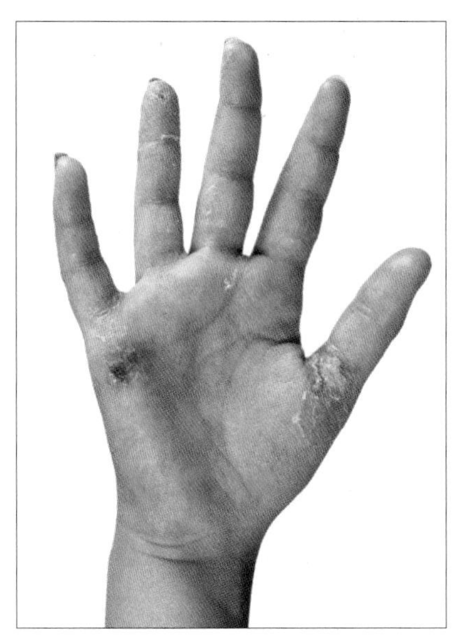

▲ Dermatitis

▲ Clean and tidy salon

Prevent cross-infection and cross-infestation

Always ensure your workstation and shampoo areas are clean and tidy to prevent cross-infection and cross-infestation. Wipe clean work surfaces, trollies and basins, and then sterilise them with an anti-bacterial spray. At the end of the colour service, make sure any waste materials are disposed of in a lidded bin, tint bowls are cleaned and put away and all stains are removed from the basin, so the area is ready for the next client.

Working safely and hygienically

When colouring hair and using chemicals such as lightening products and hydrogen peroxide, it is essential that you work safely. Spilling products on your skin can cause allergic reactions or burns, and incorrect storage such as leaving lids off bottles can put others at risk. Always mix colours in a ventilated area, follow the MFIs, wear your PPE and protect your client.

HEALTH AND SAFETY

Always cover and protect any cuts or open wounds to prevent cross-contamination and further harm.

ACTIVITY

List all the safe and hygienic practices you can think of. Consider the safety of the salon, your client, yourself and others.

HEALTH AND SAFETY

Refer to Chapter 1 for more in-depth information on working safely and hygienically.

Methods of cleaning, disinfecting and sterilising

When mixing colours, it is really important that your tint bowls and brushes are clean. If they are stained with previous colours, it may affect the end result of your client's hair.

Tint bowls and brushes should be washed in warm soapy water and rinsed until the water runs clear. Test that the bristles of the tint brush are clean by wiping them on disposable paper towels and checking that colour is not present – particularly near to the base of the bristles. Towels and gowns should be washed after every service.

Disinfect or sterilise bowls, brushes, work surfaces, combs, clips, re-usable colour-meches (if used) and all tools and equipment used in readiness for the next client.

HEALTH AND SAFETY

Refer to the Chapter for more in-depth information on sterilising and disinfecting.

Follow all safety considerations:

PREPARE FOR COLOURING AND LIGHTENING SERVICES

When preparing for colouring and lightening services you must:

- consult with and question your clients
- identify any contra-indications that may affect services
- carrying out relevant hair tests
- understand the principles of colour selection
- know the effects the products will have on the hair structure
- choose suitable tools, equipment and products
- know the different methods of applying and removing colouring and lightening products
- test and monitor development during services
- provide advice and recommendations for the service.

Question clients prior to and during services

You have a legal responsibility to question your clients about their hair before you commence with the service. You must record your client's responses to questions asked in case of any future legal action.

HANDY HINT

Record your client's responses to questions on a consultation sheet or record card. This will help you with future consultations, and you can use this information in the event of a problem, particularly if your client is intending to sue you or the salon.

Confirm the desired effect with your client

The consultation process is a very important part of the service. Ask plenty of open questions to identify the client's requirements: what are they hoping for and what is their vision of the end result?

Some examples of questions you could ask include:

- When did you last have colour put on your hair?
- What colours/products (if any) do you have on your hair?
- Do you want to cover any white hair?
- Do you want to go lighter or darker, or stay the same depth/darkness?
- Do you want to change the tone – add warmth or cool tones?
- Do you want your colour to be permanent or gradually fade out in time?
- Do you want an all over colour or **highlights/lowlights**?
- Do you have a colour/shade in mind or an image of what you would like?

You should use visual aids, such as colour charts or magazines, to ensure that you and your client have the same vision. This will enable you to choose the most suitable products, techniques, tools and equipment to achieve their desired result.

Ensure that you use positive body language together with open and closed questions to identify your client's needs. When giving your client effective aftercare advice, maintain eye contact and speak politely and clearly.

Colouring services are one of the most popular services in the salon – clients colour their hair for many reasons and you will need to identify which colouring service best meets the needs of your client.

KEY TERMS

Highlights – sections/woven pieces of hair that are coloured a lighter shade.

Lowlights – sections/woven pieces of hair that are coloured a darker shade.

▲ Use colour charts as visual aids

HANDY HINT

Reasons why clients colour their hair:

- cover white hair
- darken
- lighten
- change tonal colour
- add texture and enhance their style
- change their look.

ACTIVITY

Can you think of any other reasons why your clients may colour their hair?

ACTIVITY

When you are consulting with your clients you are using your English skills. Speaking clearly and ensuring that both parties have understood will help you to achieve the correct colour service and end result. When recording your client's answers to questions, make sure you write accurately and neatly, so that the information can be read and referred to at a later date.

In pairs, carry out role-play consultations to improve your skills in communicating and asking suitable probing questions.

Contra-indications and how they affect colouring and lightening services

Sometimes a service cannot be carried out because of **contra-indications.** You must ask your client whether they have had any **adverse reactions** to medication, products or services in the past. You must clearly write any answers to these questions on the client's record card in case of any future legal action that might take place. During the consultation check the condition and appearance of the hair and scalp to allow you to assess the options available.

KEY TERMS

Contra-indication – a reason that prevents a service or treatment from being carried out.

Adverse reaction – an unfavourable response to a product.

ACTIVITY

List the types of questions you could ask the client to identify contra-indications. How would you record them?

HANDY HINT

You should draw on the knowledge you gained in Chapter 1 on 'Advising and consulting with clients'.

Use the table below to learn how to find out about clients' contra-indications.

Contra-indication	How to find out	What to do	Why it affects the service
History of previous allergic reaction to colouring products	Ask your client if they have ever had an allergic reaction to colouring products before, including home colours or professional products.	Carry out a skin test, following the MFIs.	A client with a history of previous allergic reactions to colour is more at risk of future allergic reactions. You may need to offer an alternative colour service or advise that colour services are not carried out.
Other known allergy	Ask your client if they have any allergies, such as a nut allergy. Some products contain almond oils, so must not be used on a client who is allergic to nuts.	Carry out a skin test, following the MFIs.	A client with a history of other allergic reactions is more at risk of allergic reactions to colour. They may also be sensitive to some of the ingredients. You may need to offer an alternative colour service, or advise that colour services are not carried out.
Skin disorders	Ask your client if they suffer from any skin problems such as eczema or psoriasis.	Visually check the scalp, looking for skin disorders, infections, infestations and any cuts or abrasions.	Some skin disorders will prevent colour services from being carried out. Infections or infestations – no colour service to be carried out. Open cuts or wounds – no colour service to be carried out. Psoriasis or eczema may not affect the service unless the areas are open or sensitive for the client.
Incompatible products	Ask your client about their previous hair services and treatments, in and out of the salon, as they may react with professional products. Typically Henna and products containing metallic salts are products that are incompatible with other permanent colours and peroxide.	Visually check the hair for any signs of hair discolouration, and if in doubt, carry out an **incompatibility** test.	If your client has any product or service that is incompatible with the chosen service, then you cannot proceed with the colour. Alternative options may be available.

→

Contra-indication	How to find out	What to do	Why it affects the service
Medical advice or instructions	Ask your client if they are taking any medication or have been given medical advice that may affect the service, result or the condition of the hair.	Visually check the hair to see if it appears healthy. Is there any new hair growth or damage?	If a doctor has advised against colour services, then always follow their advice and do not put your client at risk of injury or reaction, or risk the salon being sued.
Evident hair damage	Ask your client how they treat and style their hair on a daily basis, for example, using straightening irons or curling tongs.	Visually check the hair for damage. Carry out porosity and elasticity tests.	If your client's hair is damaged then do not add additional chemicals to the hair. Consider alternative, milder colour options or alternative services while you treat the hair's condition.
Age restrictions	Ask your client their age to ensure they are at least 16 years old.	Ask to see photo ID if you are unsure of your client's age	If you client is under 16 years of age and the MFIs state the colour is not intended for use on persons under the age of 16, do not carry out the service – offer alternative services.

KEY TERMS

Incompatible – unsuitable.

Evident – easily seen.

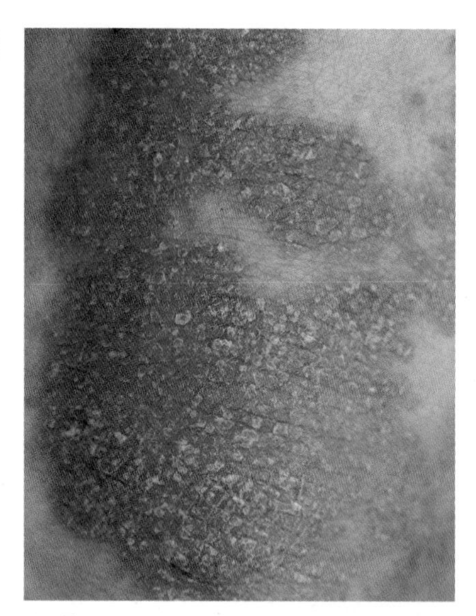

▲ Eczema

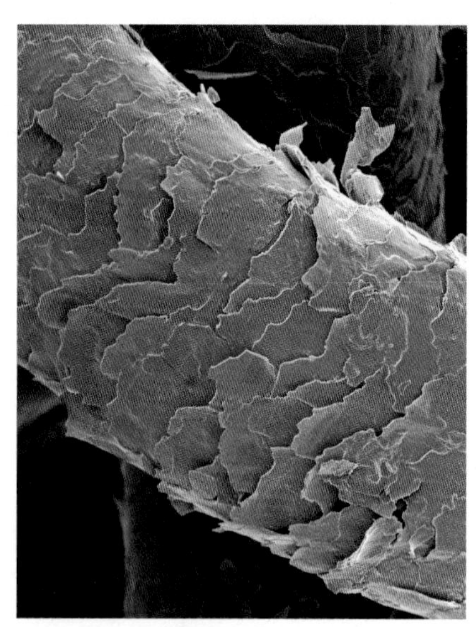

▲ Damaged cuticle

ACTIVITY

Any concerns regarding contra-indications must be reported to the relevant person. Which contra-indications would you need to refer and who would you refer them to in your salon?

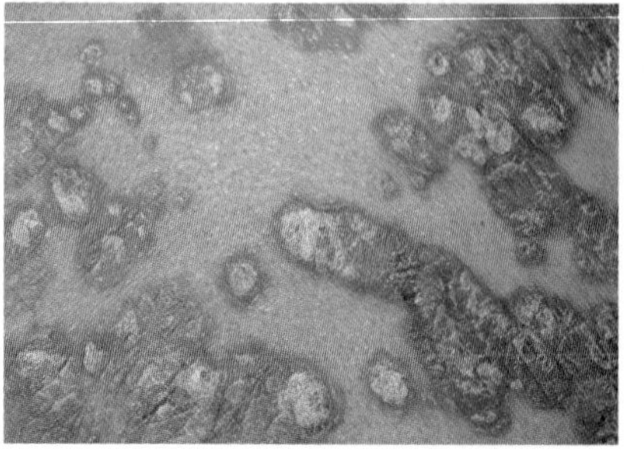

▲ Psoriasis

Carry out colouring and lightening tests

During the consultation and the service itself you will need to conduct some hair tests to confirm that your client's hair is suitable for the service required. You must follow the MFIs to ensure you adhere to health and safety procedures. The results of these tests must be recorded on the client record card and if any adverse reactions occur you must seek guidance from the relevant person. Remember to work within the limits of your authority and report all adverse reactions.

The table shows the different hair tests before and/or during the service.

Type and purpose of test	When and how to carry out the test	Expected results, impact on service and action to take if results are adverse
Skin sensitivity test to test for an allergic reaction or sensitivity to the product.	24–48 hours *before* a colour service. Always follow MFIs as these may vary. As a guide, clean an area in the inner elbow or behind the ear. Then apply the client's chosen colour (possibly mixed with peroxide, depending on MFIs) to the area and leave it exposed to dry.	A negative reaction is no change to the skin area – proceed with service. A positive adverse reaction is red skin and/or sore areas that may weep and itch. Do not apply colour to the scalp as the client may suffer a severe reaction such as anaphylactic shock. Re-test with an alternative product in 24–48 hours' time.
Incompatibility test to identify if any **metallic salts** are present, which will react with professional colouring products. 	*Before* the colouring or lightening service, if you suspect metallic salts are present in the hair. Take a small cutting of the client's hair and place it in a 20:1 solution of 20 ml liquid peroxide and 1 ml (2 drops) ammonium hydroxide (perm lotion). Leave for up to 30 minutes.	Nothing will happen if the result is negative – you can proceed with the service. If the result is positive and adverse, it means there are metallic salts present. The hair cutting may change colour and the solution may bubble, fizz and/or give off heat. Do not apply chemical products to your client's hair as they may experience scalp burns and/or damage to, or disintegration of, the hair. Offer an alternative service that is chemical-free and re-test in 2-3 weeks' time.

→

Type and purpose of test	When and how to carry out the test	Expected results, impact on service and action to take if results are adverse
Porosity test to identify if the cuticles are smooth or rough.	*Before* any service on dry hair. Take a few hairs and slide your fingers along the hair shaft in the direction of point to root.	The hair cuticle should feel smooth if the hair is non-porous and you can proceed with chemical services. If the result is adverse and the hair feels very rough or raised, the hair is very porous. Do not use chemicals as they may cause damage to the client's hair or the desired outcome may not be achieved. If the hair is slightly porous, or porous on mid-lengths and ends only, consider a **porosity leveller**, treatment, or **Olaplex restructurant**, and cut the hair prior to the service.
Elasticity test – to test the strength of the cortex.	*Before* any service on wet hair. Take one or two hairs and mist them lightly with water, then stretch the hair a couple of times between your finger and thumb.	Good elasticity means that wet hair should stretch about 30 per cent more than its original length and return when released. If the result is adverse the hair is weak and lacks elasticity. When stretched it may snap or stay in its stretched length – do not use chemicals as they will cause damage to the client's hair or the desired outcome may not be achieved. Offer penetrating treatments, or **Olaplex** restructurant, or conditioning colours, such as semi-permanent colours.
Test cutting/colour test – to see if the desired result is achievable	*Before* a colour or lightening service. Apply the chosen colour to a section of the hair (either a test cutting or on the head).	The desired result should be achieved, or further development may be required. If the result is adverse the desired result is not achieved with the colour test. Identify why and try an alternative product, re-testing before applying the colour.
Strand test – to see if the colour result has been achieved, or if the lightener development is sufficient.	*During* the colouring or lightening service. Wipe off the colour or lightener from a few strands of hair.	If permanent colour is developed, then the desired result should be achieved. If the bleach is regularly checked, the level of lift should be achieved without damage to the hair. Further development may be required if the colour result has not been achieved. If the colour is not achieved, leave the hair to develop for longer (if condition allows). If the colour is too light, remove the lightener immediately, apply a conditioning treatment and then tone with a semi-permanent toner (do not use chemicals).

HANDY HINT

If the test results show any signs of damage or breakage to the hair, do not proceed with the service. Report this to a senior member of staff and advise your client to have penetrating conditioning treatments. Re-test the hair a few weeks later.

HANDY HINT

Results from the hair tests could prevent colouring services from being carried out and affect your choice of products.

ACTIVITY

Practise porosity, elasticity, incompatibility, skin and colour tests on a colleague. Record the outcomes accurately on a record card and keep this for future reference.

Did your tests achieve the expected outcomes?

ACTIVITY

Explain the services or options you would offer your client if:

- they suffered an allergic reaction to permanent tint
- they had porous hair
- they had weak elasticity
- the results of an incompatibility test produced heat and bubbling
- the colour test did not lift sufficiently to meet with the client requirements.

Review results of hair tests

Once you have carried out the hair tests it is important to review the results and identify if the service is suitable to go ahead.

If a client has had a reaction to a skin test, or you have identified the presence of metallic salts in the hair, you must discuss this with your client. It is important they understand why a service cannot be carried out, or why you are suggesting alternative options that are more suitable.

Failure to carry out these vital tests could lead to legal action against you or your salon and you could lose your job if your client suffers an allergic reaction or hair damage as a result of a service. Always record the test carried out, the outcome and result of the test, and advice provided on a client record card.

Completing client record cards

It is important to record the outcome of the service and results of tests for the following reasons:

- to record the service carried out for future reference

KEY TERMS

Metallic salts – these can be found in some home hairdressing products and contain lead/ metallic compounds or a variety of other metals which react with professional colouring chemical ingredients.

Porosity levellers – products which coat the cuticle layer of the hair to aid the levelling of porosity.

Olaplex restructurant – restructures the hair internally by linking broken disulphide bonds in the cortex of the hair.

HEALTH AND SAFETY

The potential consequences of failing to carry out a test could result not only in significant damage to your client's hair and client dissatisfaction, but also in legal action.

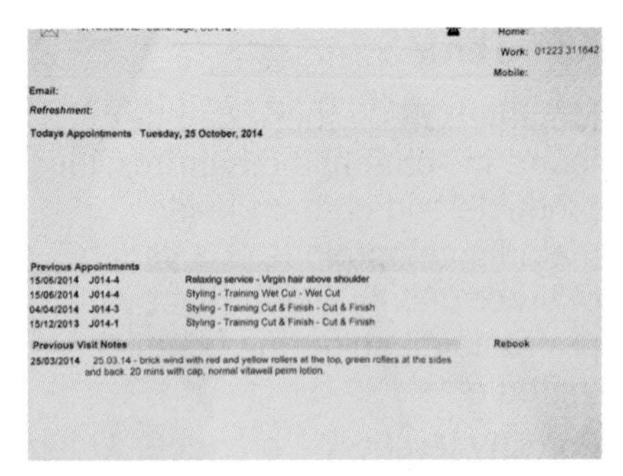

Home:
Work: 01223 311642
Mobile:
Email:
Refreshment:
Todays Appointments Tuesday, 25 October, 2014

Previous Appointments

15/06/2014	J014-4	Relaxing service - Virgin hair above shoulder
15/06/2014	J014-4	Styling - Training Wet Cut - Wet Cut
04/04/2014	J014-3	Styling - Training Cut & Finish - Cut & Finish
15/12/2013	J014-1	Styling - Training Cut & Finish - Cut & Finish

Previous Visit Notes — Rebook

25/03/2014 25.03.14 - brick wind with red and yellow rollers at the top, green rollers at the sides and back. 20 mins with cap, normal vitawell perm lotion.

▲ When completing record cards, always follow the Data Protection Act

- to provide evidence of the test result and service outcome in case of any future legal action
- to maintain the professional image of the salon.

During and after the service, ensure the client details are correct, easy to read and up to date on the record card. Make sure you enter all of the service details, including client answers to any questions about their hair, and whether they are happy with the service outcome. Always keep client information confidential and follow the requirements of the Data Protection Act.

ACTIVITY

You are using your English writing skills when completing record cards correctly – always make sure the details are accurate.

ACTIVITY

List the information that should be entered on a client record card after a colouring service.

Skin sensitivity test instructions

MFIs for skin sensitivity tests can vary between manufacturers, so always read the instructions and follow them explicitly. If you are unsure whether your client is under 16 years old, remember to ask them for ID.

Some manufacturers provide skin test patches that you can issue to your client and advise them on the MFIs for home use. Check your salon's insurance company allows this method of skin testing.

Principles of colour selection

Your colour theory and knowledge is vital and you will refer to this throughout your whole career. In this section of the chapter you will look at the relationship between science and hair colouring products in particular. You will also consider the principles of colour selection – how to choose the right colour correctly while following the International Colour Chart (ICC).

Along with understanding the principles of colour selection, you also need to understand how the client's natural pigment impacts on the colour process and how colouring and lightening products change the structure of hair. The different strengths of hydrogen peroxide will affect the levels of lift achievable, while temperature affects the application and development of products. Various porosity levels will influence the choice and application of products and the final result, so it is fundamental to understand these too.

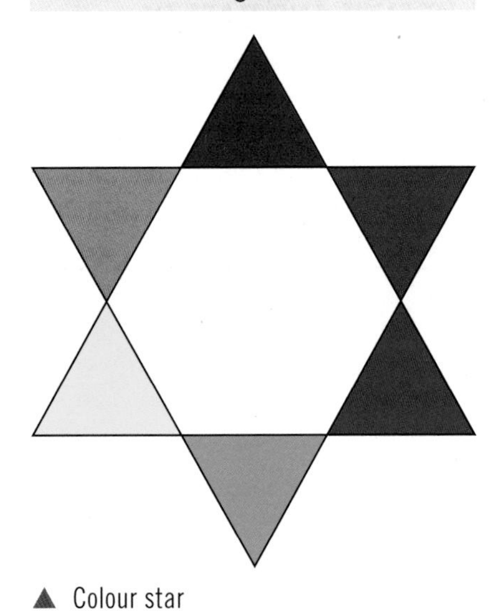

▲ Colour star

The colour star (or wheel) is used by artists and anyone else who mixes or uses colour. The principles of colour are the same for painting a picture as for colouring the hair. Our hair is made up of natural pigments containing primary and secondary colours. When you add artificial colour to the hair, you rely on your understanding of the colour star.

Primary colours

The colour star is made up of the three primary colours: red, yellow and blue.

Primary colours cannot be made by mixing other colours together. However, by mixing the primary colours together, we can make secondary colours. All other colours are made by mixing primary and/or secondary colours together.

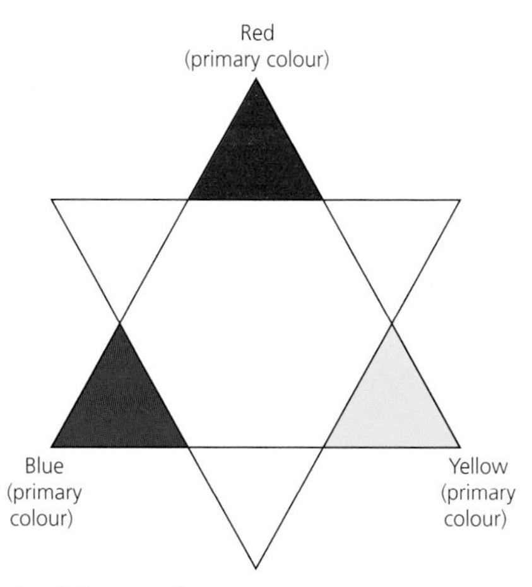

▲ Primary colours

Secondary colours

Primary colours are mixed together to form the three secondary colours: orange (created by mixing red and yellow), green (created by mixing yellow and blue) and violet (created by mixing blue and red).

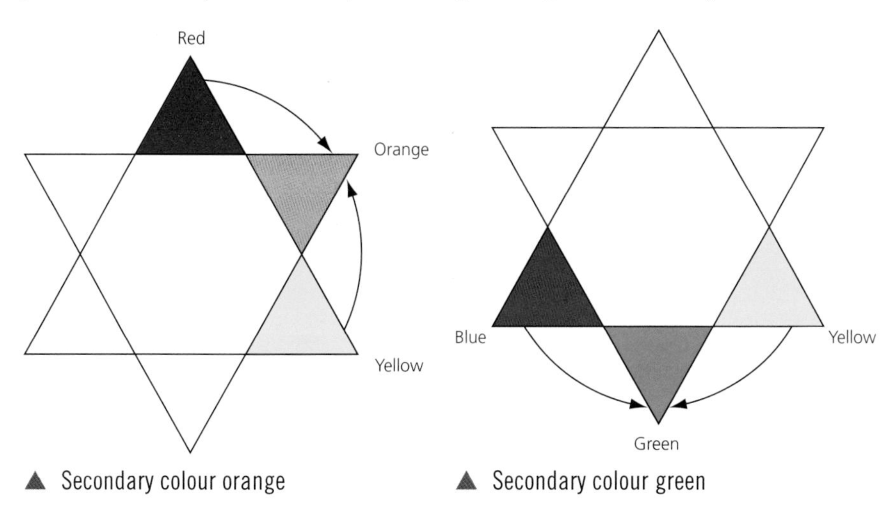

▲ Secondary colour orange

▲ Secondary colour green

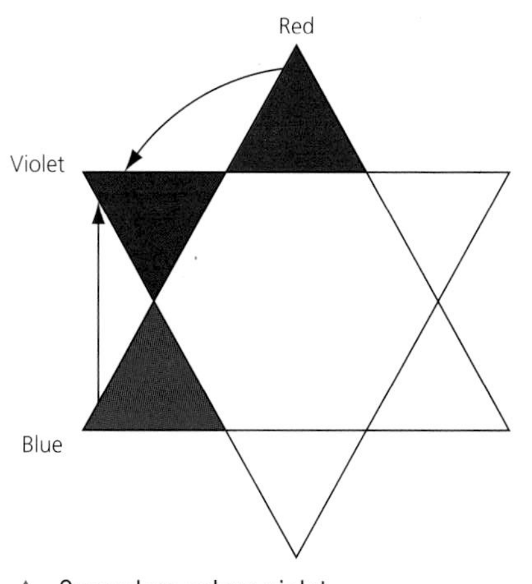

▲ Secondary colour violet

When you mix all the primary colours together you create a neutral brown colour.

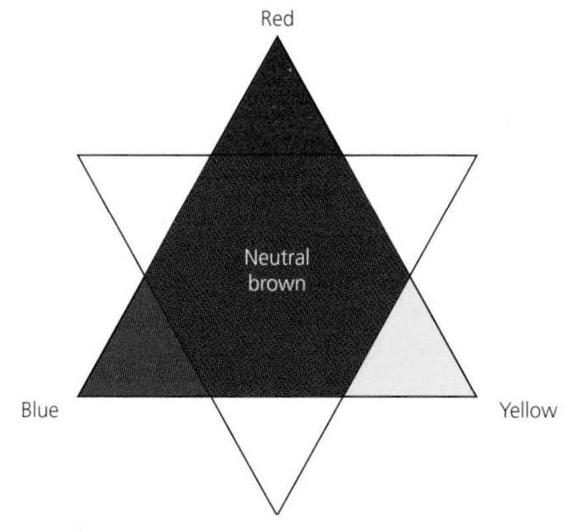

▲ Neutral brown created by mixing all primary colours

HANDY HINT

To help you remember the order of the colour star, try to memorise 'Richard Of York Gave Battle In Vain'.

Richard	Red
Of	Orange
York	Yellow
Gave	Green
Battle	Blue
In **V**ain	Indigo/Violet

ACTIVITY

Paint your own colour star and compare your secondary colours with your colleagues'.

Mix the three primary colours together. Did you get a neutral brown? Compare the results with your colleagues'.

HANDY HINT

In hairdressing we refer to yellow as *gold*, orange as *copper* and indigo as *violet*.

Tertiary colours

In the same way that mixing primary colours together gives you secondary colours, primary and secondary colours can also be mixed together to create tertiary colour. There are six tertiary colours – combinations of primary and secondary colours – red-orange, yellow-orange, yellow-green, blue-green, blue-violet and red-violet.

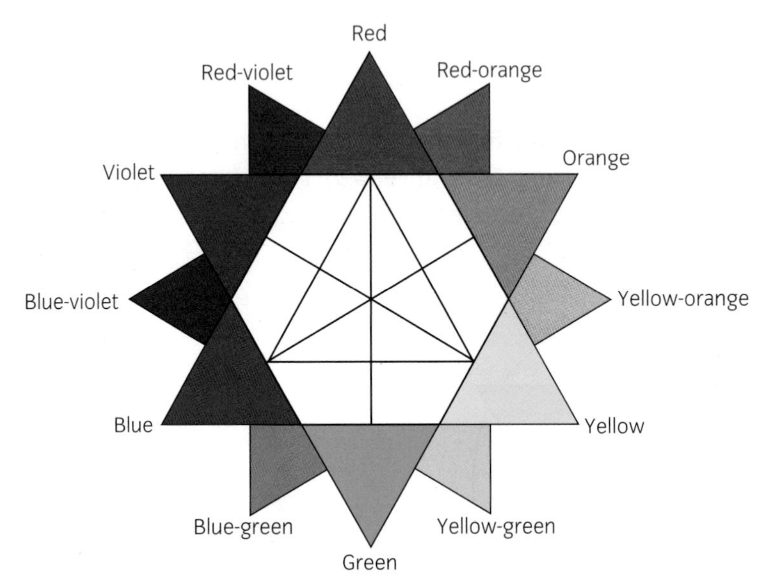

▲ Tertiary colours

International Colour Chart

The International Colour Chart (ICC) is the numbering system that all manufacturers follow. Everyone uses the same numbers to describe a colour's depth.

When you refer to your client's hair colour, you look at the depth and the tone of the hair. The depth is how light or dark the hair is, and the tone is the colour you see. If you describe someone as a redhead, you are describing their tone. If you describe someone as bleached blonde, you are referring to the depth of the hair.

Depths of hair

The natural depths of hair range from 1 (black) to 10 (lightest blonde).

The range of depths, from lightest to darkest, is as follows:

10 lightest blonde
9 very light blonde
8 light blonde
7 medium blonde
6 dark blonde
5 light brown
4 medium brown
3 dark brown
2 brown
1 black

ACTIVITY

Work with a colleague to try to identify each other's natural hair depth.

Tones in the hair

Unfortunately, manufacturers do not follow the same numbering system when describing tones. They all use a number system which you will need to learn. Once you have mastered the ICC, it will be easier to learn the tonal colours that your salon uses. You will need this understanding throughout your hairdressing career, but you can always refer to the colour chart if in doubt.

The tone numbering system describes the colour you see. All manufacturers use a similar description of the tone, but the numbering system will vary. Depths and tones are usually written in numbers for the stylist's use and given descriptive names for the client's benefit. For example, the description for depth 8 (light blonde) may be written as 8/0, 8–0, 8.0 or 8N depending on the manufacturer. The 0 refers to the tone.

Description of tone	Wella	L'Oréal	Goldwell
Natural	/0	/0	N – natural
Ash	/1 or /9	/1 or /2	A – ash
Blue ash	/8	/1	BV – blue violet
Green ash	/2	/7 (Mat)	NA – green
Gold	/3	/3	G – gold
Red	/4	/6	R – red
Mahogany	/5	/5	RB – red brown
Brunette/Mocha	/7	/8	B – brown

ACTIVITY

Work with a colleague to try to identify each other's tones. Is the colour warm or cool?

In the colour chart, the first digit after the depth is the stronger 'primary' tonal colour. For example 8/3 is depth 8 (light blonde) with a stronger 'primary' tone of 3 (gold): this could be described as a light golden blonde. Stronger 'primary' tones are often mixed together to create the secondary tones or tertiary tones: the second digit indicates these.

Description of tone	Wella	L'Oréal (as a guide)
Natural ash	/01	,01
Natural gold	/03	,03
Copper (red and gold)	/43	,46 or ,44 or ,64 or ,45
Copper (gold and red)	/34	,43 or ,34 or ,04 or ,33
Violet red	/46	,45 or ,56
Mahogany red	/56	,45 or ,56
Golden brown	/73	,35 or ,53 or ,31
Violet/Cendre/Iridescent	/89 or 81, or 98	/12 or /21

For example, using Wella, 6/43 is depth 6 (dark blonde) with a tone of /43 (red and gold). This colour could be called dark red gold blonde or dark copper blonde.

If the mixed tone were more gold than red, it would be shown as 6/34. This would still be a dark copper blonde, but the copper tone created would not be as vibrant as 6/43.

Colour tones

In hair, red, gold and copper colours are known as warm tones; blue, green and violet are known as cool tones.

By mixing more or less of each primary colour we can create different shades. For example, if you mix red with yellow, you make orange (copper). If you add more red than yellow, the resulting tone would be a brighter copper than if you mixed more yellow than red. The various possible shades of copper can be seen on any colour chart.

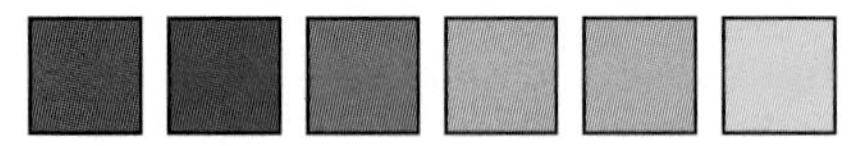

▲ Variations in the amount of red and gold mixed together affects the vibrancy of the copper created

ACTIVITY

See how many shades of orange you can make.

Neutralising unwanted tones in the hair

The principles of the colour star not only work to create colours and various shades, but also to **neutralise** any unwanted tone in the hair. Colours opposite each other on the colour star will neutralise each other. For example:

- red neutralises green and green neutralises red
- yellow neutralises violet and violet neutralises yellow
- orange neutralises blue and blue neutralises orange.

KEY TERM

Neutralise – to make neutral or balance each other out.

If a colour result has a green tone, you would need to add a red toner to neutralise it; if too red, you would add green. If highlight results are a little too gold (yellow), you would neutralise the tone with a violet toner and vice versa. When highlighting naturally copper (orange) toned hair, you should use a high lift tint with a blue tone.

Neutralising tones work by mixing all three primary colours. When neutralising unwanted golden tones, use a violet toner because yellow is a primary colour and when you add violet (which is made with red and blue primary colours) all three primary colours have been mixed together, creating a neutral tone.

Unwanted green tones are neutralised in the same way. Green is a secondary colour made up of yellow and blue primary colours – when neutralised with red, all three primary colours have been mixed together to create a neutral tone.

This same principle works for neutralising orange tones. Orange (red and yellow) mixed with blue creates a neutral tone.

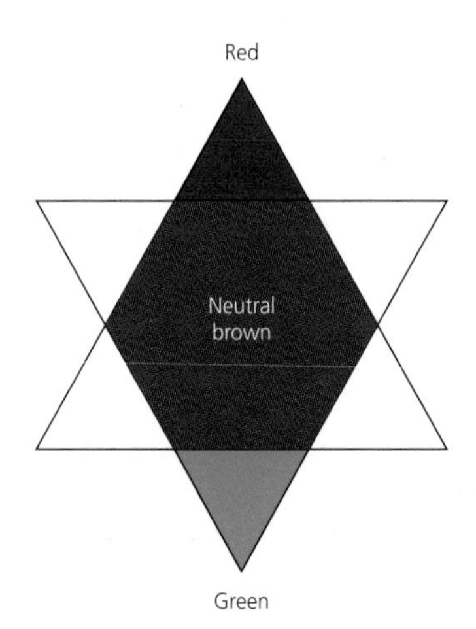

▲ Neutralising golden tones

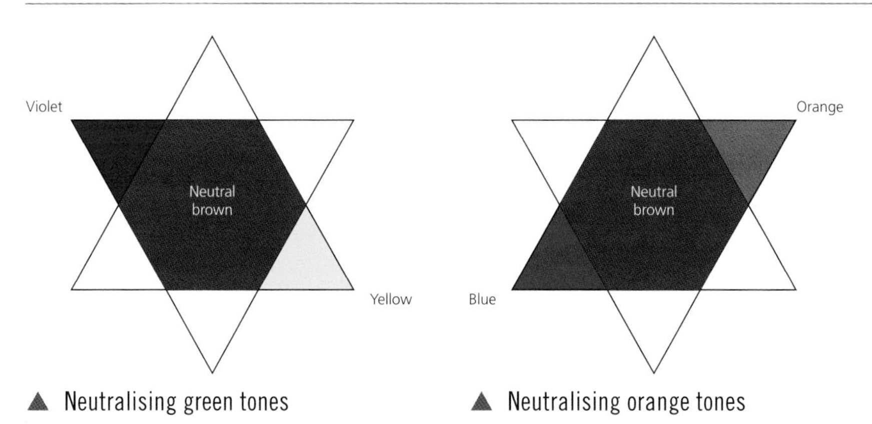

▲ Neutralising green tones

▲ Neutralising orange tones

Removing depths and tones

When you lighten hair, you lose **pigments** in a certain order: red, orange and then yellow. Red tones are larger molecules and therefore can be removed from the hair more quickly. Yellow tones are tiny molecules and it can take much longer to remove these. The yellow pigments from depths 8, 9 and 10 are the hardest to remove. If you remove too many yellow pigments, you risk breaking and damaging the hair.

Tones	Depths	
Very pale yellow	10	Lightest blonde
Pale yellow	9	Very light blonde
Yellow	8	Light blonde
Yellow/orange	7	Blonde
Orange	6	Dark blonde
Orange/red	5	Light brown
Red	4	Brown
Red	3	Dark brown
Red/blue	2	Darkest brown
Blue red	1	Black

▲ Tones in the depths of hair

▲ Tone swatches

ACTIVITY

1 If you lighten the hair colour from depth 5 to depth 8, what colour pigments (tones) will you remove? What tones will your client be left with?
2 If you lighten the hair from depth 7 to depth 9, what colour pigments (tones) will you remove? What tones will your client be left with?
3 If you darken the hair from depth 5 to depth 3, what colour pigments (tones) will you have added?

KEY TERM

Pigment – the substance that colours our tissue (hair and skin).

Impact of natural pigment on the colour process

The cortex contains all the natural and artificial colour pigments of the hair. It is the layer of the hair where all chemical action takes place. You can see the hair's colour through the transparent cuticle.

Natural hair colour varies from person to person, depending on the colour pigments. The pigments are called **melanin** and consist of two types: eumelanin and pheomelanin.

Eumelanin

Eumelanin (dark hair) is made up of black to light brown colour pigments. These are large colour molecules with varying amounts of all three primary colours, but predominately contain blue and red pigments.

Pheomelanin

Pheomelanin (lighter hair) is made up of blonde colour pigments. These are tiny molecules of colour spread throughout the cortex, with varying amounts of red, yellow and orange colour molecules, but predominately contain yellow pigments.

If you looked at two heads of hair, one dark brown and one light brown, both would have the same amount of colour pigment, but the amounts of blue, red and yellow melanin would vary. These different combinations give us depths and tones.

Clients with darker hair (more eumelanin pigments) who want a much lighter result may need to have their hair **pre-lightened** before applying the final colour choice. This technique involves lightening the hair with a lightening product and suitable strength peroxide to the desired level of lift, before adding your chosen tone. The tone can be added with a semi-permanent, quasi-permanent or even a permanent colour with low-level peroxide.

KEY TERM

Melanin – pigments that give colour to the hair and skin.

Pre-lightened – method used to lighten darker hair with a lightener prior to applying desired colour and tone.

Effects of artificial and natural light on the hair

The salon's lighting system is very important to enable the client to see their colour result accurately, effectively and in the best possible light.

Natural daylight is the ideal way to show the hair's true colour. Natural light is referred to as white light, but it is made up of all the colours of the spectrum – red, orange, yellow, green, blue, indigo and violet. If you see white, that is because all seven colours are being reflected to your eyes from the object you are looking at. If you see one colour, such as red, the other six colours are being absorbed. If you see black, then no colour is being reflected into your eyes and all are being absorbed.

▲ Hair colour under electric bulbs

▲ Hair colour in natural daylight

▲ Hair colour under fluorescent tubes

Electric bulbs can make the hair look warmer in appearance and neutralise blue or ash tones because of the yellow tinge given off by the bulb. Fluorescent tubes can make the hair appear more ash in tone as they give off a bluish tinge and remove the warmth from the hair.

ACTIVITY

Compare colour swatches in natural and artificial light and discuss your findings with colleagues and your tutor.

Effects of colouring and lightening products on the hair structure

Clients may choose partial-head or full-head colour, or a highlighted effect. Whether you're colouring the hair with a temporary colour, a permanent colour or using lightening products, it is essential that you understand their effects on the hair's structure.

Effects of temporary colour

Temporary hair colours are not such a popular service as permanent colours, but they can be quickly applied for a short-term look.

Temporary colours contain large colour molecules which coat the outside of the cuticle and stain the hair shaft. If the hair is porous and the cuticle is raised, the colour might grab and coat the cortex, which can cause the colour to last longer and/or give an uneven colour result.

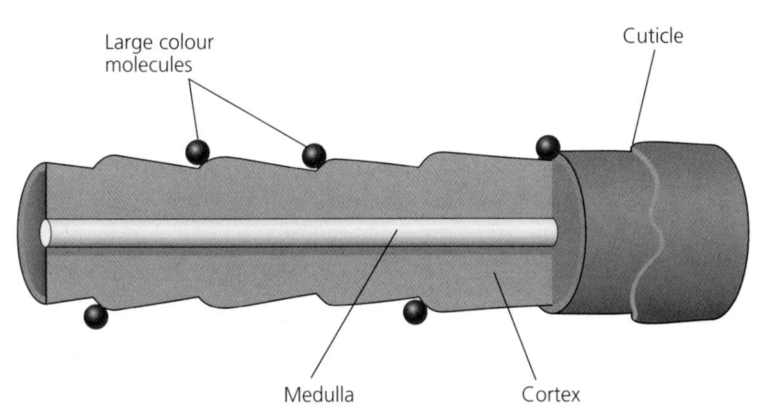

▲ Effects of temporary colour molecules on the hair

Effects of semi-permanent colour

Semi-permanent colours are a great way to introduce colouring services to your clients. They are quick and easy to apply and develop, and the client is not committed to the colour.

Semi-permanent colours contain large and small colour molecules. The larger colour molecules coat and stain the outside of the cuticle, whereas the smaller molecules coat the inside of the cuticle and the outer layer of the cortex.

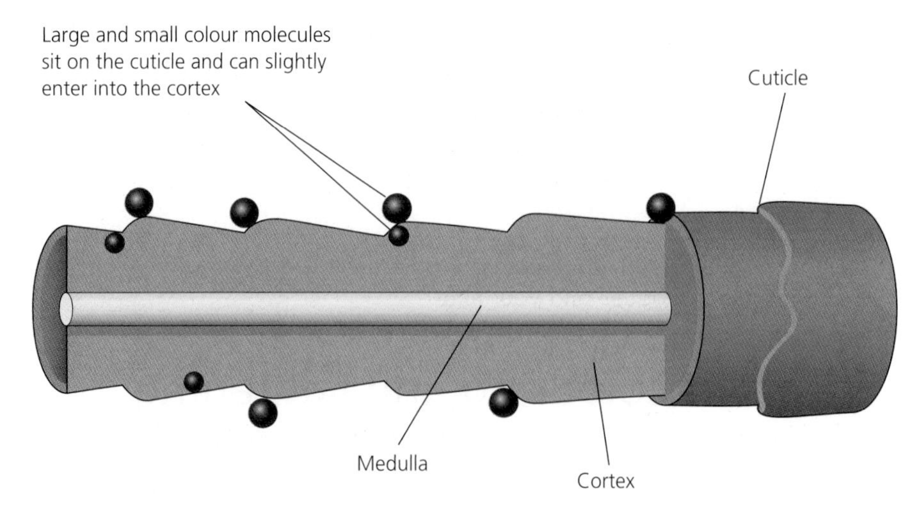

▲ Effects of semi-permanent colour molecules on the hair

Effects of quasi-permanent colour

Quasi-permanent colours are a popular service in salons. When used effectively the colour is not permanent so there is a minimal commitment.

Quasi-permanent colours contain small- and medium-sized colour molecules. The small molecules coat the cuticle and lie in the cortex, whereas the medium colour molecules penetrate into the cortex. When the weak developer is mixed with the quasi-permanent colour it oxidises and swells the cuticle slightly, allowing the deposit of depth and tone into the cortex.

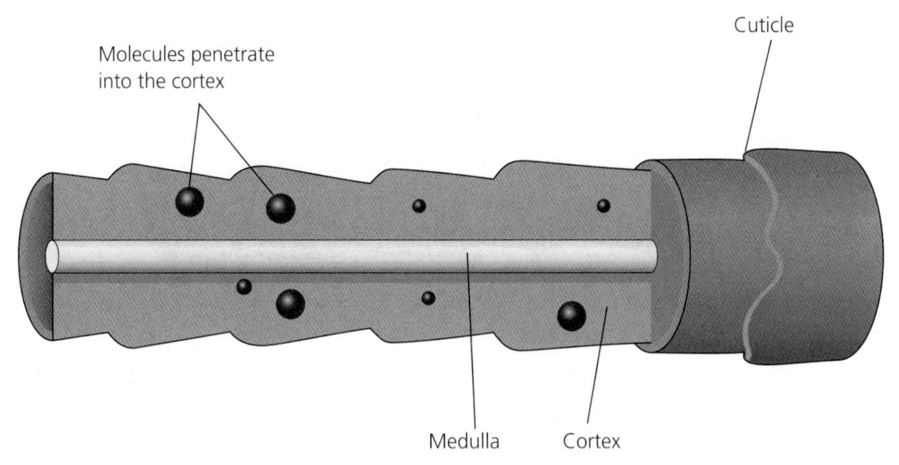

▲ Effects of quasi-permanent colour molecules on the hair

Effects of permanent and high-lift colour

Permanent and high-lift hair colours are the most popular colour treatments in salons. They can be used to create many effects and variations, such as regrowth and full-head colour services, and highlighting and lowlighting effects. Combinations of these services can be used. For example, you can combine a half head of woven highlights with a full head of colour in between the packets (folded foils).

Permanent/high-lift colours contain **ammonia** and are alkaline; therefore they open the cuticle layer of the hair. Ammonia raises the pH of the hair to pH 10, so the hair swells and the active ingredients can penetrate the cortex. They can be used to lighten or darken the hair, depending on the strength of peroxide used. The stronger the peroxide used, the higher the lift, and the greater the effect on the cortex of the hair. Up to five levels of lift are achievable when ammonia, within a high-lift colouring product, is mixed with high strength peroxide.

KEY TERM

Ammonia – an alkaline gas.

The colouring products contain small colour molecules that expand and join together during the development process. The peroxide, when mixed with the ammonia from the colouring product, swells the cuticle and allows the small molecules to enter into the cortex. This allows the colour to deposit the required depth and tone.

The products must be fully developed to allow the colour to reach its desired depth, deposit the tonal colours and neutralise; colour molecules need time to swell and join in the cortex to become permanent.

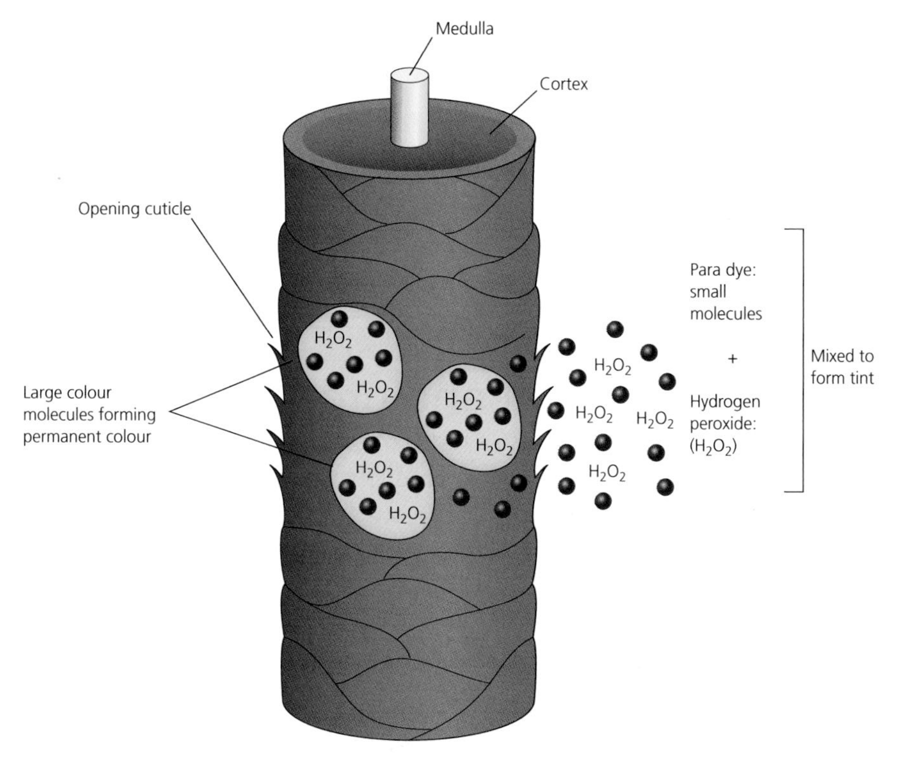

▲ Effects of quasi-permanent colour molecules on the hair

Effects of lightening products

Lightening products enable clients to achieve the lightest blondes and lighten artificial colour in the hair. They can be used to create varying effects, including regrowth, partial and full-head colour services, and highlights.

These products can be used with any strength peroxide for off-scalp techniques, such as highlights. Peroxide with a strength of 6 per cent must be used for on-scalp techniques, such as re-growths. Lightening products can achieve up to five or six shades of lift.

HEALTH AND SAFETY

Ammonia has been used safely in colouring products for over 50 years. After development the ammonia evaporates, leaving the hair conditioned and healthy.

KEY TERM

Oxy-melanin – a colourless molecule.

The lift achievable and development time varies, depending on the peroxide strength and the depth of your client's hair in relation to the target shade. Lightening products affect the hair by oxidising the natural and artificial colour pigments in the cortex. Ammonia, when mixed with peroxide, releases oxygen; the oxidisation process causes the melanin to become **oxy-melanin**.

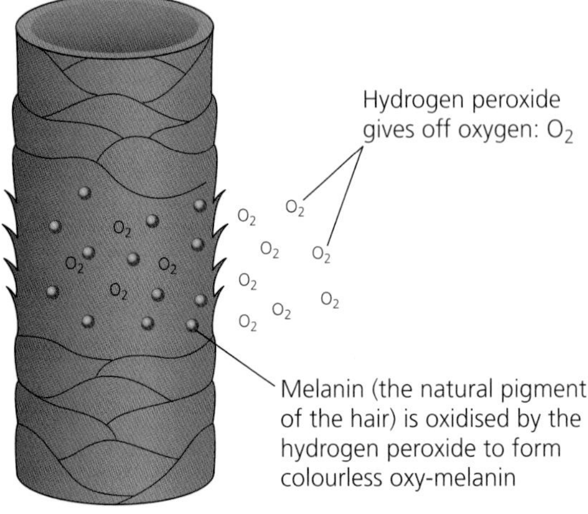

▲ Effects of lightening products on the hair

▲ Colour remover

Effects of colour remover

Colour removers or colour reducers are similar to lightening products, but work on artificial colour only (and not natural hair pigments). They use hydrogen to shrink the oxidised colour molecules.

Tools, equipment and products

When colouring hair you will use a range of colouring tools and a selection of colouring and lightening products which, when mixed with developers or hydrogen peroxide, will create a variety of looks.

The tools and equipment you will use will depend on the colouring service chosen.

For regrowth and full-head applications you will need:

- a brush – to brush through the client's hair and remove tangles
- a wide-toothed comb – to section the hair during the application
- section clips – to section the hair and to secure the towel around the client
- a tint bowl and brush – for the application of products
- weighing scales – if you weigh tint and peroxide in your salon
- a measuring jug – to measure the peroxide solution
- a timer – to time the development process accurately
- an accelerator – to reduce development time.

For highlighting applications you will need all of the above, plus:

- a pintail comb – to weave the hair if you are completing woven highlights

- a selection of clips – to section and secure the hair and to secure the towel around the client
- either foils, meches, wraps or clingfilm for woven highlights, or a spatula for pulled-through highlights.

▲ Foil

▲ Meche

▲ Wraps

▲ Spatula

Colouring, lightening and toning products

When colouring and lightening hair there is a vast range of products to choose from:

- temporary colour
- semi-permanent colours
- quasi-permanent colours
- permanent colours
- lighteners
- toners.

Choosing suitable colouring products

You must choose the most suitable products for your client's requirements. The products you choose to colour your client's hair will depend on:

- why your client is colouring their hair
- how long they want the colour to last
- their chosen shade, depth and tone
- previous services on the hair
- their natural depth and tone
- their current hair colour
- the levels of lift required
- the percentage of white hair.

The table below shows which products are most suitable for your client's requirements, together with their characteristics.

Colouring product	How long does it last?	Effects and coverage of white hair	Levels of lift achievable	Hydrogen peroxide strength (developer)
Temporary colour	1 shampoo	Generally used for whole head coverage, toning of colour and blending of white hair. They work well for replacing lost tone in between colour services.	None – they add tone only.	Not applicable
Semi-permanent colour	6–8 shampoos	As for temporary colour	None – they add tone only.	Not applicable
Quasi-permanent colour	12–24 shampoos	Generally used for whole head coverage, darkening and toning of colour and coverage of 50 per cent white hair. Good for neutralising colour and replacing lost depth and/or tone.	None – it darkens or adds tone only.	Referred to as a developer, but it is a weak peroxide – as a guide 3% or 10 volume.
Permanent colour	Permanent	Used for partial colour, such as high/low lights regrowth and full head colours. Provides up to 100 per cent coverage on white hair.	Depending on the natural depth of hair and peroxide strength, lifts up to three shades. Also darkens and deposits tone.	3% or 10 volume 6% or 20 volume 9% or 30 volume 12% or 40 volume

Colouring product	How long does it last?	Effects and coverage of white hair	Levels of lift achievable	Hydrogen peroxide strength (developer)
High-lift tint	Permanent	Used for partial colour, such as balayage, highlights, regrowth and full head colours. Blends in white hairs but generally does not cover white hair.	Depending on the natural depth of hair and peroxide strength, lifts up to four to five shades. Also deposits tone.	9% or 30 volume 12% or 40 volume
Lightening products (bleach)	Permanent	Generally used for partial colour such as balayage and highlights. Blends in white hairs only but generally does not cover white hair. Can be used for on-scalp techniques too.	Depending on the depth of hair and peroxide strength, lifts up to six shades. Also removes tone.	Off-scalp techniques. 6% or 20 volume 9% or 30 volume 12% or 40 volume For on scalp-techniques: 6^
Toners	Semi-permanent	Generally used for whole head coverage and neutralising of unwanted tones.	None – used to remove unwanted tone only.	Varied options – you can use 6% or 20 volume but generally 3% or 10 volume developer is used, or a true semi can be used.

There are two categories of colouring products:

1. Non-commitment colours – these colours wash out but require more frequent applications.
2. Commitment colours – these are longer lasting and are grown or cut out of the hair.

▲ Powder lightener

Non-commitment colouring services

Temporary and semi-permanent colours are referred to as non-commitment colours. They are pH 4.5–5.5, so their acidity is the same as that of the hair and skin and therefore they do not affect the cuticle or the cortex.

Temporary colouring products

You apply these products directly to the hair before or after styling. They are available as mousses, lotions, gels, sprays, rinses, creams and even hair mascaras. They stain the hair and are used in the same way as styling products. Mousses, gels, lotions, rinses and creams are usually applied to wet hair, and sprays and hair mascaras to dry hair. Temporary colours are removed from the hair with the next shampoo.

The table shows why your clients may or may not choose a temporary colour service.

▲ Temporary colour 'painted in' to hair

Reasons to have temporary colour	Reasons not to have temporary colour
No commitment Lasts only one shampoo Adds shine Adds tone Neutralises unwanted tone Chemical-free Enhances current look Introduction to colour Quick fashion effect No development time	Only lasts one shampoo No lift possible Colour may be uneven or last longer in porous hair

Always follow the MFIs when using colouring products and wear PPE to prevent staining the skin and damaging your clothes.

HANDY HINT

Hair mascaras or hair chalk can be used to paint colour onto the hair, to add texture and create a highlighted effect.

Semi-permanent colouring products

These conditioning colours generally come in liquid or cream form and can be applied directly to pre-shampooed hair. Apply them either from the bottle or by measuring the product into a bowl and applying with a sponge or brush. Semi-permanent products are rinsed from the hair after the development time. Follow the manufacturer's instructions and apply a conditioner if required.

The table shows why your clients may or may not choose a semi-permanent colour service.

HANDY HINT

True semi-permanent colours are not mixed with a developer or peroxide.

Reasons to have semi-permanent colour	Reasons not to have semi-permanent colour
No commitment Introduction to colour Full-head coverage No regrowth Lasts only six to eight shampoos Adds shine, tone and depth Neutralises unwanted tone Can be used for colour correction services Chemical-free Skin test is not always required (but always check MFIs) Mostly allergy-free Enhances current look and refreshes existing colour Quick service and fashion effect Blends up to 20 per cent of white hair	Only lasts six to eight shampoos Vibrancy of colour gradually fades with each shampoo No lift possible Colour can only blend white hair Colour may be uneven or 'grab' in porous hair which means the colour molecules will attach to the cuticles and last longer than they are intended to

▲ Semi-permanent colour

Commitment colouring services

Quasi, permanent and lightening products are alkaline; this means they lift the cuticle during development and affect the cortex. As these colours have a long-lasting effect on the hair, they demand a commitment to colour. These colours introduce a developing agent or peroxide to the colour.

Quasi-permanent colouring products

Quasi-permanent colouring products are mixed with a developer (mild or weak peroxide) to pre-shampooed hair and can be applied either straight from an applicator bottle or using a bowl and brush/sponge.

The table shows why your clients may or may not choose a quasi-permanent colour service.

Reasons to have quasi-permanent colour	Reasons not to have quasi-permanent colour
Adds depth and tone Covers up to 50 per cent white hair Lasts 12–24 shampoos Introduction to permanent colour Weaker chemicals used Used for colour correction Fashion colours Refreshes faded colours	No lift possible Overuse can lead to a regrowth area Skin test is required Contains chemicals Colours gradually fade

▲ Quasi-permanent colour

Permanent and high-lift colours

Permanent and high-lift colours are generally supplied in 60 ml tubes and are always mixed with peroxide. You apply them to clean, dry hair using a bowl and brush.

The table shows why your clients may or may not choose a permanent or high-lift colour service.

Reasons to have permanent/ high-lift colours	Reasons not to have permanent/high-lift colours
Adds depth and tone Lightens by up to three shades for permanent colours Lightens by up to four or five shades for high-lift colours Permanent colours cover 100 per cent white hair Used for fashion effects (foils/ balayage) Permanent result Used for colour correction Fashion/vibrant colours Change of image Adds texture Covers regrowth	The result is permanent Skin test is required Contains chemicals Vibrant tones gradually fade Committed to colour Regrowth occurs every four to six weeks

▲ Permanent colour

▲ High-lift colour

HANDY HINT

Tint does not lift tint! If there is tint already on the hair and lift is required, you will have to use a lightener.

▲ Lightener

KEY TERM

Consistency – density or thickness.

▲ Lightener cream with ash tone

Always mix your colours and follow the mixing ratios according to your manufacturer's instructions, as these will vary between manufacturers.

Follow the MFIs for the development of colours and time them correctly using a timer. This will ensure the correct development time, allows the colour product to lift and deposit the tone, and enables you to achieve the best results for your client.

Using different types of lighteners and toners

Although normal tints and high-lift tints lighten the hair, they are not 'lightening products'. When discussing lightening products, we are referring to bleach products and these come in many varieties.

Lighteners can be a bleach powder, cream or a gel, and they are always mixed with peroxide. They are applied to clean, dry hair using a bowl and brush. Some lightener products, such as foil highlights, must be applied using off-scalp techniques; other lighteners are designed to be applied directly onto the scalp. Always read the instructions to ascertain if the product is an off-scalp or on-scalp lightener.

Lightener powder

Lightener/bleach powders can be blue or white powders and are most commonly used for highlighting methods and off-scalp techniques. Some lightening powders can be used on the scalp but always read the manufacturers' instructions to be sure.

Some lightening powders have to be measured and others are mixed to a preferred **consistency**. Add lightening powder to a bowl and mix with the peroxide to make a paste (always check the manufacturers' instructions to find out whether there is a mixing ratio).

Some lighteners are available with neutralising tones – this means you can remove golden and warm tones from the hair while lifting with a lightener.

Lightener gel

Gel lighteners/bleaches are normally used for scalp applications. This thicker type of lightener contains a booster or activator which is pre-mixed with the gel and the peroxide to obtain maximum lift while limiting the harm to the hair's condition. There are many varieties available, so you must refer to the MFIs for methods of mixing and applying the products.

The table shows why your clients may or may not choose a lightening colour service.

Reasons to use a lightener	Reasons not to use a lightener
Lightens by up to six shades Removes depth Removes tone Removes tint from the hair Fashion effects (foils) Permanent result Change of image Adds texture Covers regrowth	The result is permanent Contains strong chemicals Committed to colour Regrowth occurs every four to six weeks

Toners

Toners are generally used to remove unwanted tone after a colour service. For example, if the end result of a colour is too yellow then a violet toner can be applied. Toners can be in the form of liquid temporary colours, a true semi-permanent colour, a quasi-permanent colour and sometimes even a permanent colour with a low-level hydrogen peroxide or developer.

ACTIVITY

Using your salon brand of products, identify all the products and colours that could be used to neutralise and tone hair.

HEALTH AND SAFETY

Manufacturer's instructions are provided to ensure you work safely and do not put yourself or others at risk. Always follow your MFIs when working with colouring and lightening products and mix and measure the products correctly. This will ensure you produce the best possible result for your client and ensure colour accuracy.

Pre-lightening hair

Depending on the client's requirements, a permanent tint may not produce the levels of lift required. Always remember that you cannot apply a permanent tint to lift permanent tint already on the hair – tint does not lift tint.

If there is permanent colour already on your client's hair and the desired colour choice is lighter, then you will need to pre-lighten the hair with a lightening product first. Equally if the level of lift required by the client is not achievable using a permanent colour with 12% hydrogen peroxide, then you need to pre-lighten the hair with a lightening product first.

ACTIVITY

▲ Laura

Laura would like a depth 9 and is currently a natural depth of 7. How many shades of lift are required? What strength peroxide would you use?

▲ Samira

Samira would like a depth 7 with red tones and is currently a natural depth 4. What colour would you suggest? What strength peroxide would you use? Describe the colour in client-friendly words.

▲ Darcy

Darcy is 14 years old and would like a few blonde highlights to brighten her natural base 7 hair. What advice would you give Darcy?

▲ CJ

CJ would like a very light blonde and is currently a natural depth 6. What colour are you aiming for? Would you use a permanent, high-lift or bleach colour? What strength peroxide would you use? Would you suggest a full-head colour or a highlight technique?

▲ Georgie

Georgie would like a depth 6 and is currently a natural depth 8 with some highlights. What strength peroxide would you use?

Effects of different strengths of hydrogen peroxide

Ammonia is a key ingredient in quasi-permanent and permanent hair colours. At room temperature ammonia is colourless with a pungent smell. It can be highly irritating to the skin and respiratory system.

Hydrogen peroxide is often written as H_2O_2. It is a colourless liquid, made of water (H_2O) and oxygen (O_2). Hydrogen peroxide therefore contains concentrated oxygen. Hydrogen peroxide is an acid, about pH 3–4. It is the most common chemical used in hairdressing to provide oxygen. Its purpose is to lighten the natural and artificial colour pigments, and to develop the colour of oxidation tints (permanent colours).

When hydrogen peroxide is mixed with the ammonia in the permanent colour, it activates the **oxidation** process and begins to work. The ammonia swells the cuticle, allowing penetration of the hair colour into the cortex and the peroxide provides the oxygen to oxidise the hair's colour pigment.

KEY TERM

Oxidation – a chemical process that combines a substance with oxygen.

Strengths of peroxide

Peroxide comes in varying strengths; some weaker strength peroxides are referred to as developers.

Peroxide strengths are sometimes still described as volumes but more popularly referred to as percentages.

- Volume strengths of peroxide describe the parts of free oxygen that may be given off during development. For example, '20 volume' gives off 20 parts of free oxygen.
- Percentage strengths of peroxide describe the percentage of pure peroxide. For example, in 6% peroxide, 100 grams of solution would be made up of 6 grams of pure peroxide and 94 grams of water.

The table shows the strengths of different peroxides and their uses.

▲ Hydrogen peroxide 6% or 20 volume

Percentage of peroxide	Volume of peroxide	Uses
1.5% 3% 4%	As a guide, these weak solutions are referred to as '10 volume' and 'developers'.	To darken, to add/neutralise tone and quasi-permanent colours.
6%	20 volume	One shade of lift, to darken, to add/neutralise tone, to cover 100% white hair.
9%	30 volume	As a guide, two shades of lift with a normal tint, or three shades of lift with a high-lift tint.
12%	40 volume	As a guide, three shades of lift with a normal tint, or four to five shades of lift with a high-lift tint.

HANDY HINT

The stronger the peroxide, the more oxygen present, and therefore the more lift/lightening is achievable. Levels of lift vary between manufacturers, so always read the instructions.

HEALTH AND SAFETY

Hydrogen peroxide is a very strong chemical and you must take care when using these products.

HANDY HINT

Some manufacturers describe 3% peroxides or higher as suitable for achieving permanent colour results and not just for quasi-permanent colours, so always read manufacturer's instructions.

Developer strength for quasi-permanent colours

To decide on the developer strength, consider the vibrancy of the depth and tone, and how long the colour will last. As a guide, 3% (10 volume) is used by most manufacturers. However, some also offer 1.5% or 4% strengths. The benefit of 1.5% developers is that the colour is more subtle and will not last as long, giving the client freedom to change their colour more often. Using 4% developer will give a longer lasting effect and red/violet tones will be more vibrant.

Mixing ratios

Tubes of colour and tint generally come in 60 ml tubes and a minimum quantity of a ¼ tube (15 ml) is often used. To help you mix accurately, these ¼ tube (15 ml) measures are marked on the side of the tube.

Quasi-permanent colours are mixed at a 1:2 ratio of colour to developer. Therefore, 15 ml (¼ tube) of tint would be mixed with 30 ml of developer.

Normal tints are mixed at a 1:1 ratio of tint to peroxide. Therefore, 15 ml (¼ tube) of tint would be mixed with 15 ml of peroxide.

High-lift tints (those that give maximum lift for blonde colour results) are generally mixed at a 1:2 ratio of tint to peroxide. Therefore, 15 ml (¼ tube) of tint would be mixed with 30 ml of peroxide.

HANDY HINT

When you mix colours you are using your maths skills. Always check the size of a full tube, so you can calculate ¼ tube and ½ tube measurements accurately.

HANDY HINT

Make sure you read the MFIs correctly to ensure you measure and mix the correct quantity and ratio of hydrogen peroxide.

ACTIVITY

Using your salon's range of colouring products, identify how many millilitres of tint and peroxide (or developer) you would need for the following:

- ¾ of a tube of quasi-permanent colour
- a full tube of high-lift tint
- 1½ tubes of normal permanent colour.

ACTIVITY

You will be using your maths skills when you:

- estimate the length of hair
- estimate the percentage of white hair
- work out the strength of hydrogen peroxide required.

Calculate how much product and peroxide you would need for the following clients:

1. A client with short dense hair who is having a regrowth service.
2. A client with fine hair, that sits just above the shoulders, who is having a full head colour.
3. A client with type 4 layered hair with medium density that sits just below the shoulders, who is having woven natural low-lights.

▲ Mixing of colour

Influence of porosity levels

You must consider the condition and porosity of your client's hair before deciding on the colour choice and the techniques to be used. Porous hair will not withstand further harsh chemical treatments, and colouring or lightening products must not be overlapped.

ACTIVITY

Discuss what colour services and products would be available to clients with porous hair. Explain why some products or services could not be offered.

Effects of temperature

The temperature of the salon will affect your colour and lightening development times, as well as the outcome. Some manufacturer's instructions also state whether you should apply colours to the roots first or start with the mid-lengths and ends – this is because of the heat given off from the head area at the roots of the hair.

Testing the hair and scalp prior to and during colouring and lightening

The hair and scalp must be checked prior to the service to ensure there are no contra-indications which will prevent the service from being carried out or the desired result from being achieved. Some colours develop at varied rates and others need a set development time, so colours should be monitored throughout the service too.

Monitoring and development

Most semi-permanent, quasi and permanent colours have varied but fixed development times set by the manufacturer. Always follow the manufacturer's instructions for development time, as the final few minutes is often when the tone is deposited and the true colour developed.

▲ Development time is reduced if heat is used

An approximate guide for development time (without additional heat) is:

- Semi-permanent – 15–20 minutes
- Quasi-permanent – 20 minutes
- Permanent colour – 30–40 minutes
- High-lift colours – 45–60 minutes.

At the end of the fixed development time carry out a strand test to check the tone has been deposited and the colour is even throughout.

As most lightening products do not have a fixed development time it is vital that you visually check the result at regular intervals. Carry out a strand test to check if the colour result has been achieved.

Methods of applying and removing colouring and lightening products

After a thorough consultation and with a thorough knowledge of your chosen products, you are now able to carry out the most suitable colouring service to meet your client's requirements. All that is left for you to do is to choose the correct technique to achieve the client's requirements.

▲ Quasi colours can be applied quickly at the shampoo area

KEY TERM

Anti-oxidant – a substance that stops the oxidation process.

▲ Regrowth colour application

▲ Full head colour application

The colour, lowlighting and highlighting techniques you will carry out are:

- Full head application of quasi-permanent
- Regrowth application of permanent colour
- Full head application of permanent colour
- Woven highlights and or lowlights
- Sliced highlights and or lowlights.

Full head application of quasi-permanent

Quasi-permanent colours are normally applied on pre-shampooed hair. As the product is more fluid than permanent colour, and it is applied to wet hair, larger sections can be taken. The service is normally carried out either at the workstation or the shampoo area, and the colour applied from roots to tips and gently massaged through.

Once developed, the quasi-permanent colour must be rinsed off the hair, followed by a shampoo. An **anti-oxidant** conditioner should then be used to return the hair to pH 4.5–5.5.

Regrowth application of permanent colour

Regrowth applications are applied to clean, dry hair using a cross-sectioning pattern. The colouring product is applied to the roots only and left to develop. Colour refreshing techniques may also be used to brighten up faded ends.

Full-head application of permanent colour

For a full head application, the same cross-sectioning pattern is used. Depending on the colour choice and lift required, the colour is either applied:

- at the roots, mid-lengths and ends at the same time and then left to develop evenly, or
- to the mid-lengths and ends first, left to develop for about 20 minutes and then the colour is applied to the root area.

Applying colour at the mid-lengths and ends first gives the colour a chance to develop before being applied to the warm root area (which will develop more quickly). This technique is required for most high-lift colours and vibrant tones to ensure an even coverage. Always make sure you work with clean methodical sectioning, to ensure an even coverage of product.

ACTIVITY

A client arrives at the salon requesting a full head colour service. What tests should be carried out before the service commences?

Highlighting techniques

Permanent, high-lift and lightening products can be used for creating highlighting and lowlighting effects. These techniques are useful when clients want to see a proportion of their natural hair colour or an additional colour alongside a lighter highlight. The techniques available are pulled-through or woven/sliced highlights. Always consider the hair's length, density and texture before you make your choice.

▲ Woven highlight technique

Woven/sliced highlighting techniques

Woven and sliced highlights are produced using foils, meches or wraps and are suitable for any hair length. It is very important to consider the client's requirements and expected results, and the density and texture of the hair, when deciding on the quantity of hair to be woven.

The woven technique is very flexible as you can use various colours and products alongside partial or whole head colouring techniques.

T-bar and half head sectioning patterns are commonly used in salons for quick, cost-effective highlighting.

▲ Sliced highlight technique

Pulled-through highlighting techniques

Pulled-through techniques are becoming as popular as woven techniques and can be used to achieve quick effective methods of highlighting. There are several methods that you can use.

Spatula highlights

Spatula highlights is a quicker technique to create a woven pulled-through highlighted look. These are more suitable for one-colour highlighting on longer hair. Generally, permanent and high-lift tints can be used with this method, as some lighteners swell and this could create an uneven, patchy result.

At the end of the service, rinse the product from the hair until the water runs clear, shampoo and then use an anti-oxidant conditioner.

▲ Pulled through technique - Spatula highlights

HANDY HINT

Spatula highlights is a pulled-thorough highlighting method – the hair is woven first and then pulled through from the roots to the ends on the spatula as the colour is applied.

Balayage

Balyage, dip-dye and **ombré** are very popular colouring services, as they are quick colouring services delivering low maintenance colour results. There are many ways in which to apply these types of techniques, but as a guide, the hair is sectioned in a circular sectioning pattern around the head. Then, starting at the back, take a triangle shaped section of hair and place it onto a large colouring board or colour spatula. Apply the chosen colour in a freehand technique lightly near the roots and more heavily as you progress towards the end, as this colour is mostly concentrated around the mid-lengths and ends. Various sized sections can be taken throughout the sectioning pattern, depending on the amount of colour required and the hair's density.

▲ Pulled through technique - Balayage highlights

KEY TERM

Ombré – shaded.

▲ Colour placement systems

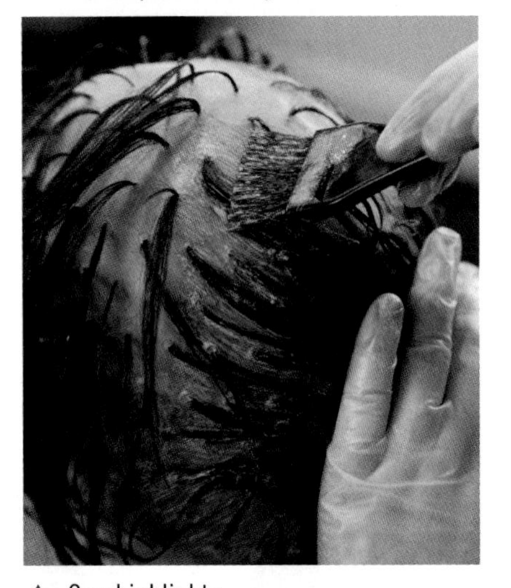

▲ Cap highlights

ACTIVITY

Use the internet to research the history of balayage and ombré. Look at the variety of ways in which these techniques can be applied and the results they produce.

Colour placement system

A colour placement system is one that does not use any clips and each tool is used only once. The hair is sectioned in a circular way and colour cones placed onto the hair that are covered in colouring products. The next section is taken and a slightly larger colour cone placed over the top of the previous section. Colour is then applied and the process continues. See the step by step for colour placement systems at the end of this chapter.

Cap highlights

Cap highlights can be used if only one additional colour is required and the hair is short. Always remember to add talcum powder to the inside of a cap before you pull it onto the head; otherwise it can cause discomfort for your client.

You should pull the hair through the holes to achieve the desired thickness of highlights.

At the end of the service rinse the product from the cap, apply conditioner to the hair to gently ease the cap from the head, shampoo the colour from the hair, and apply an anti-oxidant conditioner.

HANDY HINT

Lowlights are colour effects darker than the client's natural depth colour; highlights are colour effects lighter than the natural depth colour.

ACTIVITY

CASE STUDY 1: ASTI

Asti would like light blonde highlights but your test results show metallic salts are present in the hair. What action should you take? Would you proceed with the service? What further services would you recommend for Asti?

CASE STUDY 2: BAILEY

Bailey has heavily bleached hair and the porosity and elasticity tests show the cuticle is rough and the cortex is weak. She would like to return to a medium brown colour. Which service would you recommend for Bailey?

CASE STUDY 3: MARLEE

Marlee has type 4 African-type hair and would like a whole head colour. This is her first colouring service. Her hair is in good condition but she has psoriasis and very sensitive skin. What tests would you carry out and, depending on the results, which services would you recommend for Marlee?

HANDY HINT

Prepare your materials in advance of the service. Set up your trolley, pre-cut and/or pre-fold your foils, or prepare your chosen highlighting materials in readiness for highlights.

HANDY HINT

Prepare your client's hair in readiness for the service by detangling the hair and sectioning it into manageable size sections. Protect the skin prior to service, using a barrier cream if required.

Provide clients with advice and recommendations

At the end of the consultation you and your client should be confident that the desired result is achievable. Before you begin, make sure your client has been informed of the likely cost and duration of the service. This should include the development time and confirmation of the expected result.

At the end of a hair analysis and client consultation you should have completed the checklist shown in the diagram.

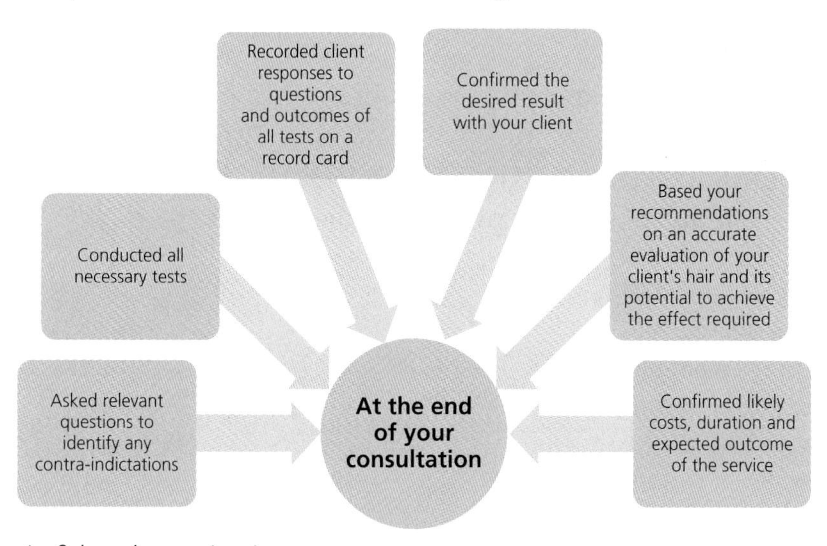

▲ Colour placement systems

COLOUR AND LIGHTEN HAIR

Before you can begin to colour your client's hair, you need to:

- question your client about the service
- understand the different methods of applying and removing colouring and lightening products
- know how to deal with influencing factors
- know how to deal with colouring and lightening problems
- identify the types and causes of problems that may occur during colour processing.

Importance of questioning clients

To confirm a service is suitable and can proceed you need to question your client (as well as check their hair and scalp). During the consultation you need to identify:

- the age of the client (to check they are at least 16 years old)
- the client's requirements
- their previous hair history
- any barriers to the service
- their hair and scalp condition
- whether the result will be achievable
- the best product, service and technique to use.

Throughout the service you should continue to question your client to confirm the service is proceeding to their satisfaction and to keep them informed of the progress of the service.

Different methods of applying and removing products

▲ Section the hair accurately

We have previously looked at methods of applying colours – full head colours, regrowth services and methods of highlighting the hair. Whichever method you choose, it is important to section the hair accurately. When sectioning and weaving the hair you need to secure and control the hair effectively, as this enables you to work methodically and achieve an even colour result.

Factors influencing the service

During your consultation you must consider these factors:

- hair classifications
- hair characteristics
- temperature
- existing colour of hair
- percentage of white hair
- test results
- strength of hydrogen peroxide
- hair length
- skin tone
- time interval from last chemical service
- recent addition or removal of hair extensions.

Many factors affect natural and artificial hair colour, causing damage or the colours and tones to fade from the hair. Make sure you consider these factors when you add colour, as they determine the types of product, service and technique you may use.

By considering all of these factors, you can ensure the colour suits your client and will not affect the hair by damaging the cuticle and the inner cortex. The cuticle must be smooth and in good condition to be able to sustain further chemical treatments. The cuticle is opened during chemical services to allow the colour to penetrate into the cortex. If the cuticle is rough and raised, the hair is porous, which could affect the colouring result or cause further damage to the hair.

Hair classifications

Hair classifications refer to how straight, wavy, curly or very curly your client's hair is.

Straight hair (type 1)

Fine or thin straight hair tends to be very soft, shiny and sometimes oily. Oily hair will need to be pre-shampooed prior to the colour application to ensure there are no barriers to the colour. Type 1 hair can have a tightly compact cuticle so the hair may be resistant to colour and you might need to **pre-soften** the hair before colouring.

When colouring hair that is coarse and straight, highlighting and lowlighting techniques can help to add texture to a hairstyle, so recommending this technique may benefit the client, depending on the hairstyle worn.

▲ Straight hair

KEY TERM

Pre-soften – a technique where 6% liquid peroxide is applied to the hair before the tint application to open the cuticle. (For more information on pre-softening hair, see 'Covering white hair' later in this chapter.)

HANDY HINT

Straight hair can be oily, as the sebum produced by the sebaceous glands has a direct pathway to travel straight along the hair shaft.

Wavy hair (type 2)

Wavy hair can sometimes be frizzy, too, so you will need to consider this, especially if you are contemplating using a lightening product on the hair. Coarse wavy hair can be resistant. If hair is resistant and there is white hair present, you may need to pre-soften the hair to ensure even depth and tone coverage on the white hair.

▲ Wavy hair

Curly hair (type 3)

Loose and tight curls tend to have a combination texture. This may affect the condition of the hair, so consider what products would ideally suit the hair's condition and texture. This type of hair can often be thick and abundant, so more product may be required. If you are carrying out woven highlights, it can be more difficult to secure the colour meches or foils near the root, so you may wish to straighten the hair before you start the service. Some curls can also be frizzy, so you may recommend avoiding lightening products where possible.

▲ Curly hair

Very curly hair (type 4)

Hair that is very curly, whether soft or wiry, tends to be very fragile and is likely to tangle easily. It is very important to use pH-balancing products on curly hair to help keep the cuticle closed and maintain a pH of 4.5 to 5.5.

If you are weaving the hair or carrying out pulled-through highlights you may need to shampoo and dry the hair into a smoother style; otherwise these techniques may cause your client discomfort. Always consider which products will best suit the fragile hair.

▲ Very curly hair

HANDY HINT

Curly and very curly hair is more susceptible to cuticle damage because of its shape. The curly pattern of the hair causes bends in the hair and this in turn raises the cuticles. Curly hair can be highly porous, as the natural hair oils (sebum) cannot travel the length of the hair shaft as easily as they can on straight hair.

Hair characteristics

Hair characteristics refer to the hair's condition, porosity, elasticity, density and texture.

Characteristic	Influence on service
Hair condition	The hair's condition may be very strong and resistant; pre-softening may be required if covering white hair or a stronger developer if using a quasi-permanent colour. If the hair's condition is poor and weak, recommend that non-chemical colours should be used.
Hair porosity	Porous hair will restrict your choice of products, as lightening products may cause damage. Resistant, non-porous hair may require longer development times for permanent hair colouring products. Uneven porosity may result in an uneven colour, so you need to consider what products and services will be suitable.
Hair elasticity	If the hair is weak in elasticity then you will need to avoid using chemicals on the hair. Semi-permanent products will add shine to the hair. Conditioning treatments prior to the service will help prepare the hair for future services.
Hair density	Your client's hair density will determine which techniques you use, how much product is required and how long the service may take to complete. You may need to adapt the size of your sections or weaves. Fine weaves in dense hair result in a subtle colour; thick weaves on finer hair could create a heavily highlighted effect, which may not suit the client's requirements.
Hair texture	Texture is the fineness or thickness of each strand of hair. A client may have fine hair but a lot of it, or coarse hair that is sparse in texture. The texture of the hair may affect the amount of product required, the time the service takes to complete and the size of your sections when colouring the hair.
Hair growth pattern	Not many hair growth patterns affect the colouring and lightening services but it is advisable to work with any strong hair movement, rather than try to fight it. Identifying the growth patterns will help you work with natural partings in the hair and identify how the client wears their hair. Trying to hold a foil in place during woven highlights on a cowlick or going against a widow's peak can cause the stylist problems. Adapt your sectioning patterns to work with any hair growth patterns or strong movement in the hair.

Temperature

Warmer or cooler temperatures can have an effect on colouring development times. Warmth speeds up development times and lightening products develop more quickly under heat. Cooler temperatures, on the other hand, increase development time.

Accelerators generate heat, adding to the heat naturally arising from the head. If you are completing a full-head colouring service, you may need to start your application at the mid-lengths and ends of the hair because these are furthest away from the source of heat (the head). After allowing the mid-lengths and ends to develop for 20 minutes, start the root application, so that the whole head colour develops evenly. Accelerators can reduce the development time by about 50 per cent, but not all MFIs recommend the use of accelerators, so always check your instructions.

KEY TERM

Accelerators – an electrical appliance used to provide heat, which accelerates (speeds up) development.

▲ Accelerator

ACTIVITY

Using your salon brand of colouring and lightening products, identify how using heat/accelerators affects the development time of each product and note these down. Using your maths skills, identify how much time could be saved each day by using heat, if a stylist carried out an average of three colours per day.

HANDY HINT

Cool temperatures increase colour development time.

Warm temperatures reduce colour development time.

Existing hair colour

You must consider your client's existing hair colour to identify the following:

- Is the target shade lighter, darker or the same depth as the existing shade?
- Is the colour of the hair natural or artificial?
- Has the previous colour faded?
- How many shades of lift are required to achieve the target shade?
- Can you use a tint to achieve the required lift or do you need to use a lightening product?

HEALTH AND SAFETY

Before using electrical items, make sure you check them visually for any cracks in the main body or plug. Check that the wires are tangle-free and not frayed. If you identify any problems or faults with electrical equipment, remove it from the salon, label it as faulty and report it to a senior member of staff.

Percentage of white hair

The percentage of white hair is important because it can affect the products used and services available to the client. When colouring white hair, you must consider the following:

- Is the white hair strong and resistant?
- Do you need to pre-soften the hair?
- If your client wants a semi-permanent colour, will it blend enough white hair?
- If your client wants a quasi-permanent colour, will it cover enough white hair?
- Does your client want a permanent colour to cover 100 per cent white hair?

Test results

You must consider the results of all hair and skin tests carried out to ensure the client will not suffer an allergic reaction and that the hair is suitable for the service.

▲ Colour test on a strand of hair

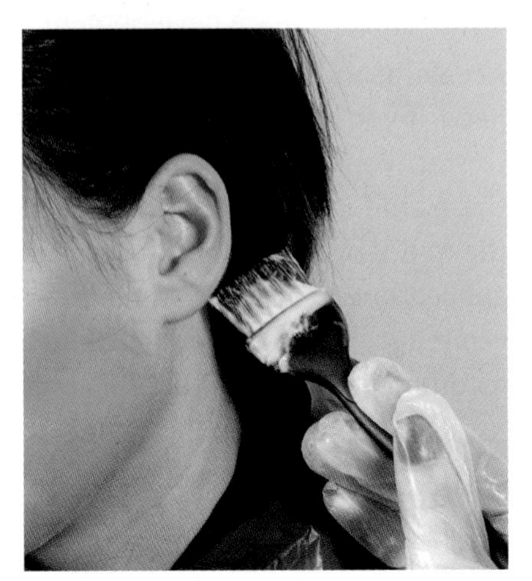

▲ Skin test

Strength of hydrogen peroxide

Hydrogen peroxide and developers can be used to lighten or darken the hair depending on the strength used.

Hair length

The length of your client's hair will determine which techniques you use, your sectioning pattern, how much product is required and how long the service may take to complete.

Short hair is often easier to manage, but you still need to work methodically and take clean sections to ensure even coverage.

Longer hair will benefit from being clipped and secured into manageable sized sections to make it easier to control. Longer or thick, coarse hair, will require more product than short or fine hair. Colouring services on longer/thicker hair will generally take the stylist more time to complete, due to controlling and securing the hair sections and to ensure even coverage of the product.

Skin tone

You need to check that the client's chosen hair colour will complement their skin tone. To help identify whether a client's skin tone is warm or cool, you should look for some tell-tale signs.

In general, natural redheads, reddish golden browns, deep browns and golden blonde hair colours have warmer complexions. Their skin may be paler with pink, peach, copper or gold undertones. People from Latin America, Africa or Europe with freckled complexions generally have warm tones. Depending on the hair's depth, colours such as caramel, copper and yellow–gold suit warm skin tones.

For cooler skin tones – skin that is pale to medium with little colour in the cheeks – look for hair colours that are naturally bluish-black, dark brown or medium ash blonde. True olive skin, such as Asian, Latino and Mediterranean skin, suits cool red colours, such as burgundy, as the hair is naturally dark. Naturally lighter hair would require lighter cool ash shades.

HANDY HINT

Red or flushed complexions will look redder if you colour the hair with red or warm tones. Pale complexions will look even paler if you colour the hair with darker tones.

Time interval since last chemical service

Previous services can affect the condition and the result of your colouring service. If your client has recently had a perm or relaxing service you should not use colouring chemicals on the hair for a couple of weeks, and longer if the condition does not allow. However, a semi-permanent colour may be applied directly after a perm or relaxer service and could replace any tone that has been lost due to the chemicals in the perm or relaxer.

HANDY HINT

Always check the manufacturer's instructions for guidance on when you can colour or lighten the hair after a perm or relaxer service.

Recent removal of hair extensions

If your client has recently had weaved or bonded extensions removed, the hair and scalp may be delicate. Extensions can damage the hair and cause traction alopecia if the client does not follow the correct aftercare advice or if the hair extensions are left in too long or secured too tightly. Therefore, it is critical you complete a thorough examination of the hair condition and scalp area before colouring hair after removal of hair extensions.

Clip-in hair extensions rarely cause any damage to the hair, so once removed from the hair, colouring services can be carried out.

For bonded hair extensions, a releaser solution or **acetone** is applied to the resin bond to dissolve it and release the extension from the hair. Some manufacturers allow colouring products to be applied immediately after the removal of hair extensions. The hair must be cleansed first with a detoxing shampoo (to remove the acetone from the hair) prior to the colour application.

KEY TERM

Acetone – soluble material or chemical solvent.

Ideally, after the removal of hair extensions, additional chemical services should be avoided for a week or two if possible, and even longer if the hair is damaged or the scalp is sensitive. Always check with your supplier and manufacturer's instructions before applying a colour service.

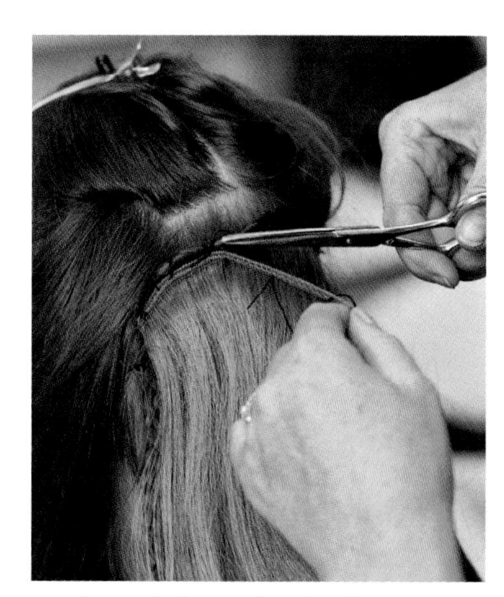

▲ Removal of sewn-in extensions

Judge the quantity of hair to be woven

When carrying out highlights you need to decide if the look required is more suitable to woven or sliced highlights, or a combination of both – which is often the case. You then need to decide on the amount of hair to be woven and this will depend on the following:

- The desired result – is the colour required subtle highlights or lots of colour? Do you want thin weaves or thicker bold colours? Will you need several colours applied finely or one colour and lots of packets?
- Style worn – the placement and amount of woven packets you put in may vary around the head to suit the style worn. Are you carrying out a full head, half head, or T-bar sectioning patten?

- The density and texture of your client's hair – the finer or thinner the hair, the fewer highlights required and the denser the hair, the more weaves and packets required. Also the thickness of each weave will vary to suit hair type and colour required.

Dealing with colouring and lightening problems

You will encounter the occasional problem during a colour service that needs to be rectified. Some problems can be avoided by:

- applying colour refreshing techniques
- applying products correctly around the hairline and avoiding colour staining around the hair line and by using techniques that use products that have been **emulsified**
- restoring hair back to its natural pH level and preventing dry and damaged hair
- not disturbing areas still developing, when products need removing.

KEY TERM

Emulsify – the mixing of a small amount of water with the colouring product to ensure thorough removal from the hair and scalp.

Colour refreshing techniques

Hair depth can naturally lighten with sunlight, humidity and wind, because hair is exposed to oxygen in the air. Hair tones can also be lost in sunlight or UV light, particularly red and violet tones, as their larger colour pigments sit nearer the surface of the hair.

As permanent colours can often fade between salon visits, clients may be advised to have their mid-lengths and ends refreshed along with a regrowth touch-up. The techniques and services you suggest will vary according to the amount of depth and tone lost.

Regrowth using a refreshing technique for mid-lengths and ends

If your client has minimal loss of depth and tone:

1. Complete the regrowth colour application.
2. Develop for the full development time.
3. Add 10–15 ml of water to the hair and emulsify the product through the mid-lengths and ends.
4. Leave for 3–5 minutes.
5. Remove the colour in the usual way.
6. Record the process on the client's record card.

If your client has significant loss of depth and tone:

1. Complete the regrowth colour application.
2. Develop for 10–15 minutes.
3. Mist the mid-lengths and ends with water.
4. Apply a quasi-permanent colour to the mid-lengths and ends.
5. Develop for a further 20 minutes.
6. Remove the colour in the usual way.
7. Record the process on the client's record card.

▲ Loss of depth and tone – requiring a regrowth colour and refreshing techniques

If your client has loss of tone only (for example, faded red tones):
1 Complete the regrowth colour application.
2 Develop for 20 minutes.
3 Add 10–15 ml of water to the hair, and emulsify the product through the mid-lengths and ends.
4 Develop for a further 10–15 minutes.
5 Remove the colour in the usual way.
6 Record the process on the client's record card.

If your client is changing the tonal colours of their hair, but maintaining the depth, complete the application as follows:
1 Complete the regrowth colour application.
2 Add 10–15 ml of water to the hair and emulsify the product through the mid-lengths and ends.
3 Develop for the full development time.
4 Remove the colour in the usual way.
5 Record the process on the client's record card.

Methods of removing colouring and lightening products

At the end of an on-scalp colour service, you will need to thoroughly remove the products from the hair. After a highlighting service you will also need to carefully remove materials, such as cap, meche or foils from the hair. When products and materials are being removed from the hair you must continue to wear your gloves and PPE.

Removal of materials

Apply water over the meche's seals, or unfold the foils to loosen them.

Remove the meches or foils carefully from the hair and thoroughly rinse the area. Once all foils or meches are removed, gently shampoo the hair, using a shampoo for coloured hair and condition using an anti-oxidant conditioner.

Emulsify colour prior to removal

It is important that all colouring products are removed effectively from the hair to prevent scalp irritation and hair damage. To remove colouring products you must emulsify the product thoroughly at the end of the development time using the following method:
1 Apply a small of amount of water to the hair.
2 Emulsify the product into the moistened hair using a rotary massage technique.
3 Rinse the emulsified product until the water runs clear.
4 Shampoo the hair using a shampoo for coloured hair.
5 Condition the hair using an anti-oxidant conditioner.

HANDY HINT

Colouring products must be thoroughly removed from the hair to prevent further development or damage to the hair and scalp. Emulsifying will enable the colour to be loosened from the hair and prevent staining to the skin and scalp.

HANDY HINT

Apply products carefully and cleanly to minimise the risk of the product being spread to your client's skin, clothes and surrounding area.

ACTIVITY

List three reasons why it is important to use products economically.

▲ Add a little water and then massage the hairline to emulsify and remove colour from the hairline and scalp.

HANDY HINT

Tint removes tint. If you encounter any staining of colour around the hairline and ears, you can apply some tint from the bowl and massage gently into these areas prior to the colour removal process.

Lightening products used for regrowth and full head services must be thoroughly removed from the hair at the end of the development time using the following method:

1 Apply a small of amount of water over the hair.
2 Gently emulsify the water into the lightening product, using a gentle rotary massage technique – be gentle with the hair because it will be in a delicate state, and the scalp may be tender.
3 Rinse the emulsified hair until the water runs clear
4 Gently shampoo the hair, using a shampoo for coloured hair.
5 Condition the hair using an anti-oxidant conditioner.

THE HAIR PROFESSIONAL IN THE WORKPLACE

A true professional will always follow manufacturer's instructions when measuring, mixing and timing colouring and lightening products to ensure an accurate result is achieved and to prevent any damage to the hair and scalp.

Restoring hair's pH balance

After all chemical services an anti-oxidant conditioner should be used to stop the oxidation process. This closes the cuticle and returns the hair to its natural state of pH 4.5–5.5. It prevents colours from fading, the hair from becoming dry/brittle and causing damage to the cuticle or cortex.

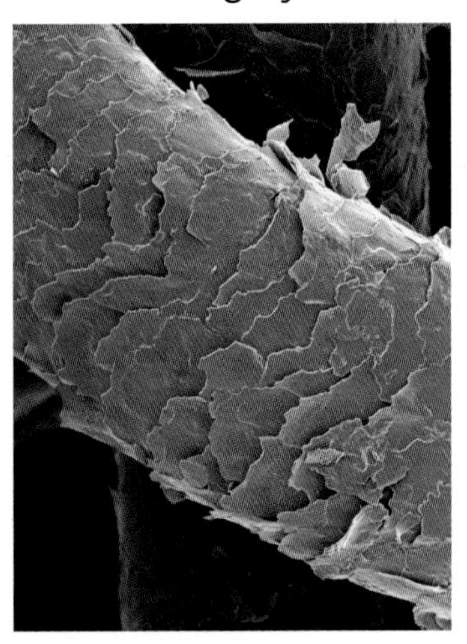

▲ Damaged cuticle layer

▲ Post-colour care

Avoid disturbing areas still processing when removing product

If you are using lighteners, some meches may need to be removed while others are still developing. To do this, secure the meches that are still developing and ensure they do not move and cause seepage.

At the end of the service, carefully remove all remaining meches or foils from the client's hair without causing discomfort. Once the materials are removed from the hair, remove the product in the usual manner.

ACTIVITY

You encountered the following problems when removing products or materials from the hair:

1 As you remove developed colour meches, you disturb foils or meches still developing.
2 You identify a colour bleed/seepage at the root area of a couple of foil packets.
3 You identify over processed highlights.

What action will you take and who will you report this to?

Problems that may occur when applying colour

You may encounter some problems when colouring the hair. The table below shows the causes and remedies to common problems.

Colouring problem	Cause of problem	Resolving the problem
Skin staining	Poor application Dry skin/hairline Did not use barrier cream	Use a stain remover. If not too late, emulsify colour at the basin.
Uneven colour result	Poor mixing of product Uneven application Porous hair prior to application Incorrect selection of colour for white hair Underdeveloped	Apply a quasi-permanent colour if suitable. Spot tint/bleach uneven areas.
Poor coverage on white hair	Resistant hair Did not pre-soften Incorrect choice of colour Incorrect strength of peroxide used	Pre-soften hair in future. Reapply product if hair condition allows.
Seepage	Poor application Incorrect mixing of product Incorrect use of foils or meche	Spot tint to cover seepage of product.
Allergy and/or scalp irritation	Product too strong Allergy to product Possible cuts or abrasions	Remove product immediately. Rinse with cool water. Refer to GP if required.
Over processed result, or deterioration of hair condition	Overdeveloped Peroxide too strong Too much heat used Overlapped previous colour	Remove product immediately. Apply conditioning treatment to the hair. Recommend Olaplex treatments to repair the structure of the hair.
Under processing	Underdeveloped Peroxide strength was not strong enough Wrong colour/product choice Did not consider tones present in the hair	Use a violet toner. Re-lighten if hair condition allows.

HANDY HINT

At the end of the service you should confirm your client is satisfied with the end result. You may need the record card if the client is unhappy with the service or wants to take legal action. The record card provides evidence to support any defence and shows that professional standards were met.

HANDY HINT

Remember not to mix your lightening product too thinly, as it will seep out of the foils or through the holes in the cap. If the lightener is too thick it will dry out too quickly. Try to mix it to a cream which will just about support your tint brush in an upward position, without you holding it.

HANDY HINT

Take extra care when using lightening products on previously chemically treated hair. Ensure your application is not overlapped, as this will cause greater porosity, damage to the hair's condition, and potentially uneven colour results.

▲ Electrical heat appliances can cause colour loss

ACTIVITY

Find out from your salon manager what the limits of your authority would be if you had to solve the colouring problems listed in the table above. Who would you refer colour problems to if you could not resolve them?

Potential risks of using lightening products

There is a potential risk of damage to your client's hair if you overlap lightening products or use lightening products on previously chemically treated hair. Always ensure you test the condition of your client's hair and check the hair's history before you apply lighteners.

It is imperative that you follow your specific manufacturer's instructions relating to skin tests to ensure your clients are not at risk of an allergic reaction and to prevent any legal consequences. Remember to check the age ID of any young-looking clients to confirm they are over 16 years old, as it is illegal to colour the hair of anyone under this age.

Make sure you monitor and develop lightening products properly, if there is not a fixed time for development; check the process visually on a regular basis to ensure the end result is not over-processed.

Provide aftercare advice and recommendations

Colour services are very costly to the client and providing aftercare advice on maintaining the colour is vitally important.

You may need to recommend lifestyle alterations to your client, to ensure both the colour and condition of the hair are preserved. This may include advising wearing a hat on sunny or windy days, or warning about the effects of chlorine on hair colour. Chlorine can cause hair to dry out and become brittle, the colour to fade and even a colour reaction. You might recommend shampoos that remove chlorine from the hair, and additional shampoo and conditioning products that will enhance the colour and improve durability.

Excessive use of electrical heat appliances will also cause the colour to fade and the hair to lose condition. You should advise your client appropriately and suggest regular conditioning treatments.

Time interval between services

Depending on the service carried out, you may need to advise your client on time intervals between other services or future colouring services.

ACTIVITY

Ask your salon manager or another stylist how long they would suggest a client waits before having the following services:

- hair extensions
- permanent blow-dry
- permanent wave.

Present and future products and services

Finally, you should advise your client when to return to the salon for additional services, or for their next colouring service. Explain how long they should expect the current service to last, and advise them on what to look for as a guide for when they should return. This may include white hair becoming noticeable around the hairline, a visible regrowth or colour fade.

Make suitable suggestions for additional services such as their next haircut or treatments you have recommended. Suggest that your client books their next appointment while they are still in the salon. This helps the salon to maintain regular trade and revenue, and allows your client to look forward to their next appointment.

ACTIVITY

Identify the products available in your salon that you could recommend to clients after a colouring service.

ACTIVITY

1 If a client wanted to rebook for their next colour service, when would you suggest they rebook? How many weeks for:
- a regrowth tint?
- a full head of woven highlights?
- T-bar section of woven highlights?
- pulled-through capped highlights?
- balayage or dip dye?

2 Using your maths skills, how many times a year would your client visit for the above services?

3 Use your salon price list to work out how much money the salon will generate from this client and the services they receive each year.

RESOLVE BASIC COLOURING PROBLEMS

You will now look at the types and causes of colouring lightening problems and how to rectify them, as well as the reasons for pre-softening and pre-pigmenting hair and methods of how to do this.

Colouring and lightening problems

Some basic colouring problems you may have to rectify are:
- neutralising colour tone
- restoring depth and tone – requiring pre-pigmenting services
- colouring resistant hair – requiring pre-softening services.

To correct these colouring problems you must:
1. Assess the condition of the hair and check the corrective service can go ahead.
2. Identify the main cause of the problem.
3. Identify suitable corrective product(s) to use.
4. Identify suitable corrective technique(s) to use.

▲ Colour star

Neutralising colour tone

Colour tones may need to be neutralised because of:

- poor diagnoses of natural tone
- wrong colour choice
- underdeveloped products – insufficient lift or deposit of tone/ development of tone
- hidden tones within the hair (often golden/copper tones).

If the tonal end result of a colour is not to the client's requirements then you may need to neutralise the colour. When neutralising colour tone you must refer to your colour star.

If hair is too gold, then you must neutralise with violet – this could be a semi- or quasi-permanent colour or a silver/violet toner provided by the manufacturer.

If the hair colour is:

- too copper (orange), you need to neutralise with a blue base ash
- too red, you need to neutralise with a green base ash
- too violet or grey, you need to neutralise with a warm gold (yellow)
- green, you need to neutralise with a red tone colour.

For more information refer back to the section on the principles of colour earlier in this chapter.

HANDY HINT

Clients have sometimes experienced recently applied highlights turning green in swimming pools; this is due to the chlorine reacting to the porous hair. A quick remedy for clients on holiday (and not near their favourite salon) is to rinse tomato sauce through the hair – the red from the sauce neutralises the green caused by the chlorine. Recommending chlorine-removing shampoos or clarifying shampoos for your clients who swim regularly will prevent this scenario.

Restoring depth and tone

Hair may lose depth and tone as a result of:

- using harsh shampoos and conditioners
- time spent in sunny climates
- overuse of heated electrical appliances
- the hair being porous at the start of the last colour application which has resulted in the colour not being held.

Replacing lost tone is much easier than replacing loss of depth. A loss of minor depth and tone can be replaced with a refreshing technique. Loss of tone can be refreshed with a semi-permanent colour or a quasi-permanent colour, but if the hair has lost a lot of depth and needs to be darkened then the hair may need to have a **pre-pigmenting** process first.

KEY TERM

Pre-pigmenting – a technique to replace the pigments that have been removed during the lightening stages of hair colouring.

Pre-pigmenting

Hair that has been lightened in a colouring process has had many of the pheomelanin pigments removed. When hair is either darkened again or you need to restore lost depth and tone, the hair will need a pre-pigmenting service first. If you fail to undercoat the hair with these vital pigments before colouring, then the hair is likely to be a khaki green colour.

Normally it is red, orange and gold (yellow) colours that are required for pre-pigmenting. There are lots of products you can use, for example, a temporary colour mousse, a semi-permanent colour or a pre-pigmenting spray. After pre-pigmenting the hair, you can apply your target shade.

The diagram opposite shows the tones that are removed from the hair as it is lightened. These tones must be replaced before applying the target shade.

For example:

- Roxanne had a hair colour 6.3. This has faded in the sun and is now an 8.0. You must pre-pigment the hair with an orange undercoat before applying 6.3 to her hair.
- Darcy-belle had her porous highlighted hair re-coloured to her natural depth of 5. This has gradually faded out as the hair is porous. To restore her depth and tone again you will need to pre-pigment the hair with reddish-orange before adding the target base 5 colour.

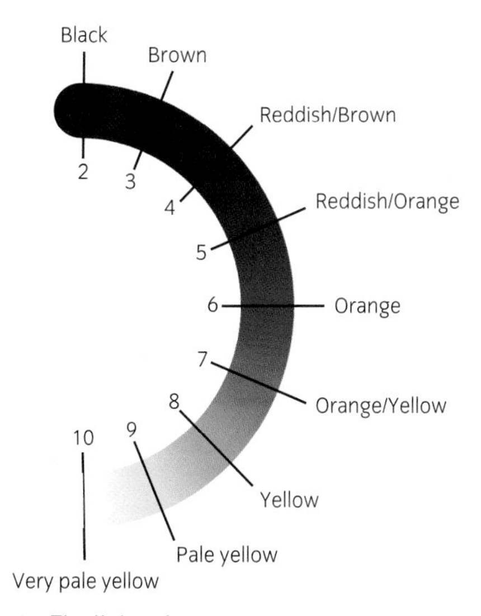

▲ The lightening curve

▲ Pre-pigmenting

Colouring resistant hair

Clients with a high percentage of white hair tend to find that colour coverage can be less effective – white hair is often resistant to the colour because of the tightly compacted cuticle. To overcome this, you may need to pre-soften the hair.

Pre-softening

This technique involves applying neat (undiluted) 6% liquid peroxide to the hair, prior to the colouring service. It can be used before a full-head or regrowth application using the following method:

1. Apply the liquid peroxide to clean dry hair using a bowl and brush.
2. Using either a hand held hairdryer or by placing your client under a hood dryer, dry the solution into the hair.
3. Do not rinse out the solution and, once dry, continue with the application process as normal.
4. Record the process on the client's record card.

This technique uses added heat from the hairdryer to open the cuticle, allowing the peroxide to enter the cortex, ready for the colouring process.

ACTIVITY

What pigment tones need to be replaced if you are going to the following depths?

- From a base 10 to a base 8.
- From a base 9 to a base 7.

HANDY HINT

When pre-softening the hair, make sure you only use liquid peroxide (and not cream) so that the peroxide can swell the cuticle layer and allow the colour to penetrate into the cortex effectively.

WHAT YOU MUST DO

For your practical assessments you must:

- apply safe working practices when colouring and lightening
- prepare for colouring and lightening
- colour and lighten hair
- resolve basic colouring problems
- carry out colouring and lightening services.

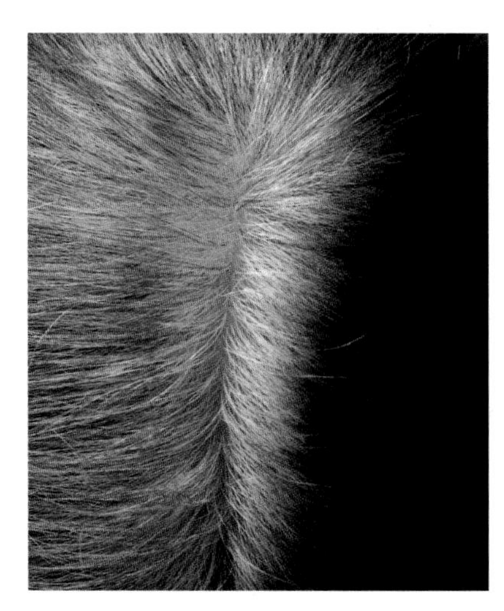

▲ Covering white hair can be a problem

▲ Prepare for services

Apply safe working practices

You must:

- prepare for colouring and lightening services
- apply safe and hygienic methods of working
- consult with clients about services and outcomes of tests and confirm the desired result
- assess any colouring problems and take appropriate action to resolve problems using the relevant corrective action.

Prepare for colouring and lightening services

For your assessments, you must prepare for colouring and lightening services by:

- preparing your client to meet salon requirements
- protecting your client's clothing throughout the service
- ensuring your personal hygiene, appearance and personal protection equipment meets accepted industry and organisational requirements
- applying safe and hygienic methods of working throughout services.

Apply safe and hygienic methods of working

You must maintain your responsibilities for health and safety throughout the service and wear personal protective equipment when using colouring and/or lightening chemicals. Always ensure you position your client to meet the needs of the service without causing them discomfort and adapt your own posture and position while working to minimise fatigue and the risk of injury. Your work area must be kept clean and tidy throughout the service and you must use working methods that:

- minimise wastage of products
- minimise the risk of cross-infection
- make effective use of your working time
- ensure the use of clean resources
- minimise the risk of harm or injury to yourself and others
- promote environmental and sustainable working practices.

Throughout the service follow workplace and suppliers' or manufacturer's instructions for the safe use of equipment, materials and products and dispose of waste materials correctly. You must constantly monitor:

- colouring and lightener development
- condition of the hair
- scalp sensitivity
- condition of the lightener.

▲ Consult with clients

Consult with clients about services and outcomes of tests

You must explore the variety of looks possible with your client using relevant visual aids and confirm with clients the desired effect.

Assess and resolve colouring problems

You must adapt your techniques to assess and resolve problems, taking into account any factors that may influence the achievement of the required result. You must resolve any problems occurring during the colouring and lightening process using the relevant corrective action.

Carry out colouring and lightening services

When carrying out colouring and lightening services you must:

- complete the service within a commercially viable time while using colouring and lightening effects in an innovative way to achieve the required look
- use lightening application techniques suitable for achieving the desired look and follow manufacturer's instructions
- combine and place products in a way that complements the hairstyle and use techniques that minimise the risk of products being spread to your client's skin, clothes and surrounding areas
- apply lightener products and carry out hair tests at frequent and regular intervals
- ensure the application of toners to lightened hair achieves the desired effect when used, which is to the satisfaction of your client
- remove colour and/or lightener from the hair to minimise discomfort to your client and damage to the hair and scalp and ensure the application of toners to lightened hair achieves the desired effect, when required.

▲ Carry out colour services

Commercially viable service times for colouring

It is important to work effectively in the salon. Your salon will have calculated the cost for each service, including material and labour costs; therefore all services must be completed within an allocated time frame. The table below shows the guide times for typical colouring services.

Colouring service	Guide to service time
Semi-permanent/quasi-permanent	Applied to pre-shampooed hair. Application time around 20 minutes including consultation, shampooing and product application. Additional development time around 20 minutes (see MFIs). Total service time around 40 minutes.
Regrowth permanent	Application time around 30 minutes including consultation, product preparation and application. Additional development time around 30–50 minutes (see MFIs). Total service time 60–80 minutes.

→

Colouring service	Guide to service time
Full head permanent colour	Application time around 40–60 minutes including consultation, product preparation and application. Additional development time around 30–50 minutes (see MFIs). Total service time 70–110 minutes.
Pulled-through highlights	Application time around 30 minutes including consultation, technique application, product preparation and application. Additional development time around 30–50 minutes (see MFIs). Total service time 60–80 minutes.
Full head highlights	Application time around 90-120 minutes including consultation, product preparation and application. Additional development time around 30–50 minutes (see MFIs). Total service time 120–170 minutes.
Partial head highlights	Application time around 60 minutes including consultation, product preparation and application. Additional development time around 30–50 minutes (see MFIs). Total service time 90–110 minutes.

ACTIVITY

Compare these colouring service times to your salon requirements and note any variation.

HANDY HINT

Allocating time frames to each service means that the charge to the client covers all relevant costs, enabling the salon to remain profitable and commercially viable.

ACTIVITY

Using your salon price list, work out the cost and duration of Georgina and Kerry's services:

Georgina wants a half head of woven highlights, with a cut and blow dry.

Kerry wants a full head quasi-permanent colour and a finger dry.

Prepare for colouring and lightening

To prepare for the service you must:

- consult with clients about services and outcomes of tests
- provide clients with advice and recommendations on the service(s) provided
- select suitable products, tools and equipment.

Consult with clients

Always ask your client relevant questions to identify if they have any contra-indications to colouring and/or lightening services (such as open sores on the scalp, previous allergic reactions or hair colourants applied at home). Record their responses to questions asked. Conduct all necessary tests following manufacturer's instructions and recognised industry procedures and record the outcome of tests on the client's record card. Make sure you seek assistance from the relevant person when contra-indications or reactions to tests cause doubts as to the suitability of the service for your client.

▲ Select a suitable service

Provide clients with advice and recommendations

The advice and recommendations you give to your client must be based on an accurate evaluation of your client's hair and its potential to achieve the effect required. Always inform your client of the likely cost, duration and expected outcome of the service and then prepare their hair and protect their skin, where necessary, in readiness for the service.

Select suitable products, tools and equipment

After you have completed necessary tests, consulted with your client and considered any relevant factors, you must choose suitable products, tools and equipment. You must prepare all materials to meet the application requirements and prepare products according to manufacturer's instructions.

▲ Provide aftercare advice to your client and recommend products

Colour and lighten hair

When carrying out colouring and lightening services you must:

- confirm the desired effect with your client prior to the application of products
- section the hair cleanly and evenly to assist the accurate application of products
- apply products, taking into account relevant factors influencing the service
- use colour and lightening techniques suitable for achieving the desired look, following manufacturer's instructions, and apply products in a way that minimises the risk of the product being spread to your client's skin, clothes and surrounding area
- time the development of products following manufacturer's instructions and confirm the required result has been achieved by taking strand tests at suitable times throughout the process
- massage the hair and scalp to emulsify the colour, as necessary, prior to removal, following manufacturer's instructions and remove the hair products that have developed, avoiding disturbance to areas still processing
- remove colouring or lightening materials from hair with minimum discomfort to your client and leave the hair and scalp free of products after the desired effect is achieved

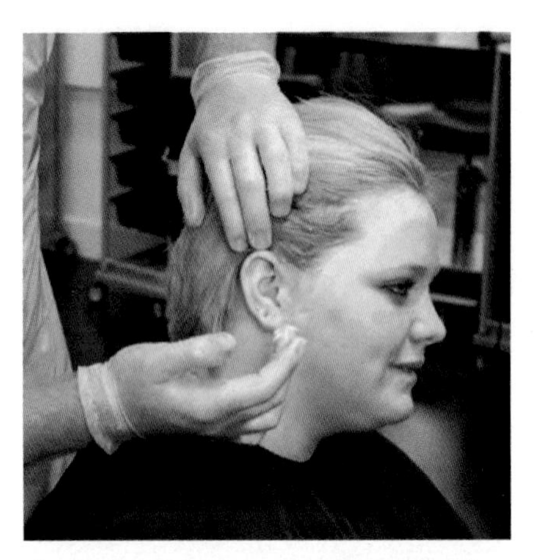

▲ Apply barrier cream to prevent staining

- identify any problems during the service and resolve them within the limits of your own authority, referring problems that cannot be resolved to the relevant person in your salon
- achieve the desired effect to the satisfaction of your client.

Provide clients with advice and recommendations

You must provide your client with advice and recommendations on the service provided, including:

- how to maintain their colour
- time intervals between services
- present and future products and services

Resolve basic colouring problems

You must assess any colouring problems and take suitable action, using methods to:

- assess the condition of the hair
- identify the colouring problem
- identify suitable colour correction products
- identify suitable colour correction techniques.

You must explain to your client the options available for resolving their colour problem and refer your client for specialist colour correction work, if necessary. You must use colour correction techniques effectively to achieve the required colour.

STEP BY STEP

In this part of the chapter you will look at how to:

- carry out a semi-permanent colouring service
- carry out a quasi-permanent colouring service
- apply permanent and high-lift products to the hair.

Carry out a semi-permanent colouring service

STEP 1 – Gown and protect your client and shampoo their hair, but do not add conditioner.

STEP 2 – Apply the semi-permanent colour evenly direct from the applicator bottle.

STEP 3 – Sit the client comfortably for the development time, then add water to emulsify and rinse thoroughly, but do not shampoo the hair. Condition the hair and style as required.

Carry out a quasi-permanent colouring service

STEP 1 – Gown and protect your client. Apply colour choice to pre-shampooed hair at the shampoo area, using a bowl and brush or an applicator technique and allow to develop.

STEP 2 – After the development time, add some water, emulsify and rinse thoroughly.

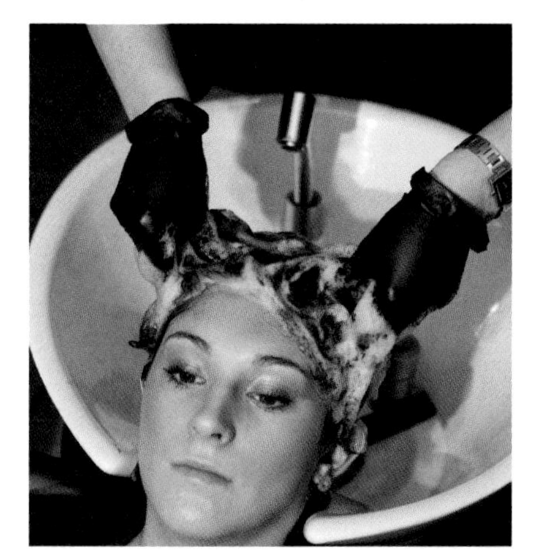

STEP 3 – Shampoo and condition the hair and style to finish.

STEP 4 – The final look.

HANDY HINT

Quasi-permanent colours can also be applied on wet hair at the workstation by sectioning the hair and applying in the same way as a full head colour application. Apply the colour from root to point in medium-sized sections.

HANDY HINT

If quasi-permanent colours are used too regularly, a more permanent colour effect can occur and definite regrowth can be seen at the roots.

Apply permanent and high-lift products to the hair

Permanent and high-lift products can be used for regrowth and full-head colouring services.

Permanent regrowth service

STEP 1 – Gown and protect your client and apply barrier cream.

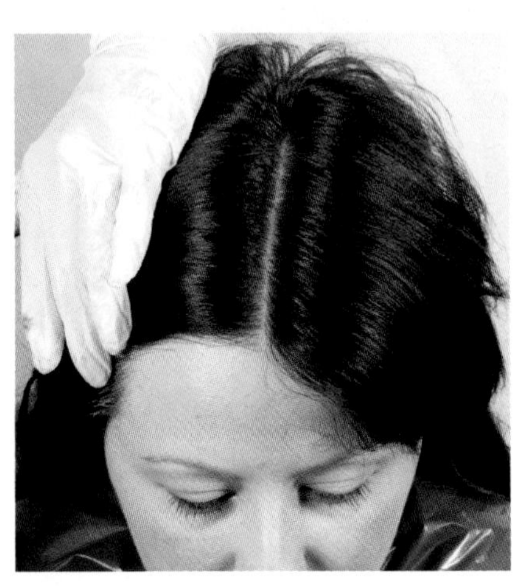

STEP 2 – Section the hair cleanly into four sections (cross section).

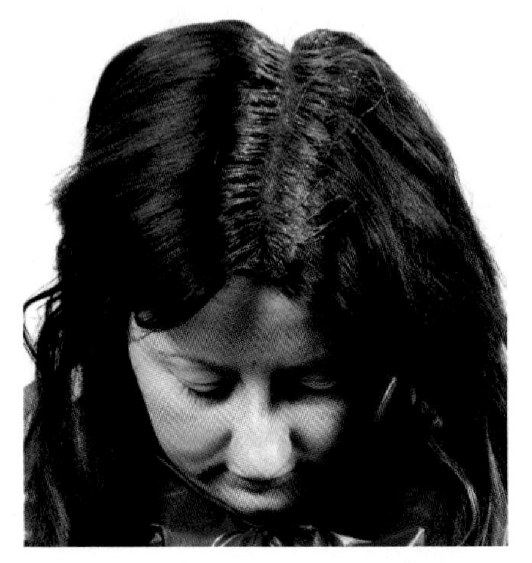

STEP 3 – Apply the colour evenly and cleanly to the root area.

STEP 4 – Follow your section pattern for a thorough coverage.

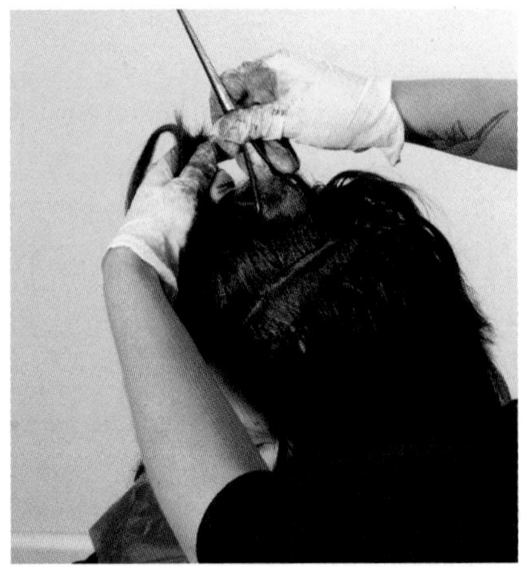

STEP 5 – Cross-check your sections to ensure even coverage.

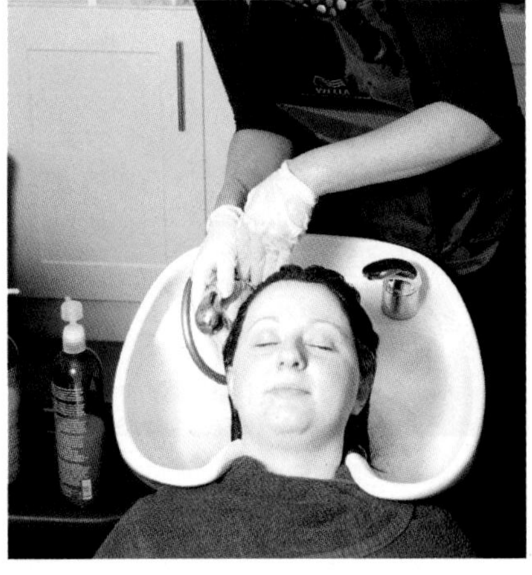

STEP 6 – After development and checking of the colour, rinse, emulsify, shampoo and condition.

HANDY HINT

Always follow the MFIs when using colouring products to prevent damage to your client's hair or skin, to achieve the correct result and to avoid any legal action.

HANDY HINT

To help you mix your tint accurately, most colouring tubes are clearly marked along the sides to show every quarter of a tube.

Full head woven highlights

Full head woven highlights with permanent colour and meche:

STEP 1 – Divide the hair to be coloured into manageable sections and weave your section.

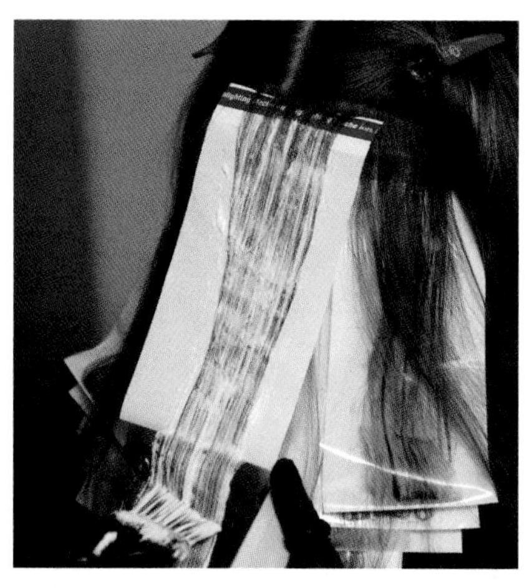

STEP 2 – Apply the product evenly without overloading the root area.

STEP 3 – Work in a methodical manner towards the top of the head. When you have completed all the hair, leave it to develop

STEP 4 – The finished look.

Pulled-through Balayage highlights

STEP 1 – Model before.

STEP 2 – Cross-section the hair into four. Starting at the nape area, take a horizontal section of hair about 2 cm thick and secure the rest.

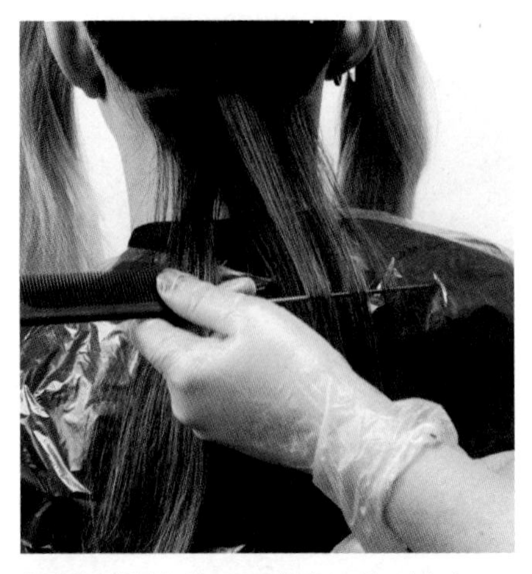

STEP 3 – Divide the nape hair section into two, and weave the section of hair to the desired thickness.

STEP 4 – Hold the hair out from the head about 45° with tension and gently tease the root area to break up the weaved section line.

STEP 5 – Apply the lightener to both sides of the section, near to the root area, and as you go further down the hair's length apply the lightener to the mid-lengths.

STEP 6 – Apply a lightener with a lower level of peroxide to the ends of the hair to refresh and lighten the ends.

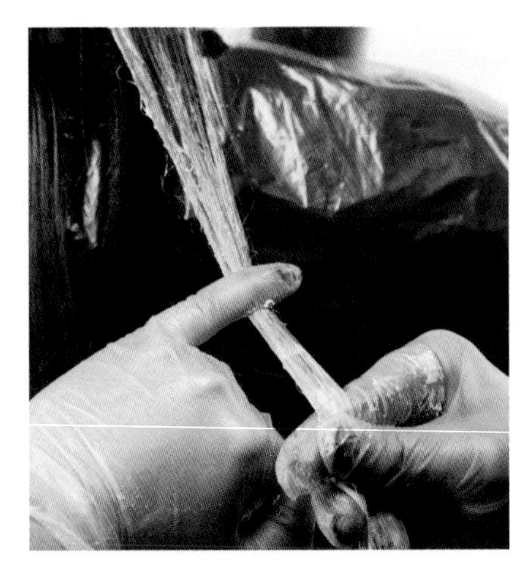

STEP 7 – Using your fingers, gently smudge the applied colour to blend and soften the line and the varied levels of peroxide.

STEP 8 – Place the lightened section of hair into the foil, cover the hair with another foil and fold securely. Repeat this on the other side.

STEP 9 – Take sections 2–3 cm thick, working progressively through the back and up to the crown section.

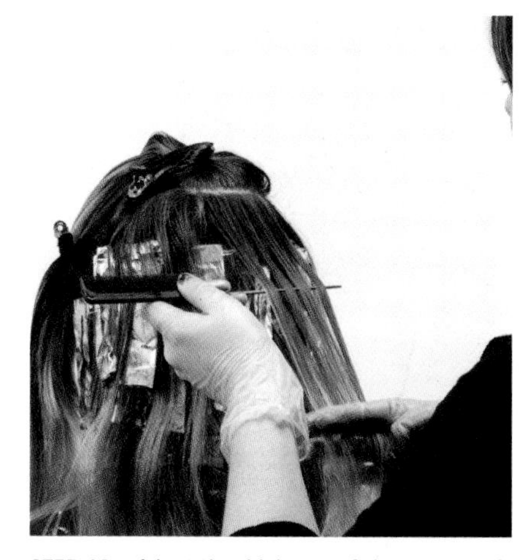

STEP 10 – Adapt the thickness of the weaves, if required, to suit the client's requirements. Carry out the same process on both sides of the head, remixing your lightener or changing the level of peroxide for even development if required.

STEP 11 – Work to the parting of the hair. When completed, visually monitor the development of the lightener and remove when developed.

STEP 12 – The finished result.

Pulled-through spatula highlights

STEP 1 – Section the hair and weave a small section.

STEP 2 – Place the spatula at the root area and apply the product onto the spatula. Slowly pull the spatula away from the root area.

STEP 3 – Gently lay the coloured hair onto the non-coloured hair. Continue with your next weave and apply the colour carefully. Work neatly through the sections to the top of the head.

STEP 4 – The finished look.

Pulled-through colour placement system (dip-dye effect)

STEP 1 – Place the small twister (size 1) on the scalp and turn clockwise 360°.

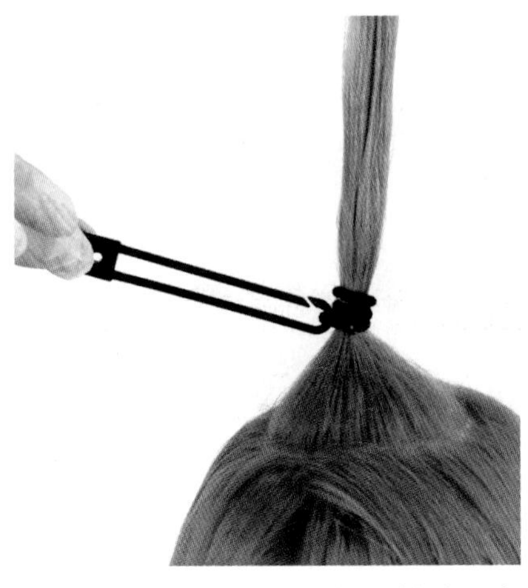

STEP 2 – Secure the sectioned hair with the soft band and attach the hook.

STEP 3 – Thread the hooked-sectioned hair through the first shade and secure with the hook – this hair has not been coloured.

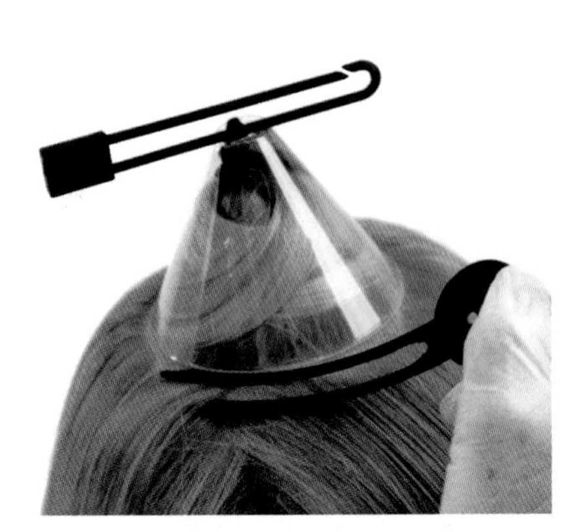

STEP 4 – Using the twin tail comb for accuracy, take the next section of hair.

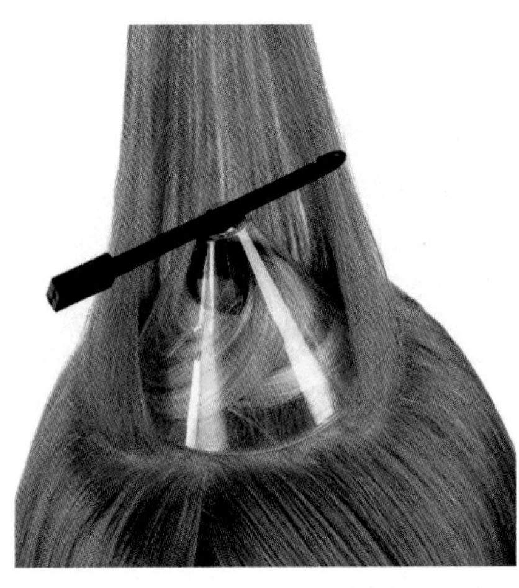

STEP 5 – Complete the section of hair around the shade.

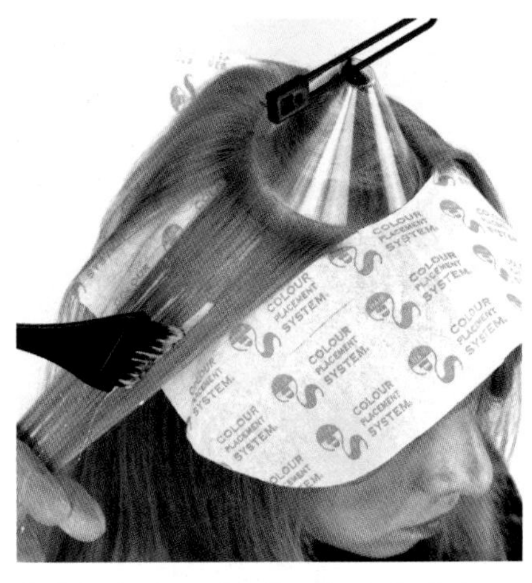

STEP 6 – Apply a colour guard over the first shade and lay the sectioned hair over the top.

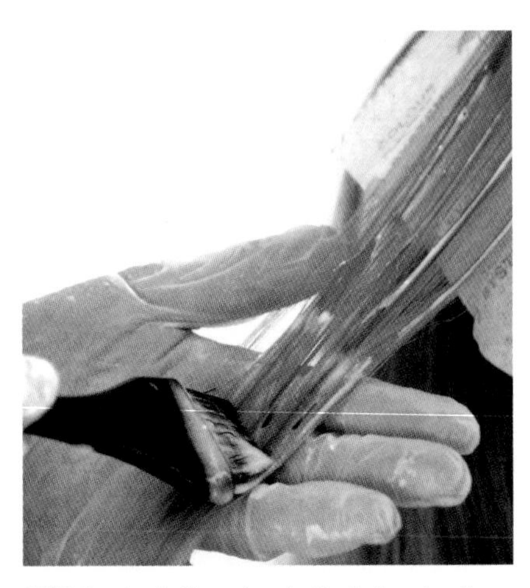

STEP 7 – Apply the colour to the hair using the colour guard to protect the root area.

STEP 8 – Wrap the coloured hair around the shade securely.

STEP 9 – Cover the coloured hair with the next sized shade and secure with the hook.

STEP 10 – Repeat the 360°-sectioning pattern and colour application as required.

STEP 11– Add a few woven highlights or slices of colour to the mid-lengths.

STEP 12 – Leave colour to develop, following the manufacturer's instructions.

Half head of woven and sliced highlights with colour correction techniques (restore lost depth and tone)

This colour service includes a half head of woven and sliced highlights with lightener and 6% peroxide. After the foil packets are completed, the remaining hair was pre-pigmented with orange pre-pigmenting spray and then a quasi-permanent colour was applied directly over the top to restore depth and tone. At the end of the service the highlights were toned with a 9.16 and 1.9% developer to refresh the ends and tone the highlights.

STEP 1 – Model before.

STEP 2 – Section the hair to suit the client's parting and to enable the colours to enhance the contours of the face.

STEP 3 – Secure the remaining hair in a ponytail, secured with a covered band to colour later.

STEP 4 – Take your first section, angled from temple to ear, and weave small and medium sections.

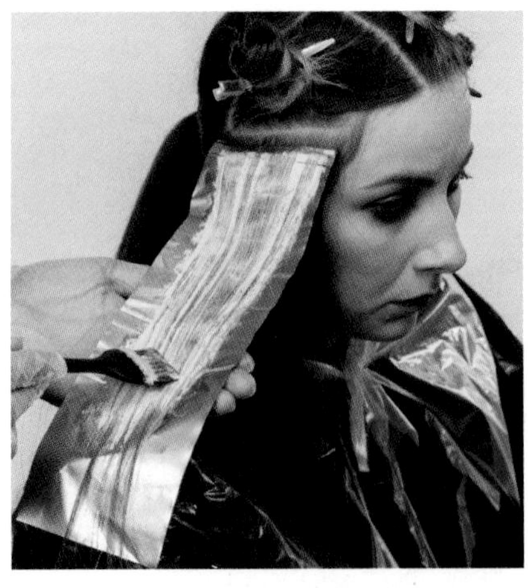

STEP 5 – Add the foil at the root area and apply the colour to the roots and middle areas, leaving out the hair that has been previously coloured and lightened.

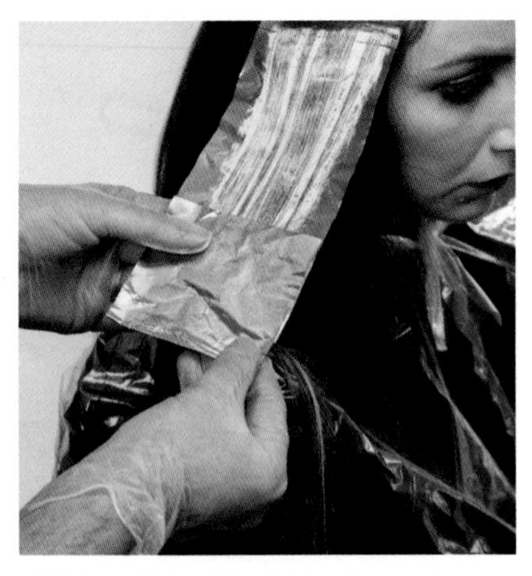

STEP 6 – Fold the foil a third of the way, leaving out the non-coloured ends.

STEP 7 – Fold the foil again towards the root area.

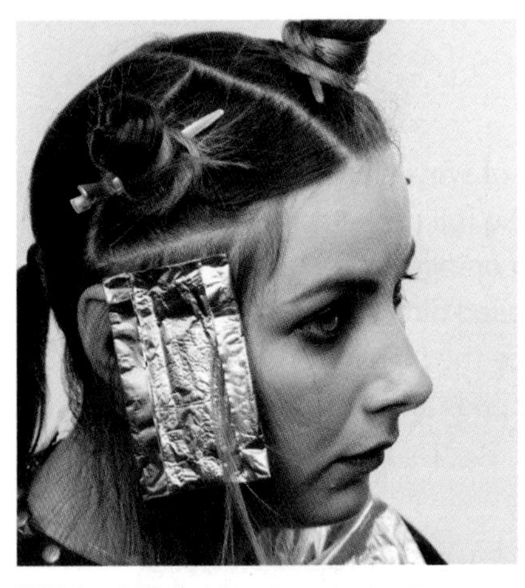

STEP 8 – Fold the edges to secure in place.

STEP 9 – Slice the next section of hair and apply colour to the roots and mid-lengths.

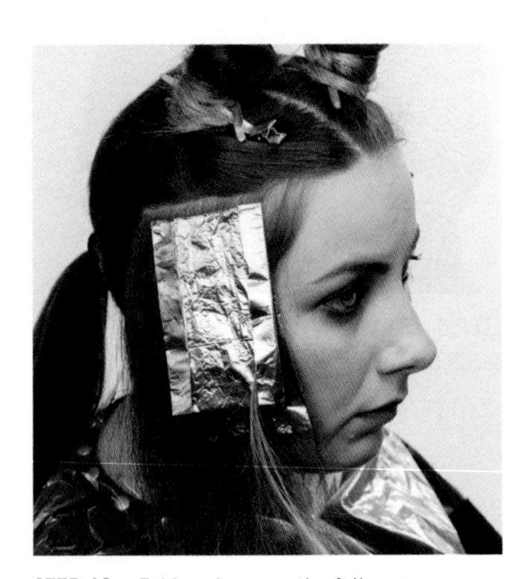

STEP 10 – Fold and secure the foil.

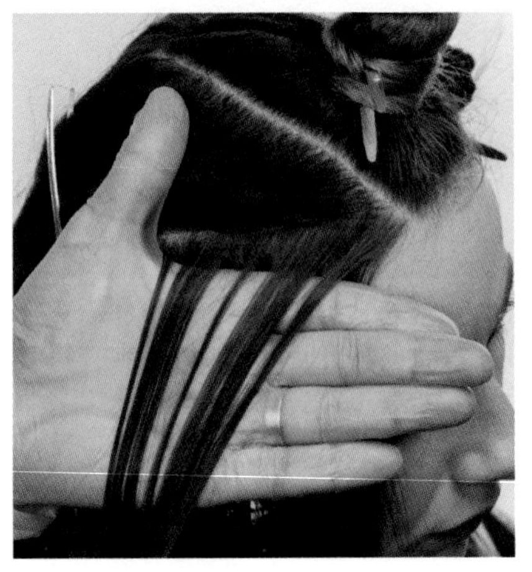

STEP 11 – For the next section, weave the hair and colour.

STEP 12 – Continue the sides with one weave foil and then one slice foil.

STEP 13 – On the top section, start at the crown and work towards the front – weave one, slice one.

STEP 14 – Remove the pony tail and apply pre-pigment spray and apply quasi-permanent colour to mid-lengths and ends.

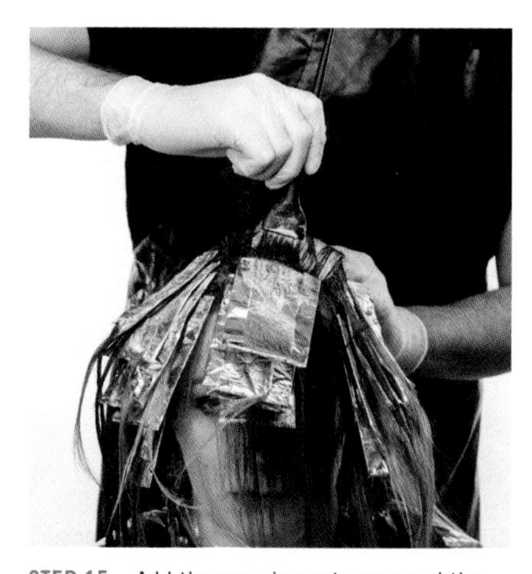

STEP 15 – Add the pre-pigment spray and the quasi-colour touch in-between each weave and slice through the top and sides. Monitor the development of the lightener and remove as level of lift is achieved. Apply a toner to tone highlights and refresh ends.

STEP 16 – The final look. In this example, as the highlights developed, the stylist removed the pony tail and pre-pigmented the hair with an orange pre-pigment spray, before applying a quasi-permanent 6/0 with a 4% developer to provide a long-lasting glossy look (Step 14).

Regrowth lightening and neutralising colour tone

STEP 1 – Consultation is carried out to identify the problem areas and best products to use to create the desired result.

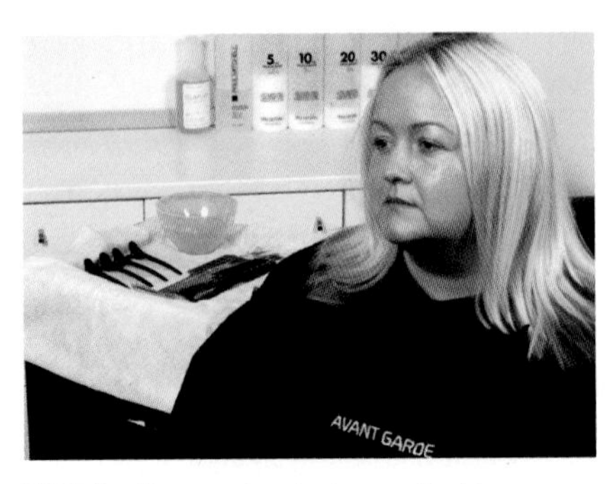

STEP 2 – Gown and protect your client in readiness for the service.

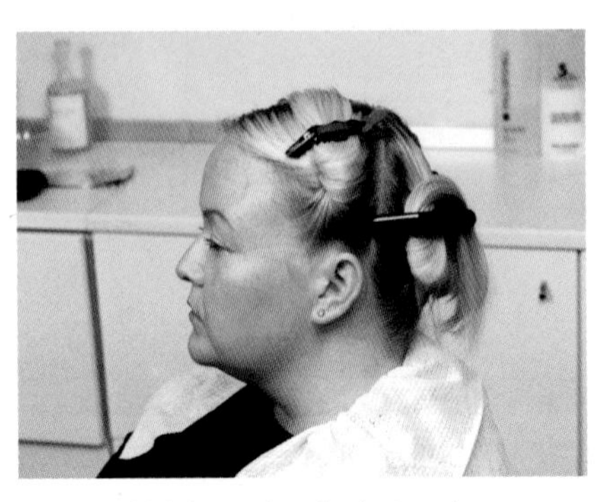

STEP 3 – Hair is sectioned prior to colour application.

STEP 4 – The lightning product is weighed and mixed correctly with 6% (20 vol) peroxide following MFIs.

STEP 5 – Apply the lightening product directly onto the scalp and the root area to lift the natural depth. Apply with a brush, working from the back forwards, keeping the product away from the face. Finish the application with the finer more fragile hair and the front hairline area last to help protect it.

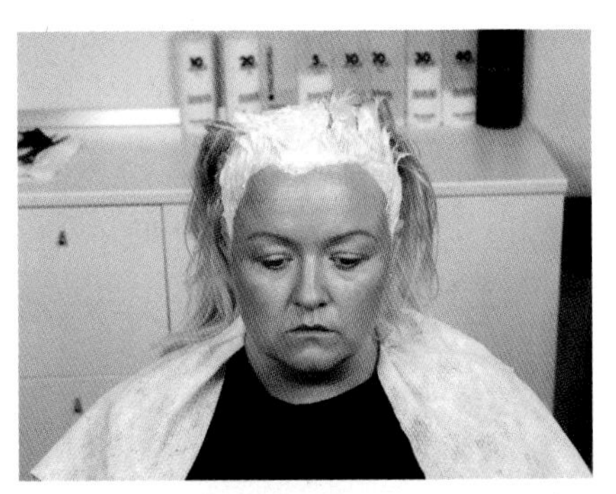

STEP 6 – Complete the root area application and leave to develop, visually checking the levels of lift.

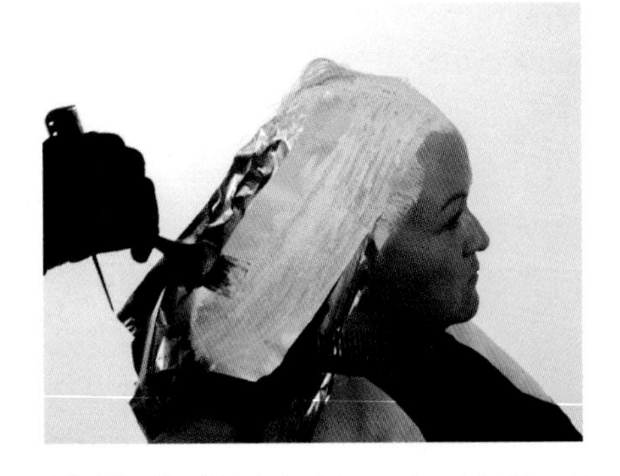

STEP 7 – Use foils to isolate previously lightened hair, and freshen up with 1.5% (5 vol) peroxide/developer and lightener to clean up the yellow-toned hair and develop for 35 minutes. Check visually every five minutes.

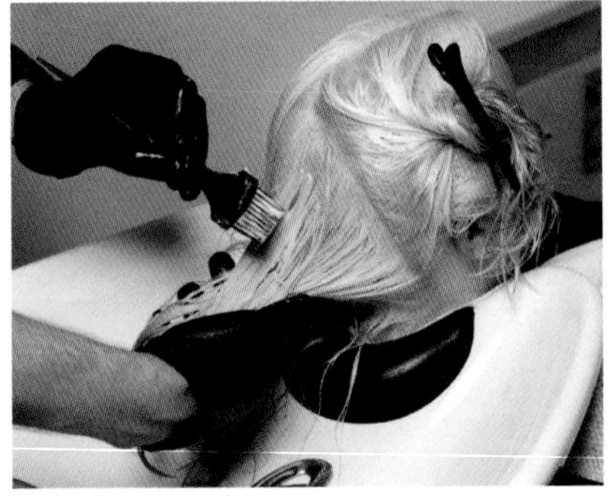

STEP 8 – Once levels of lift are achieved and lightener has developed, a pearl toner is applied, to give cooler and warmer results – toner is developed and rinsed off when tone is achieved.

STEP 9 – The final result.

Test your knowledge

Question 1

Describe the purpose of three tests carried out before or during a colour service.

Question 2

State the potential consequences of not carrying out hair and skin tests.

Question 3

What colour choices are available to clients requiring 100 per cent white hair coverage?

Question 4

Explain how lightening products affect the hair.

Question 5

If a client required three shades of lift with a permanent tint, what strength peroxide is required?

Question 6

What course of action should be taken when removing colour from the hair to prevent skin staining?

Question 7

After receiving a colour woven highlight colour service, your client's result is slightly patchy and too golden in colour.

- Describe the causes of these problems.
- How would you remedy these problems?

Multiple choice questions

8 Which of the following is the legislation that should be adhered to when using colour?

a Trades Descriptions Act

b Data Protection Act

c RIDDOR

d COSHH

9 Which of the following is a hair classification that affects the colouring techniques to be used?

a Very curly, frizzy hair

b Fine textured, white hair

c Naturally coloured, wavy hair

d Medium textured, straight hair

10 Which of the following is noted as depth number 3 on the International Colour Chart (ICC)?

a Light brown

b Dark brown

c Light blonde

d Medium blonde

11 Are these statements true or false?

Statement 1: Depending on the natural depth of hair and peroxide used, high lift tint will lift up to seven shades.

Statement 2: Toners are used to remove unwanted tone left behind after lightening.

a True, true

b True, false

c False, true

d False, false

12 Which of the following techniques is used when re-colouring previously lightened hair?

a Pre-softening

b Pre-lightening

c Pre-bleaching

d Pre-pigmenting

13 Are these statements true or false?

Statement 1: One of the differences between quasi- and semi-permanent colour is that a quasi is mixed with a developer.

Statement 2: Quasi-permanent colours act in the same way as semi-permanent colours; they just last a little longer.

a True, true

b True, false

c False, true

d False, false

14 Which of the following is best used on the scalp for lifting up to six shades?

a Gel bleach

b Blue bleach powder

c Permanent colour

d White bleach powder

15 Which of the following is NOT an effect of using a pH balancing conditioner?

a It brings the hair back to its natural pH
b It closes the cuticles
c It stops creeping oxidation
d It fixes an uneven colour result

16 Which of the following identifies the chemical process and the most commonly used chemical for permanently colouring hair?

a Reduction and hydrogen peroxide
b Polymerisation and hydrogen
c Polymerisation and oxygen

17 Which of the following correctly describes eumelanin?

a Large colour molecules ranging from black to blonde
b Large colour molecules ranging from black to light brown
c Small colour molecules ranging from blonde to lightest blonde
d Small colour molecules ranging from blonde to brown

This page intentionally left blank.

CHAPTER 9

SOPHIE HENDY – TOMMY'S HAIR COMPANY

My name is Sophie Hendy and I am just about to complete my Level 3 Apprenticeship in Hairdressing through work-based learning. I started my career at Tommy's Hair Company in Llandudno as a Salon Assistant working towards achieving my Level 2 Hairdressing and Barbering, before becoming a stylist.

I love the challenge of competing in hairdressing competitions. In 2016, I was chosen as one of eight Apprentices from the UK to compete in the Worldskills UK final in Birmingham. I won an award for my empathy and teamwork and I have made the top eight again for the final in 2017 where my ambition is to win a medal.

My Apprenticeship has enabled me to develop my creative skills in a way which has enhanced my professional profile. I research, plan and create a range of images for my competition ideas and work collaboratively, sharing my ideas with my colleagues who often compete alongside me.

Competition work allows me to hone my skills, making me a better stylist back at the salon – especially my time management skills which are crucial for a busy salon. Reaching the Worldskills UK final generated a lot of publicity resulting in more clients and income for the salon.

When I started, I was 18 and extremely shy and struggled with reading and writing due to my Irlen's Syndrome. My Apprenticeship has pushed me to adapt my work and education around the challenges of Irlen's, which has improved my confidence. The work-based environment has made me overcome my shyness as you have to deal with customers on a daily basis. I always stayed away from doing gent's hair as I was really nervous and I didn't know what to say to them. I really wanted to start the barbering Apprenticeship to help me with the higher-level skills competitions. I was thrown in the deep end, I had to speak to the male clients and I have realised that that is the best way to learn and progress.

This chapter maps to:

- Unit 11 Cut facial hair into shape (Level 2 Diploma for Hair Professionals – Barbering)

INTRODUCTION

For many years, beards and facial hair were often associated with sandal-wearing hippies or men who were too lazy to groom themselves properly! However, during the noughties, facial hair and celebrity 'designer' beards became increasingly popular and statistics show that men with facial hair now outnumber those without.

Barbershops have noticed an increase in clients visiting the salon to have their facial hair trimmed and styled, and most have been quick to capitalise on this trend by offering a wide variety of different facial hair services. Whatever your client's choice, facial hair grooming is now a very popular service at the barbers, and these are technical skills that you must master.

After reading this chapter you will:

- know how health and safety policies and procedures affect facial hair
- apply safe working practices when cutting facial hair to shape
- know how to cut facial hair to shape using basic techniques
- be able to design and create a range of facial hair shapes.

HEALTH AND SAFETY POLICIES AND PROCEDURES

When preparing to shape facial hair, you must follow good health and safety practices by:

- following your salon procedures and all of the health and safety legislation
- preparing a clean working environment
- maintaining your personal hygiene and presentation
- carrying out a consultation with your client
- gowning and protecting your client for the facial hair cutting service
- behaving in a suitable manner that does not cause risk of injury to you and those around you.

HEALTH AND SAFETY

Your role requires you to adhere to the requirements of health and safety legislation. Particular attention should be given to the Electricity at Work Act and COSHH – for more information on the health and safety Acts refer to Chapter 1.

You must protect your client by using towels, gowns and eye pads for eye protection. Eye pads can be damp cotton wool pads or soothing eye pads with added ingredients such as vitamin E or Aloe vera.

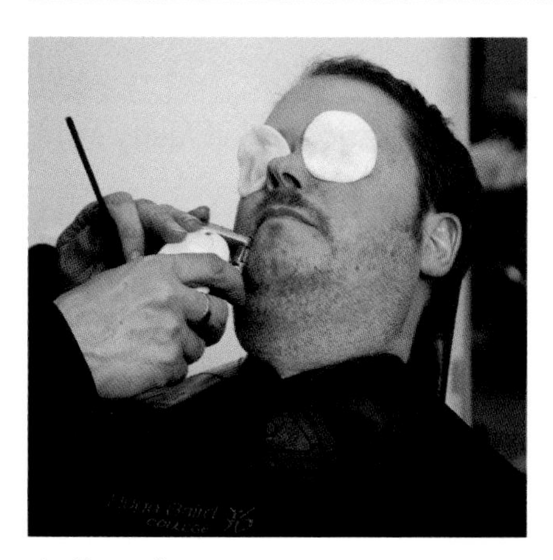

▲ Eye pads

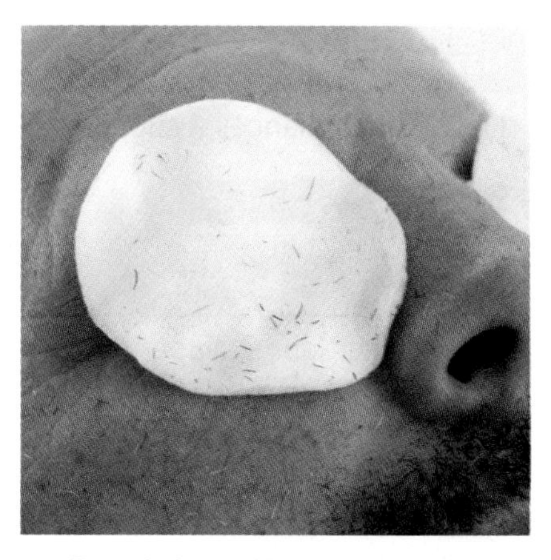

▲ These hairs could have entered the client's eyes if pads had not been used

▲ Soothing eye pads

Personal presentation

You must always be prepared for the working day ahead. Arrive at work clean and showered, wearing deodorant, with fresh breath and dressed in clean clothes. Your own hair and/or facial hair must be well groomed and well presented. Avoid wearing any accessories that might get caught in your client's hair or put you at risk of contact dermatitis.

HANDY HINT

As with all services, your personal hygiene, protection and presentation are important during facial hair cutting services.

Potential hazards and possible risks

Cutting facial hair involves using sharp tools and cutting very close to, if not onto, your client's skin, and this increases risk to you and your client. Care must be taken when using and transporting sharp tools to avoid risk of injury. Dispose of used razor blades in a sharps bin. Collection of these bins can be arranged by your local council and sometimes with your local pharmacy.

Some further potential hazards and risks are shown in the table below.

Hazard	Potential risk
Sharp objects Razors and scissors	Risk of injury to self and client
Infected clients Razor bumps	Cross-contamination

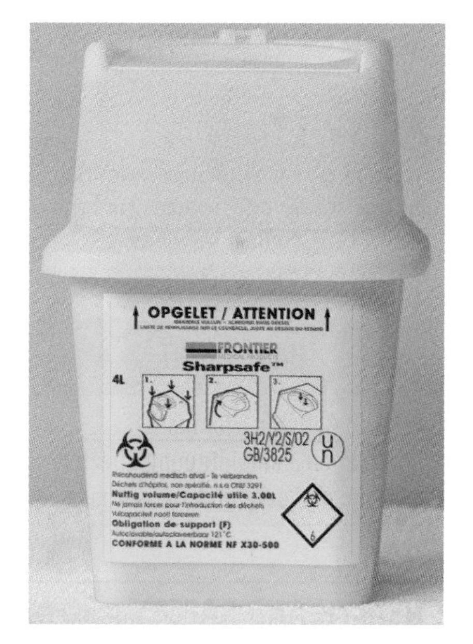

▲ Sharps bin

Hazard	Potential risk
Electrical appliances – clippers Frayed wire	Risk of electric shock if faulty or used incorrectly
Hair on the floor – slippery surface Hair cuttings	Risk of slipping over/injury
Spillages Water spillage	Risk of slipping over/injury

ACTIVITY

In pairs or small groups, identify further safety considerations for facial hair cutting services.

HANDY HINT

Refer to Chapter 1 for more information on maintaining effective, hygienic and safe working methods.

HEALTH AND SAFETY

When using electrical appliances, you must follow the Electricity at Work Regulations. Always be mindful of trailing wires, as these can cause trip hazards. For more information visit www.hse.gov.uk and search for information on the Electricity at Work Regulations.

Throughout the facial hair cutting service remember to:

- maintain responsibilities for health and safety
- use your time effectively
- prepare your tools in advance of the service and keep your work area clean and tidy
- take care with your cutting tools and follow MFIs, supplier and workplace instructions
- prevent cross-contamination by working safely and hygienically
- sweep the floor during and after the service
- dispose of waste in an environmentally friendly manner
- check the positioning of your client throughout the service
- maintain a good body posture
- remove loose hair cuttings from your client to maintain their comfort.

Safe and hygienic working methods and practices

Make sure your work area and trolley are ready for your client's arrival. Workstations and barbers' chairs must be hair-free, cleaned with warm soapy water and wiped or sprayed with disinfectant. Your cutting tools must be sterilised before and after use; this is particularly important if you are using razor blades or cutting very close to the skin.

HANDY HINT

For facial hair cutting services you will need to clean and sterilise your tools and equipment before use. You may require the following tools and equipment for the service:

- a selection of combs
- scissors
- clippers
- clipper attachments
- trimmers
- razor.

Prepare your client

Always gown and protect your client's clothing and eyes from hair clippings and follow your salon requirements for client preparation. Most salons will use a gown and towel, but how the towel is folded or draped around the client's neck may vary. Some salons will use a gown fitted closely around the neck and therefore may not use a towel.

If you are cutting the head hair and facial hair, then you should shampoo the hair prior to the service. If you are carrying out a beard and moustache cut, then the face should be washed with a facial soap and water. If the facial hair is a full beard, you could apply a conditioner to the hair to soften it slightly. However, due to the coarseness of the hair, the conditioner will not work as well as it does on head hair. If you are trimming a moustache only, then a facial wipe would suffice to cleanse the facial hair. Comb all beards and moustaches through with a wide-toothed comb to untangle the hair and to allow all of the hair to be cut.

Make sure that your client is well protected and that you remove loose hair clippings from him on a regular basis throughout the service. Loose hair can penetrate into the skin and cause infections, such as boils. Both you and your client are at risk of infection from loose hair clippings.

HANDY HINT

If you are cutting facial hair, tuck tissue or cotton wool in the top edge of the towel to prevent the coarse hair from falling down the client's clothes. Use cotton pads on his eyes to protect him from stray hair cuttings.

Positioning of you and your client

The comfort of you and your client is paramount during this service, as both of you need to stay still during the service. Any sudden movements could cause your client to be cut by the scissors or razor.

Your position

You should always stand with your body weight evenly distributed; this will ensure that you are evenly balanced and that you are not putting undue stress on your back. You should place your work area and trolley to your preferred side of working and never over-stretch to reach for your tools.

▲ Keep your work area clean and tidy

ACTIVITY

Identify your salon requirements for protecting clients' eyes and clothes from hair clippings.

HANDY HINT

Protect clients from hair clippings to ensure they are comfortable at all times and to prevent any stray hairs from entering the skin or eyes.

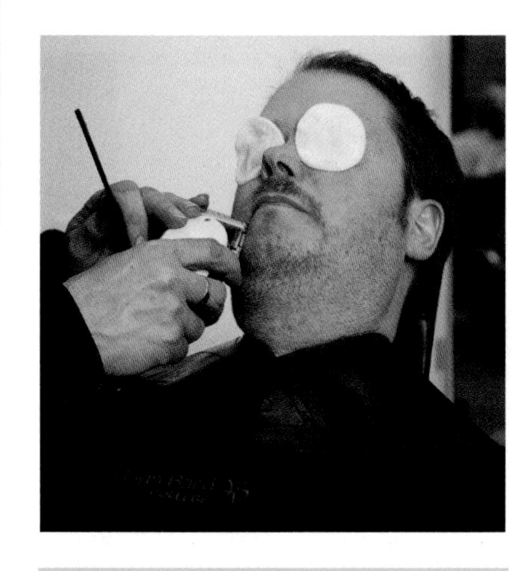

HANDY HINT

For a barber, poor posture can lead to fatigue and back injuries.

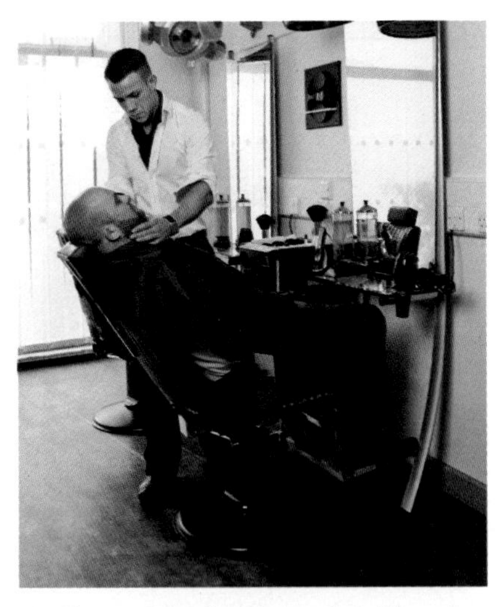

▲ Ensure your client is comfortable and their neck is supported

HEALTH AND SAFETY

WARNING! Always support your client's neck – if positioned in an unnatural way and/or left unsupported, your client could incur a neck injury or even suffer a stroke.

HANDY HINT

Barber's chairs are much heavier and bulkier than salon chairs. If you need to move them, do so carefully so you do not injure yourself.

Your client's position

Ensure your client is seated comfortably in the barber's chair. Check that his legs are not crossed and that both feet are either on the floor or supported by the footrest. Although your client's comfort is important, it is just as crucial that he is sitting squarely and not off balance. When your client's body position is suitable, recline the chair and adjust it to a suitable position/height for you to work. During the facial hair cutting, you will need to ask your client to move his head in various directions, so that you can cut around the neck area and follow the contours of the face and neck.

It is important that you use the correct type of barber's chair. Support your client's neck on the neck-rest, ensuring he is comfortable and to allow you access to the whole of his face and neckline.

Safety considerations

The diagram shows the safety considerations that must be taken into account.

- Hair clippings on the floor make for a slippery surface, so sweep the floor after every client and, if necessary, during the service.
- Dispose of any used cotton wool (and plasters) in the designated salon waste bin with a lid to prevent any cross-contamination.
- Always follow the suppliers' and manufacturer's instructions for the safe use of equipment, materials and products to ensure they are used safely and correctly and produce the best possible result for the client.

ACTIVITY

What would the risks and potential consequences be if a razor blade were disposed of in the salon waste bin?

HANDY HINT

Position your cutting tools for ease of use, using your trolley to your left if you are left-handed and on your right, if you are right-handed.

ACTIVITY

State the different types of working methods that promote environmental and sustainable working practices, including correct methods of waste disposal. Refer back to Chapter 1 if you struggle to answer this activity.

▲ Dispose of waste in a lidded bin

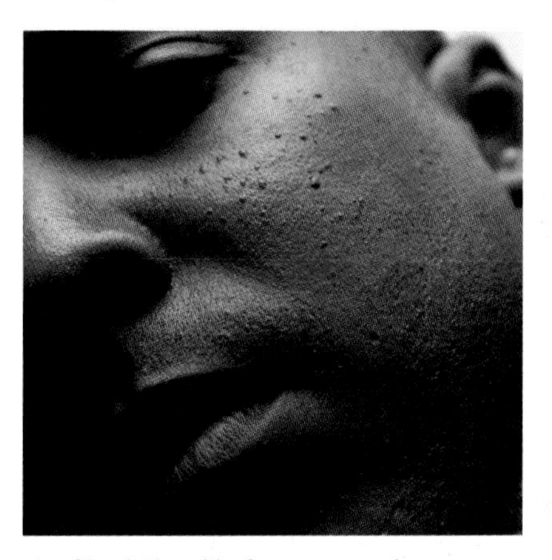

▲ Check the skin for scars, moles, acne or skin disorders

Client safety

Before you begin any facial hair cutting, you must check beneath the facial hair for open wounds, cold sores that might not be visible due to hair growth and for signs of infection or infestation. Some clients might have facial hair to hide scar tissue, acne, facial moles or other potential skin disorders. If infectious these might pose a risk of cross-contamination to you, or cause discomfort to your client if they are caught with a comb.

If you accidentally cut your client's skin or lip, you must administer some minor first aid. First, put on some gloves to prevent cross-contamination, then stem the blood flow with clean, dry cotton wool and remove all loose clippings from the surrounding area. If necessary, apply a suitable plaster, checking first that your client does not have an allergy to plasters. Remember to record the incident in the accident book.

Prevent cross-infection and cross-infestation

Although many of the tools that you will use will be similar to those used for cutting head hair, you are cutting very near to the skin and lips, so you need to take extra care.

Cleaning, disinfecting and sterilising

You must clean and disinfect or sterilise your cutting tools after every service to maintain a good reputation, ensure a professional image and to prevent cross-infection and infestation. You must ensure that you protect yourself and your client from the risk of cross-contamination. Make sure all your towels and gowns are contamination-free, and scissors and combs are sterile. If you encounter any infections or infestations you will need to sterilise your tools effectively and boil wash all towels and gowns. Use heat, such as boiling water or an autoclave, for scissors and combs. Remember that a UV light will only maintain sterilisation – it is not an effective method of removing infections or infestations from your tools.

If you are using razor blades, you must use a fresh blade for every client, unless of course the razor blades are not disposable. Non-disposable razors must be sterilised in an autoclave, sanitised in a UV cabinet or disinfected with a chemical solution or wipe.

HANDY HINT

Make sure any wounds are free from hair clippings to prevent infections.

HANDY HINT

Remember: you sterilise in an autoclave, sanitise in a UV cabinet and disinfect with chemical solutions or wipes.

Before and after using electrical or rechargeable clippers, you must remove all the hair clippings from in between the blades, spray the blades with a clipper disinfectant solution and oil them before storing them away or reusing them.

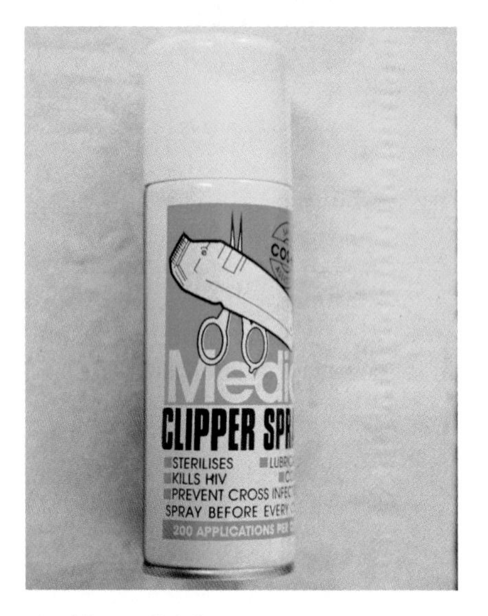

▲ Clipper disinfectant

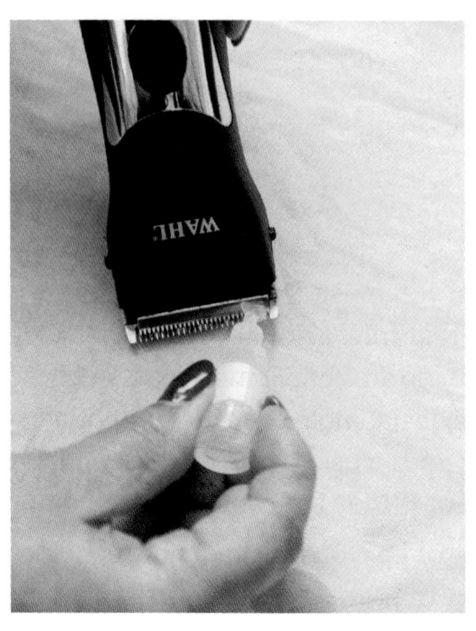

▲ Clipper oil

▲ Barbicide

CUT FACIAL HAIR TO SHAPE USING BASIC TECHNIQUES

To cut facial hair correctly you must consult with your client and understand the factors that may affect the service.

Consult with clients

You will need to question your client before and during the service to check the service is proceeding as planned, and use the correct techniques to achieve the service objectives. A series of open questions, starting with 'what', 'how', 'when' and 'why', will help you to obtain specific answers from your client about his requirements. Finish the conversation with closed questions to confirm you both understand what is required.

Open questions include:

- What would you like done today?
- When was your facial hair last trimmed or shaped?
- How much length would you like removed today?
- What (if any) style changes would you like today?
- What (if anything) do you not like about your facial hair?

Closed questions include:

- Do you want width or bulk removed from the shape of the beard?
- Are you growing part of your facial hair?

It is important you use the correct tools, equipment and products and understand the effects they achieve. At the end of the service you should always provide your client with aftercare advice.

Factors that may influence services

Vellus hair found on the head and face in **prepubescent** males becomes **terminal** hair or **androgenic** hair on the face and body after puberty. During puberty the male hormone androgen is produced – the primary androgen is mostly known as testosterone. After puberty the soft, fine, vellus facial hair is replaced with androgenic hair or terminal hair, which is much thicker and coarser, and this is when facial hair cutting services are required. Every man's facial hair is as different as every head of hair – it will vary in density and texture depending on the age of the client, their ethnicity and genetics.

▲ Asian men typically have less facial hair

KEY TERMS

Vellus hair – short, thin, light-coloured hair found on the body during childhood.

Prepubescent – before puberty.

Terminal/androgenic hair – thick, long, darker hair found on the body after puberty.

Hispanic – of Spanish descent.

Your client's ethnicity will affect the amount of facial hair he has – Asian men have the least terminal hair and **Hispanic** and Middle Eastern men typically have the most.

Beards and facial hair have become an important fashion accessory for men, with more and more celebrities sporting these looks. R&B and hip hop music artists, movie stars, models and sportsmen have brought beards and designer stubble looks back into fashion and the media.

Although the factors that you need to consider for cutting facial hair are very similar to those for cutting head hair, there are some important differences. Facial hair is generally cut much shorter in length than head hair and therefore can grow out of style much more quickly. You will need to ensure that your client's requirements will suit his lifestyle, so that the shape and style of the beard or moustache will last and can be maintained, as and when required.

▲ Johnny Depp and other celebrities have brought beards back into fashion

It is becoming increasingly acceptable to wear facial hair in the workplace and it does not look out of place with a suit, or with jeans and casual wear. The 'unshaven look', however, is not easy to achieve and requires a lot of care and attention. Some of the designer-stubble styles need maintaining every couple of days, and the initial days/weeks of growing facial hair might make your client look scruffy, so planning when to grow a beard also needs to be discussed. Before the chosen style is decided, check that your client has the time to maintain the desired look.

Some jobs can affect whether men can have beards. Firefighters, for example, will need to ensure that any breathing apparatus fits snugly around their mouth and airways and a thick beard could prevent this. When consulting with your client about his facial hair requirements, you must discuss whether this might impact on his job and make judgements as to which style would be most suitable.

▲ Firefighter with breathing apparatus

Your client's choice of sport can have an impact on his facial hair decisions, too. Boxers, for example, may not be allowed facial hair, because it can cushion a blow, or if the punch lands on the face at a bad angle it can pull the hair from the skin. You should always discuss your

▲ Some men maintain a beard for religious purposes

client's choice of leisure activity to identify whether this may have an effect on the service.

THE HAIR PROFESSIONAL AT WORK

Respect the diversity of your clients and remember that facial hair and beards may be a requirement of some religions and cultures.

The following factors will need to be considered, as these can influence your client's decision on the chosen design and style:

- head, face shape and facial features
- facial hair classification
- facial hair characteristics
- hairstyle and client's wishes
- adverse skin conditions
- facial piercings and tattoos.

HANDY HINT

When discussing the facial hair design, you should always consider your client's age and the suitability of the chosen style. As their beard hair turns white, the shape of the beard might look slightly uneven or patchy.

Head, face shape and facial features

It is important that the facial hair/beard complements the client's current hairstyle. A bald head and a big beard may look out of place on some clients, so always check if the two need to be balanced.

If your client has a round face, suggest a squarer cut and finish for the beard or moustache. For square faces and jaw-lines suggest a rounded beard or curved moustache.

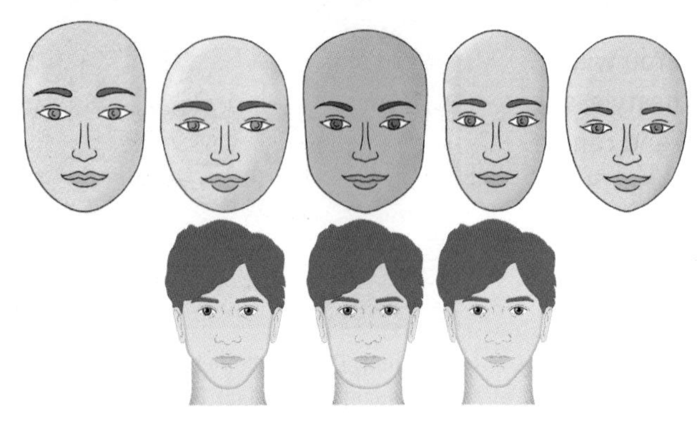

▲ Face shapes can affect the beard style

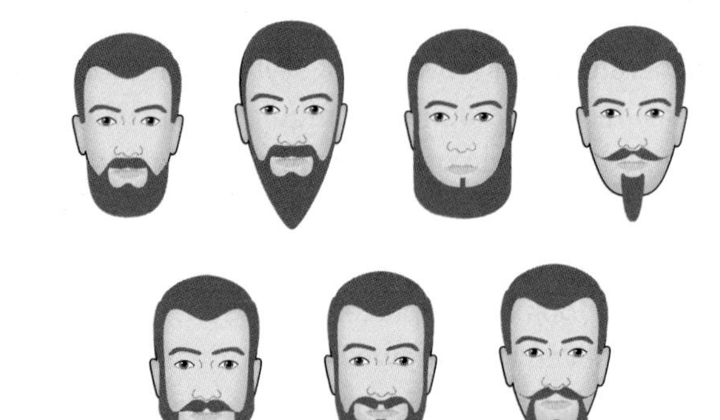

▲ Different facial hair shapes

▲ Check all facial features for balance

Facial features

Cutting the facial hair of clients with dimples can sometimes cause you difficulties in achieving a balanced result. To ensure the end result is even, ask your client to poke their tongue in the dimple area to push the cheek area outwards when you cut/clipper the hair.

Clients with heavy-set chins generally prefer a fuller beard and moustache to balance this feature.

Clients with small mouths tend to suit smaller/thinner moustaches, and those with large noses suit a thick or wider moustache which will minimise the look of this larger feature.

The shape and positioning of your client's nose can also affect the balanced look of the facial hair, so remember to check all facial features.

Facial hair classifications

The table below shows the various hair classifications and their impact on the service.

Hair classification	Consideration and impact on service
Straight hair	Fine/thin – may result in a patchy end result. Avoid very short beards. Full beards may take several services for the desired result to be achievable. Medium – although straight, this type of hair can be easy to work with as it often has body and volume. Coarse – as this type of hair can be extremely straight you need to ensure you go over the facial hair in all directions to ensure the result is even throughout.
Wavy hair	Fine/thin – due to the 'S' pattern in this type of hair, ensure you go over the facial hair in all directions. Medium – can be a little frizzy. The hair may need to be conditioned before starting the service. Coarse – very frizzy and is likely to need to be conditioned before the service. This type of hair may also be abundant and thick, so you will need to go over the facial hair in all directions to ensure an even finish.
Curly hair	Loose curls – this type of facial hair may be of combination texture and therefore difficult to ensure an even finish. It may be thick and full, so full beards are achievable, but make sure you cross-check the end result thoroughly. Tight curls – as for loose curls.
Very curly hair	Soft – this type of hair is very fragile, so take care with your tools. The hair is often tightly coiled, so again, cross-check thoroughly. Wiry – as for soft very curly hair, but this type of hair has more of a 'Z' pattern shape and the curls may be less defined. Very curly hair grows out of the follicle at an acute angle and is therefore more prone to becoming an ingrowing hair. Take extra care with very curly hair, particularly on black skin, as this skin type is also more prone to scarring.

HANDY HINT

If the beard hair is curly, this might affect the achievement of the desired style, particularly for longer beards.

Facial hair characteristics

Hair characteristics include:

- density and texture
- elasticity, porosity and condition
- growth patterns, distribution and quality.

Texture and density

Clients who request a full beard but who have sparse or no hair around the mouth should be advised to have a disconnected beard and moustache, so that the look balances.

It might not be possible to achieve a thin or fine moustache if the facial hair growth is naturally very dense or abundant. You might need to cut the facial hair with clippers, as cutting dense hair could take too long using a **scissor over comb** technique.

KEY TERM

Scissor over comb – cutting the facial hair by moving the comb through the facial hair and removing the hair length above the comb.

Asian hair is very straight and there tends to be less facial hair, so full beards may take a long time to grow, or be finer and patchy as a result.

▲ Fine beard

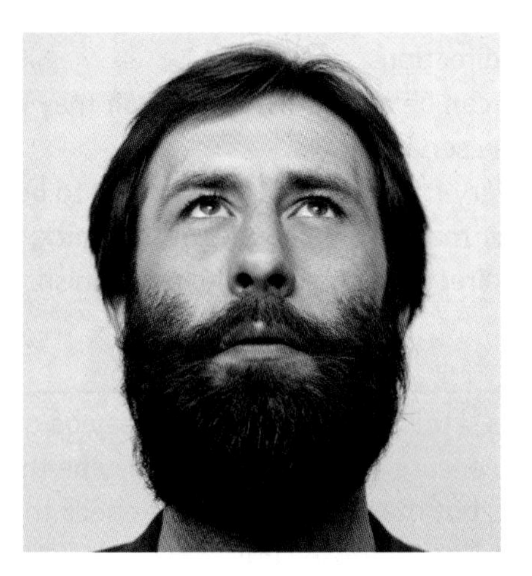

▲ Medium beard

▲ Coarse beard

Elasticity, porosity and condition

If facial hair is of poor elasticity or porous then extra care will need to be taken with your tools as the hair is more fragile. Be careful not to snag the facial hair and cause any discomfort for your client.

HANDY HINT

As with all services, remember to carry out elasticity and porosity tests on the facial hair, particularly on longer beards.

Hair growth patterns, distribution and quality

As with head hair, facial hair can have varied growth directions and this can affect the finished shape, look uneven or grow out unevenly and untidily. A whorl growth direction needs to be cut or clippered in several directions, to ensure all the hairs are cut to the same length.

You will need to consider the distribution of hair, as one side of the face might have more hair than the other. The quality of the facial hair might not suit certain styles, so check both sides of the face when you are consulting and discussing style requirements.

HANDY HINT

You will need to consider the length and type of hair your client has. If he wants a different beard style, you need to identify whether the beard needs further growth or needs to be cut shorter to achieve the desired shape.

Hairstyle and client's wishes

Most clients choose facial hairstyles to complement their haircut. Always look at their current hairstyle and offer advice on facial hairstyles that will blend or match. Always consult with your client to identify their wishes and to ascertain whether their desired result is achievable.

Adverse skin conditions

Some adverse skin conditions or contra-indications may affect the service. If the skin condition is infectious or contagious you must not proceed with the service.

Along with any adverse skin and scalp conditions mentioned in Chapter 1, you will also need to be mindful of the adverse skin disorders in the table below when cutting facial hair. Always check in the beard growth for any signs of infection.

Condition	Description	Cause	Infectious?	Treatment
Barber's itch (sycosis barbea)	Folliculitis – inflammation and infection of the hair follicles on the hairy parts of the face.	Bacterial infection	Yes, can be spread by infected shaving tools.	Do not carry out the service until the condition has cleared up. Refer to GP if it does not clear up after improved hygiene.
Boils/abscesses	Raised, inflamed pus-filled spots.	Infection in the hair follicle	Yes	Do not carry out facial hair cutting treatments – refer to GP.
Cold sores (herpes simplex)	A cold sore on the facial area or lip.	Virus infection	Yes	Do not carry out facial hair cutting treatments – refer to pharmacy for treatment.

Condition	Description	Cause	Infectious?	Treatment
Impetigo 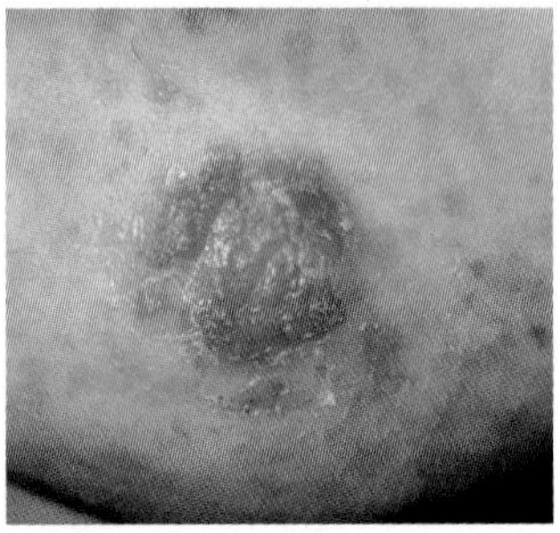	Yellow crusts on the skin, often around the mouth area	Bacterial infection – often a secondary infection caused by scratching the skin.	Yes	Do not carry out facial hair cutting treatments – refer to GP.
Psoriasis 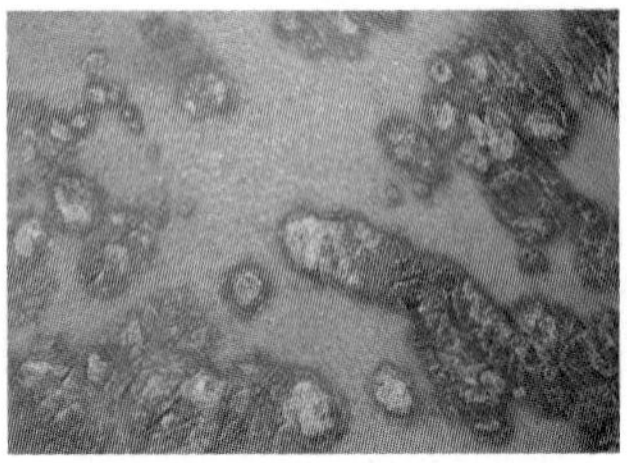	Silvery yellow scales and thickening of the skin, with tender pink skin underneath the scales.	Unknown	No	Services can be carried out, but avoid using open-blade razors on psoriasis – refer to a dermatologist or GP.
Cysts 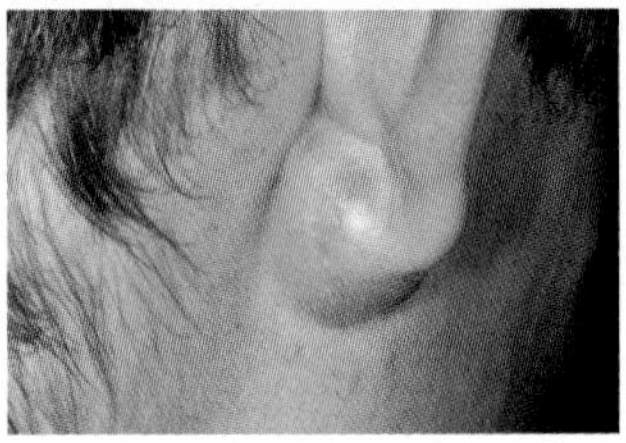	The most common cyst on the face and neck area is a sebaceous cyst – a small pea-sized, lump/bump that is filled with fluid called sebum or pus if infected.	Blocked sebaceous gland	No – unless the cyst is infected.	Services can be carried out, as these cysts are often painless, but can become painful if they are knocked or combed, and could get infected if they are accidently cut with clippers or scissors. Sometimes cysts disappear by themselves, or they can be drained by a GP.
Moles and skin tags 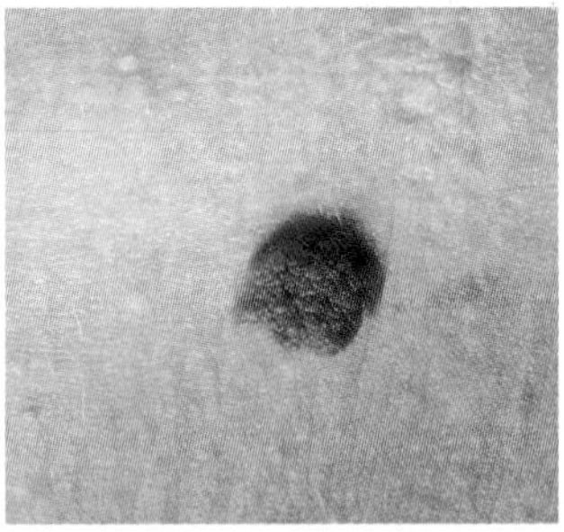	Skin lesions – either under or on the skin.	Some are caused by a pigment growth in the skin – **melanocytes** – causing a dark colour. Others occur from a **subdermal** growth.	No	Continue with the service but be careful not to catch the skin tag or moles with your tools. If the mole looks like it is infected or has grown in size, refer to GP.

KEY TERMS

Melanocytes – melanin-producing cells.

Subdermal – under the skin.

In grown hairs (razor bumps)

In growing hairs are just like they sound – hairs that grow inwards and cause a mild infection or discomfort. Repeated close shaving causes the hair to get trapped under a layer of skin but it continues to grow. The service can continue, as it is not an infectious condition, unless the follicle has become infected, and then the service should not go ahead. You should always advise your client to use treatments and products at home and to exfoliate the skin regularly.

HANDY HINT

The effects of continual close cutting to the skin can result in barber's itch and the risk of developing in growing hairs. You should advise your client on aftercare to prevent or remedy these ailments. Regular exfoliation of the skin can often help.

Scarring

Skin is a seamless organ and any tears in it get repaired but leave behind scars from the healing process. This is normally caused by accidents or injury to the skin. Scarring is not an infectious condition, but the area may be tender, so proceed with care with the service and take care with your tools.

Skin elasticity

From the age of 30, your client's skin elasticity will be affected by collagen and elastin degradation and this will increase with age. Therefore, more care will be required and the facial styles worn will need to be adapted to suit older, looser skin.

Facial piercings and tattoos

Always check the face and eyebrow area for any piercings; you must be extremely careful not to catch these with the comb or your cutting tools.

The size or design of a tattoo can affect the balanced look of facial hair, so you need to consider this when discussing the type of facial hair shape and when checking the balanced end result. Some clients may wish to show off their body art designs, while others may choose to have their tattoos covered up by the facial hair – so make sure you check prior to starting the service.

Tattoo designs are sometimes completed in stages and the healing stages can take 5–10 days. During this time, the skin is tender and the tattoo design is at risk of damage if the skin is disturbed, so advise your client to wait until the peeling stage of the tattoo has finished and the skin has regenerated.

Importance of questioning clients

As we have mentioned in previous chapters, it is very important that you are polite to your clients and speak to them in a friendly manner. Engaging in neutral conversation about topics such as recent football

HANDY HINT

If your client has any facial scarring, this can be disguised more easily with a beard or moustache.

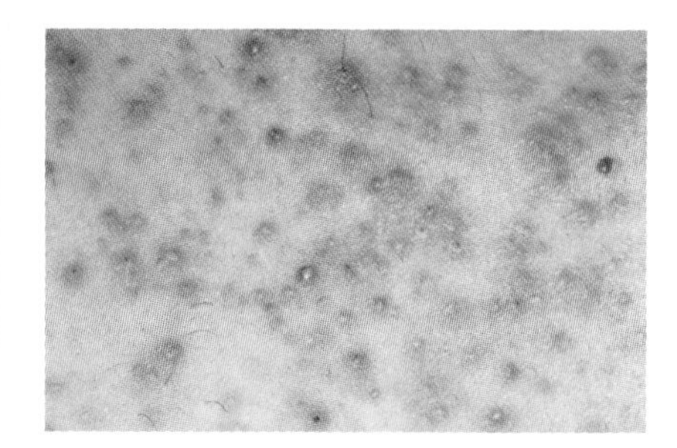

▲ Ingrown hair

▲ Scar tissue/scarring

▲ The skin's elasticity is lost as we get older

▲ Piercings can catch on tools

▲ Smartphones are a great consultation tool

HANDY HINT

When speaking to your client and colleagues, always demonstrate respect. Speak confidently and politely, expressing yourself clearly and portraying positive body language.

ACTIVITY

Use the internet to search for sites about beards and moustaches. How many websites on beards and facial hair can you find?

ACTIVITY

Ask a colleague to pretend to be your client. Ask them to visualise a style and then ask the relevant questions to identify the image and look they require.

results and which teams they support may help to relax your client. Always speak clearly and demonstrate positive body language at all times. When speaking with clients or your colleagues, be respectful and respond to their needs.

You should use client-friendly terminology and speak in a reassuring and confident manner. Make sure you really listen to what your client is asking of you and respond by nodding and maintaining eye contact to prove you are listening. Before your client arrives, it is good practice to read your client's record card. During or after the visit record any changes or update the record card with details of the latest service.

Consultation techniques

The consultation with your client for a facial haircut is no different to any other consultation – you need to identify the service objectives. There are over 40 different styles of beards and moustaches and you will need to confirm which one of these your client desires and assess the potential of his hair to achieve the look required.

To help your client choose a style for his facial hair, use magazines and mobile devices, or print off from the internet photos of celebrities with facial hair. Always listen carefully and hear what your client is asking you to achieve for him. Repeat any instructions back to clarify what has been agreed and discussed.

THE HAIR PROFESSIONAL IN THE WORKPLACE

Refer to Chapter 1 for more information on client care and effective communication.

Always carry out an in-depth consultation with your client to find out what they would like. Establish any factors that may affect the service by checking the hair classifications, hair characteristics, head and face shape, the client's wishes and their style requirements. Remember to check for any ingrowing hairs, adverse skin conditions and facial piercings, and check the client's skin elasticity.

Apply correct techniques during services

In this part of the chapter you will look at the techniques used during services:

- scissor over comb
- clipper over comb
- clippering with grade attachments
- freehand.

Create and follow a guideline for tapered beard lines, beard outlines and moustaches

When cutting the beard or moustache, you must work in a methodical manner – establish a cutting guideline and ensure you follow it throughout. We will explore these in detail in the step-by-step section later in the chapter.

Cut different facial hair shapes using basic cutting techniques

Scissor over comb

Scissor over comb is a popular technique that is used for beard and moustache trimming and shaping. It allows for graduation in the shape but you will need to be very accurate with your cutting.

When you are using scissor over comb techniques, ensure that the beard has been washed and towel-dried thoroughly, then place your comb on the skin and work upwards from the neck area towards the lower lip. You can use either side of your comb, or angle the comb at 45° to achieve shorter or longer lengths, depending on your client's requirements.

Some barbers prefer to use this technique to demonstrate their skills and personalise the look, but this is not always possible on thick or dense hair, so clipper over comb techniques might be used instead.

Clipper over comb

Clipper over comb is used in a similar way to scissor over comb, but produces quicker results. Using the clipper over comb technique still requires accuracy with your hand and comb balance; otherwise the result will be uneven.

Clippering with grade attachments

In the same way that you might clipper the back and sides of a haircut with clipper grades attached to clippers, you can do so for beard-trimming. If using clippers with a grade, you will need to decide the size of the grade required and this will depend on your client's requirements. When the desired length has been agreed, attach the appropriate clipper grades and work through the facial hair from the neck upwards. When you have cut the beard or moustache to length, remove any unwanted hair outside the outline of the shape by removing the clipper grades and cutting the hair against the skin.

Clipper grades range from grade 0.5 (the shortest) up to grade 8 (the longest). Each full grade leaves the hair longer by about 3 mm, starting from 3 mm up to 24 mm – refer to Chapter 5 for a reminder.

ACTIVITY

If grade 1 is 3 mm and each grade increases by 3 mm, what is the size of the following grades?

- Grade 2
- Grade 4
- Grade 5
- Grade 8.

HANDY HINT

Clipper blades should be correctly aligned and checked before each service to ensure the blades are level and they cut evenly without pulling on the hair.

HANDY HINT

When you are cutting a full beard, it is advisable to remove all excess bulk from the beard first, so that you can see the natural hairline of the facial hair. When this is done, you can cut in your outline shape, with either clippers or mini-clippers.

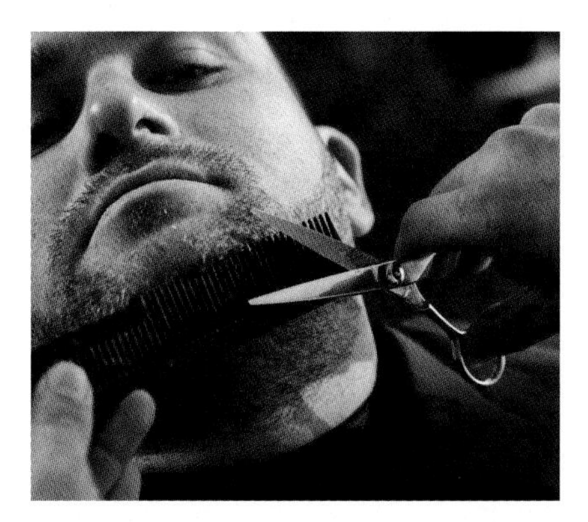

▲ Scissor over comb

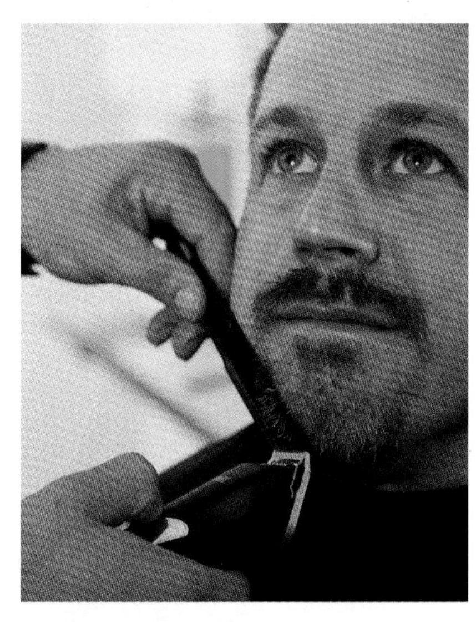

▲ Clipper over comb

▲ Clippering with grade attachments

HANDY HINT

For both scissor and clipper over comb techniques, remember to work with the various directions of the hair growth.

HANDY HINT

The benefit of carrying out clipper over comb techniques is that it allows you to see the areas of different densities of hair growth and to adapt your cutting/clippering direction to suit.

▲ Freehand using mini-clippers/trimmers

ACTIVITY

What action would you take if you dropped the electrical clippers and the blades were now making a terrible noise when switched on?

Freehand

Use freehand to finalise the detail of the shape to:

- create a blunt line above the lip
- shape and blend into the sideburn area
- enhance the outline shape of the beard or moustache.

Take extra care when you are cutting near the ears and especially around the lip area, as the skin might not be as easy to see through the hair growth and you might cut your client.

These cutting techniques can be used together or separately to create the following looks:

- tapered beardline
- full beard outlines
- partial beards – goatee, chin curtain
- moustache only
- eye brow trim.

Outline shapes

With so many beard and moustache designs and styles to choose from, make sure you do not forget to discuss the finer details, such as the hairline and outline finish, with your client.

Beards generally mean chin and cheek hair. Therefore, the hair on the neck is often cut back to the skin or much shorter than the beard length itself. You will need to check the following with your client: does he want a full beard? Where does he want the cheek and the neck hair to stop and be blended out to?

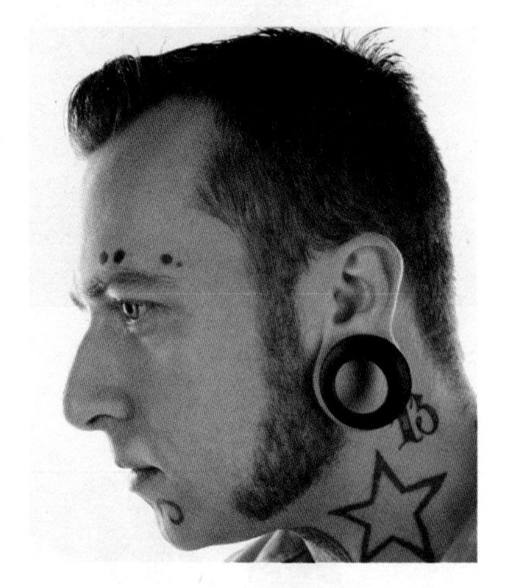

▲ Sideburns

If he has sideburns, does he want them blended into the beard or left longer?

▲ Partial beard

Does he want a partial beard – facial hair that is neither a full beard nor a moustache?

▲ Chin curtains

Does he want a chin curtain – beard hair that travels from ear to ear along the chin but does not meet up with the lower lip or have an accompanying moustache?

▲ Mutton chops

Does he want mutton chops – thick sideburns extended down and stopping at the lips, leaving the chin hair-free?

▲ Soul patch

Does he want a soul patch – a small patch of facial hair just below the lower lip and above the chin?

▲ Goatee

▲ Chin puff

▲ Chin strip

▲ Stubble

Does he want stubble – a neatened, several-day full-beard growth?

Does he want a goatee – a narrow beard which sits under the mouth and around the chin and is not attached to a moustache, or a chin puff – a narrower version of the goatee, or a chin strip – a thin strip of beard from middle of the lip down to the chin?

With so many beard and moustache options to choose from, make sure you discuss with your client the cheek hair, neck hairline, sideburns and moustache shapes and hairlines. When you have agreed where you are cutting to along the natural hairline, make sure you remove all the hair outside of this outline shape.

KEY TERM

Mandible – jawbone.

KEY TERM

Chevron – v-shaped stripe.

ACTIVITY

Research the following facial hair shapes and create a facial hairstyle book.

- Pharaoh – a beard starting from the base of the chin, it can be any length.
- Curtain rail – a narrow beard following the **mandible**.
- Lipline moustache – a horizontal moustache about the width of a pencil.
- Mexican moustache – a moustache following the natural line of the upper lip and extending down towards the chin.
- Pencil moustache – a narrow moustache following the natural line of the upper lip.
- Rooftop moustache – a moustache that extends from under the nose to form a straight '**chevron**' shape.

Cross-checking the facial haircut

It is just as important to cross-check facial hair, as it is a haircut. Check the length and balance on both sides of the face to ensure it is even and the weight of the shape is evenly distributed.

Working with growth patterns

When cutting the facial hair, consider the angles of hair growth and move your clippers in various directions to ensure hair is cut evenly from the beard or moustache. Check the natural weight distribution of hair growth throughout the beard and adapt the shape and length accordingly to ensure a balanced result.

To achieve an accurate end result follow the process shown in the diagram.

Ensure your client is comfortable and protected throughout the service.

↓

Adapt your cutting angle and degree of graduation to maintain balance or increase length, according to the style requirements.

↓

Controlling your tools correctly, remove any unwanted hair outside the desired outline shape using T-liners or mini-clippers, or use a razor for an extra clean finish.

↓

Check weight, balance and shape
It is important to use your mirrors to make sure the cut is the right shape and evenly balanced; regularly cross-check your cut to ensure even weight distribution.

↓

Check the desired result is to your client's satisfaction, and remove excess ear and nostril hair as part of the service.

Cutting angles

The angle at which the cutting tools and the head are positioned will affect the weight distribution, balance and degree of graduation of the facial hair.

At the end of the facial haircut you must check the look is even and symmetrical, and that the overall balance suits your client's facial contours. Remove any unwanted hair outside the desired outline shape to ensure a clean finish to suit the client's requirements and carry out an eye brow trim to finish the look – this is shown in the step-by step section later in this chapter.

Tools, equipment and products

You will use a variety of tools and equipment when creating facial hairstyles such as tapered and full beard lines and partial beards and moustaches, including:

- scissors
- razors
- clippers
- clippers with grade attachments
- trimmers and T-liners
- combs.

You will not require the use of a razor, unless the outside edges are being cut away cleanly.

Size and types of clippers, clipper blades and attachments

The table below shows the safe use and maintenance of cutting tools.

Tools and equipment	How to use and effects achieved	Maintenance
Scissors	During the service, use scissors with scissor over comb techniques to achieve the desired lengths and trim the hair to shape.	Before and after every service – clean with hot soapy water and remove all hair clippings, then disinfect in a chemical Barbicide solution, sterilise in an autoclave or sanitise in a UV light cabinet. Oil blades after sterilising.
Clippers	During the service, use clipper over comb techniques to achieve the desired lengths. Clippers can also be used pointing the blades directly onto the skin to achieve a shaved line and to remove hair back to the skin.	Before and after every service – remove the hairs from the blades, spray with a disinfectant and oil the blades.
Clipper grade attachments	During the service, use clippers with various grades attached to achieve different lengths.	Before and after every service – clean grade attachments with hot soapy water and remove all hair clippings, then disinfect in a chemical Barbicide solution or sanitise in a UV light cabinet.

Tools and equipment	How to use and effects achieved	Maintenance
Trimmers and T-liners	During the service trimmers and T-liners are used to create small precise lines in the beard line or moustache.	Before and after every service – remove the hairs from the blades, spray with a disinfectant and oil the blades.
Combs	Before service – use the comb to untangle the beard and moustache before cutting. During service – use with scissor or clipper over comb techniques to guide the hair when cutting to the correct hair length. Either end of the comb can be used, depending on the hair length required.	Before and after every service – clean with hot soapy water and remove all hair clippings, then disinfect in a chemical Barbicide solution or sanitise in a UV light cabinet.

HANDY HINT

Always carry your scissors in a pouch or case and **palm** them when not in use.

KEY TERM

Palm – hold your scissors in the palm of your hand with the blades closed.

▲ Re-align your clipper blades when they need levelling

Test and level clippers

Clipper blades must be correctly aligned and checked before each service to ensure the blades are level and they cut evenly without pulling on the hair.

To check the blades are aligned and will not 'pull' on the hair, test the blades on the back of your hands. If they bite or mark the skin, the blades are offset and need to be levelled. To do this, un screw the blades and re-align them, ensuring the top blade is slightly seated back from the fixed blade, before screwing the blades together again.

Products

You can use oil or wax to aid styling and to finish the look of facial hair. Both products are suitable for the coarseness of facial hair and add control, particularly for fuller or dense beards.

Provide aftercare

As with every service that you provide, you must offer aftercare advice to your client. This should include:

- products to use at home (including products for exfoliation)
- recommendations for any equipment for home maintenance
- how to maintain their current look
- additional services that are available
- when he should return for his next appointment.

Present and future services

Shaving styles for men are very individual and personal, and some clients like to personalise their beards. This might be in the form of colouring or bleaching their facial hair. If your salon offers this service, discuss with your client any ideas you have for making his beard individual to him.

Time intervals between services

The recommendations you make will very much depend on the style you have created. Maintaining a rugged look requires more regular upkeep; otherwise it quickly becomes a scruffy look. These styles might need grooming every three days or so. A full-beard style might last from three to five weeks, depending on the length of the beard and the rate of hair growth; you will need to personalise this part of the service to suit each individual look and every individual client.

Maintenance and retail opportunities

Products

You should recommend to your client that he regularly exfoliates the skin outside the facial hair shape to prevent ingrowing hairs and an increased risk of 'barber's itch'. Show your client how to carry out this exfoliating treatment; suggest how often the treatment should be carried out and demonstrate the products that are available for him to purchase and use at home in between salon visits.

If your client suffers with dry skin and very coarse beard hair, you can recommend shampoos and conditioners to be used on the beard (these are suitable for full beards only). Equally, for clients with less facial hair or those that close shave more regularly, you can suggest a gent's skincare range to help moisturise the face.

Equipment

If the style requires minimal trimming on a regular basis, it is likely that your client will want to maintain this himself in between visits. Suggest clippers for trimming facial hair or razors if he is removing his facial hair. Demonstrate the areas of the cheek or neck that he should clipper cut, explaining how to do it and advise how often he should do it.

The hairiness of men varies from person to person. Men with very hairy chests might need guidance on where to stop shaving the neck hair before it becomes removal of chest hair. A clean-shaven neckline can help to lessen the overall look of a hairy chest.

HANDY HINT

Advise your clients not to use a razor or clippers with blunt blades; these are a common cause of minor skin infections and may lead to in growing hairs.

HANDY HINT

Facial hair grows at the same rate as head hair – about 12.5 mm each month. Advising your client when to rebook for their next facial hair cut will depend on the length of the facial hairstyle.

ACTIVITY

If your client wanted to grow a long beard – about 5 cm long – how many months would he need to grow his beard for?

▲ Exfoliating treatment

HANDY HINT

Advise your client to oil their clipper blades to keep the blades lubricated and extend the life of the clippers.

▲ Use a tablet to explore images of facial hair designs

CREATE A RANGE OF FACIAL HAIR SHAPES

When creating a range of facial hair shapes you will follow many of the same practices as you did for cutting facial hair using basic techniques, such as:

- questioning clients prior to and during cutting services
- consulting with clients throughout the service.

It is important to explore different ideas with your client before they confirm the look they require. Tablets and smartphones are great tools – try using apps such Pinterest and Instagram to look for specific images of facial hair designs.

Factors that may influence services

Regardless of the shape you are creating and the techniques you use, these factors can impact on the facial haircut:

- head and face shape
- hair classifications
- hair characteristics
- hairstyle
- adverse skin conditions
- facial piercings
- client's wishes
- ingrown hairs
- skins elasticity
- scarring.

When designing new beard shapes, it is important to consider the facial contours, as this allows you to highlight cheekbones and narrow fuller faces.

Choosing the optimal beard shape

You have already explored face shapes earlier in the chapter. You will now look at matching beard shapes and styles to particular facial characteristics to achieve the optimal beard shape.

- Long narrow faces – avoid long chin length beards; keep hair cut short at the chin. The '5 o'clock shadow' or '2 days' stubble' looks work particularly well on longer faces with narrow chins.
- Pointed chin on a short face – keep a full beard, quite long, to add length but round off the bottom of the chin area to avoid adding a point.
- Pointed chin on a longer face – a rounded goatee style can work well.
- Rounded chins should avoid bushy sideburns with a long beard; instead aim for a narrow goatee. The moustache should ideally meet the goatee to narrow the area. Alternatively a longer beard cut into a V-shape at the chin will narrow the roundness.
- Overly square face – suggest your client grows a full face beard; keep the sides short and the chin area longer.
- Rectangular face – suggest a chin curtain or short box beard, keeping the sides fuller.

- A very hairy chest – suggest a clean-shaven neckline to allow for a clear gap between the hairy chest/back and the facial hair.

HEALTH AND SAFETY

Continual close cutting to the skin can cause in growing hairs. Provide your clients with advice on how to remedy this in between salon visits by exfoliating and using moisturising products at home.

▲ Clean-shaven neckline

Traditional and current facial hair shapes

Beard shapes differ immensely when you look at them closely. You can have variations of:

- moustache only
- partial beard with a moustache
- tapered beard lines
- full beard outlines
- full beard with a moustache.

You looked at moustaches, partial beards and full beards without moustaches earlier in this chapter. You will now look at combining these beards with moustaches.

Partial beard with a moustache

▲ Anchor beard shape – a beard shaped like an anchor from the centre of the bottom lip and around and up the chin.

▲ Goatee and moustache – a goatee partial beard and an attached blended moustache.

▲ The extended goatee – broader than the traditional goatee and has an attached moustache.

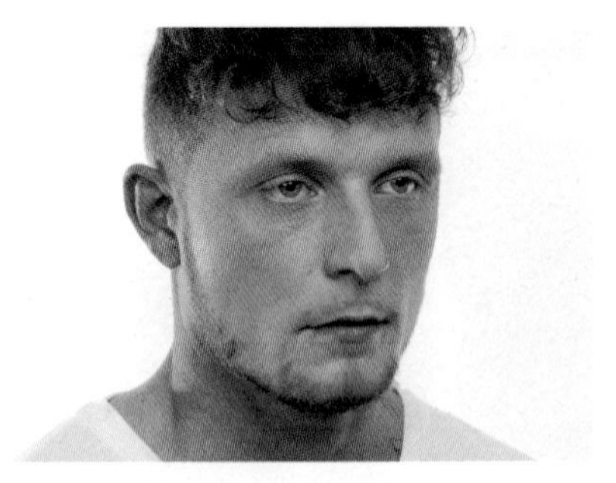

▲ The Balbo – where a goatee and a moustache feature but are not connected

▲ Short tapered beard

Tapered beard

The beard hair is short and cut into defined lines at the edges around the face and under the chin; the beard generally stops when the face meets the neck, leaving a clean-shaven neckline. The sideburns are very short and fade into the beard near the middle of the cheek area. The beard is tapered and then rounded under the chin. If accompanied with a moustache, this should blend into the beard and be uniform in length. Your client could grow a soul patch for a fuller appearance, if preferred. This beard will need maintaining regularly as it needs to be kept short, neat and tidy.

Full beard outlines

Full beard outlines are the most popular style at the moment in the UK, with one in three men with facial hair having a full beard style. There are many different ways to wear a full beard, to suit every face shape, lifestyle and personality.

The table below describes the various types of full beard and their associated maintenance.

Beard	Description	Maintenance period
Thin full-face beard	This is one of the shortest full beards a man can have and it can perfectly fade into the hairstyle. The sideburns are thin and fade into the main beard. The edges around the face are shapely, defined, curved and trimmed neatly. The moustache is a thin line of stubble that meets the beard close to the lower lip. The beard line continues under the chin and finishes at the base of the neck.	This beard will need maintaining regularly as it needs to be kept short, neat and tidy.
Lined full beard	The sideburns are grown and extended into the full beard around the mid-ear area. The beard edge is cut cleanly (often with a razor) in front of the ear and down to the neck area. The beard is kept full, with a pronounced soul patch, but the moustache needs to be kept short and not meet the beard.	This beard will need maintaining regularly as the clean lines need to be kept short, neat and tidy.

Beard	Description	Maintenance period
Bold and thick full beard	Very popular at the moment, the sideburns are grown and blended into the beard and cut to the same length throughout. The facial edge is angled down diagonally across the cheek and curved upwards into a soul patch. The beard is slightly longer at the chin with a rounded end. The moustache is a thin line of hair that meets the beard and travels down to the corners of the mouth.	This beard will need maintaining regularly as the cheek lines need to be kept neat and tidy and the length maintained.
The uniform full beard	This beard and moustache is uniform in length throughout. It is about 6 cm long and is a perfect beard for a working professional who wants a longer beard. The beard extends past the chin and is rounded neatly; the neckline is sometimes left cleanly shaven. The moustache blends uniformly into the beard.	This beard is fairly easy to maintain with regular trims.
The faded full beard	This is a long square-shaped beard, often with a handlebar moustache. The sideburns fade into the main beard and the beard is about 10 cm long. The base of the beard is trimmed into a flat straight line.	Due to the length of this beard, it will not need to be trimmed as often as a short beard. The length and shape will need regular maintenance and the beard will need to be conditioned and combed regularly.
The wild full beard	The sideburns fade into a wild full beard and the sides are not trimmed. The cheek area is kept neat with clean sharp edges; the moustache is grown longer so it can curl slightly upwards at the ends. The hair is kept long below the chin and the point of the beard is cut off at the end.	Due to the length of this beard, it will not need to be trimmed as often as a short beard, but some shaping will be needed and the beard will need to be conditioned and combed regularly.

ACTIVITY

Use the internet to search for celebrities wearing various beards and identify which movies are influencing facial hairstyles.

▲ Chin strap and goatee

HANDY HINT

Use and maintain cutting tools and equipment correctly and test and level your clippers before every service.

Apply correct techniques during services

You will need to cut facial hair using different cutting techniques to achieve the desired result. You must create, establish and follow your guidelines to create an even and balanced look.

More advanced cuts will require you to use the same basic techniques, but in addition you will add fading and more blending techniques to allow for flexibility and variety in the styles created. As your experience and confidence grows, you can combine looks such as a chin strap and goatee or soul patch to personalise the look you are creating; you will need to personalise your cutting techniques too.

Both during and at the end of the service it is important you cross-check the facial haircut to ensure a balanced end result. You will need to consider weight distribution and work with the natural growth patterns of the facial hair throughout.

Tools, equipment and products

For all facial haircuts you are likely to use the following tools and techniques:

- scissors for trimming length and creating shape
- clippers and attachments for removing bulk length and clipper over comb for tapering various lengths
- trimmers for creating clean lines round the cheeks and hairlines, and the finer details such as removing lengths from moustaches.

Wax and oils are used to soften and condition coarse hair and aid styling, such as when creating a curl shape or twisting a moustache into a point.

Problems that may occur during services

There are many problems that can occur when cutting facial hair, so it is important you understand what action to take to remedy each problem.

Problem	Cause	Remedy/action
Beard is too short	Barber error Poor consultation	Apologise to client and create a suitable shape that the beard can grow into.
Beard is uneven or unbalanced	Barber error	Apologise to client and re-cut to balance the shape, avoiding taking the style too short where possible.
Client is dissatisfied with end result	Barber error Poor consultation	Apologise to client and create a shape and style that is to the client's satisfaction or allows the beard to grow into the shape in time.
Cut skin/bleeding	Barber error Cutting of the skin/catching skin tags Blades on clippers are not aligned/oiled/maintained	Apologise to client and, wearing gloves, apply a styptic match to the cut or nick on the skin.

Provide advice and recommendations

At the end of the service it is important to provide advice and recommendations on the products and services provided in the salon.

You should advise your client on:

- how to maintain their current look, including what equipment to use or purchase for home maintenance
- how to exfoliate the skin in between visits (if relevant) and what products to use for this
- time intervals between salon services and visits
- present and future products and services that would benefit the client
- any additional services or products that you recommended during the service.

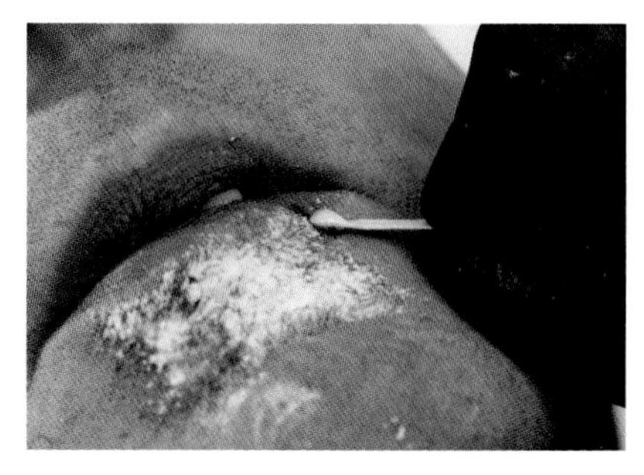

▲ For minor cuts or nicks to the skin, use a styptic match to stop the blood flow

WHAT YOU MUST DO

For your practical assessments you must:

- maintain safe working practices when cutting facial hair to shape
- cut facial hair to shape using basic techniques
- design and create a range of facial hair shapes.

Maintain safe working practices

Before the service, prepare your client to meet salon requirements for facial hair shaping services.

You must apply safe and hygienic methods of working throughout services, as shown in the diagram.

You must use working methods that:

- minimise the risk of cross-infection
- make effective use of your working time

- ensure the use of clean resources
- minimise the risk of harm or injury to yourself and others
- promote environmental and sustainable working practices and dispose of waste materials correctly.

When you are ready to carry out facial hair shaping services you must select suitable products, tools and equipment and complete the service within a commercially viable time.

Cut facial hair to shape using basic techniques

Always consult with clients to confirm the desired look and identify factors likely to influence the service prior to cutting. During the service confirm with your client the look agreed.

Cut beards and moustaches to maintain their shape

Carry out the service as shown in the diagram below.

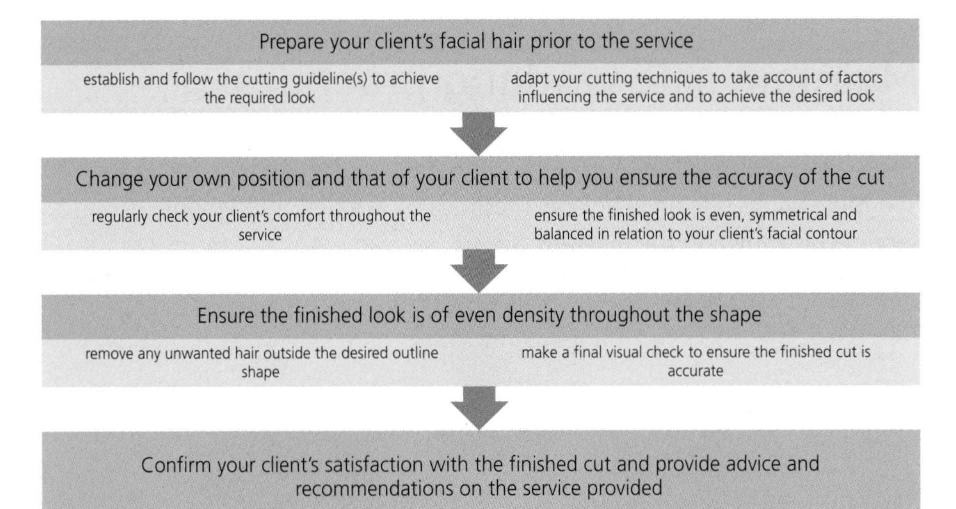

Design and create a range of facial hair shapes

You must complete all of the above and:

- explore a variety of new facial hair shapes with your client using relevant visual aids
- recommend a new look that is suitable for your client's head and face shape
- base your recommendations on an accurate evaluation of your client's facial hair and its potential to achieve the new look
- design and create a variety of facial hair shapes
- personalise your cutting techniques to take account of factors that will influence the desired look
- take action to resolve any problems arising during the cutting service

- create facial hair outlines that are accurate, clearly defined and achieve the look required by your client
- ensure the finished look is of even density throughout the shape.

STEP BY STEP

Do not try to 'run before you can walk'! Before you try to begin creating new facial hair designs, you first need to master the basic skills of facial haircuts. You will now look at how some of these are achieved.

Cutting a traditional moustache using freehand techniques

STEP 1 – After removing excess length with scissor over comb techniques, create the top lipline shape with mini-clippers.

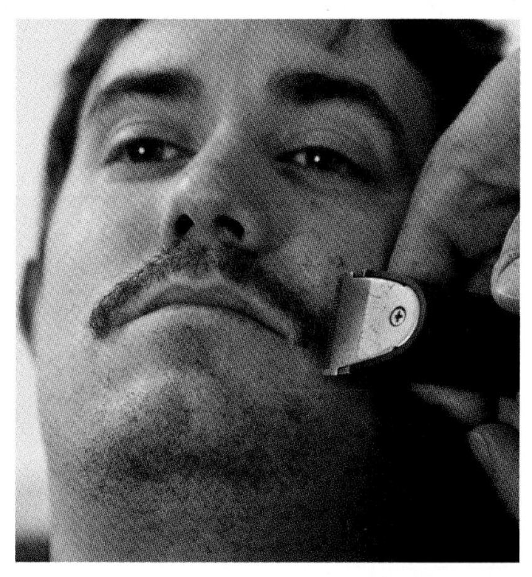

STEP 2 – Agree the width of the moustache and use clippers, blade down onto the face.

STEP 3 – Check the balance on both sides.

STEP 4 – Create the bottom lipline and shape to personalise the moustache.

Cutting a straight line top-lip moustache using clippers

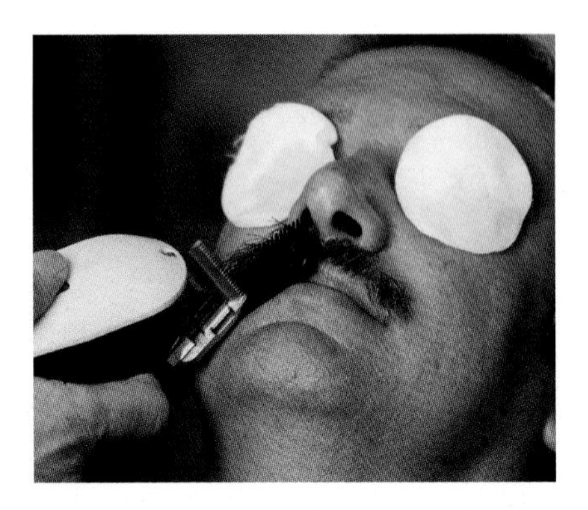

STEP 1 – Cut the length of the moustache with the clipper over comb technique.

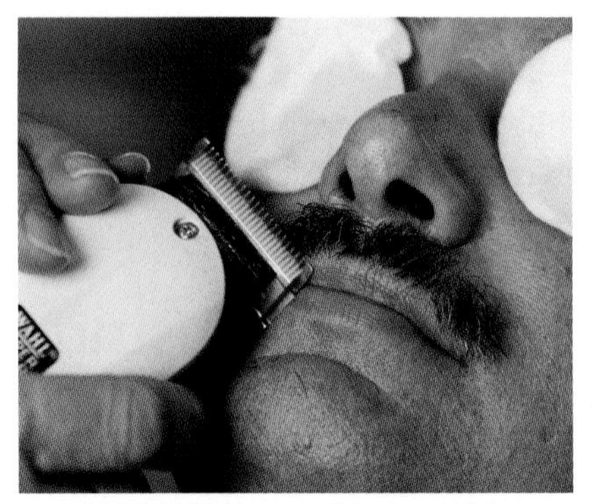

STEP 2 – Remove the outline length from the bottom of the lipline using freehand technique with clippers.

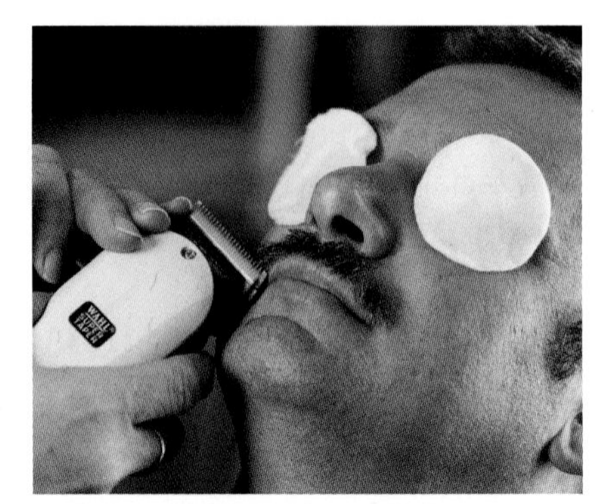

STEP 3 – Continue the process.

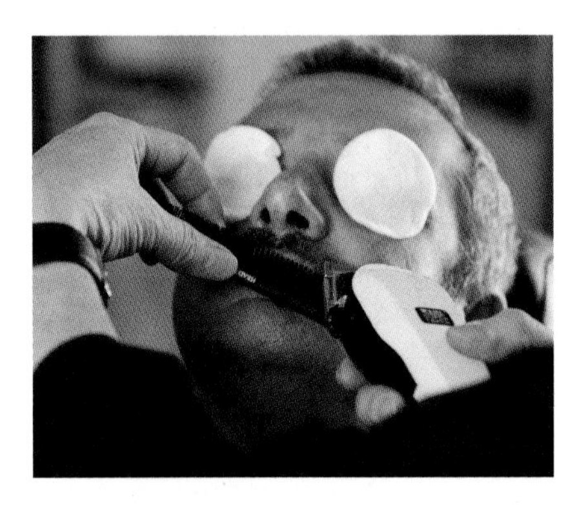

STEP 4 – With the new shape in place, check the internal lengths are cut to the agreed length using clipper over comb techniques.

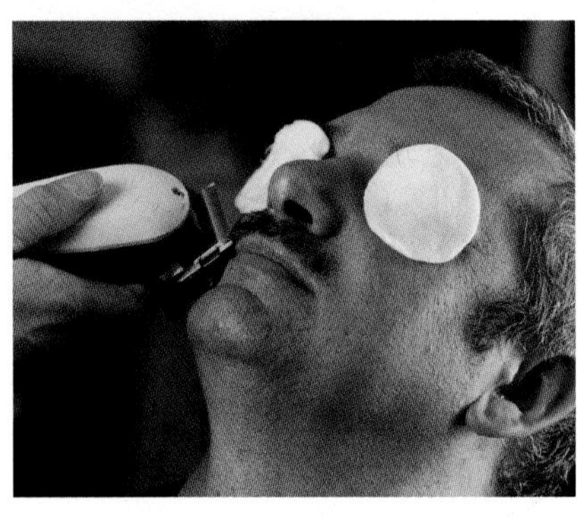

STEP 5 – Agree the width of the moustache and cut using freehand technique with clippers.

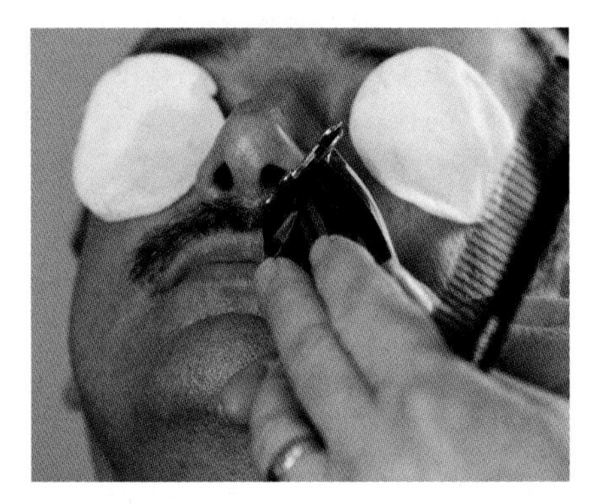

STEP 6 – Check the moustache for balance on both sides, tidy up any loose hairs and show the finished result to your client.

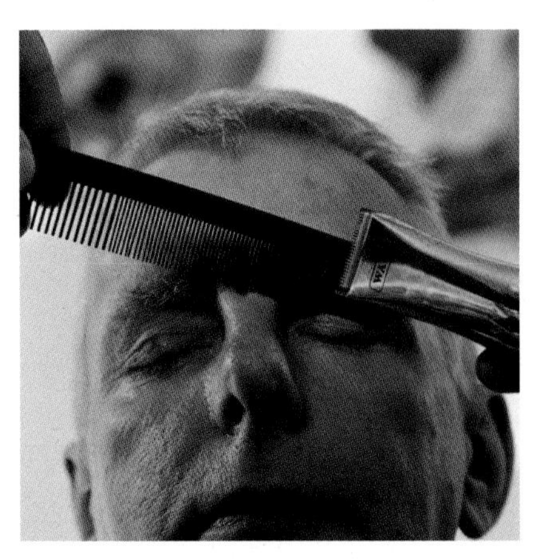

▲ Eyebrow trim

ACTIVITY

Practise cutting various moustache styles on a training head.

HANDY HINT

At the end of every facial haircut, ask your client if he would like his eyebrows trimmed. Some clients are surprised by this question, but reassure them that eyebrows are also facial hair, and trimming them enhances the whole image of the beard and moustache. Refer to Chapter 5 for a recap on how to trim eyebrow hair to shape.

Cutting a current fashion moustache with a tapered beard

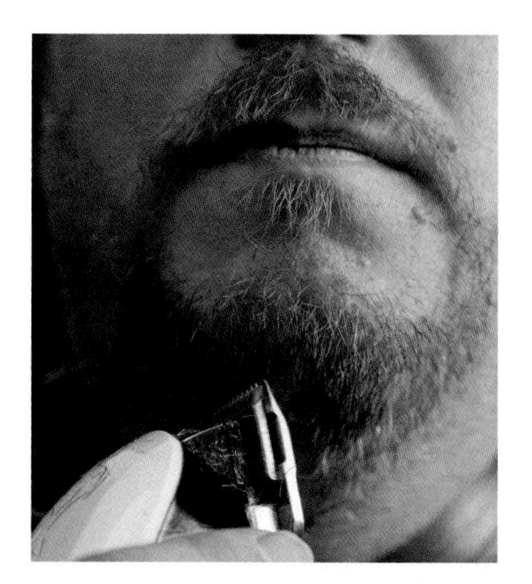

STEP 1 – Before commencing, lift the chin upwards for ease of working.

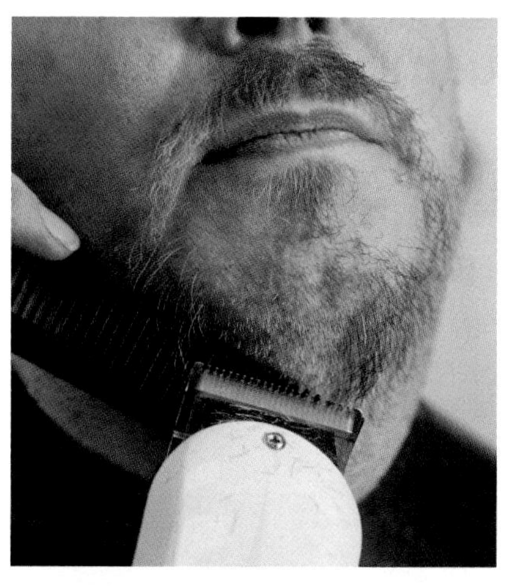

STEP 2 – Remove the excess length of the beard with the clipper over comb technique, tapering the length into the neckline and below the chin.

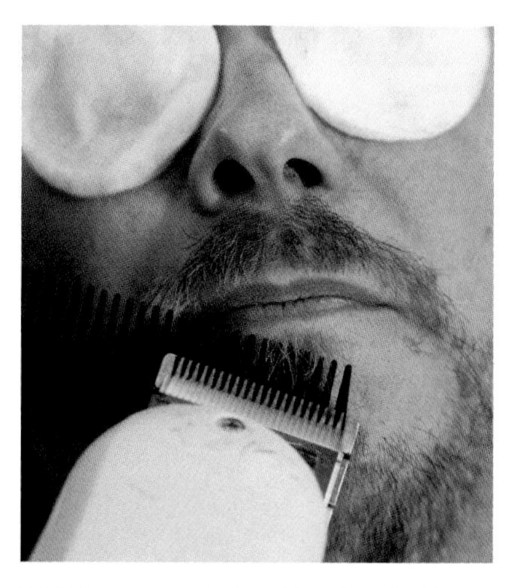

STEP 3 – Remove the beard length under the lipline using the clipper over comb technique.

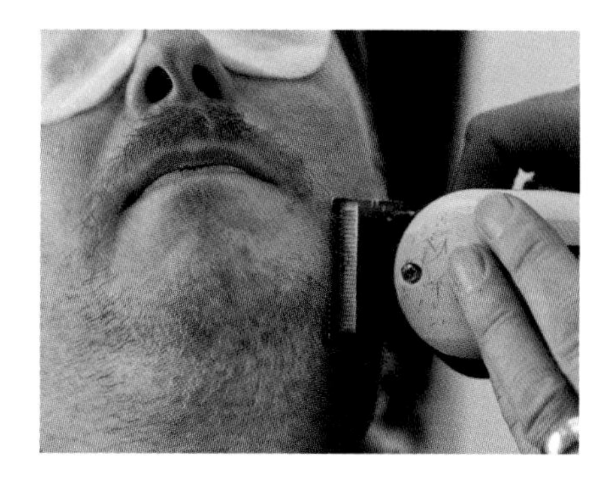

STEP 4 – Adjust the clipper grade length and remove the unwanted facial hair.

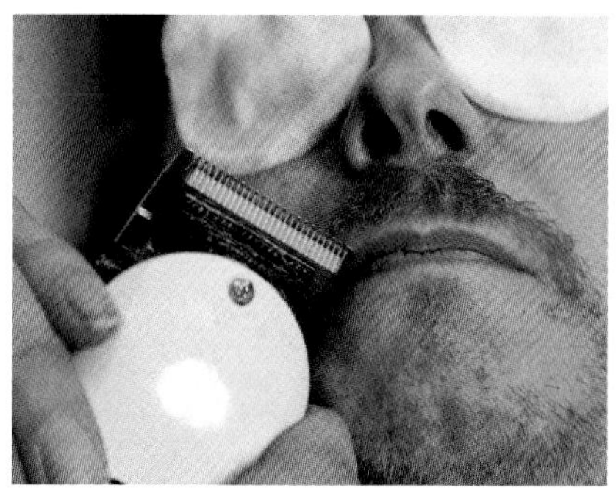

STEP 5 – Tilt the clippers to the side and create the lipline moustache length required.

STEP 6 – Using the mini-clippers, define the lipline shape.

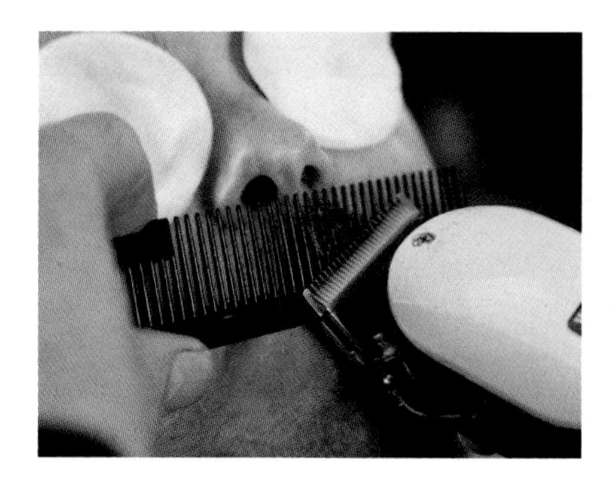

STEP 7 – Using the clipper over comb technique, remove the moustache length.

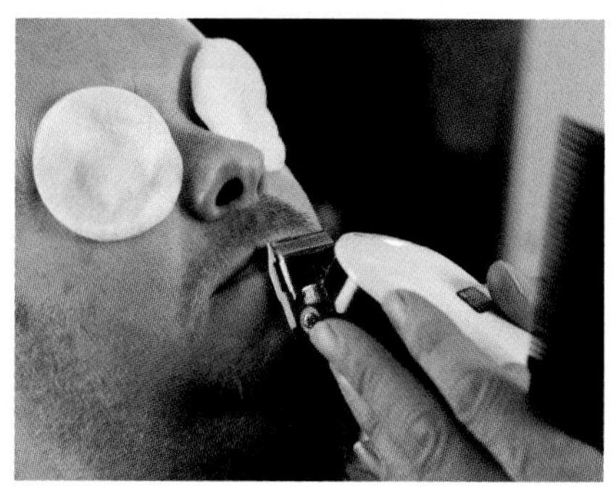

STEP 8 – Check the moustache length is defined before you show the client the end result.

HANDY HINT

It is good practice to cover the eyes with cotton pads to prevent stray hair from entering the eyes.

Now that your skills are developing and your confidence is growing, you can begin to create more facial hair shapes.

Cutting a goatee-tapered beard line using the scissor over comb technique

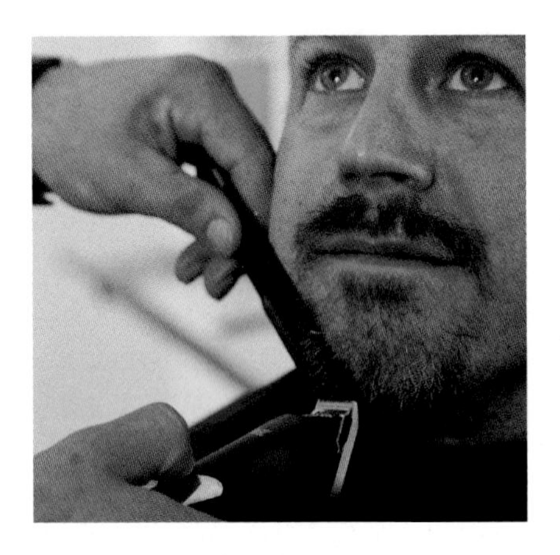

STEP 1 – Remove the excess length with the clipper over comb technique.

STEP 2 – Shape the goatee beard and cut to the desired length with the scissor over comb technique.

STEP 3 – Trim the moustache length with clippers and grades.

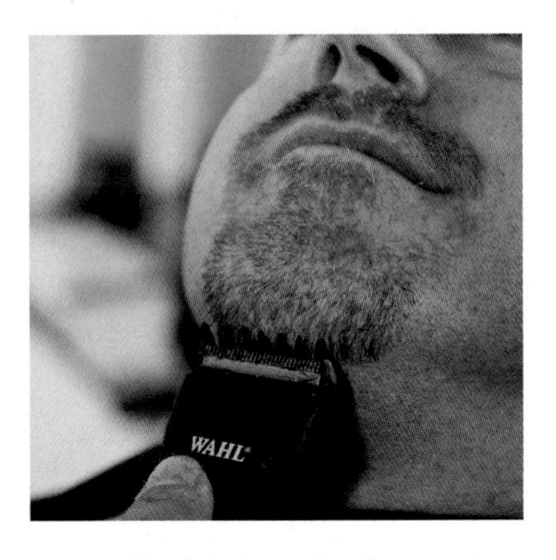

STEP 4 – Trim the goatee using clippers and grades.

STEP 5 – Use mini-clippers to create the lipline shape.

STEP 6 – Check your client is happy with the finished result.

ACTIVITY

Practise cutting a goatee beard on a training head.

HANDY HINT

Remember that the angles in which the cutting tools and the head are positioned will affect weight distribution, balance and degree of graduation of the facial hair.

Cutting a short full beard outline with a moustache using clipper over comb techniques

You can cut full beards by using uniform layers on longer beards, or scissor or clipper over comb techniques on shorter, full beards as shown below.

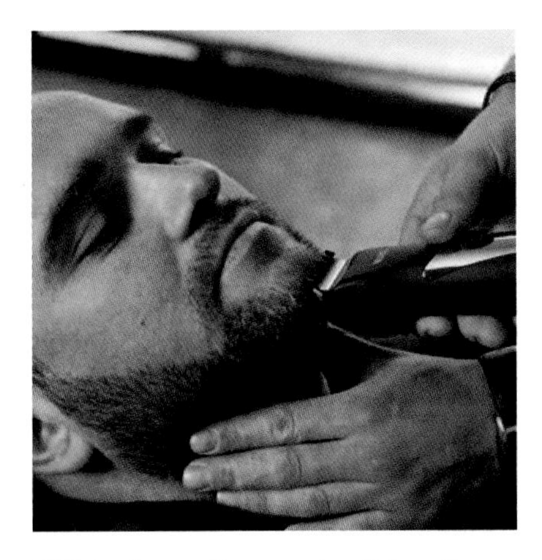

STEP 1 – Remove the excess length from the beard.

STEP 2 – Lift the head and cut, blend or remove the length under the chin.

STEP 3 – Trim the moustache to the agreed length.

STEP 4 – Blend and personalise the facial hair with clipper over comb techniques to taper the beard outline

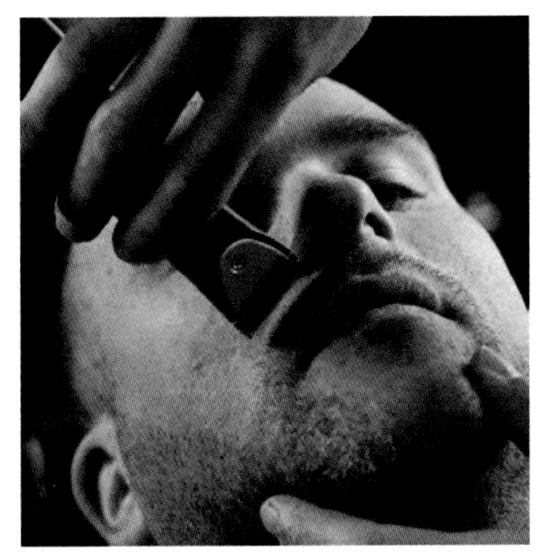

STEP 5 – Personalise the moustache outline.

STEP 6 – Ensure the client is happy with the finished look.

HANDY HINT

Work with the natural growth patterns of facial hair and consider the weight distribution within the facial haircut.

HANDY HINT

Make final visual checks to ensure the finished cut is accurate.

ACTIVITY

Practise cutting a full beard on a training head.

HANDY HINT

Cross-check the cut to ensure the finished look is symmetrical and even in shape and density. Check the weight distribution and balance.

HANDY HINT

Ask your client to move their head for you so you can follow all the contours of the neck and face shapes and remove any unwanted hair outside the desired outline shape.

Chin strap goatee beard with a moustache

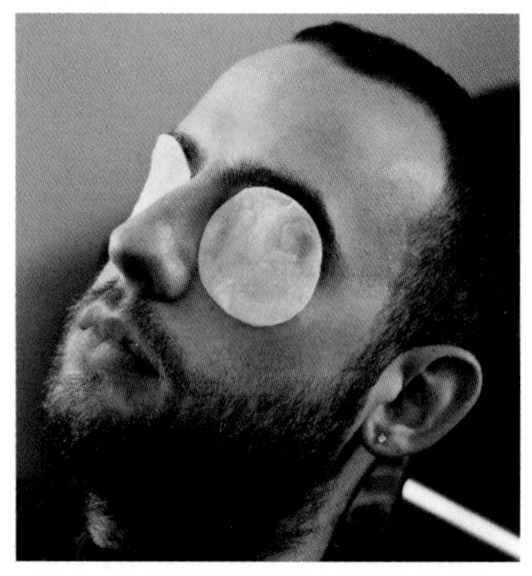

STEP 1 – Cover the client's eyes with pads and ensure his head is supported on the neck rest.

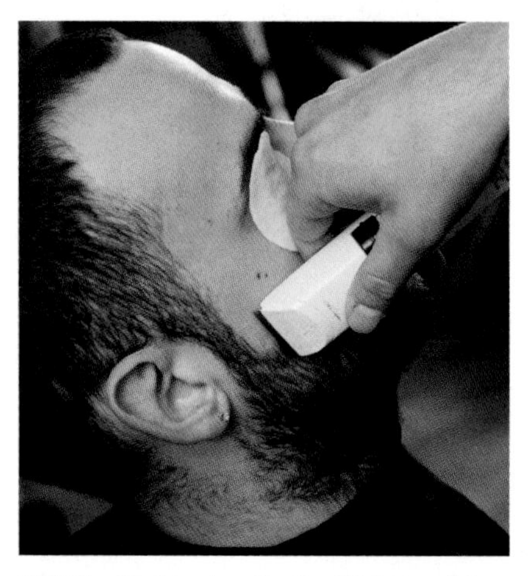

STEP 2 – Start by choosing the thickness of the chin strap, then follow the sideburn down the cheek with mini-clippers.

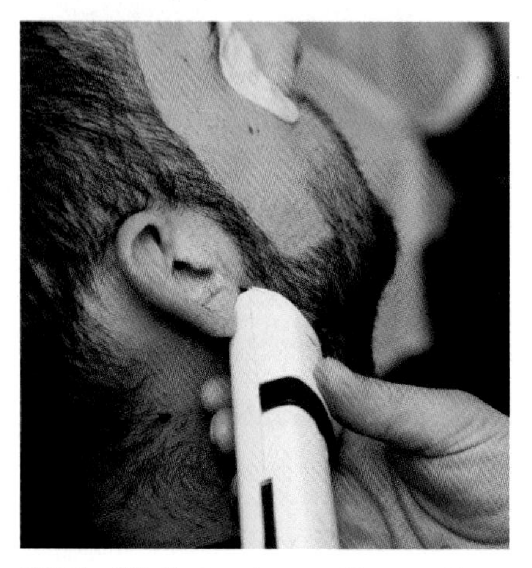

STEP 3 – Tidy the temple area with a smooth curve from the sideburn to the temple; follow this down onto the neck area.

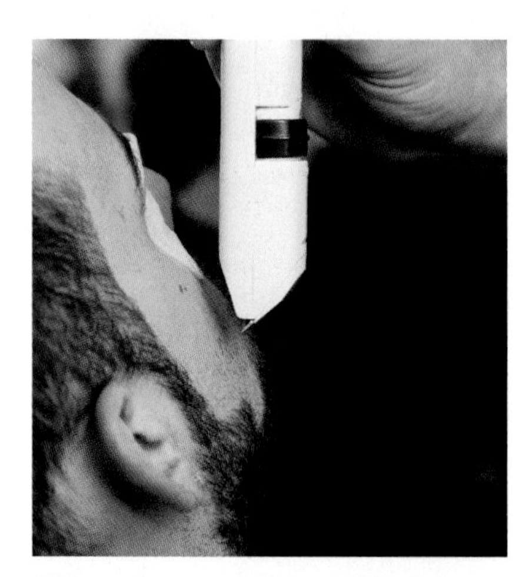

STEP 4 – Shave the cheek area to the desired height until you reach the desired angle for the sides of the goatee.

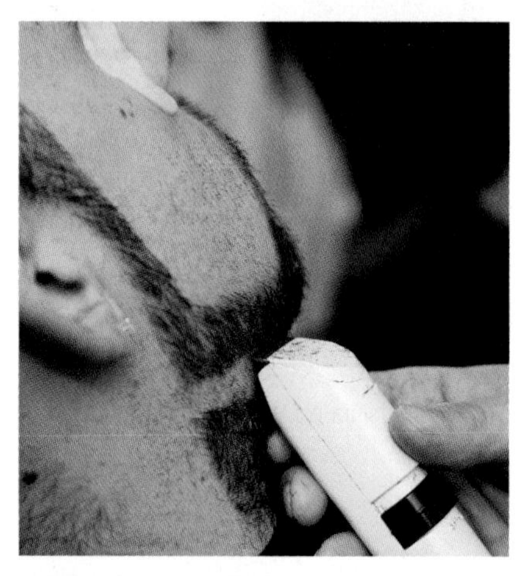

STEP 5 – Shave parallel to the top of the chin strap underneath the jawline, ensuring that the same thickness is maintained throughout. Keep the lines clean and precise.

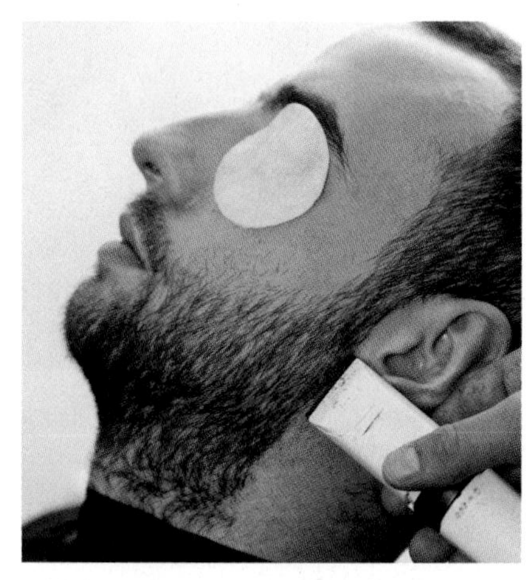

STEP 6 – Repeat steps 2 and 3 on the other side. Make sure the line is sharp on the back of the sideburn.

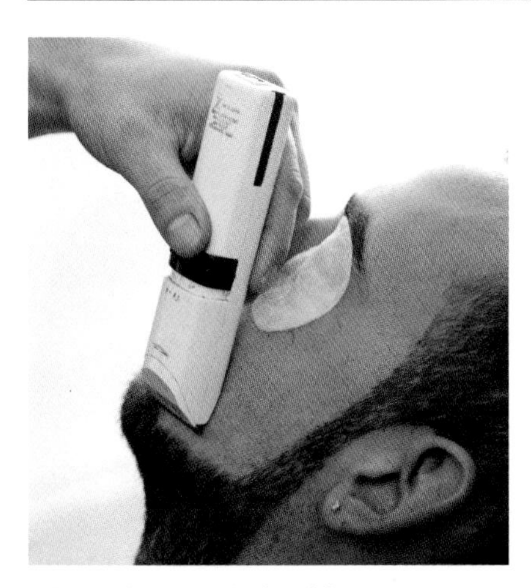

STEP 7 – Repeat steps 4 and 5.

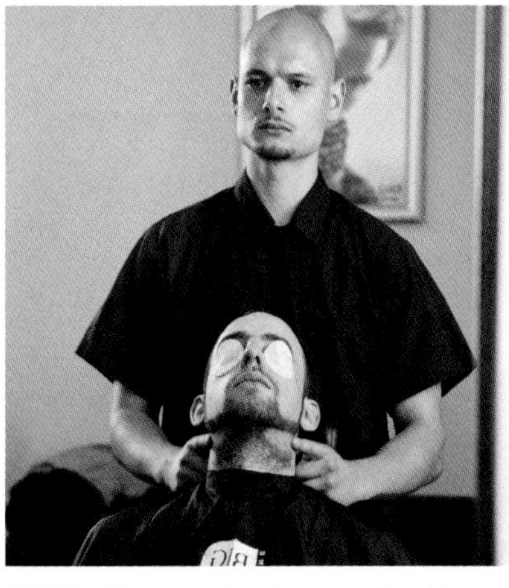

STEP 8 – Use your mirror to ensure the chin strap is balanced on both sides.

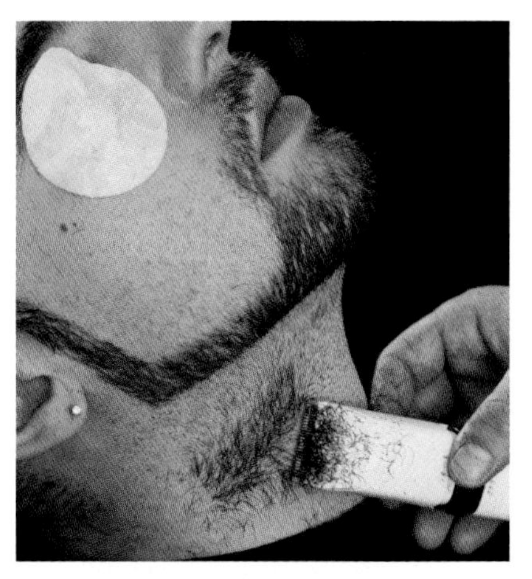

STEP 9 – Join both sides up by shaving away the area underneath the chin, making sure the shape is still balanced. Remove all the remaining hair from the neck area.

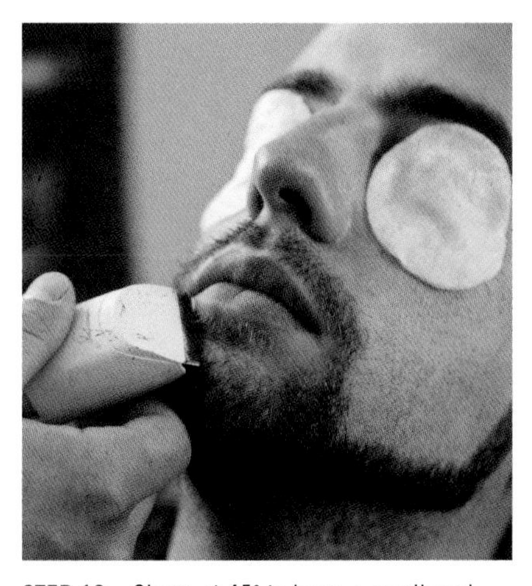

STEP 10 – Shave at 45° to leave a small soul patch under the bottom lip.

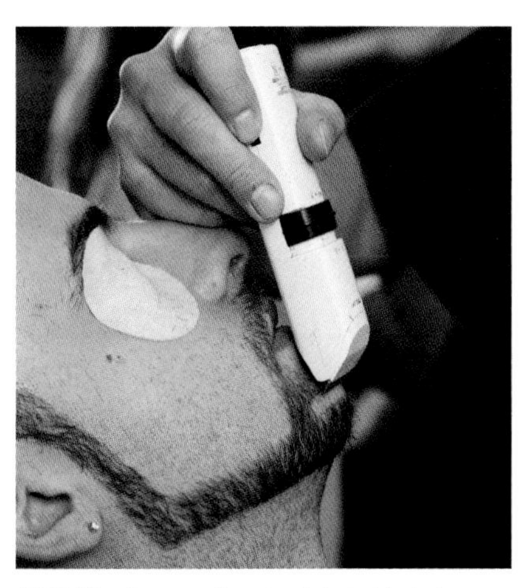

STEP 11 – Remove the remaining chin hair, continuing the chin strap's thickness across the lower chin.

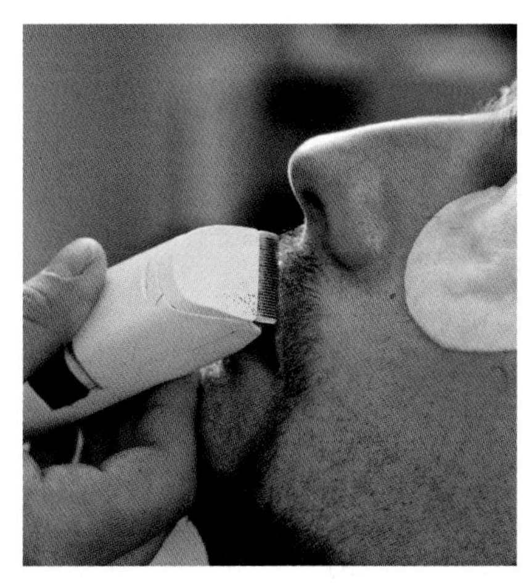

STEP 12 – Line the bottom of the moustache by resting the back of your hand on the client's chin for support to increase accuracy.

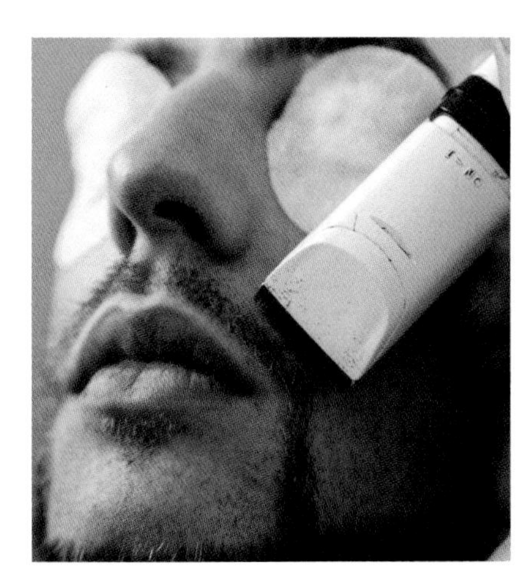

STEP 13 – Line up the top of the moustache to the same thickness as the side of the goatee for balance.

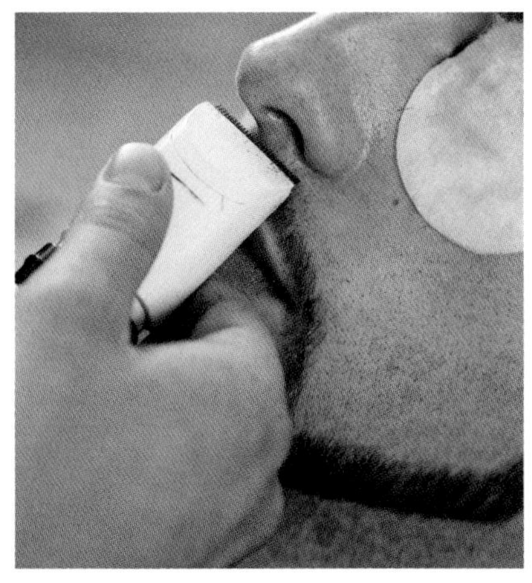

STEP 14 – Line up under the nose area with the clipper pointing towards the nose to get to this hard-to-reach area.

STEP 15 – The finished look.

Full beard

STEP 1 – Rest a long comb against the face, and angle it away from the face. Use clippers to cut the beard and graduate to maintain length.

STEP 2 – Taper the top of the beard into the haircut, gradually getting shorter towards the sideburns.

STEP 3 – Using freehand clippering techniques, cut the beard outline shape and remove length and bulk.

STEP 4 – Taper the edges using a freehand technique with clippers to obtain the outline shape in front of the ears.

STEP 5 – Continue this technique, creating the overall beard shape and length.

STEP 6 – Lift the head and remove length and density of hair under the chin.

STEP 7 – Use freehand clippering throughout to create the rounded tapered beard shape required.

STEP 8 – Repeat on the other side.

STEP 9 – Visually check for balance and shape on both sides and adapt length as required.

STEP 10 – Add oil to soften the beard hair.

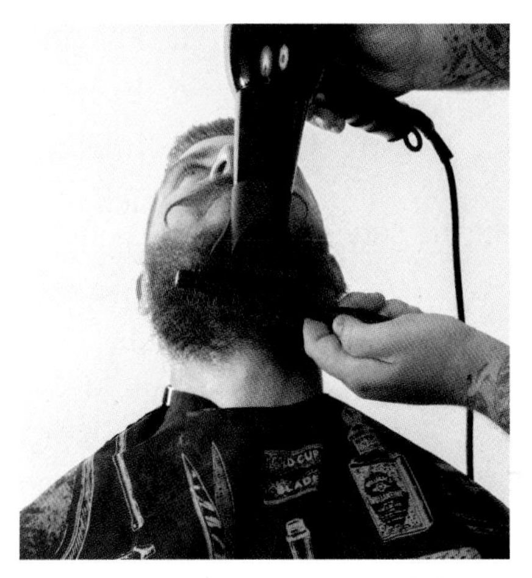

STEP 11 – Blow-dry the beard to smooth the hair, using a small to medium-sized radial brush. Apply a very small amount of deluxe pomade gel to curl the ends of the moustache.

STEP 12 – The finished look.

Test your knowledge

Question 1

Describe the safety considerations for using a razor.

Question 2

A client requests a full beard. How would you adapt the facial hair cutting service for a client with straight type 1 fine sparse hair?

Question 3

Describe androgenic alopecia.

Question 4

How can very coarse, tightly curled facial hair impact on cutting services?

Question 5

Which facial hairstyles would best suit a client with a heavy set chin?

Question 6

How would the following factors affect the service?

- Adverse skin conditions
- Hair characteristics
- A recent tattoo.

Multiple choice questions

7 Why should a barber's chair be used when cutting facial hair?

- **a** To minimise the risk of cross-contamination of tools
- **b** To ensure the service can be carried out hygienically
- **c** To keep the client comfortable and expose the neck area
- **d** To make sure the client is happy with the service and will pay the agreed price

8 Which one of the following facial hairstyles would best suit a client with a long face and a thin pointed chin?

- **a** Short stubble
- **b** A rounded goatee
- **c** Chin curtains
- **d** A full beard

9 What is the cause of the common facial cyst?

- **a** Blocked sebaceous glands
- **b** Fungus
- **c** Bacteria
- **d** Infected follicles

10 Which of the following skin disorders are contagious?

Cold sores
Cysts
Skin tags
Impetigo

- **a** Cold sores and cysts
- **b** Cysts and skin tags
- **c** Skin tags and impetigo
- **d** Cold sores and impetigo

This page intentionally left blank.

YOLANDA DOUGLAS – THE HAIR PROJECT

My name is Yolanda Douglas and I'm currently completing the City & Guilds NVQ Level 3 in Hairdressing at the Hair Project. I chose to complete an Apprenticeship because I wanted on-the-job learning where I could develop and accelerate my skills as a stylist in a real salon environment. Through my Apprenticeship, I have been able to work at the Errol Douglas Salon in Knightsbridge, where I'm able to go out and assist the creative team on all types of shoots and events while still getting all the experience I need in the salon. That's what's great about the Apprenticeship – you never know what opportunities will come your way! My Apprenticeship journey is a great example of this – I became a finalist in the HJ's British Hairdressing Business Awards, Junior of the Year final!

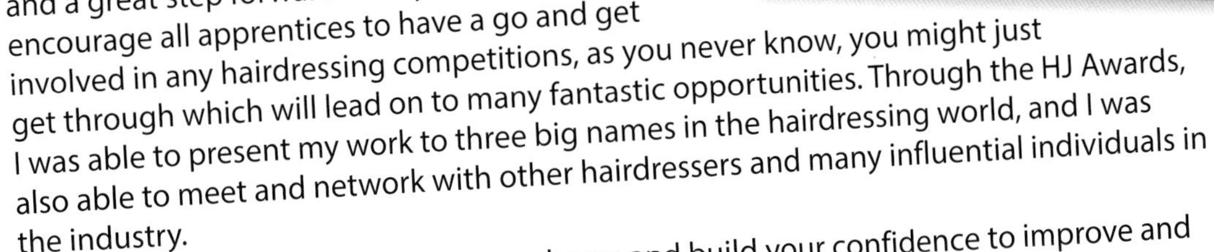

The Awards process was an amazing experience and a great step forward for my career – I would encourage all apprentices to have a go and get involved in any hairdressing competitions, as you never know, you might just get through which will lead on to many fantastic opportunities. Through the HJ Awards, I was able to present my work to three big names in the hairdressing world, and I was also able to meet and network with other hairdressers and many influential individuals in the industry.

Completing an Apprenticeship can push you and build your confidence to improve and expand your skills – when I started my Level 3, I really struggled with men's haircutting, but with my mentor Curtis' help I've learned how to overcome my inhibitions. That's why I chose to style a gent for my soirée!

This chapter maps to:

- Unit 12 Provide shaving services (Level 2 Diploma for Hair Professionals – Barbering).

INTRODUCTION

All men have to decide whether to grow their facial hair or opt for a cleanly shaved face. Although facial hair has become extremely fashionable in recent years, combinations of cleanly shaved areas of the face with partial beards has once again made shaving services popular in barbershops. Virtually all men who choose not to wear facial hair must shave every day; barbershops are therefore ideally placed to promote this service alongside men's hair services.

After reading this chapter you will:

- understand how health and safety affects shaving services
- apply safe working practices when preparing the hair and skin for shaving
- know how to prepare the hair and skin for shaving
- know how to shave hair and apply finishing products.

HEALTH AND SAFETY POLICIES AND PROCEDURES

When working closely on the skin with sharps and razor blades, it is vital that you follow health and safety guidelines and legislation.

You are responsible for the safety of your client during salon services, so always ensure client comfort and protect his clothing from hair clippings with gowns, towels and/or tissue paper. When carrying out facial hair shaving with a razor you must wear gloves at all times and check your client's face for any contra-indications or adverse skin conditions.

The European Agency for Safety and Health at Work has issued an **EU directive** requiring gloves to be worn to provide added protection for you and your client when shaving. For more information, go to: https://osha.europa.eu/en/tools-and-publications/publications/literature_reviews/occupational-health-and-safety-in-the-hairdressing-sector. Please be aware this legislation may change in the near future.

KEY TERM

EU directive – a legal Act which countries who are members of the EU must follow.

Maintain personal hygiene and safe practices

As you will be working in such close proximity to your client, your own personal hygiene and presentation is very important in maintaining health and safety in your workplace. Make sure you:

- maintain good personal hygiene by showering daily and wearing deodorant
- wear clean, ironed clothes to project a professional image for you and your salon
- keep your breath fresh throughout the day.

▲ Well-prepared and well-groomed barber

Potential hazards and possible risks

Along with the salon hazards you encounter every day, cross-infection and infestation are the main risks when shaving, so ensure you wear gloves to protect you and your client.

When using razors, health and safety requirements must be followed to prevent the risks of cross-contamination to you and your client. Cutting razor bumps is a primary risk, so having tissues close by will allow you to act quickly, applying pressure to the area to stop bleeding. Using a **styptic stick** will close up the cut. Advise your client that regular exfoliation and closing pores with cold water will help prevent razor bumps, while using a vitamin E cream will help keep the skin moist and less irritable.

HEALTH AND SAFETY

Refer to Chapter 1 for more on health and safety and Chapter 9 for specific information on preparing for facial hair services.

KEY TERM

Styptic stick – a medicated stick that restricts blood flow and stops bleeding.

▲ Styptic stick

Safe and hygienic working methods and practices

Safe and hygienic working methods and practices are shown in the diagram below.

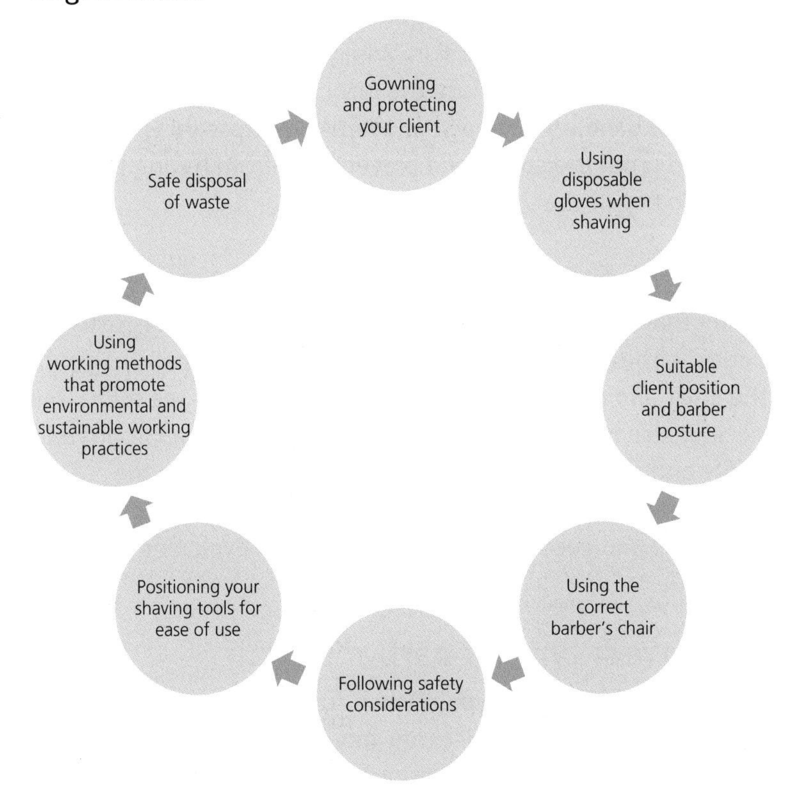

Each client should be given:

- a gown to protect their clothing from hair clippings
- a neck strip to give further protection to their skin from the gown
- cotton eye pads to protect their eyes from hair clippings.

A waterproof gown is best for shaving, as this will avoid water or product damage to your client's clothing as well as reducing mess in the salon environment.

HANDY HINT

Protect the eyes with a towel if it is more comfortable for the client, as the eyelids can get cold from wet cotton pads after a while.

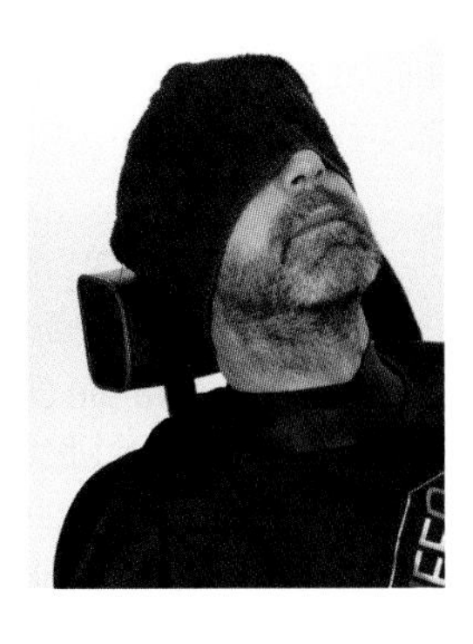

HANDY HINT

Specialist moisturising eye pads can be used instead of standard cotton eye pads to help reduce swelling or relieve tired eyes.

▲ Fab eye pads

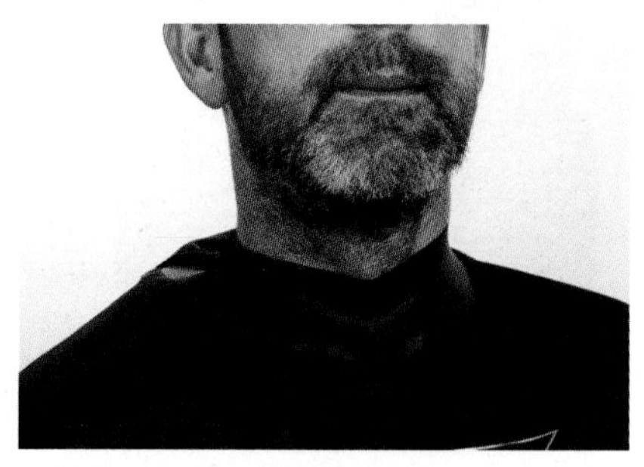

▲ Neoprene collars in barbering capes fit snuggly to the skin to prevent hair clippings from entering the neck area

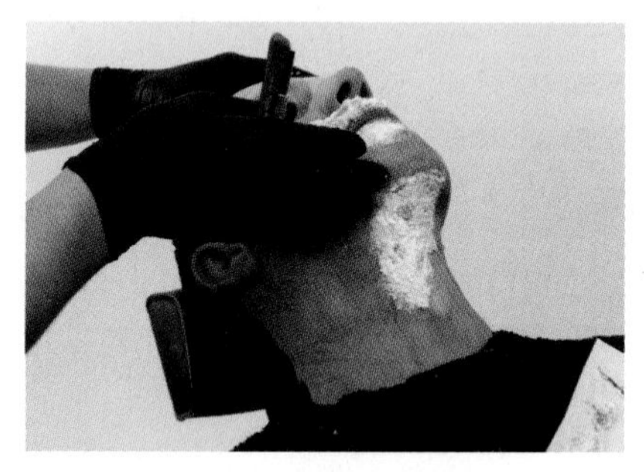

▲ Always cover the blade when repositioning your client's head during the shaving service

HANDY HINT

You should make sure the chair is positioned at the correct height and reclined appropriately for shaving comfort. Ensure your back is kept straight whenever possible.

Use a neck brush continuously to keep hair clippings off the client. This keeps the client comfortable and less prone to movement which could disrupt the service and risk the quality of the cut.

HANDY HINT

Some salons use an eye mask to hold the eye pads in place when the client is repositioned during a shaving service. This is important because during shaving services the head must be moved, especially when using clippers, and there is a risk that hair clippings may enter the eye and cause the client discomfort.

ACTIVITY

Name four items that can be used during shaving to protect the client from hair clippings. Remember that the client's head is being moved throughout the shaving service.

You must always wear gloves when handling razors. Hold the razor blade on the blunt edge to slide on; this gives grip and also, in the event of a cut, the gloves will be cut before the skin. When you need to reposition your client's head, make sure you close the razor and cover the blade completely with the handle. Keeping your sharps box close by you during the service will aid prompt disposal and prevent you from having to move too far when disposing of the used blades.

Client positioning and barber posture

When providing shaving services, it is important that the client is sitting fully in the chair with their back against the chair frame. This allows you to recline the chair and position the neck at 90°, so you can see fully under the neck. It also means that the skin can be stretched appropriately to ensure a safe and clean shave. It is crucial that you maintain the correct posture during shaving services, as you will be standing for long periods of time and need to minimise the risk of developing back problems or fatigue.

Using the correct type of barber's chair

It is important to use the correct type of chair for the comfort of you and your client throughout the service. You should be able to recline the chair and see the face and neck in a position that allows for easy access to all areas of the face and neck. At the start of the service, turn the chair towards the client to avoid them climbing into the chair and getting tangled in wiring or twisting their back.

The headrest is the most comfortable way for your client to be shaved and for you to conduct a shaving service. Use the headrest in conjunction with the recliner lever for a 45–90° resting angle. Always inform the client of headrest adjustments. Use your hand to support the head and avoid any sudden jolting movements.

HEALTH AND SAFETY

You should always ask the client to raise their head slightly while you adjust the height of the chair. The headrest should be wiped down prior to each service to avoid cross-infection.

HEALTH AND SAFETY

When reclining the chair, it is important to keep on the back foot to support the chair back with your own weight. This is most important when dealing with men weighing around 15 stone and over, as the chair will drop suddenly, throwing out your back and that of your client. Take care to use the correct handling techniques to avoid causing harm to your back.

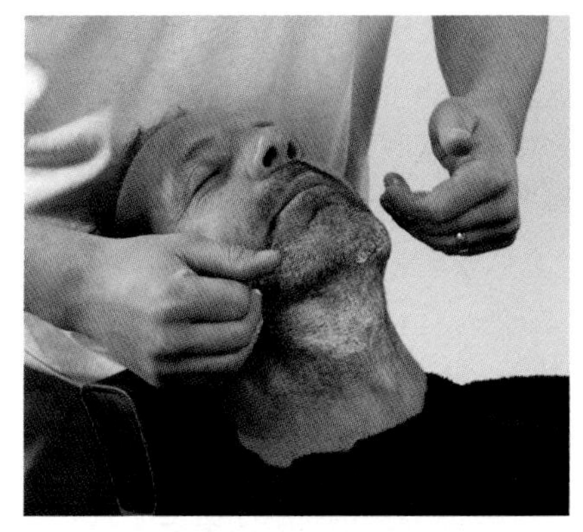

▲ Use the correct type of barber's chair

Have the chair reclined back fully and use appropriate cutting techniques, such as the **rake cut**, to prevent hair clippings from going into the eye area. During the shaving service, refrain from entering into general conversation with the client, as you need the client to keep as still as possible to prevent hair going into the mouth and to avoid cutting the client.

KEY TERM

Rake cut – cutting with the lever on the clipper at 90°.

Waste disposal

Using the right amount of product will avoid waste and reduce the risk of contact with the client's eyes. Read the manufacturer's instructions to understand how much product to use, and how to avoid waste and spillage. Avoid watering down products too much as this leads to overspread.

After shaving, used razors (sharps) must be disposed of in a sharps bin.

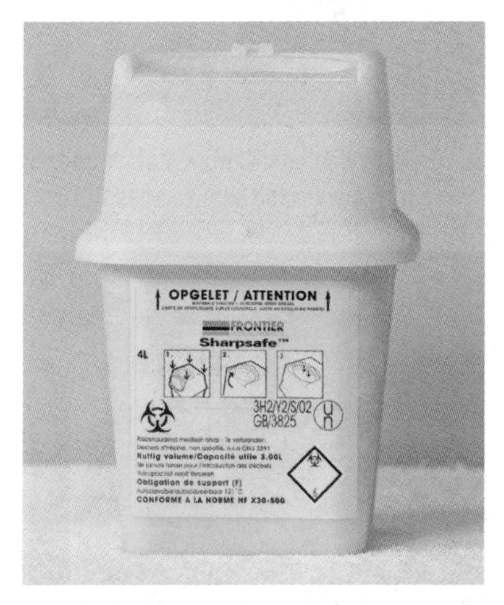

▲ Sharps bin

THE HAIR PROFESSIONAL AT WORK

To ensure environmental and sustainable working practices, always use products sparingly to prevent waste and to avoid too much build-up of product.

Prevent cross-infection and cross-infestation

You must protect your clients from cross-infection and infestation. The points below explain how you can do this.

- Wearing gloves in preparation for and during the service will prevent cross-infection in general and particularly in the unfortunate event of any cuts to the skin.
- Styptic sticks/matches are useful to have to hand in case there are any cuts to the skin. They stop bleeding and the risk of spreading infection.
- Change razor blades before each service in front of the client for a hygienic professional salon image.
- Sterilise all tools and equipment before and after service using clipper disinfectant sprays and Barbicide to prevent cross-infection and infestation. Clippers must be sprayed to kill germs and razors must be replaced. Used razors should be discarded in a sharps box.

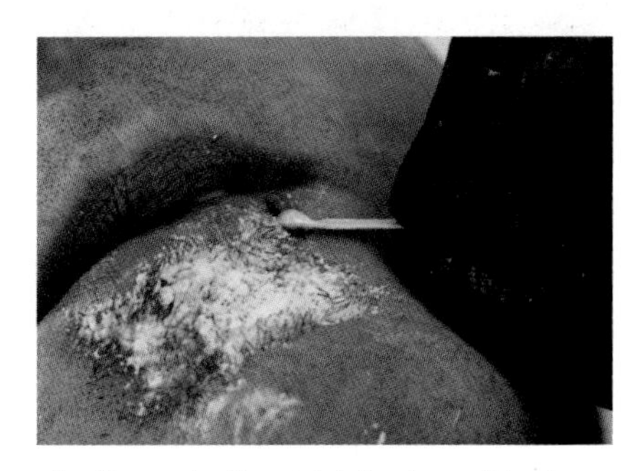

▲ Use a styptic match to stop a bleed after a cut or nick to the skin

▲ A tidy salon ready for clients

▲ Prepare your client, work station and your trolley for the service ahead

▲ Barbicide

HEALTH AND SAFETY

Gloves must be worn to perform shaving services, as close contact with the skin is needed to achieve the closest shave possible.

Maintain a clean and tidy work area

Your station should be clean and tidy before and throughout the service to help maintain a professional image. When operating an appointment system, it is essential to be organised and have the tools and equipment needed for the service to hand. This increases your efficiency and minimises preparation time between clients.

When using tools, equipment and products, always follow the manufacturer's and salon's instructions to keep you, your colleagues and your clients safe from harm. Checking tools prior to service and ensuring they are fit for purpose and clean to use will prevent accidents.

Cleaning, disinfecting and sterilisation

Cleaning in the barbershop is essential as hair clippings and scalp particles can be deposited all around the salon. Having a small hand-held vacuum cleaner for workstations can help, or use disinfectant wipes. Make sure you maintain a hygienic salon by:

- applying anti-bacterial spray with a paper-tissue roll – this is a very effective and inexpensive way of removing clippings from surfaces
- using Barbicide or clipper spray for clippers and combs – this is crucial and it is recommended that you do this in front of clients to demonstrate and promote the barbershop's good hygiene practice
- cleaning scissors with disinfectant wipes – make sure you wipe the scissors from the bevel back towards the point, keeping fingers flat on the blade and being mindful of the cutting edge and the point
- brushing clippers free of hair clippings and then spraying with a clipper disinfectant in an angled, downwards position across the blades to prevent solution dripping back into the machine
- replacing disposable razors for each client to prevent cross-infection and infestation
- washing your hands prior to every service – this is vital and using a hand sanitiser after the service will ensure you are germ-free
- laundering towels and gowns to combat cross-infection and infestation – although it is now common not only to use a clean gown for every client but also a neck strip to prevent the gown touching the client's skin.

Work safely and hygienically

Hygienic working practices are covered in detail in Chapter 1. The points below are specific to providing shaving services.

- Check tools prior to service, ensuring they are clean and sterilised and that electrical equipment is safe and fit for purpose, with safe wiring and levelled clipper blades.
- Maintain a clean and tidy work area throughout the service, keeping disinfectant wipes close by to clean hair from workstations.
- Keep your client free from hair clippings during and at the end of service to prevent hair clippings going into his eyes, causing discomfort and risking hair splinters.

- Undertake a full consultation before beginning the service as this will allow you to minimise your client's risk of discomfort and avoid accidents. Inspect the beard using a comb or gloved hands to lift against the directional growth of the hair, as this allows you to check the skin for any contra-indications that may affect the chosen style. Some clients may have razor bumps, facial alopecia, facial moles, scar tissue or acne, and in such cases, the comb should be used with caution to avoid causing discomfort.

PREPARE THE HAIR AND SKIN FOR SHAVING

Preparing the hair and skin for shaving services includes:

- checking and identifying any factors that may limit or affect services
- choosing the correct tools and equipment
- understanding the structure and functions of skin
- recognising scalp and facial skin disorders
- preparing the hair and skin in readiness for the service
- understanding how the function of lathering affects the hair and skin
- understanding how heat affects hair and skin
- understanding the effects of continual close cutting of hair on the skin
- understanding how ageing and environmental factors affect the facial skin and muscle tone.

Influencing factors

Always carry out a full consultation with your client to check for any contra-indications that could prevent the service being carried out.

The diagram below shows the factors that may affect shaving services and which may require you to alter your service.

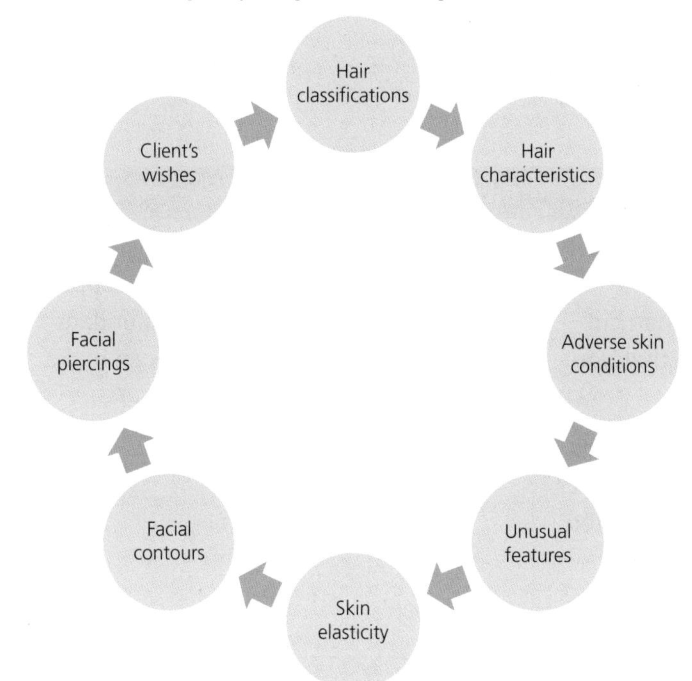

Hair classification

There are different types of hair classification that you will come across when providing shaving services and they are graded depending on the structure of the hair:

- Type 1 – straight hair
- Type 2 – wavy hair
- Type 3 - curly hair
- Type 4 – very curly hair.

For both a clipper shave and wet shave, you will need to consider the following in relation to the hair type:

- Directional growth patterns – these are important and you will need to observe them in order to follow the movement of the hair. (Revisit Chapter 9 for more detail on hair classifications.)
- Density (especially if you are leaving facial hair) – type 3 and 4 hair is likely to be denser than type 1 and 2.
- Products used on the hair and how these will affect the way the hair sits. For example, smoothing products may be used for type 3 and 4 hair.
- Skin challenges – razor bumps, pimples, skin tags, scars and dry or flaky skin (this applies to all hair types).

Type 1 hair can be fine, so hair clippings are more likely to fly about when you are carrying out a clipper shave. Use eye pads to prevent these clippings getting in the client's eyes.

Hair characteristics

There are many hair characteristics that you will come across, and it is important to know these because they will determine which shaving method – clippers or razor – you should use. The hair characteristics that you will need to consider are:

- density
- texture
- growth pattern
- length.

Hair characteristic	Clippers	Razor
Density	Only important if you want to cut facial hair shapes. Identify the sparsest areas first, then cut the abundant areas to match, so that you achieve a uniform look.	Similar method to using clippers. Recommend using the three-step clipper shave prior to using a razor, as abundant hair is strong and coarse which can make shaving difficult.
Texture	Can be challenging to gain a uniform look. Starting with the highest attachment, cut your length down gradually to the desired result. Can also use a clipper over a comb or freehand cutting with clippers/scissors.	Similar method to using clippers.

Hair characteristic	Clippers	Razor
Growth pattern	To avoid client discomfort, you must remove the hair in the direction of hair growth. Be aware of the width of the blade and make sure that you only cut directly with or against the directional hair growth. If combining partial beard shapes with areas of clean face shave, observing the growth pattern can determine which technique is used in order to achieve a uniform look.	The direction of hair growth will determine the direction of the shave. Your first stokes should always be with the directional growth and then against. Different techniques (backhand, freehand and reverse freehand) will be determined by whether you are left- or right-handed.
Length	Combing the hair against the directional growth will allow you to spot any sparse areas. This determines what length you leave the hair in order to cover these areas. Eye pads must be used if the hair is long to prevent hair clippings entering your client's eyes.	You may need to use clippers before a wet razor shave if the hair is long. This is because the hair length may be long enough to hide the facial skin and therefore hide any factors that could hinder the service. The shorter the hair length, the easier it is to use a wet razor.

Adverse skin conditions

Adverse skin and scalp conditions such as psoriasis, cysts, impetigo, scars and moles, infections and infestations can all affect whether a service can be carried out. This is especially true when using razor blades on the skin and if the client's condition is infectious. Some non-infectious conditions do not prevent the service from being carried out but may affect *how* it is carried out. Extra care must be taken to avoid causing discomfort or aggravating a condition.

Refer back to Chapter 2 for more information on the following non-infectious and infectious adverse skin conditions.

- Non-infections conditions:
  - Eczema
  - Psoriasis
  - Alopecia
  - Scars
  - Keloids
  - Moles
  - Cysts
  - Skin tags.
- Infectious skin conditions and infestations:
  - Ringworm/tinea captitis
  - Impetigo
  - Folliculitis
  - In grown hair
  - Scabies.

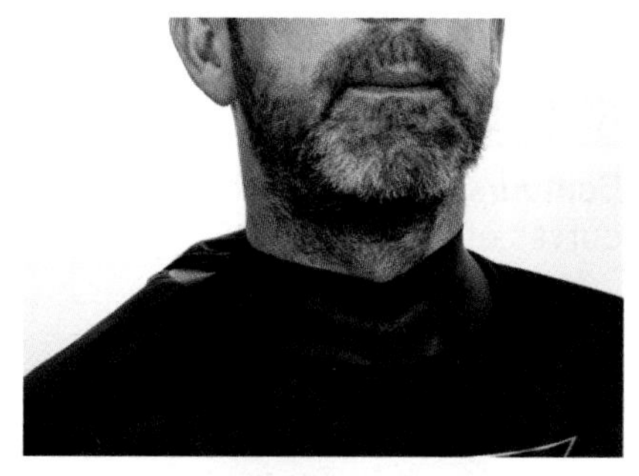

▲ Coarse, dense hair

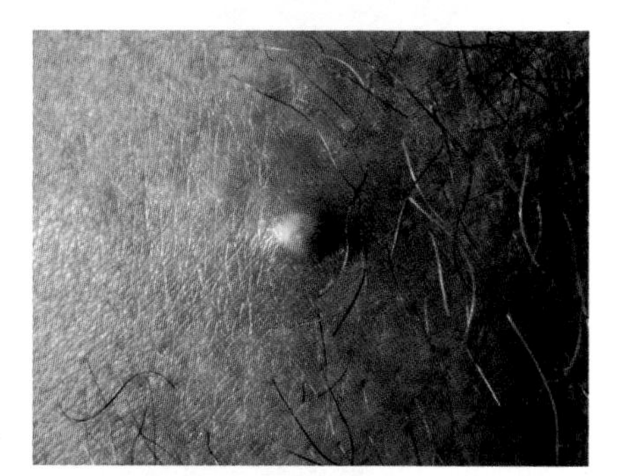

▲ Infectious conditions

HANDY HINT

You will look at recognising scalp and facial hair disorders later in this chapter.

KEY TERM

Philtrum – the area between your nose and your mouth which is formed by two ridges/lines and a valley.

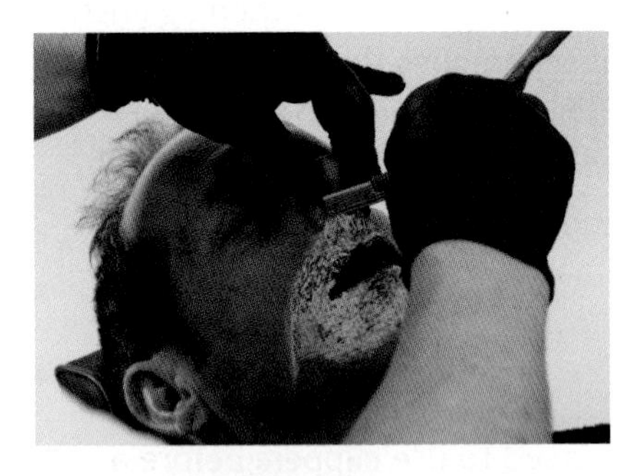

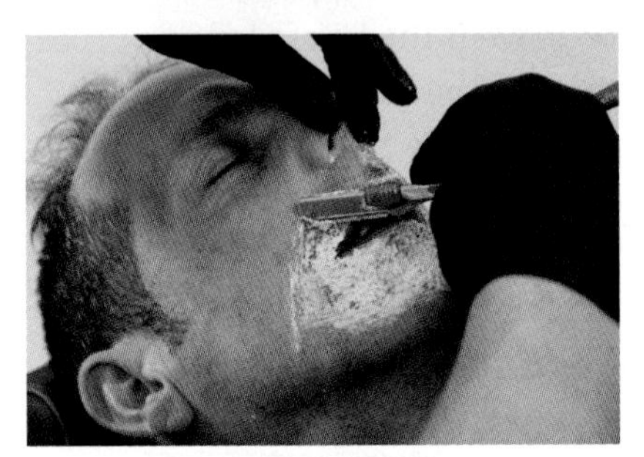

KEY TERM

Contours – outlines, shapes and curves of the face.

▲ You need to consider the facial contours – particularly on a square face with a chiselled jawline

▲ Facial piercings in the philtrum

HEALTHY AND SAFETY

Shaving services must not be carried out on skin that is infectious or on clients with infestations.

Skin elasticity

Good skin elasticity is preferable when shaving because it lends itself to a better and smoother shave, giving the client more comfort throughout the service. Using a good moisturising shaving gel will nourish the skin and improve elasticity by retaining moisture.

Unusual features

When carrying out wet shaving services you will work all around the mouth and lip area, the nose and **philtrum** area, the chin, cheeks and neckline including around the Adam's apple. If any of these areas are unusually large or small and misshaped you must adapt the service or shaving angle to suit.

HEALTH AND SAFETY

Take care when shaving around the philtrum: gently lift the nose straight up and stretch it slightly, then shave downwards.

HEALTH AND SAFETY

Take care at the lip area and lift the blade upwards and over the lip area. Glide the razor diagonally downwards, following the line of the lip.

Facial contours

The facial **contours** must be taken into consideration when choosing a shaving method for a client. It can be challenging, as there are lots of factors that can determine which method is best, due to the elasticity of the skin, body fat and bone structure. The more angular the bone structure, the more the skin is stretched, resulting in a smoother shave.

Facial piercings and tattoos

Piercings and fresh tattoos can present a challenge for razor and clipper shaving, as both can disrupt a clean shave. Piercings should be removed before a shave, where possible. If there is a fresh tattoo in the shaving area, it is not advisable to shave until it has fully healed.

Hair growth rate

The average rate of hair growth is 12.5 mm per month. If a client shaves quite regularly, then the rate of hair growth can change and it will grow back more quickly. A typical client could be shaving once a week to stay clean shaven but over time will find that he has to shave more frequently, maybe every two days. Many men have to shave every day.

Client wishes

Along with all the above factors to consider, your client's requirements and wishes are equally important. You need to find out exactly what your client would like, particularly if you are combining a partial beard with a clean shaved area. If you are carrying out a full shaving service, ask your client if he has time to repeat this service regularly or if he intends to maintain his own shaving in-between salon visits.

Use and maintenance of cutting tools and equipment

Along with scissors, clippers and trimmers mentioned in Chapters 5 and 9, you will use balding clippers and open blade razors with detachable blades for a shaving service.

HEALTH AND SAFETY

Refer to Chapters 5 and 9 for a reminder of the correct use and maintenance of cutting tools and equipment.

Balding clippers

Balding clippers are just that – clippers that create a bald finish. These clippers are popular for haircuts such as skin fades, but are also a very useful tool for removing facial hair to a bald finish.

Most balding clippers come with a blade that cannot be adjusted with a lever and top and bottom teeth that are virtually parallel – this means they are very sharp, so extreme care must be taken.

Some clipper companies manufacture clippers with changeable blade heads, rather than using clipper attachments. Rather than 'grades' that clipper attachments have, these blade heads are labelled with zeros, to show how short they are: 000, 0000, 00000 or 3x0, 4x0, 5x0, for example. A 6 zero blade will provide the shortest of shaves, while a 1 zero blade is just like a normal clipper blade head. These blade heads also come with grade 1 and 1A to help blend the bald fades into hair growth and work just like clipper grade attachments 1 and 1.5.

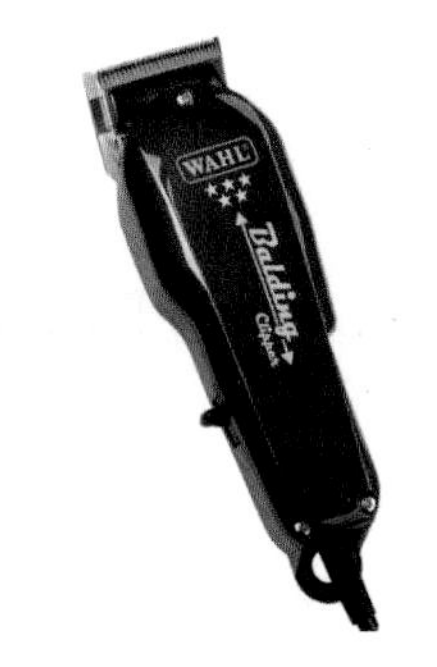

▲ Balding clippers

As a guide these lengths are:

000 blade – 0.5mm

0000 blade – 0.25mm

000000 blade – 0.2mm

When shaving, the look you wish to achieve will determine the blade you need to use. Clipper shaving requires either a 4 zero, 5 zero or 6 zero blade. Deciding which one should be used will depend on skin sensitivity and how coarse or thick the client's facial hair is. Beard outlining requires a 3, 5 or 6 zero blade, depending on the length of the hair. The shorter the hair, the more likely you may need a 5 or 6 zero blade in order to achieve a close shave.

Open blade razors with disposable blades

A wide variety of open blade razors with detachable blades are available. They all look quite similar and follow the same design principles, as shown in the diagram.

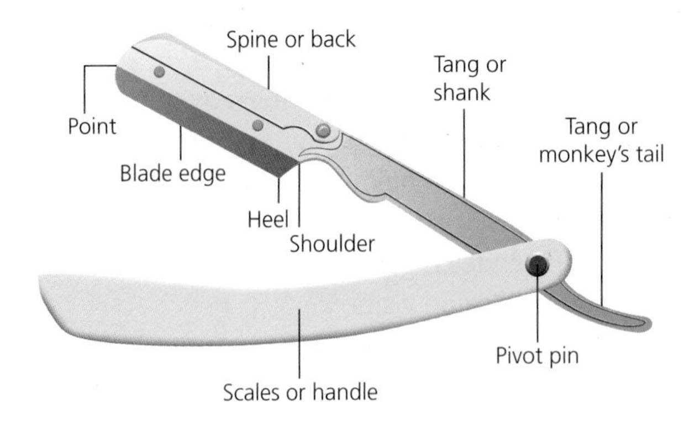

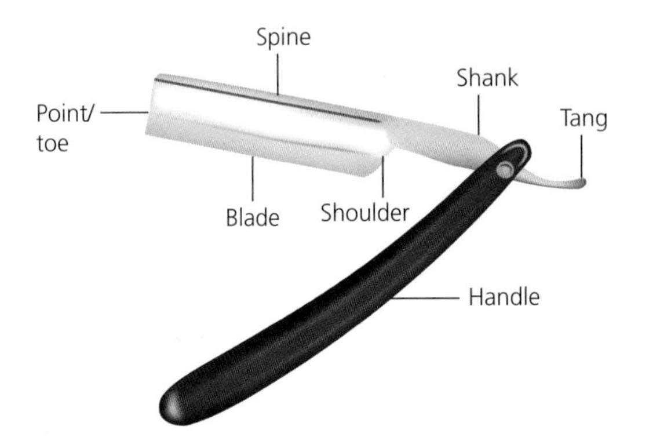

▲ Open blade razor

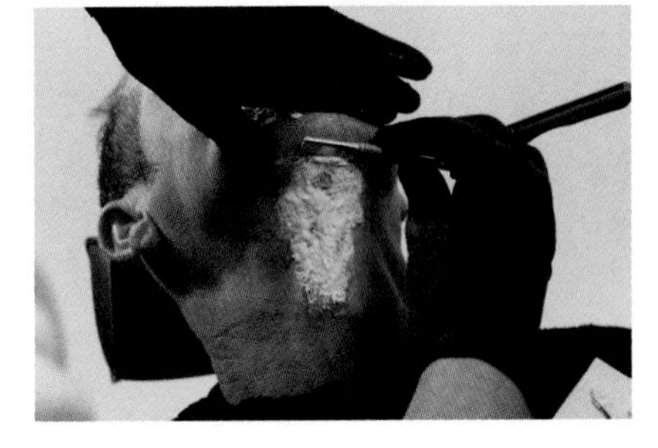

▲ Hold the razor correctly

To hold an open blade razor with detachable blades:

- open the spine or back of the blade and move the handle on the pivot pin ¾ of the way round (270°)
- rest your thumb and first two fingers either side of the spine, finger three on the shank, with the handle poking up between fingers three and four
- rest your little finger on the 'Tang' or Monkey's tail for support and balance.

Once the new disposable blade is positioned into place the blade edge is held against the skin at about 30°.

Preparing an open blade razor with disposal blade for use

- Visually inspect the razor's overall condition and suitability for use.
- Sterilise the whole razor – body and handle area – after every service.
- Carefully fit a new disposable blade for every client.
- Carefully store the razor and the spare blades in a sterile safe environment until you are ready to use it.
- Dispose of the old blades in a sharps container.

Structure and function of skin

The skin is the largest organ in your body – it protects the body from extremes in temperature and attack from foreign bodies. There are three main layers of skin:

- epidermis
- dermis
- subcutaneous layer (or hypodermis).

Epidermis layer

The epidermis is the outer layer of skin. It is the layer where hair comes out of the skin and it is made up of five layers:

- Stratum corneum – protective outer layer of horny cells which are replaced every month.
- Stratum lucidum – a clear layer which is only present when the skin is at its thickest.
- Stratum granulosum – contains the protein keratin.
- Stratum spinosum – the layer where new cells are pushed up from the **basale layer**; these cells have a role in the immune system of the skin.
- Stratum germinativum – the base layer of the epidermis where new cells are produced; this layer also contains the skin's natural pigment, melanin.

The epidermis acts as a barrier to protect the body against **microbial pathogens,** oxidant stress (UV light) and chemical compounds. It also provides mechanical resistance in the form of a physical barrier made up of **keratinocytes** bonded together to give the epidermis its strength.

The skin has a natural pH of 4.5–5.5 but any imbalances such as a more acidic pH (around 4.0) or a lack of hydration can make the skin hostile to many **micro-organic** pathogens. This means that it is crucial to give the client good advice about the correct aftercare in order to maintain the healthy functioning of their skin.

KEY TERM

Basale layer – the deepest layer of the skin.

KEY TERMS

Microbial pathogen – a pathogen is a type of microbe, such as a bacteria or virus, which has the potential to cause harm.

Keratinocytes – these produce keratin, an insoluble protein which makes the cell more resilient.

Micro-organic – relating to a tiny living cell (for example, an infection) which can only be seen under a microscope.

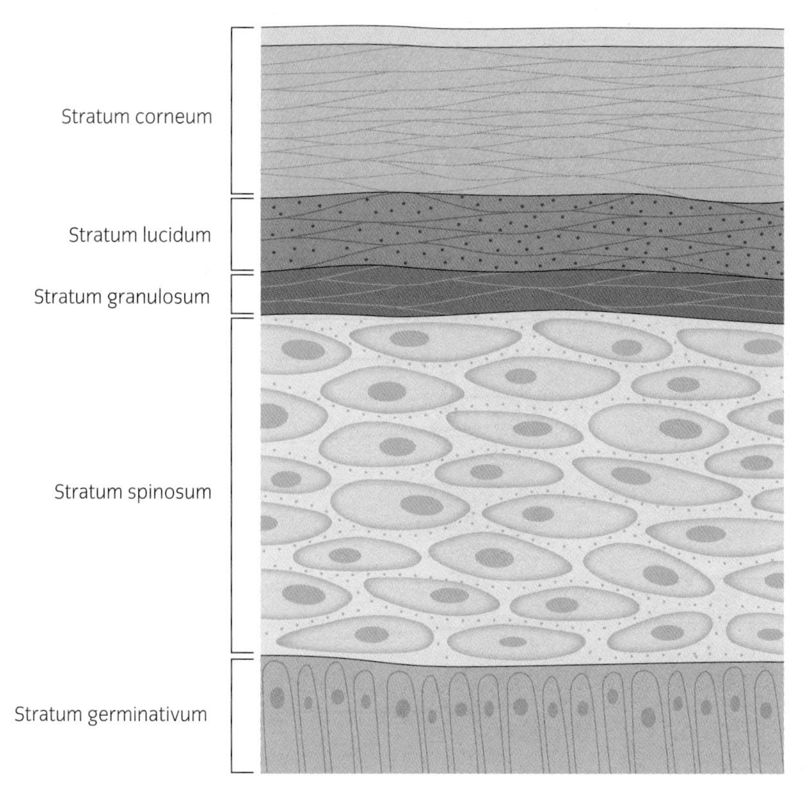

▲ The five layers of the epidermis

Dermis layer

The dermis layer is 3–5 mm thick and lies beneath the epidermis. The dermis has a high water content and contains blood vessels, sweat glands, nerve endings and sebaceous glands. The hair follicle is formed in this layer.

The main functions of the dermis are to:

- provide strength and flexibility – the skin's elasticity
- provide a system of capillaries which nourish the cells of the lower layers of the epidermis and remove waste products
- control temperature and blood pressure.

Subcutaneous layer

The subcutaneous layer, often referred to as the hypodermis, is the deepest layer of the skin. It is mostly responsible for regulating body temperature. This layer mainly consists of **adipose tissue** which is made up of a layer of fat cells. It acts as a cushion to protect vital organs and bones from minor injuries and provides some thermal insulation. The thickness of this layer varies, depending on the person's gender and age, and the area of the body.

KEY TERM

Adipose tissue – cells that store energy as fat.

Muscles of the face

The muscles of our face define our features. They give us expression and show our age. You will find it particularly helpful to know the location and action of each muscle during shaving treatments.

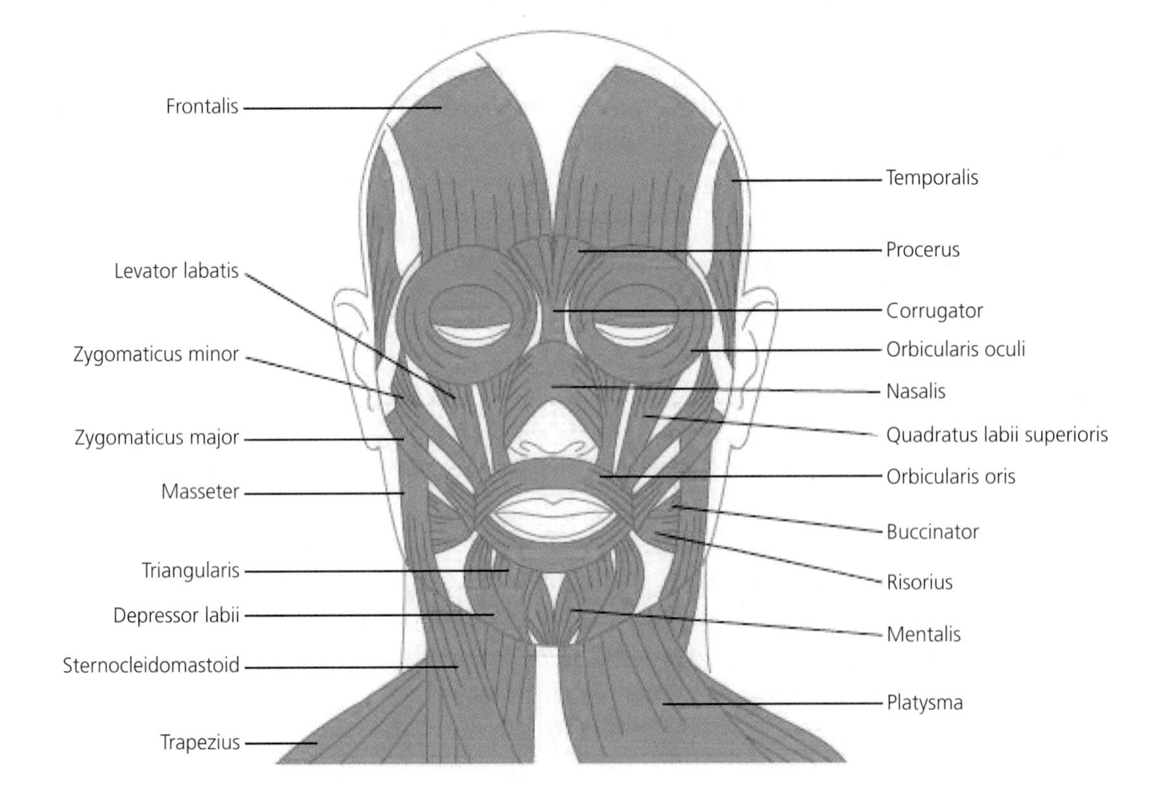

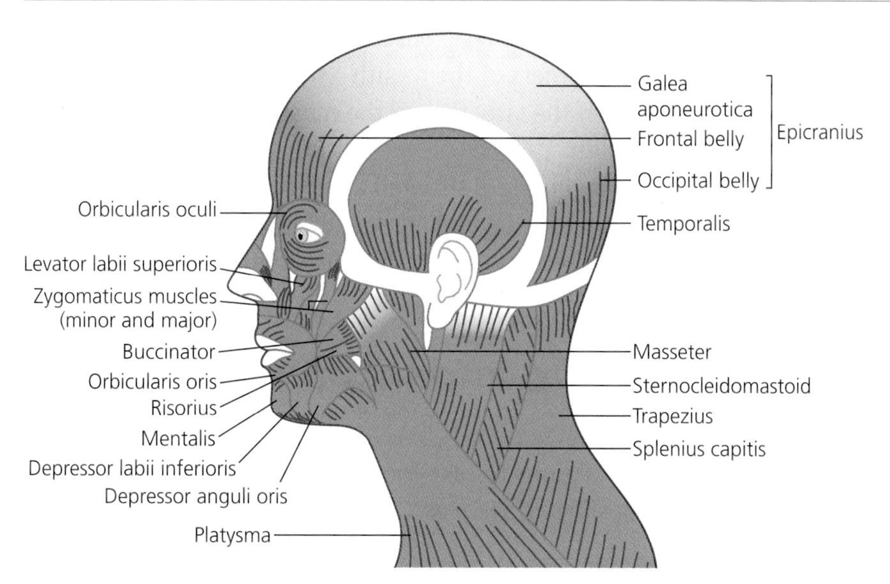

▲ Muscles of the face and head

- Frontalis – this muscle is located at the front of the head. It is responsible for facial expressions, such as raising the eyebrows and frowning by wrinkling the forehead.
- Temporalis – also known as the temporal muscle, this muscle covers the side of the head, stretching to the mandible (jaw). It raises the mandible during chewing.
- Corrugator – this muscle sits in between the eyebrows. It is close to the eye, just below the frontalis. It moves the eyebrows down and is associated with frowning and showing sadness or stress.
- Orbicularis oculi – this muscle surrounds the eye socket and is responsible for closing the eyelids.
- Procerus – this muscle is found in between the brows, extending down towards the nasal bone. It pulls the eyebrows down into a frown, causing the horizontal line that you can see in the forehead. It also aids the flaring of the nostrils.
- Nasalis – this muscle crosses the bridge of the nose. It is a strong muscle, as it is made up of many different types of muscles known as sphincters. These are generally tight and are constantly flexed. They give the structural part of the nose its shape. It also aids in the flaring of the nostrils.
- Quadratus labii superioris – this muscle is found at the sides of the upper lip. Its main function is to retract and lift the upper lip.
- Orbicularis oris – this is the muscle that surrounds the orifice of the mouth. It is also known as the 'kissing' muscle, due to the fact that it is used to pucker up the lips.
- Buccinator – this muscle aids the motion of chewing by squeezing the cheeks together. This keeps food in a suitable place in order to be broken down by the teeth.
- Risorius – this muscle can be found at the corners of the mouth. It draws back the angle of the mouth, allowing us to smile.
- Mentalis – this muscle is located just beneath the lower lip and aids in the expression of doubt and displeasure by wrinkling the chin area. Together with the orbicularis, this muscle also helps the lips to pout.

- Zygomaticus major/minor – these muscles can be found along the cheek. They raise the corners of the mouth when smiling upwards and laterally. Depending on the structure of the muscle, they can also be responsible for dimples.
- Masseter – this strong muscle is situated along the sides of the face. It is responsible for raising the lower jaw (mandible) and helps us chew food. This muscle can appear larger in those that habitually clench, grind their teeth or chew a lot of gum.

Recognise scalp and facial skin disorders

The table describes the actions to take for skin disorders you may come across when providing shaving services.

Skin disorder	Recognised by	Action
Sensitive skin	Skin that may be dry or broken.	The client should be recommended a course of facials to repair the skin prior to shaving. Using a good shaving gel will help improve the elasticity of the skin by replacing some moisture content and nourishment.
Comedones	Blocked follicles often found around the forehead or chin – black heads (open comedones) or white heads (closed comedones).	Comedones need be taken into consideration – both black and white heads should be approached with caution and avoided if possible. There are other shaving options that can be used for these areas which will not cause damage, such as an electric foil mesh shaver.
Milia	Milia are very small, raised, pearly-white or yellowish bumps on the skin. They are often found on the skin around the cheeks, nose, eyes and eyelids.	Milia are firm and squeezing has little to no impact on them. Unlike acne, these bumps can show up around the eyes and on parts of the face where there are no active oil glands. Milia are not painful in the way that acne is (where a pimple forms and then becomes inflamed and sore). Take care when shaving as milia can easily be cut.
Dehydrated skin	Dehydrated skin is very dry and can easily turn into broken skin.	Be very vigilant, as shaving broken skin can damage the epidermis even further and could easily cut the skin. If the skin is broken, facial treatments are recommended prior to a razor shaving service.

Skin disorder	Recognised by	Action
Broken capillaries	Broken blood vessels	Broken capillaries are more common in clients with fair skin than in people with a dark or olive complexion. People with dry and dehydrated skin, as well as very sensitive skin, have thinner and less protected layers of tissue, making them more susceptible to this problem. Advise your client not to scrub their face if they have broken blood vessels, as this can cause them to spread. Razor shaving is not recommended and you should suggest the client seeks the advice of a dermatologist.
Papules	Elevated parts of the skin resembling a bump but with no visible fluid.	Papules are elevated parts of the skin resembling a bump but with no visible fluid. They can open when scratched and become easily infected.
Open pores	Often associated with oily skin, pores expand when they are clogged.	Open pores do not usually affect a shave but some clients will be more sensitive to products on their skin than others. During your consultation, you should always check whether the client has noticeably open pores. It would be advisable to test some of your shaving products on the skin surface to check for irritation.
Hyperpigmentation	A patch of skin that is darker than the surrounding skin.	Hyperpigmentation can be caused by excess sun exposure or be the result of acne where the skin has broken and healed. Shaving should be fine in these cases but always check for skin sensitivity before razor shaving.
Hypopigmentation	A patch of skin that has less melanin so looks paler than the surrounding skin.	Hypopigmentation cannot affect a razor shave unless it is an extreme case, for example, when a scab has peeled off from a wound. If the scab is removed before the wound has healed, it will cause the skin to become too sensitive or fragile for razor shaving.

Skin disorder	Recognised by	Action
Dermatosis papulosa nigra	More common in dark-skinned clients, these are small raised bumps (similar to papules) on the skin that appear to be more like very dark, hardened spots.	Can be cut easily so caution must be taken when shaving.
Pseudofolliculitis	Razor bumps – also known as barber's itch.	This condition is common in dark-skinned clients and can cause ingrown hairs. It is advisable not to shave these areas but allow them to grow and treat the skin with facials. To avoid irritation, use a clipper rather than a razor to shave and adjust the blade to ensure it is not set too close.
Keloids	Keloids are an overgrown area of rubbery scar tissue, larger than the original wound. Often found in those with darker skin, due to the speed of their skin rejuvenation.	Keloids can form if you continue shaving over razor bumps, which will cause irritation, infection and scar tissue. Avoid shaving completely in these areas and advise your client to seek the help of a dermatologist immediately.

HANDY HINT

Shaving with an electric foil shaver will be far less damaging to the skin than a razor.

HEALTH AND SAFETY

It is not advisable to clipper shave or razor shave when the skin has papules but if required, then extreme caution is a must!

HANDY HINT

Make sure the towel is wet enough but not dripping wet – it needs to be more than just damp.

Prepare the face and facial hair prior to shaving

Prepare the client's face for the wet shave by using pre-heated hot towels. If your client's hair is coarse then the towel will need to be wetter and hotter than for a client with fine beard hair, to allow the moisture to penetrate into the beard hair.

HEALTH AND SAFETY

When the hot towel is in place, always check the temperature of the towel is not too hot and that your client is comfortable.

After a few minutes but before the towel completely cools down, remove it and apply an exfoliating product using effleurage massage to remove the dead skin cells. Continue to massage firmly, using petrissage massage techniques to warm the muscles and to lift the hairs.

A second hot towel should then be applied to remove the exfoliator product and to ensure the hairs are adequately lifted. Massage oil is then applied using petrissage and tapotement massage techniques to wake up the skin and encourage hairs to stand up ready for shaving. Apply a third hot towel for up to one minute, before removing in readiness for the shaving service to start.

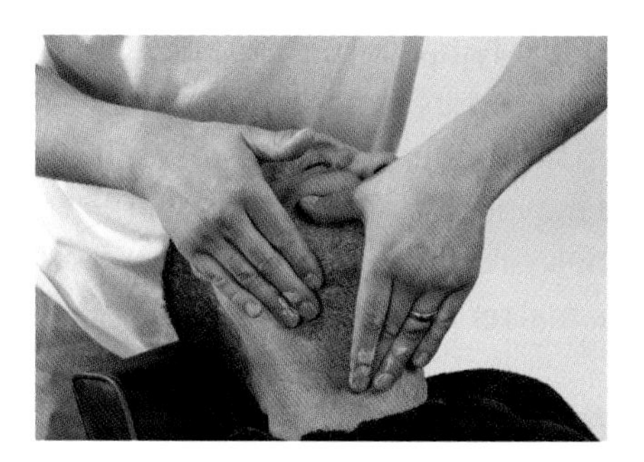

▲ Use effleurage to apply exfoliator before petrissage to warm the muscles

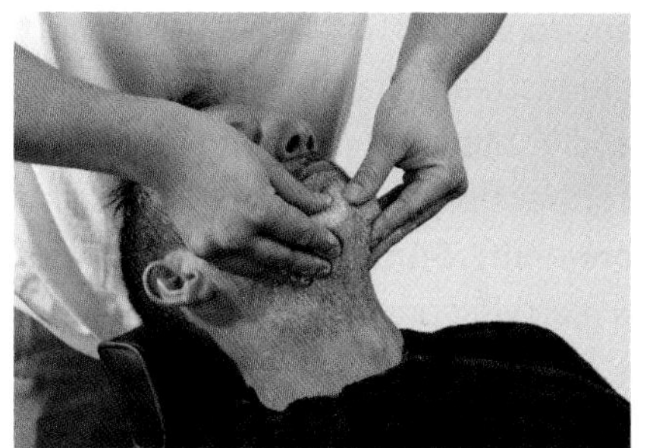

▲ Use tapotement massage with oil to encourage the hairs to stand up before shaving

HANDY HINT

Always remove the hot towels just before they cool down so the pores do not begin to close again.

HANDY HINT

Adding fragrance to the water before heating the towels, or spraying fragrance onto hot towels, can have added benefits for the client. Use lavender scent for relaxation, lemon for a crisp, fresh, citrus burst or menthol for cooling effects.

▲ Lather the cream or gel in the bowl using a brush

The barber's preferred shaving product is then prepared and lathered in a bowl with the brush. Apply the lathering cream with a brush in a circular motion, going against the hair growth to lift the hairs up. Massaging the lathering cream with your fingers will also help lift the hairs. As some lathering creams dry quickly, you may need to add more water and re-apply the cream if it starts to dry on the face during the service.

HANDY HINT

Shaving cream or gel can be used. Gel is good to use as it is clearer and you can see where you are working.

Effects of lathering on the skin and hair

The lathering of the products before a shave not only prepares the facial hair for the service but also improves blood flow to the surrounding areas.

HANDY HINT

Squeeze the brush flat between your fingers and thumb to narrow the brush for applying the lathering product to the thin moustache area.

Functions of the blood and lymph

Blood

The main function of the blood is to:

- regulate body temperature
- maintain a constant pH and water balance
- transport digested food, respiratory gases and waste material.

Lymph

Lymph is a pale milky-coloured fluid that is made up of approximately 95 per cent water and 5 per cent lymphocyte cells. Lymph is also known as tissue fluid as it bathes the tissues of the body. It is formed from plasma seeping out of the blood capillaries and contains substances that are too large to pass through the blood capillary walls, such as debris from areas of infection and cells damaged by disease.

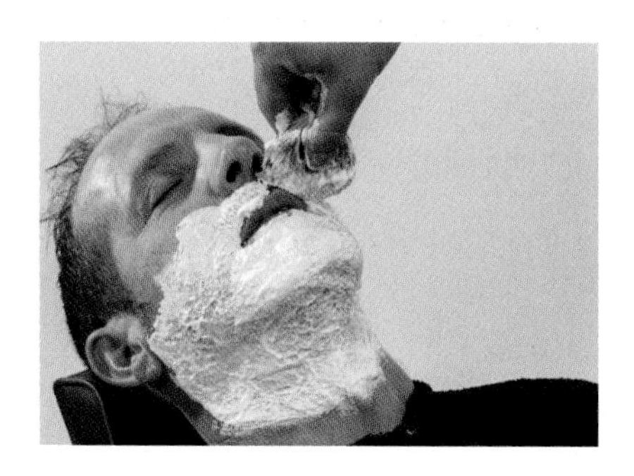

Lymph transfers nutrients such as food, oxygen and water, and collects waste, such as urea and carbon dioxide. It creates the essential environment that cells need to survive. Most lymph returns to the bloodstream via the capillary walls, but the rest becomes lymphocytes and enters the lymphatic system. Lymph moves very slowly as a result of contraction of the skeletal muscles and movement of the thorax during breathing. Some of the functions of lymph circulation include:

- carrying protein and large particulate matter away from tissues
- redistributing fluid in the body
- removing bacteria, toxins and other foreign bodies from the tissues
- maintaining the structural and functional integrity of tissue
- enforcing an immune response in the body
- producing and maturing lymphocytes
- absorbing end-products of digestion.

Effect of massage on blood flow and pulse rate

The condition of the skin improves when the blood and lymph get rid of toxins in the skin and muscles. Facial muscle massage and steaming can encourage the lymph to carry away toxins and blood to help release toxins through the skin.

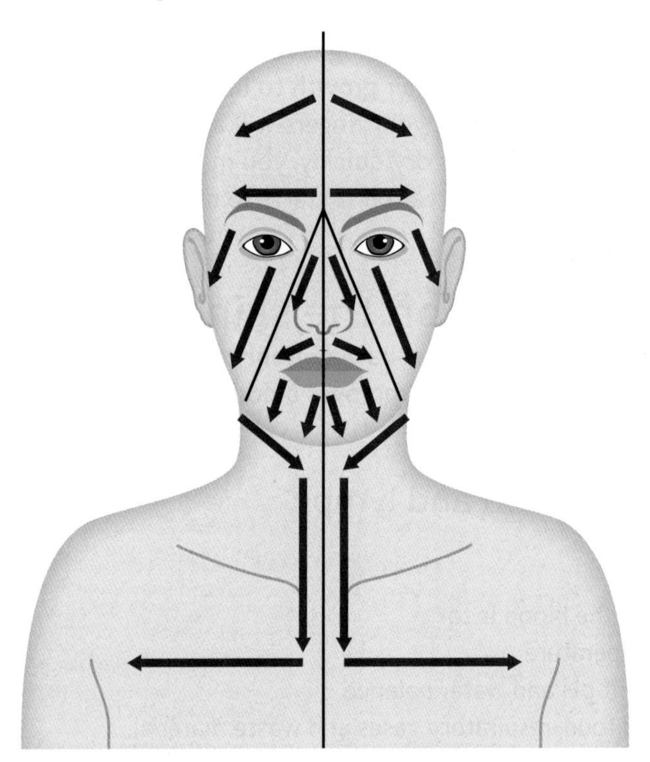

▲ Lymph drainage

Massage facilitates the circulation of blood around the body because the pressure created by the massage technique actually moves the blood through the congested areas. The release of this same pressure causes new blood to flow in. The squeezing and pulling motions of massage also flush lactic acid out from the muscles and improve the circulation of the lymph fluid which carries metabolic waste away from muscles and internal organs. This results in lower blood pressure and improved body function.

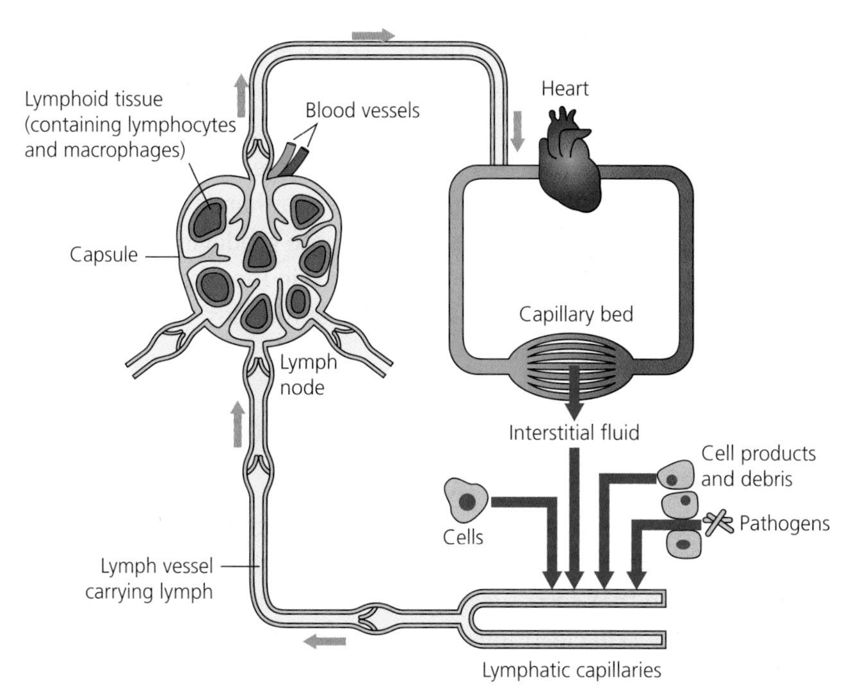

▲ Process of lymph drainage during massage

A good way to help the lymph circulate around the body is to have the client breathe in slowly and deeply during the massage. Lymph drainage massage takes place on a massage table, using oil to lubricate the skin, although it is not always necessary to use oil. In order to perform this form of massage, it is important to remember the following:

- Make sure you apply the correct pressure – firm enough that you do not slide over the skin but light enough that you do not feel the tissue below the skin. Be careful not to push too hard, as this may cause the initial lymphatic flow to stop.
- Always push the lymph towards the correct nodes. This will ensure efficient drainage of the lymph.
- Use an appropriate rhythm. This is very important in order for the initial lymphatic nodes to be opened and then be allowed to shut, so that the lymph can properly drain. An appropriate rhythm will also stimulate the parasympathetic nervous system, allowing the client to relax.
- Make sure that you use a proper sequence and order the strokes appropriately. Always start near the node that you are draining, then move further and further away, but always push the fluid back in the direction of the node. By doing this, you clear a path for the lymph to move, as well as creating a 'suction' effect that draws the lymph to the node.
- Leave the 'smoothing' or 'finishing' stroke until last. It is performed by slowly and gently stroking over the entire section that you have just worked on. This may be over an area that is only an inch or less (for example, on the face and neck).

Effects of heat on hair and skin

When you use hot towels directly onto the skin, the pores in the skin are opened and the facial hair is softened. The heat assists the shaving product to lather and swell, as well as helping to soften the facial hair or beard. Massaging with the shaving brush and your hands creates heat which helps to stimulate the sebaceous glands into producing oil, which in turn helps the razor stroke and glide over the skin more smoothly. The massage also relaxes the client and the facial muscles, which makes tensioning and shaving smoother.

Effects of continual close cutting of hair on the skin

Continual razor shaving on the face can cause damage to the epidermis, reducing the naturally occurring oils that moisturise the skin, and leading to breaks in the skin that can cause ingrown hairs. Problems can also be caused by a poor skin cleansing regime or not exfoliating. Ingrown hairs can be more of a problem for men with darker skin, as their skin rejuvenates faster than those with lighter skin. This means that new skin can easily grow over the older layers, preventing hair from growing freely and thus causing a bump which may form pseudofolliculitis.

Keloids are formed when the skin is not treated in the early stages of razor bumps and pseudofolliculitis. Razor shaving in these conditions will inevitably worsen the condition and, if left untreated, may lead to keloids.

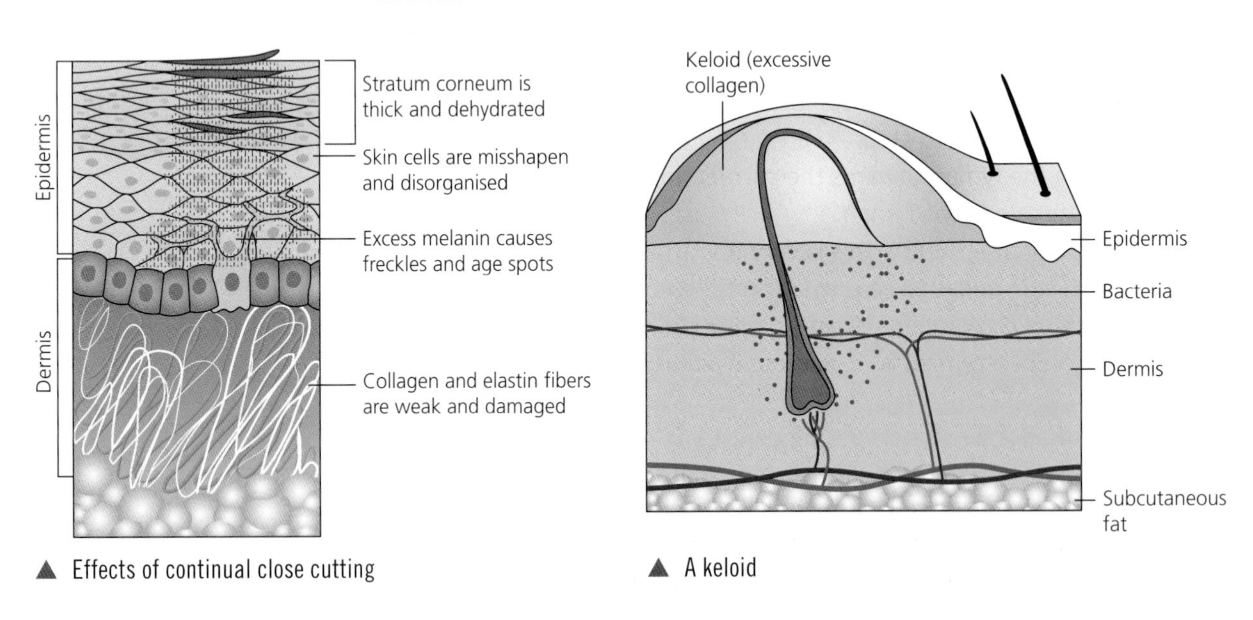

▲ Effects of continual close cutting

▲ A keloid

Ageing and environmental factors

Both natural ageing (which is outside of our control) and environmental and lifestyle factors (many of which are within our control) have negative effects on the skin and muscle tone.

Effects of the natural ageing process

As the skin ages, the number of melanocytes in the skin decreases and the epidermis becomes thinner and paler. The process of the skin losing its strength and elasticity is called **elastosis**. This is more noticeable in sun-exposed areas of the skin, because the sun's rays cause a leathery, weather-beaten appearance, common in people who spend more time outdoors. The sebaceous glands produce less oil as we age, making it harder for the skin to remain moist. The blood supply also decreases, along with fat tissue, making it less efficient at keeping the body warm and healing the body from injuries such as bruising.

A gradual reduction in muscle strength and mass occurs as we age and is called **sarcopenia**. **Metabolism** also slows down with age and, together, this means that a person will burn fewer calories. This is because our muscles help to burn calories and as we age, muscle loss means we are less efficient at burning calories. As we grow older, we need to change our calorie intake to avoid gaining weight.

KEY TERMS

Elastosis – the process by which skin loses strength and elasticity.

Sarcopenia – reduction of muscle mass and strength associated with the ageing process.

Metabolism – chemical transformations within living cells.

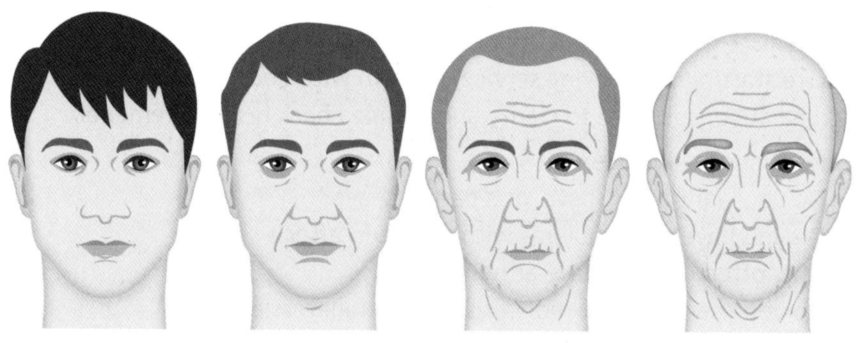

▲ How faces age over time

Effect of environmental and lifestyle factors on the condition of the skin

There are many reasons why skin damage may occur. These include:

- too much exposure to the sun
- artificial light (sunbeds)
- heat and steam
- excessive alcohol
- smoking.

Skin damage may result in the skin ageing prematurely, causing lines and wrinkles due to the breakdown of collagen and elastin which support the skin. Uneven pigmentation may also occur. In many cases, the leading cause of ageing skin is dehydration. Skin can also become dehydrated as a result of exposure to central heating (which can cause over-activity of the sebaceous glands) as well as from applying products containing harsh chemicals or from a lack of essential nutrients due to an unbalanced diet.

HANDY HINT

Avoid using heavy oils on the face immediately before and after exercising, as this can cause blocked pores due to sweat and sebum being unable to escape onto the skin surface. If this happens, the skin will feel lumpy or coarse.

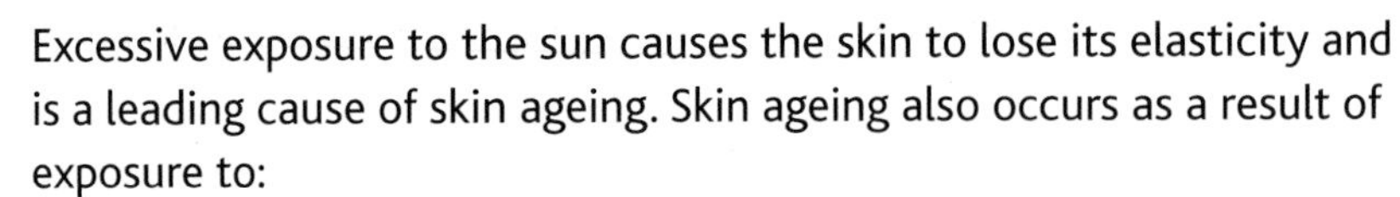

Excessive exposure to the sun causes the skin to lose its elasticity and is a leading cause of skin ageing. Skin ageing also occurs as a result of exposure to:

- wind
- cold
- artificial environments such as air conditioning
- pollution from the natural environment, such as traffic exhaust fumes and thinning of the protective ozone layer.

If the skin is exposed to these environments, over time they may cause contamination of the skin, clogged and blocked pores, irritations, allergic reactions and a tendency to comedones and oversensitivity.

SHAVE HAIR AND APPLY FINISHING PRODUCTS

When carrying out shaving services barbers wear black gloves, so the client cannot see any tiny specs of blood caused from razor bumps.

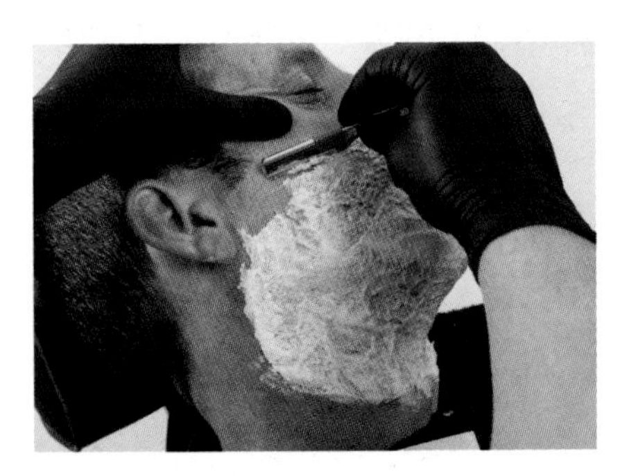

▲ Black barbering gloves

Importance of questioning clients

Before starting the shaving service, confirm with your client the look agreed at consultation to clarify and double check his requirements.

Questions may include:

- Do you want a full shave, or a partial shave?
- Do you have any problems with your skin after a shave?
- How often do you shave at home?
- Do you use any facial moisturisers or exfoliators at home?

Prepare the face and facial hair prior to shaving

Preparation is very important in a shaving service. For the client, it can have an impact on their overall experience and helps prepare their skin and hair to prevent discomfort. It provides you with an opportunity to promote extra services and products and aids your technical performance.

To prepare the face and facial hair for the shaving service you may need to remove beard length first. Remove the beard length using clippers and 0.5 grade as this allows you to carefully check for skin tags and moles prior to using the razor on the skin.

Preparation can include the application of a hot towel to open the pores and relax the client, a pre-shave balm, exfoliator, cleanser or shampoo.

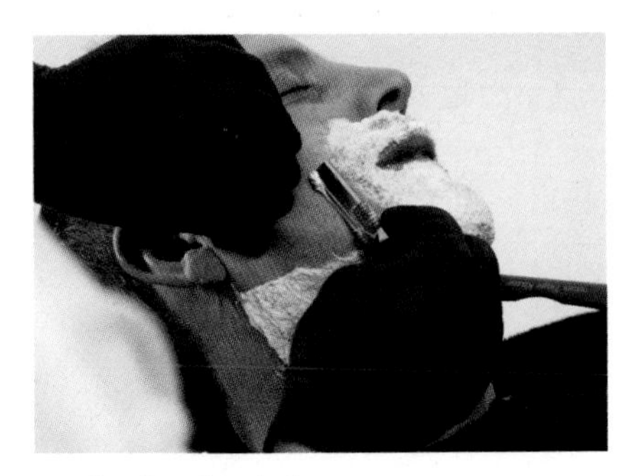

▲ Forehand technique

Apply correct technique during shaving services

To carry out the service you will need to know:

- how to carry out different shaving techniques
- why skin needs to be tensioned during shaving

- the importance of working in a way which maintains the right skin temperature throughout the shaving process
- the importance of adapting shaving techniques in relation to the direction of hair growth
- why and when to use brush and massage techniques to apply lathering products
- why and when to use sponge shaving
- reasons for and effects of using cool towels after shaving.

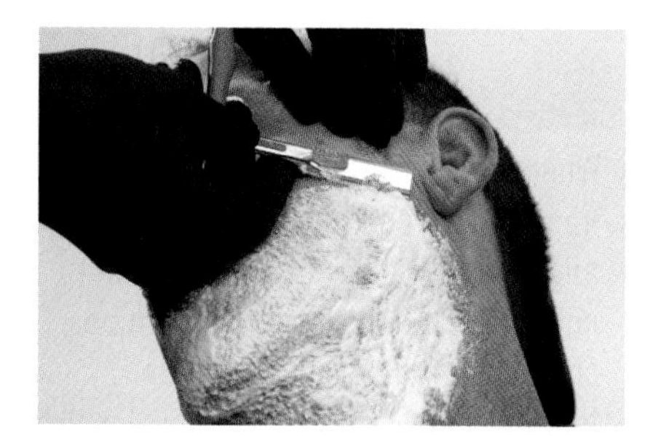

▲ Backhand technique

Carry out different shaving techniques

There are several techniques that you can use for shaving services, but the most commonly used are forehand and backhand. In general, you will use your forehand for comfort and, depending on whether you are left- or right-handed, you may need to use backhand strokes on the opposite side of your client's face.

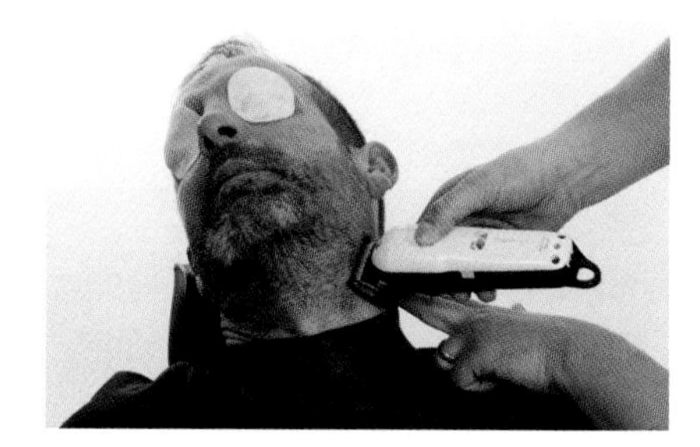

▲ Apply tension to the skin as you clipper the hair to remove length

Forehand and backhand razoring

Both forehand and backhand razoring are used for a close shave, either against or with the grain, and are dependent on area and angle, which side you are working on and left- or right-handedness.

Backhand techniques can be useful if a person has a very coarse beard as they help to achieve a closer shave. Backhand techniques can help raise the hair up before the razor passes and the hair then drops back into the follicle.

HANDY HINT

Keep the non-shaving area of skin clear of product so you can grip the skin with tension.

Importance of tensioning skin during shaving

Tension facilitates the blade or clippers, avoids cuts and ensures an even shave. It provides a smooth surface for the razor to pass over and prevents creases, which could cause cuts. Use your free hand to stretch the skin before applying the razor.

If you are removing beard hair before shaving, make sure you use the clippers and shave against the hair growth using tension on the skin. Then clipper down to 0 and remove the final length after checking skin condition.

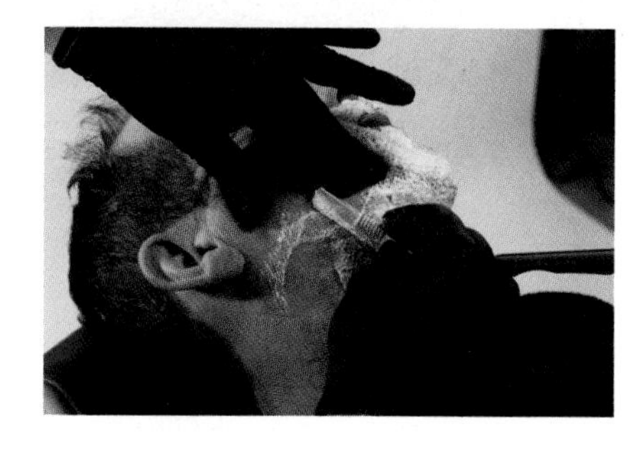

Maintain the right skin temperature throughout the shaving process

Hot towels open the pores of the skin, enabling the facial hair to stand upright and be removed more easily. As skin cools the pores will start to close again, so you must work at a **commercial pace** to remove the facial hair while the pores are still open.

KEY TERM

Commercial pace – industry-recommended time frame for a service; in the case of shaving it is about 20–30 minutes.

Adapt shaving techniques in relation to direction of hair growth

To carry out a clipper shave in the direction of growth follow these steps:

1. Ensure that your clipper is flat to the skin at 0° on the stationary blade and cut against the directional growth.

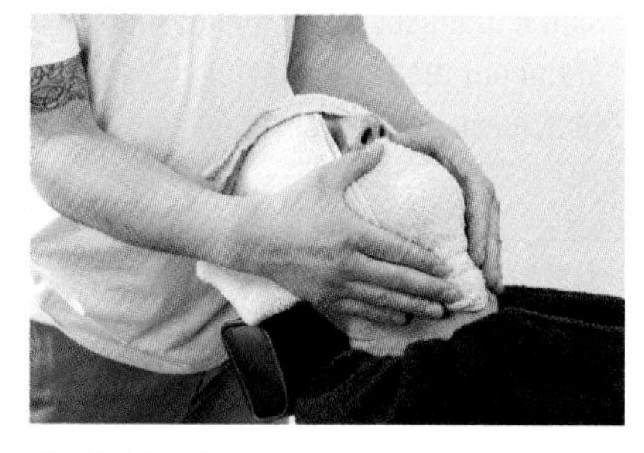

▲ Hot towels

2 With a raised clipper angle of around 45°, continue to shave against the directional growth, having the clipper in the same handling position but this time stretching the skin for a closer cut.
3 Turning the clipper on its point for a closer clipper cut, stretch the skin as much as possible and continue cutting, making sure that you are shaving with and against the directional growth.

When using the razor to shave you must adapt your forehand and backhand techniques to suit the direction of hair growth.

HANDY HINT

When cutting with clippers, it is important to check the clipper blade alignment to make sure that it will not cut the client's skin. This can be checked between your thumb and forefinger.

Brush and massage techniques to apply lathering products

Lathering techniques

Lathering is an essential part of the shaving service because it:

- lubricates the beard
- removes dirt
- makes the hairs stand out from the skin for an easier shave
- opens the pores
- stimulates the sebaceous glands and blood flow
- softens the hair.

Make sure you prepare the lathering products in good time for the service.

When applying soap, vigorously work the shaving brush with warm water into a bar of shaving soap and a mug using a circular motion.

HANDY HINT

Massaging the lathering cream with your gloved fingers will also help lift the hair.

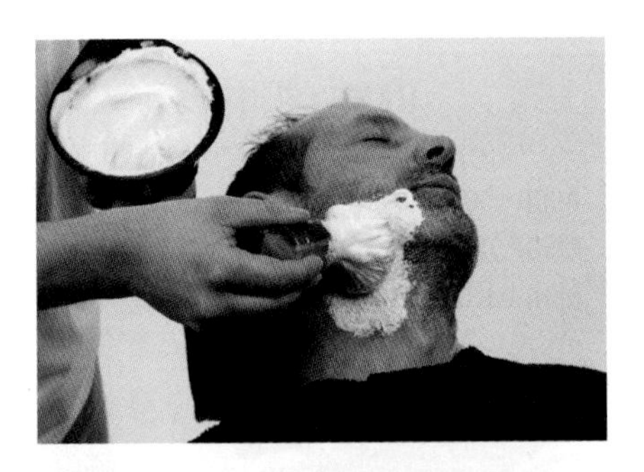

Brushing technique

The bristles of the brush help to push lather under the hair and this makes the hair stand out ready for the shaving services.

Hand technique

If your client wishes to keep their beard a certain shape, then lathering by hand gives you more control to lather thinly and see where you need to stop the razor.

HANDY HINT

If you know a client well, you may offer the hand lathering technique as this is a more personal and informal technique. The hand lathering massage technique will relax some clients, while others may find this technique an invasion of their personal space and too personal.

HANDY HINT

Apply the lathering product over the philtrum area with your fingers, not the brush, to avoid product getting in the client's nostrils or on the lips.

HANDY HINT

When you massage the lather into the beard it softens the hair, relaxes the skin and muscles and makes the hair stand out ready for shaving. Be sure to achieve an even coverage.

Sponge shaving

A sponge shave produces a very close shave. The sponge is wetted in water that is very warm but not so hot that it is uncomfortable for the client. As the sponge is drawn across the skin it lubricates it and lifts the hairs up in readiness for the razor to cut them. With one hand, the barber slowly moves the sponge across the face, maintaining the tension of the skin, and with the other hand the barber follows with the razor, trailing the direction of the sponge closely.

HEALTH AND SAFETY

A new sterile sponge is required for each client when using the sponge technique.

Use cool towels after shaving

At the end of every of part of the service, remove any excess oil, cream or soap from the skin.

The actions of applying products, lathering, massage and shaving will irritate the skin and the body will try to fight this because it will assume there is a risk of infection. As the blood capillaries work hard to fight off the expected infection the face gets very warm, so applying a cool towel will reduce this heat and slow the capillary action.

By finishing the service with the application of a cool towel over the face, you return the skin back to its normal temperature quickly, maintain client comfort, close the pores and reduce the risk of infection.

Using a facial toner and massaging in a vitamin E moisturiser help revive skin by improving its elasticity and vitality.

HANDY HINT

Remember: after any shaving services remove all lathering products.

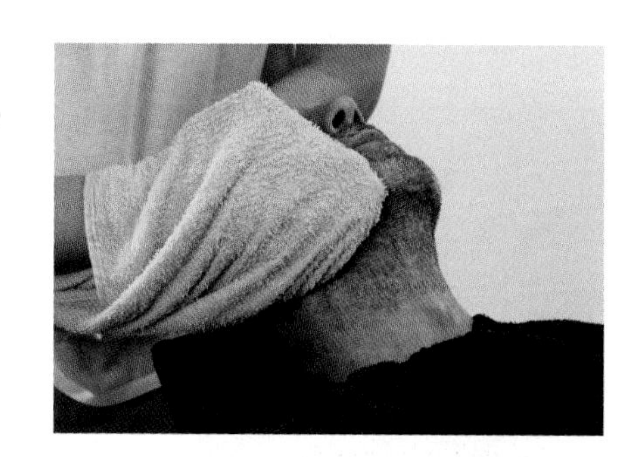

Facial massage techniques

Benefits and effects of facial massage

Massage can help to prepare the client's skin before shaving. If their skin is dry, massaging shaving gel before lathering can moisturise the skin, as well as help you determine the client's facial beard shape. This will help you to achieve a more accurate shave. The benefits of massage include stimulation of the muscles, glands and nerves. The massage increases blood flow and keeps the muscles in the face warm, aiding the shaving process.

Avoid use of cold towels before a facial massage

A face massage is a beneficial service to carry out after the shaving service, as the skin is soft and supple, and the muscles are still warm. You must not use cool towels before a massage as the temperature of the skin and muscles will be cooled down too much and the effects will be counter-productive.

Massage techniques

You will use different massage techniques around zones of the face.

The 'T' - zone goes across the forehead and down the nose.

The 'U' - zone goes down one side of the cheeks, across the chin and back up the other side of the cheeks.

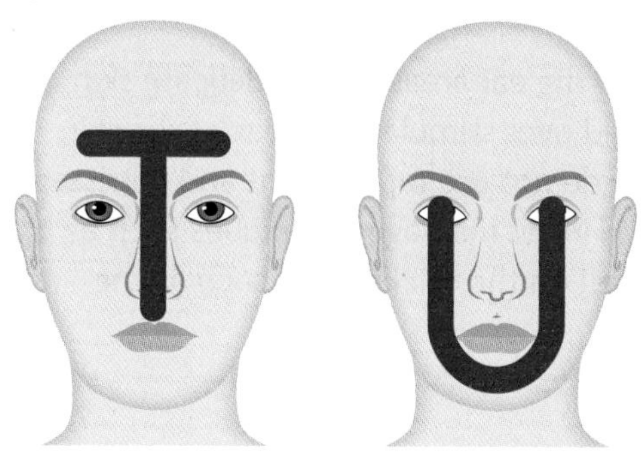

▲ Massage zones

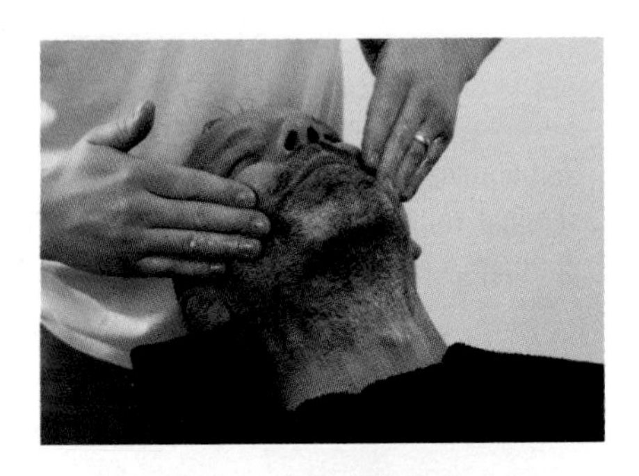

Effleurage

Effleurage is used to apply exfoliator and any massage oils to the face.

Rotary

The rotary technique should focus on the T-zone first, on either side of the nose and across the forehead, then in the U-zone across the **mandible**, chin and cheek areas. Use your fingertips in a gentle circular motion, starting from the centre, up the T-zone and then towards the side of the face and down.

Petrissage

Petrissage movements involve kneading the skin. The skin is lifted and then squeezed with a firm yet light amount of pressure, using the thumb and fingers. The benefits of this type of facial massage include stimulation of the muscles, glands and nerves.

KEY TERM

Mandible – the lower jawbone.

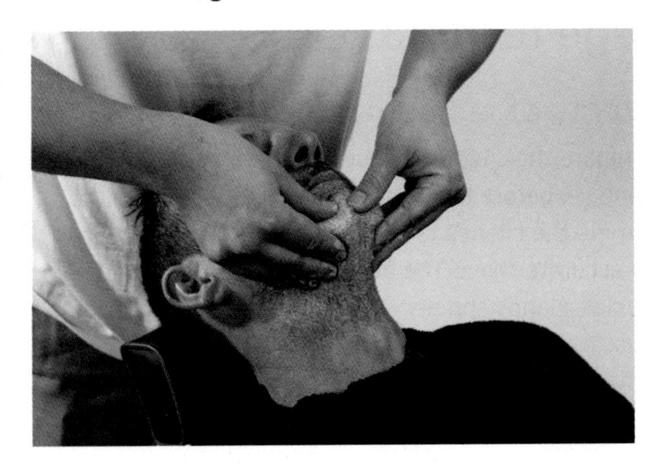

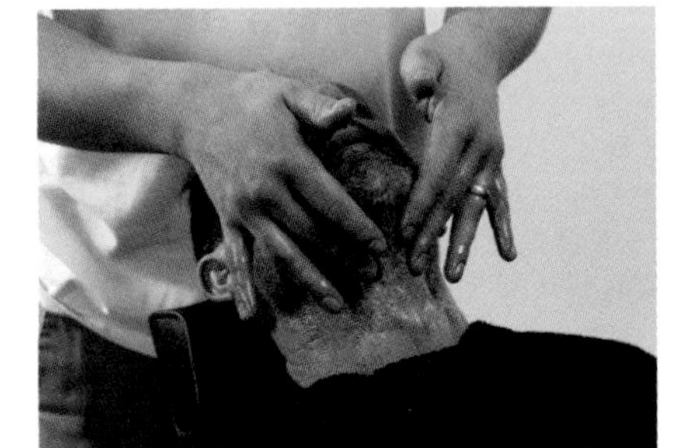

Tapotement

The tapotement technique consists of short and fast tapping movements that are said to be the most stimulating massage technique. It helps to tone muscles and can give the treated area a healthy glow. When performing such movements, you will need to keep your fingers strong but flexible. Bring the fingertips down lightly but in rapid succession, to massage the skin. Start in the centre of the face going up and always ending down to ensure more efficient lymphatic flow.

ACTIVITY

In pairs, use oils or moisturisers to massage each other's faces using different techniques. Provide feedback on how it feels.

Varying massage techniques on the different areas of the face

Care should always be taken around the ear areas and on delicate skin, such as the nostrils. You should avoid over stimulating areas of the skin prone to spots or oil production, so do not use tapotement and petrissage around the forehead or nose areas. Firmer massage techniques such as tapotement and petrissage work well on the thicker skin, such as the cheeks.

Finishing products and their effects

It is important to cleanse your client's face and make sure all lathering products have been removed after shaving and before applying finishing products. If lathering products are mixed with moisturising products, they could dry out the skin. Cleansing also helps prevent any dirt or hair clippings (or hair splinters) that are in the lather after shaving from getting into the pores.

Types of finishing products

There are many different types of products that are available for finishing services. The ones that you need to know about are:

- astringents
- moisturising creams
- aftershave balm
- powder.

Astringents

Astringents tighten, shrink and contract the skin, making pores appear smaller. They are a stronger form of toner and are formulated with an alcohol to give the skin a tight feeling. This tight feeling is a sign of dehydration and not a sign of clean skin, as many think. Experts have suggested astringents may cause more harm than help to the skin.

▲ Jack Dean Moisturising Balm

Moisturising creams

Moisturising creams are becoming increasingly popular with men as part of their everyday skincare routine. Moisturising creams soften and sooth the skin, preventing irritation like razor burn.

Aftershave balm

Aftershave balms are similar to astringents because they close the pore, but they are less harsh on the skin and often have antiseptic properties. Balms soothe the skin after shaving by reducing redness and providing soothing relief. These products often contain alcohol-free ingredients such as witch hazel, vitamin E, green tea or oatmeal to soothe the skin.

Powder

It was once traditional to use talcum powder after shaving, but nowadays many barbers disagree with this, as talc removes much-needed moisture from the skin. However, some modern-day powders will calm the skin around the face and neck area and absorb any residue oils left behind from shaving.

HEALTH AND SAFETY

If you choose to use talc, do so in a well-ventilated area as inhalation can be damaging to your health.

Removing excess moisture from skin

The skin must be left free of excess moisture at the end of the service. If necessary, use a tissue to blot the skin to remove excess moisture, both for client comfort and a more natural look. The sweat glands and sebum can now escape onto the skin surface freely. This will help to prevent blocked pores that can cause hardening of the epidermis.

Problems that may occur during service

There may be problems that arise while you are performing the shaving service and you will need to know how to solve them. Some examples of problems and how to solve them are described below.

- Burning sensation for the client – to wipe the 'burning' area with lukewarm water and then apply an Aloe vera gel to soothe the sensitive skin. Make sure that you then use slower strokes when shaving. Ask the client if they are comfortable and make sure that they are happy to leave the hair unshaved on the irritable area if necessary.
- Small cut or open wounds – use a tissue to rub some alcohol solution onto the cut as this will help to heal the wound. Apply pressure to stop the bleeding and then press a styptic match/stick onto the affected area.

Provide advice and recommendations

You should provide clients with advice on:

- how to maintain their look
- time interval between services
- present and future products and services
- skin care.

Maintaining the look

Advise clients on when to return to the salon for another shaving service to maintain their look, or provide advice on the tools required to maintain their look at home.

Time interval between services

The client's shaving regime will depend on their unique rate of growth. However, they will need to book an appointment once they start losing their initial look. On average, clients receiving a close shave may need to book weekly or fortnightly.

Present and future products and services

If during the service you discussed other salon services with your client, you should revisit this conversation at the end of the service and make recommendations for your client to consider.

It is advisable to have a full list of services with prices available for clients to see and a retail shelf of products to support every service you provide.

This will help you advise your clients on products for all their grooming needs. Being able to give advice on when their chosen style needs to be done again or what is required to style their hair and maintain their skin will give your salon a good reputation. It also means that your clients will be well groomed, which is a positive advert for the salon.

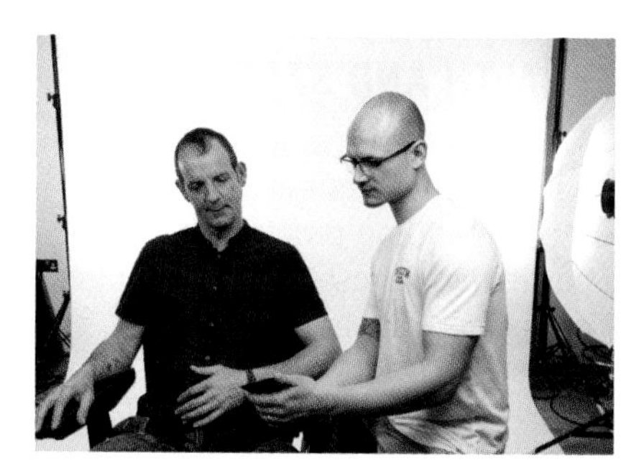

▲ Recommend aftercare products

Products and skin care

Bump spray

Bump spray is often used for razor bumps and papules to cure and prevent them becoming worse. The client should use this daily after cleansing until the bumps have gone; they should also refrain from close shaving until the skin has healed.

Exfoliator/scrub

Exfoliator or facial scrub is advised when clients are suffering from ingrown hairs. It is also used for regular maintenance to remove dead skin cells which are preventing new skin growing over old skin, making the skin appear darker and thicker. Regular removal of dead skin brightens the complexion, softens the skin and makes it more receptive to receiving moisture.

Toner

Toners cool and refresh the skin, and remove traces of grease on the skin. This helps with the drying action. The oilier the skin, the stronger the alcohol content in the toner should be.

Grape seed oil

Grape seed oil is rich in linoleic acid, which is an essential fatty acid that is important for moisturising the skin. It is a great non-greasy oil to use but could be enriched by blending it with another oil such as almond or wheat germ.

Apricot oil

Apricot oil has good moisturising and nourishing properties and is particularly helpful for dehydrated, delicate, mature and sensitive skin. It also spreads very easily and helps to soothe inflammation. Like grape seed oil, it is rich in linoleic acid, as well as antioxidants which prevent damage to the skin from free radicals.

Wheat germ oil

Wheat germ oil has a high vitamin E content as well as essential fatty acids, so it is used extensively in aromatherapy massage blends. It is said to promote a smoother, younger-looking skin and to assist in healing scar tissue as well as stretch marks. It is too sticky to use on its own but works well when blended with other oils such as almond. When it is applied to the skin, wheat germ oil is said to help promote the formation of new cells, improve circulation and help repair sun damage. It is also used to help relieve the symptoms of dermatitis.

HEALTH AND SAFETY

Always check if your client has any allergies before recommending products – particularly those containing nuts or nut derivatives.

Almond oil

Almond oil is excellent for softening and soothing the skin. It also helps the skin to balance its loss and absorption of moisture. This oil is one of the most popular of all oils used in aromatherapy and massage, since it is non-greasy, spreads easily and is great for nourishing the skin.

Gel

Gel contains water which cools the skin and provides slip, allowing it to spread more easily. Some gels can be used as shaving foam, cleansing the skin at the same time.

Tonics

Tonics soothe and brighten your skin. They can be gentle and alcohol-free, and they add a fine layer of moisture. Tonics have far less alcohol than most toners.

WHAT YOU MUST DO

For your practical assessments, you must:

- apply safe working practices when preparing the hair and skin for shaving
- prepare the hair and skin for shaving
- shave hair and apply finishing products.

Apply safe working practices when preparing the hair and skin for shaving

You must apply safe and hygienic methods of working throughout services by:

- maintaining your responsibilities for health and safety and keeping your work area clean and tidy
- following workplace and suppliers' or manufacturer's instructions for the safe use of equipment, materials and products
- using working methods that:
  - minimise the risk of damage to tools and equipment
  - minimise the risk of cross-infection
  - make effective use of your working time
  - ensure the use of clean resources
  - minimise the risk of harm or injury to yourself and others
  - promote environmental and sustainable working practices and dispose of waste materials and sharps
- wearing gloves throughout the shaving service and ensuring your personal hygiene, protection and appearance meet accepted industry and organisational requirements
- protecting your client's clothing and keeping their skin free of excess hair clippings
- positioning your client to meet the needs of the service without causing them discomfort and ensuring your own posture and position while working minimise fatigue and the risk of injury
- completing the service within a commercially viable time.

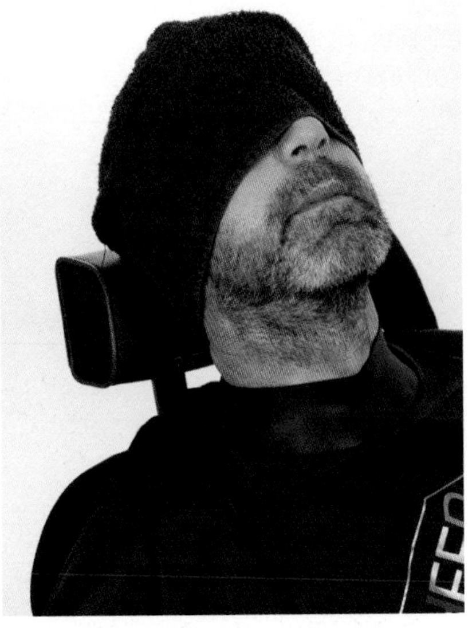

▲ Safe working – checking for skin conditions

Prepare the hair and skin for shaving

To prepare for the service you must:

- consult with clients to confirm the desired look
- identify factors that may influence the service prior to shaving
- select suitable products, tools and equipment based on the results of consultation with your client.

When preparing to carry out shaving services you must:

- prepare, apply and adapt the use of hot towels to suit the needs of the service and the comfort of your client
- cleanse and/or exfoliate your client's skin when necessary and use a pre-shave product prior to lathering the client
- lather the products so they are ready for use in time for the shaving service. You must also use lathering techniques which achieve an even coverage of product to the areas to be shaved
- apply the products in a way that takes account of factors you have identified and that minimises the risk of the product being spread to your client's eyes, clothes and surrounding area.

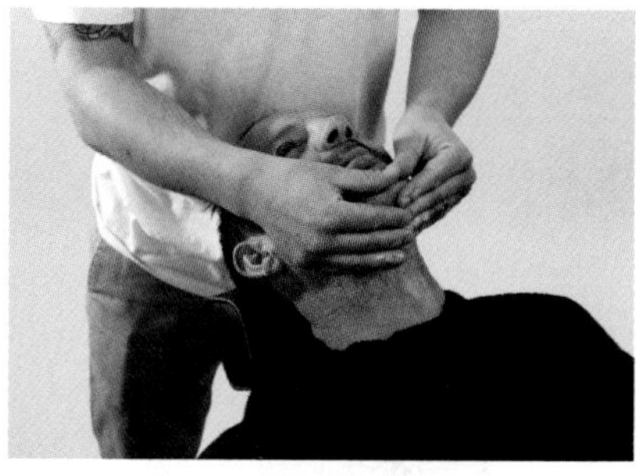

▲ Exfoliate the skin when necessary

Shave hair and apply finishing products

Before carrying out the shaving service you must:

- confirm with your client the look agreed at consultation.

As you begin the shaving service:

- adapt your shaving techniques to take account of factors you have identified
- adapt your client's position throughout the service to ensure safety and the effective removal of hair
- maintain or replace the cutting edge of razors during the shaving service as and when required, and take suitable remedial action to resolve any problems arising during the shaving service.

At the end of the service, you must:

- leave your client's skin free from lathering products after shaving
- apply facial massage techniques in a way that avoids discomfort
- apply finishing products to achieve the desired effect
- remove any excess moisture from your client's face and confirm the completed service is to the satisfaction of your client
- provide your client with advice and recommendations on the services you provided to ensure they can maintain their look and skin care routine.

ACTIVITY

Practise a clean shave with a clipper and with a razor, remembering how important the directional growth is to the comfort of the client.

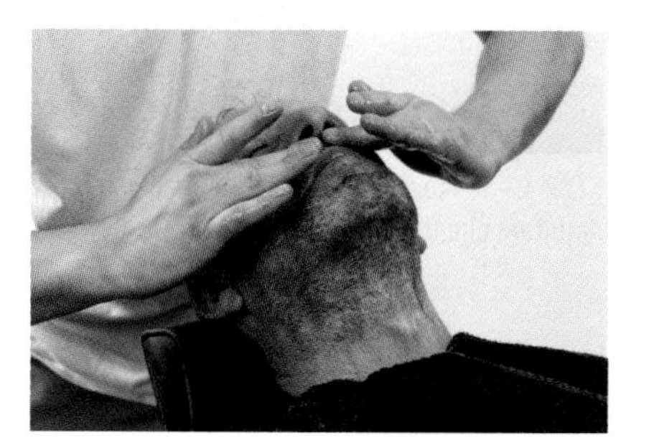

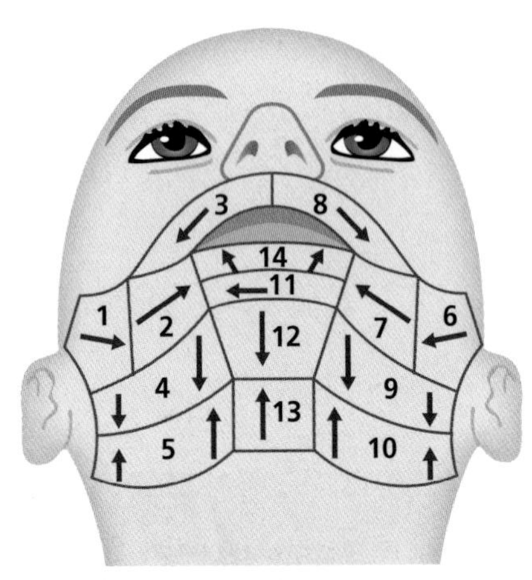

▲ Shaving strokes process

STEP BY STEP

You will carry out the following services:

- full shave
- partial shave
- beard outlines.

Full shave

The diagram below shows the shaving strokes process of a wet shave.

A full shaving service on a client with a coarse dense beard

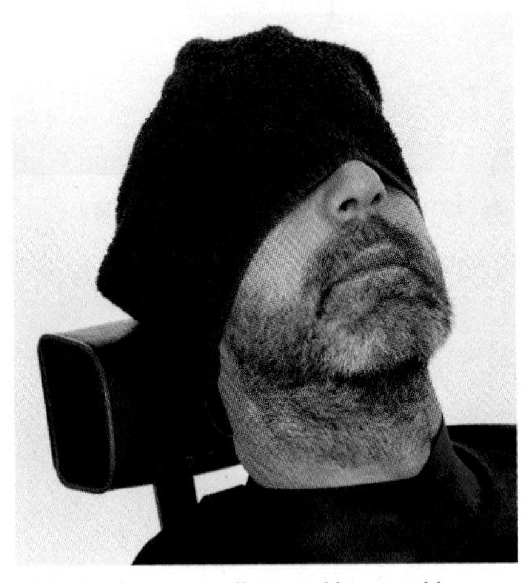

STEP 1 – Gown your client, making sure his clothes are protected and hairs cannot escape down the neck area. After the consultation protect your client's eyes with eye pads or a towel.

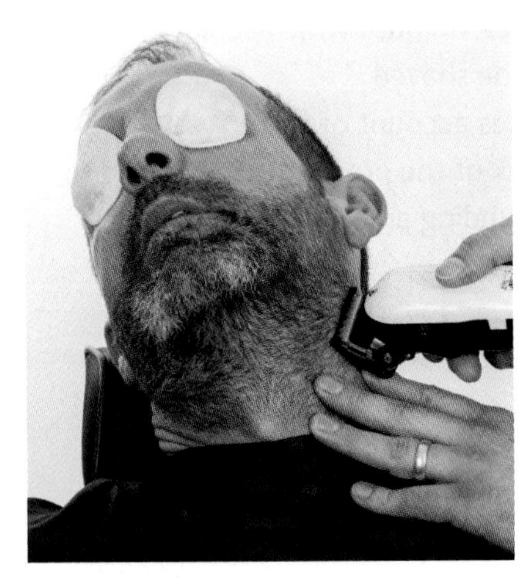

STEP 2 – Remove the beard length with clippers and 0.5 grade and maintain skin tension throughout. Check the skin for skin tags, moles, etc.

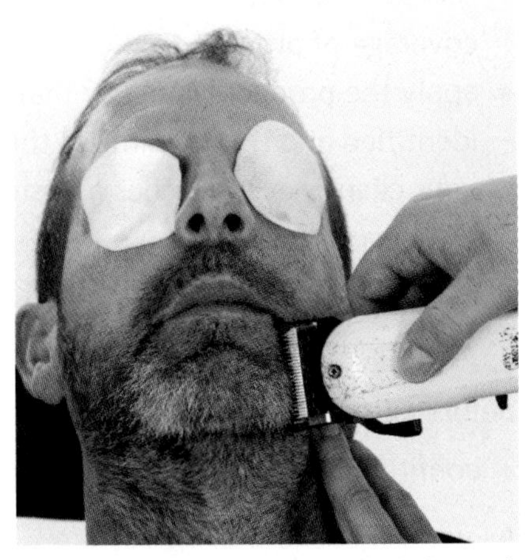

STEP 3 – Shave the face against the hair growth with tension. Take the clipper down to 0 grade to remove the final length and double check the skin condition.

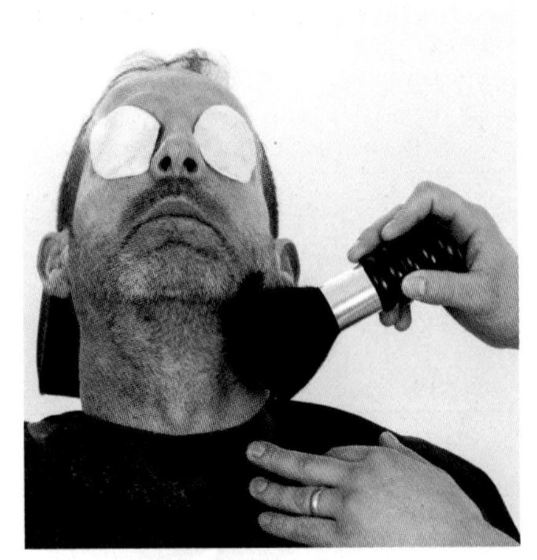

STEP 4 – Remove loose hair clippings to maintain client comfort.

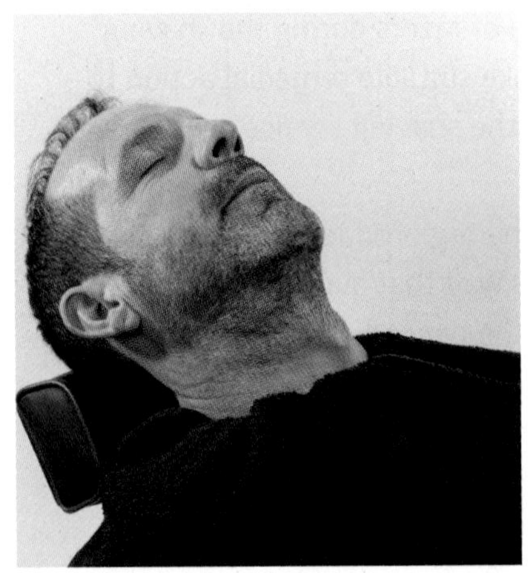

STEP 5 – Prepare the client for the wet shave with clean towels and fully support their neck on the barber's chair neck rest.

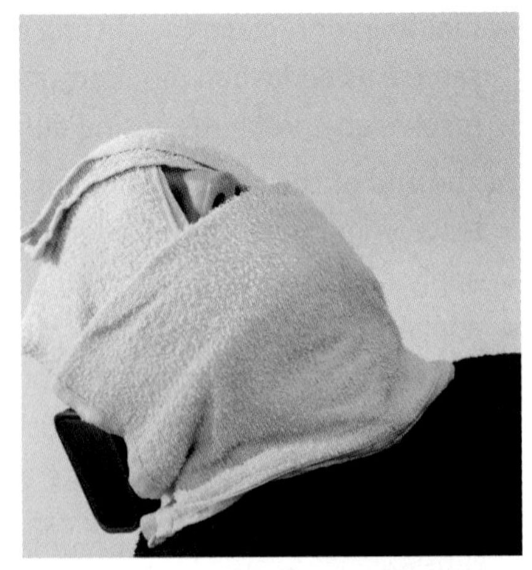

STEP 6 – Place a hot towel around the client's face, keeping the nose exposed to ensure they can breathe. Check the heat of the towel is comfortable for the client.

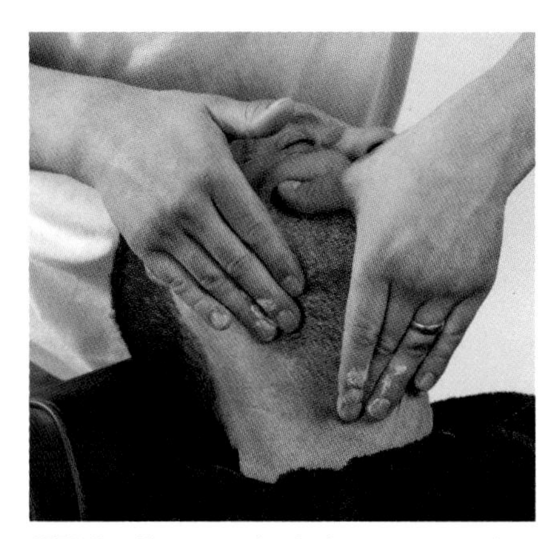

STEP 7 – After a couple of minutes, remove the towel before it cools and apply an exfoliating product with effleurage massage to remove dead skin cells. Once the muscles are warm massage more firmly using petrissage to lift the hairs. Apply another hot towel to ensure the hairs are lifted and to remove product.

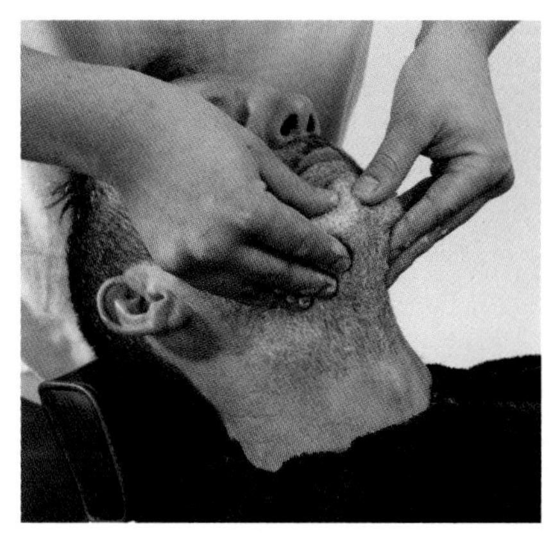

STEP 8 – Apply a moisturising oil using petrissage massage and tapotement to wake up the skin and encourage hairs to stand up in readiness for shaving. Apply another hot towel for up to one minute (if required).

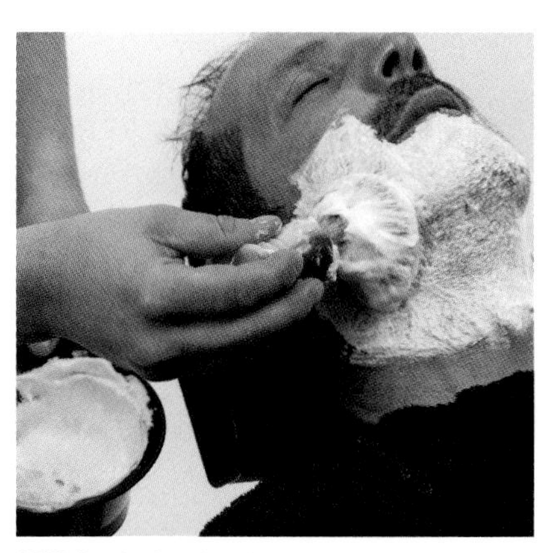

STEP 9 – Lather the shaving cream in a bowl using a brush. Apply lathering cream with the brush in a circular motion, going against the hair growth to lift the hairs up.

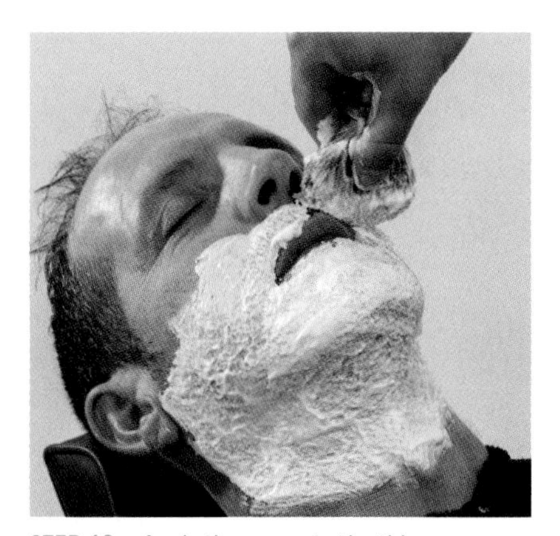

STEP 10 – Apply the cream to the thin moustache area with the brush squeezed to avoid the product entering the nostrils.

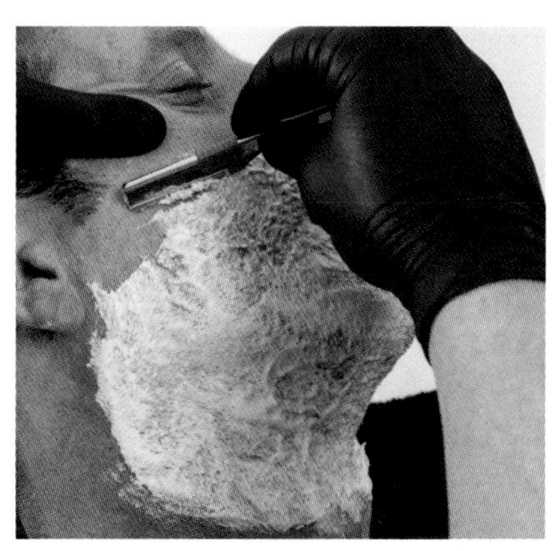

STEP 11 – Fit a new disposable blade to the razor. Adjust the angle of the client's head and, if you are right-handed, start on the right for barber comfort using forehand techniques. Holding the skin with tension and following the hair growth, shave the cheek area.

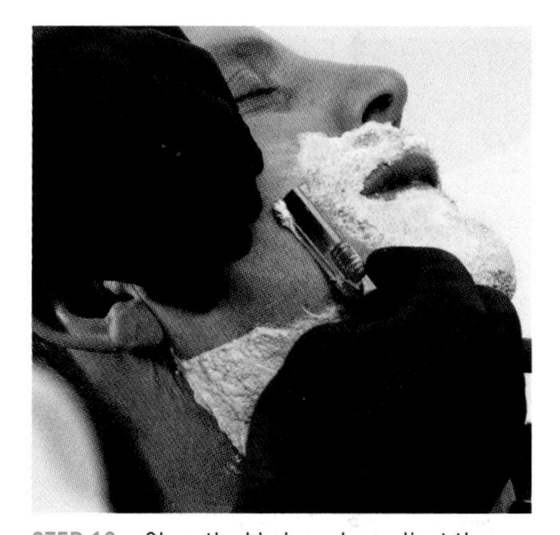

STEP 12 – Close the blade and re-adjust the head angle for the left side. Use backhand shaving techniques and, starting from the bottom of the side burn, shave the other side of the face.

STEP 13 – As you move on to the neck, stretch the skin downwards for tension, and follow the hair growth, changing angles and direction to suit. Shave upwards if the hair grows upwards and downwards if hair grows downwards.

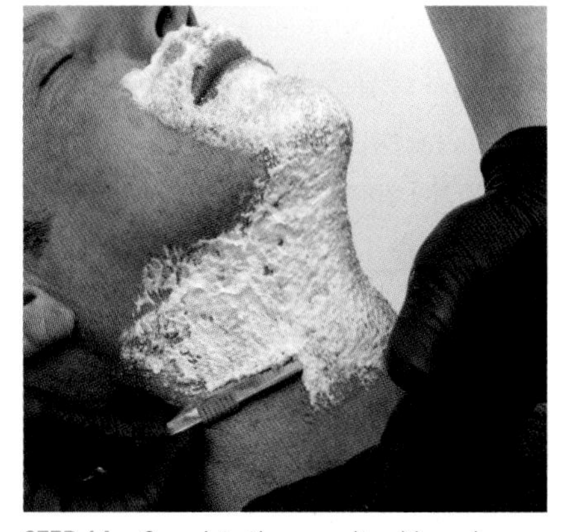

STEP 14 – Complete the opposite side and flatten the contours of the chin by applying tension.

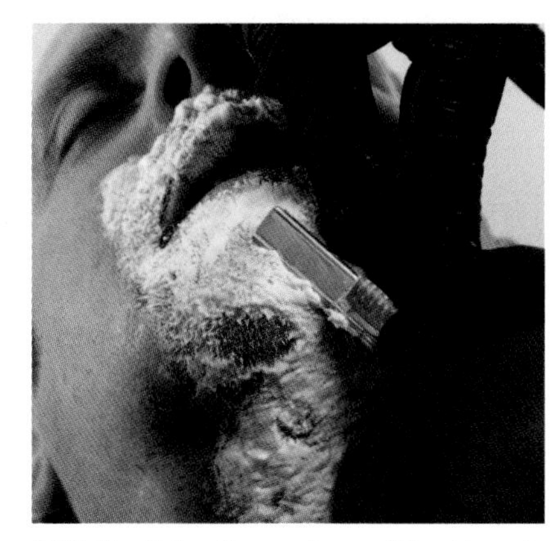

STEP 15 – Follow the roundness of the chin and stretch out the dimple area. Lift the head up to stretch out the neck skin. For extra tension, lift up the skin and shave downwards following the hair growth direction.

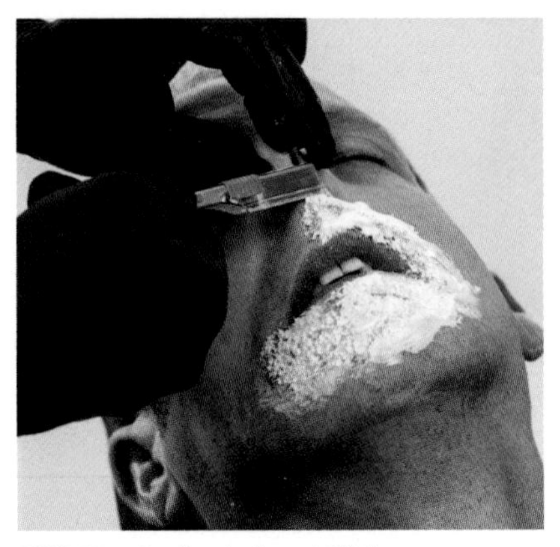

STEP 16 – Gently pinch and lift the nose, shaving slightly to the left (to suit the client's hair growth) using backhand on the other side, or changing sides to work. To shave around the philtrum, lift the nose straight up and stretch, shave downwards taking care at the lip and lift the blade up.

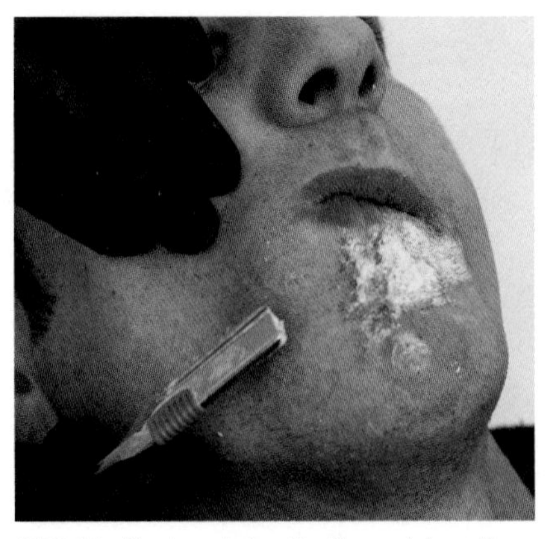

STEP 17 – To shave below the lip, work from the lower chin up to the lip, using smaller strokes due to the curvatures of the chin and the denser hair at the chin. Ask the client to poke his tongue into the lip corners to enable the close shave.

STEP 18 – Apply a warm towel, allow this to cool and then apply a cold towel to shock the pores to close. Apply an after-shave balm/astringent to close the pores and finally add a moisturiser to moisturise the skin.

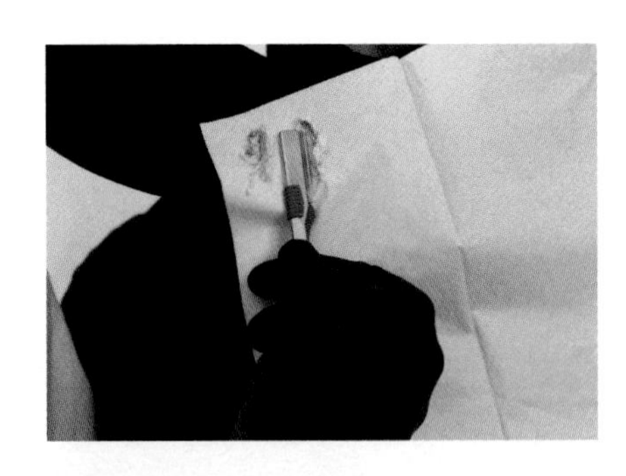

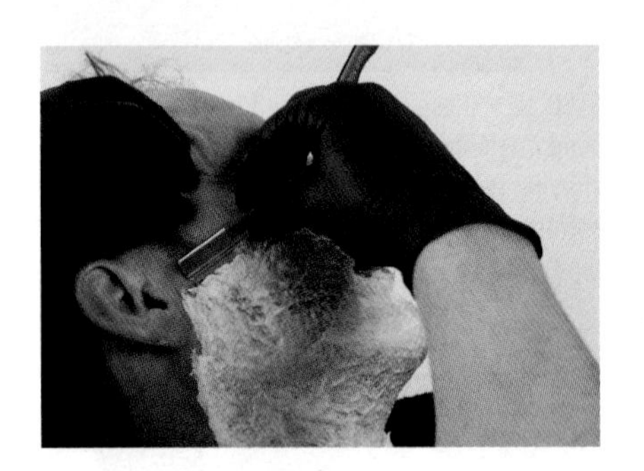

HANDY HINT

Clean the razor blade on a tissue or separate towel after every couple of strokes to remove the hair and lathering products.

HANDY HINT

The angle of the razor should held at about 30° to the face.

HANDY HINT

For the area below the lip, work from the lower chin up to the lip and use smaller strokes because of the curvatures and denser hair of the chin. Always pull the skin away from either side of the Adam's apple, rather than shave the skin directly over the Adam's apple.

HANDY HINT

Touch the area where you want the client to poke out his tongue to enable a close shave.

Visual checks

You need to carry out visual checks to ensure the shaving is accurate. If you have done a smooth razor shave, it is important to check whether there are any small dots of hair. You should wear gloves to stroke the shaved area with your fingers to feel for any differences in skin texture and if there are any rough areas that have been missed. This should be done in both directions, with and against the hair growth pattern.

Partial shave

There are many different types of traditional and current facial hair shapes that you will need to know in order to provide a good facial hair shaving service. Some examples are shown below.

▲ Facial hair shapes

HANDY HINT

Producing a partial shave service requires the same steps as a normal clean shave, but you must only focus on the particular area to be shaved. The area will depend on each individual client's wishes.

Moustache shave

Moustaches can also be clean shaved – just be very careful when shaving near the nostril. Ask your client to tuck their lips in while you push their nose from left to right, depending on which side you are shaving.

HANDY HINT

Using a T-shaped blade or trimmer blade to shape the hair can help you achieve the moustache style your client desires.

Beard outline

You can create many different possible beard outlines. Again, you use the same steps as for a normal clean shave but just focus on the area you want to leave, in accordance with the client's request. You can also use a T-shaped or trimmer blade clipper to help style the hair into the desired shape.

▲ Beard outlines

How to create and follow guidelines

In order to create and follow guidelines when providing facial hair shaving services, you will need to take the following into consideration:

- When beard shaping, examine the facial features to check for symmetry and see what style of facial hair would be most suitable for the client.
- Use the teeth of your comb to comb through the hair and achieve the correct thickness of the moustache or chin strap beard required. You

could also use the comb teeth with a clipper, so it acts as a 'ruler' to create a straight line. Always keep half of the blade on the line, so that only half of the blade is creating the new line. This will keep your angle and line straight. When razor wet shaving, try stroking the lather foam in the same direction as the growth pattern of the hair, to make it easier to see the directional growth after the first shave.

HANDY HINT

You can use an adjustable clipper, keeping the lever back fully, to trim a moustache. Place your clipper at 90° and keep the angle while rake-cutting down. This will give you around a level 1 attachment. Depending on the hair length, you can also use a number 1 attachment in the same way.

Balancing and shaping sideburns

To shape sideburns accurately and to meet client requirements, try using the back of a straight comb to create straight lines. You can also use the teeth on the clipper as a ruler – when creating a straight line, keep half of the blade on the line so that only half of the blade is creating the new line. This will keep your angle and line straight.

You could also turn the chair away from the mirror, so that your client's profile is side on, allowing you to see the half of the facial hair that has been cut and to match accordingly.

ACTIVITY

Practise maintaining symmetry and balance within beard styles using these resources to achieve accuracy:

- mirror
- comb
- teeth of the comb
- back of the comb
- clipper blade
- facial features.

Test your knowledge

Question 1

Name a potential skin problem that can occur as a result of facial shaving service.

Question 2

Describe the first step when performing a full facial shaving service.

Question 3

Describe the functions of the dermis layer.

Question 4

Describe the functions of the muscles around the nose and mouth areas of the face.

Question 5

Which layer of the epidermis is most affected by shaving services?

Multiple choice questions

6 Why must you ensure that all tools and equipment are sterilised before use?
   - a To avoid the risk of cross-contamination
   - b To avoid the risk of infection
   - c To uphold the reputation of the business by practising good hygiene
   - d All of the above

7 What is the optimum angle for the headrest when performing a facial shaving service?
   - a 30–70°
   - b 45–90°
   - c 80–120°
   - d 180°

8 Which of the following is a main function of the blood?
   - a Maintaining an immune system in the body
   - b Transporting digested food, respiratory gases and waste material
   - c Producing and maturing lymphocytes
   - d Heating and humidifying air

9 Which of the following tools would give better control when trimming a moustache into the desired shape?
   - a Clippers
   - b Scissors
   - c T-shaped blade
   - d Razors

10 Which of the following massage techniques is considered the most stimulating for the skin?
   - a Rotary
   - b Petrissage
   - c Tapotement
   - d Swedish

CHAPTER 11

PERMING HAIR (OPTIONAL UNIT)

This chapter maps to:

- Unit 6 Perming hair (Level 2 Diploma for Hair Professionals – Hairdressing).

INTRODUCTION

Perms are making a comeback, as curly and soft wavy hair is becoming more and more popular. Modern setting techniques are great, but they are high maintenance if your client wants to recreate the look themselves. Perming straight hair, or chemically rearranging African/type 4 hair, makes it possible for clients to recreate loose curls, spiral curls or a tousled look and, most importantly, maintain their look at reasonable cost at home. Perm winding is creative and improves your dexterity (skill with your hands), but understanding the science behind perming and chemical rearranging is extremely important. When perming, you are working with strong chemicals to change the hair's structure, so you must avoid damaging your client's hair.

After reading this chapter, you will:

- know how health and safety policies and procedures affect perming, neutralising and chemical rearranging services
- be able to apply safe working practices when perming hair
- understand how to prepare for perming and neutralising
- be able to perm and neutralise hair.

HEALTH AND SAFETY POLICIES AND PROCEDURES AFFECTING SERVICES

When perming and neutralising the hair, you will be using some very strong chemicals that can cause harm to yourself and your client. It is therefore important that you work safely throughout these services and ensure that both you and your client are effectively protected. Always follow the health and safety policies and procedures in place at your salon or college.

ACTIVITY

Refer to the health and safety sections in Chapter 1 and list your responsibilities under the health and safety acts.

Protective clothing and products

You must protect your client's clothing with a gown, towel and disposable plastic shoulder cape to ensure they remain dry and to avoid getting chemicals on their clothes. Before you apply the perm lotion or neutraliser, apply a barrier cream around your client's hairline to protect their skin from the chemicals. You must take particular care to avoid contact of the lotion with your client's eyes.

Always ensure that your client is comfortable, and **periodically** check they are comfortable and offer them refreshments. Ask your client to sit upright, with their back against the back of the salon chair and their legs uncrossed.

KEY TERM

Periodically – at regular intervals.

THE HAIR PROFESSIONAL AT WORK

A supply of clean towels and fresh shoulder capes should be available throughout the perming and neutralising process for your client's comfort.

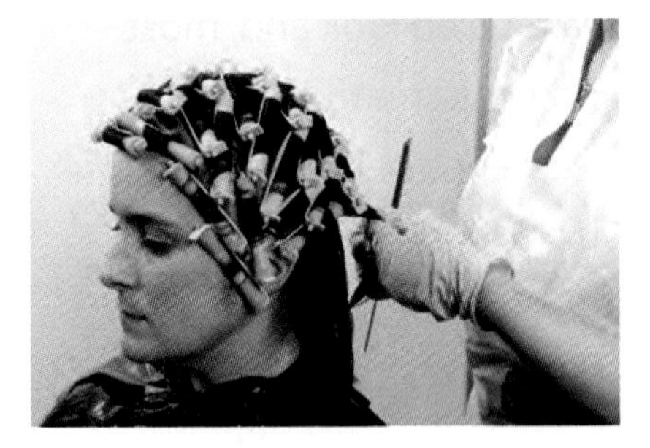

▲ Wear PPE when perming hair

You should wear gloves to protect your hands from the perm lotions, neutralisers and chemical rearranger. You should also wear an apron to protect your clothes.

Personal hygiene and presentation

You will be standing for long periods of time, so you must wear sensible, flat-soled, closed-in shoes and stand correctly.

You must maintain your personal health and hygiene throughout the service by showering daily, wearing clean clothes, using deodorant, and carefully covering and protecting any cuts or open wounds. Always check that your body odour and your breath are fresh as you are working in close **proximity** to your clients and colleagues.

KEY TERM

Proximity – closeness to, in terms of space.

HEALTH AND SAFETY

Maintain a good posture and stand with your feet apart and your body weight evenly distributed. Avoid overstretching or bending too much to prevent fatigue and back problems.

HANDY HINT

Poor standards of hygiene can cause offence to your clients, give a poor salon image and cause cross-contamination.

THE HAIR PROFESSIONAL AT WORK

Refer to Chapter 1 for more information on personal hygiene and protection, maintaining effective and safe methods for working and meeting salon standards of behaviour.

Safe and hygienic working methods and practices

Before your client arrives, ensure you are prepared to carry out the perm. Keep your work area clean and tidy to avoid potential hazards and risk of injury, to ensure the salon looks professional, and to minimise the risk of infection, infestation and cross-contamination.

Equipment and products

Your equipment should have a yearly portable appliance test (PAT) by an electrician to ensure it's safe and fit for use (see Chapter 1). Every time you use a piece of electrical equipment, you must check it visually by looking at the power cable, plug and main body to ensure that it is in good working order. This will prevent harm and risk of injury to you and others.

During a perming service you may use shampoo, pre- and post-perm conditioners, perm lotion, neutraliser, chemical rearrangers and styling products. All of these are substances which could be hazardous to your health, through **absorption**, inhalation or ingestion. Wear PPE, for example gloves, aprons, eye protection and masks (particularly if you are asthmatic), and mix the chemicals in a well-ventilated area.

KEY TERM

Absorption – the passage of a substance through the skin.

Preparing a client for a perming service

When you shampoo and neutralise your client's hair, ensure that you support their head and neck as you position them down to the basin. Take care to do this when you lift their head and neck after the shampoo and neutralising process too.

To prepare the client's hair for a perming service, the hair is shampooed with a clarifying or deep cleansing shampoo (pH 6.0–7.0) to remove any residue or styling product from the hair. Surface conditioner should not be used before the service, as it coats the hair and creates a barrier to the lotions.

Position tools and equipment for ease of use

Always make effective use of your time to ensure you work to a commercially viable time. Prepare your trolley with the tools and equipment required before commencing the service. Ensure you clean and sterilise your tools before and after use.

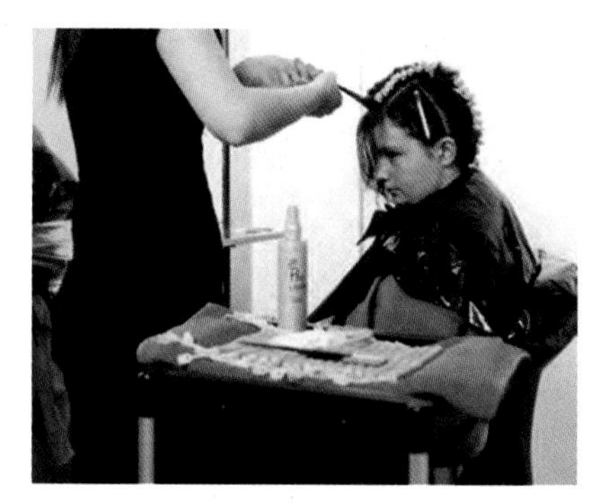

▲ Prepare your trolley in advance of the service

▲ Barrier cream

▲ Neutraliser

HANDY HINT

When working with chemicals, always follow the Control of Substances Hazardous to Health (COSHH) guidelines as well as the manufacturers' instructions (MFIs) and your salon policy. You can access COSHH regulations at:

www.legislation.gov.uk/uksi/2002/2677/pdfs/uksi_20022677_en.pdf

Always follow SHUD – this is derived from COSHH Regulations and refers to **S**tore, **H**andle, **U**se and **D**ispose of substances correctly.

HANDY HINT

Remember – the position of your client and yourself can affect the desired outcome, lead to fatigue and cause you the risk of injury.

HANDY HINT

If towels get damp from the shampoo or neutralising service, you must remove them from your client and replace them immediately with clean, dry ones.

HANDY HINT

Avoid wastage by turning off taps between shampoos and using the correct amount of product to avoid overloading the hair. This will help the environment and keep the salon profitable.

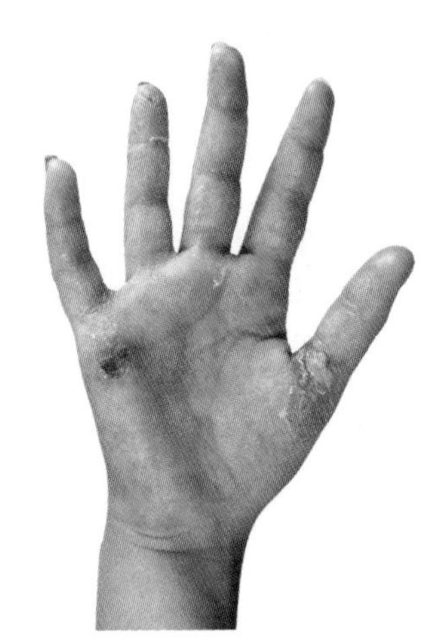

▲ Dermatitis

▲ A clean and tidy salon

HANDY HINT

Clean your tools and work surfaces with detergent and water to remove oil, products, hair and debris. Disinfect with chemical solutions or wipes, and sterilise using a UV light cabinet or an autoclave.

Correct methods of waste disposal

You must remove any used, wet or soiled cotton wool after the perm or neutralising process. This will aid client comfort and prevent perm lotion coming into contact with the skin for long periods, which can cause chemical burns to the hairline area.

You must ensure that you dispose of all salon waste in the designated waste bin and rinse any excess perm lotion or neutraliser down the sink with plenty of cold water. This will ensure that chemicals are diluted and that you work within your salon policy, follow the MFIs and local by-laws.

THE HAIR PROFESSIONAL AT WORK

Refer to Chapter 1 to recap on environmental and sustainable working practices, such as:

- reducing waste
- safe disposal of waste
- using disposable items
- reducing energy usage
- preventing pollution.

ACTIVITY

Research contact dermatitis and list three ways in which you can help prevent it.

▲ Wear gloves to protect your hands from dermatitis

▲ Neutraliser and perming lotion

ACTIVITY

Which tools should be disinfected or sterilised using the following methods?

- Autoclave
- UV light cabinet
- Chemicals

PREPARE FOR PERMING AND NEUTRALISING

You will need to carry out a thorough consultation to ensure the desired perm result can be achieved. This will include asking appropriate questions and listening to your client's responses, conducting relevant tests, analysing your client's hair and recognising any contra-indications. Once you have done this you will be able to choose the correct tools, equipment and products to prepare your client's hair for perming and neutralising.

Importance of questioning clients prior to and during services

To identify the type of perm that is best suited to your client's requirements and to achieve the desired result, you should ask a series of questions. Whether your client is new to perming or not, you'll need to ask them the same questions. Regular clients may want a change of curl, but even if a repeat service is required, you need to check if anything has changed with the condition of the client's hair, their lifestyle or their health. As with all services, it is important to use products cost effectively. This means you should be quoting the cost of the perm service based on the hair length and amounts of products required.

Here are some examples of the types of question you should ask your client:

- What do they want the perm to achieve?
- What is their vision of the end result?
- What type of curl/movement would they like?
- What size curl would they like?
- How much time do they have available to spend styling their own hair on a daily basis?
- Have they had a perm/chemical rearranger before?
- When was their last perm/chemical rearranger?
- Have they had any previous problems with a perm?
- What chemicals (including relaxer) do they currently have on their hair, if any?
- Do they have any colour on their hair and, if so, what type of colour service did they have?
- Do they have any contra-indications such as allergies?

HANDY HINT

By asking clear questions that are jargon-free (avoiding complex/technical words) and listening to your client's responses, you are using your communication skills. Confirming your understanding by repeating back what has been discussed will ensure you both agree and that you have communicated clearly.

HANDY HINT

You must always listen carefully to your client's responses and write them on their record card. Ask your client to sign the record card to confirm that what has been written is accurate and true. Ask open questions to obtain as much information as possible. When you need to clarify a response, switch to closed questions to obtain a definite reply.

▲ Check what products are on your client's hair and record their responses to questions asked

THE HAIR PROFESSIONAL AT WORK

Refer to Chapter 1 for more information on:

- maintaining customer care
- greeting clients respectfully and in a friendly manner
- identifying and confirming the client's expectations
- treating the client courteously at all times
- giving the client the information they need about the services or products offered by the salon
- recognising information that the client may find complicated and checking they fully understand.

Carry out perming and neutralising tests prior to services

The table below shows when and how perming and neutralising tests are carried out prior to services. Remember that instructions from manufacturers will vary, so make sure you always follow the MFIs in relation to these tests.

Type and purpose of test	When and how to carry out the test	Expected result	How the results influence the perming service	Action to take in the event of adverse reactions
Elasticity – to test the strength of the cortex layer.	This test is carried out before the perm service or chemical rearranger. On wet hair, stretch a few hairs.	To see if the hair stretches and returns to its original length	If the hair stretches and returns then the elasticity is good – proceed with perm or chemical rearranger service. If the hair stretches and stays stretched or snaps, the hair is in weak condition and has poor elasticity – do not perm.	If the hair is weak, do not perm but offer alternative services and courses of conditioning treatments.

Type and purpose of test	When and how to carry out the test	Expected result	How the results influence the perming service	Action to take in the event of adverse reactions
Porosity – to identify if the cuticle layers are porous or non-porous.	This test is carried out before the perm service or chemical rearranger. On dry hair, run your finger and thumb along the cuticle layer of the hair shaft towards the scalp. Check whether your finger and thumb run along the hair smoothly or whether there is resistance and the hair feels bumpy.	The test will either identify smooth cuticles meaning good porosity or raised cuticles (if there is resistance and the hair feels bumpy) meaning porous or uneven porosity on the hair.	Good porosity results will mean you can proceed with the service. Porous hair will either need a pre-perm treatment or, if very porous, do not proceed with the service.	If the hair is porous, do not perm but offer alternative services and courses of conditioning treatments
Incompatibility – to test if the hair has products on it that are incompatible with the salon's products.	This test is carried out before the perm service or chemical rearranger. Take a test cutting, place hair in a solution of 20:1 liquid peroxide and ammonia hydroxide and leave for up to 30 minutes.	Ideally no reaction will occur. If the hair bubbles, gets warm and/ or becomes discoloured, then metallic salts are present on the hair.	No reaction – proceed with service. Positive reaction – do not perm.	Do not perm if the hair reacts in the solution. Offer treatments and re-test in four to six weeks' time.

Type and purpose of test	When and how to carry out the test	Expected result	How the results influence the perming service	Action to take in the event of adverse reactions
Strand test – to establish the effect of the product on the hair and its condition, such as whether the degree of straightness/smoothness has been achieved before winding. Chemical rearranger strand test	This test is carried out prior to the rearranging process. Apply the chemical rearranger to a discreet section of the hair and carry out the full development. If the test is on the scalp, monitor every five minutes to determine if the hair has been sufficiently 'smoothed' prior to winding the perm. If the test is off the scalp, take small samples of hair from various areas of the head, secure together and apply the rearranger.	If condition of hair is good and outcome confirms this, the service can go ahead. Development time is confirmed and degree of straightness achieved.	If the results meet with your expectations, you can proceed with the service. If the hair condition is poor, you can advise on the best course of action.	Do not proceed with the service if the degree of straightness is not achieved or the condition of the hair is weak.

HANDY HINT

It is important to confirm that straightening has been achieved by taking strand tests on different areas of the head at suitable times during the chemical rearranging process. This will help you to ensure the desired result has been achieved and that it is even throughout.

If the client does not experience any adverse reaction, the results of the hair tests described above will help you decide on the rod size, lotion strength, development time and the most suitable service for your client.

Potential consequences of failing to test hair

Failure to test your client's hair means that they could experience an adverse reaction and damage to their skin, scalp and hair during the perming service. This is potentially dangerous and the client may take legal action as a result. It also reflects poorly on you as a hair professional and could impact on your salon's professional reputation.

Course of action to take in the event of an adverse reaction

Do not perm if a client has a positive reaction or if breakage occurs during a test, as the hair and scalp may be damaged.

If your client experiences an adverse reaction and cannot proceed with the perming service, you can offer them advice on penetrating conditioning treatments and suggest alternative services, such as cutting and styling services, or setting the hair to create temporary curls. Always seek guidance from your manager if you are unsure what to do about the result of a hair test. You must record every test carried out and its result on the client's record card for future reference and in case of legal action.

> **THE HAIR PROFESSIONAL AT WORK**
>
> If a perm or chemical rearranger service cannot be carried out, refer to Chapter 1 for more information on explaining clearly to clients the reasons why their needs or expectations cannot be met.

ACTIVITY

Compare the different hair textures and densities among your colleagues. Look at each person's hair length and natural movement and identify which perm lotion would be most suitable. Don't forget to consider the hair's condition and what products have already been used. Ask each person to give you an indication of what sort of curl result they would like, so you can also choose the rod size. Present your findings in an interesting way.

Recording test results

If you are going to carry out a perm service on a regular client, refer to their previous record card to check the service details and make sure that the last perm service was to their satisfaction. Whether you are repeating the same service or changing it, you will need to add the details to the record card. For every client, regular or new, always ensure that their details are correct by checking their name, address and contact details. Record the date, type of service, products used and the result, ensuring that the card is completed accurately and that it is easy to read.

You must also record any relevant questions that you asked and the client's responses. This will ensure that:

- the correct service is carried out
- the records are available for future services
- you maintain a professional image
- you have documented evidence, in case of **litigation**.

KEY TERM

Litigation – legal action.

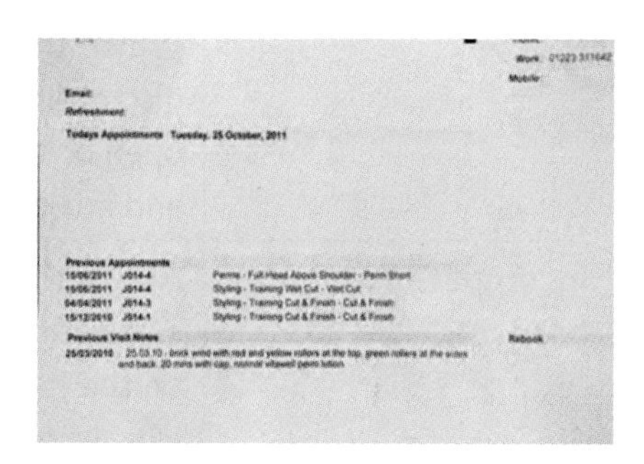
Work
Mobile
Email
Todays Appointments Tuesday, 25 October, 2011
Previous Appointments
Previous Visit Notes
Rebook

▲ Completed record card

ACTIVITY

Ask your manager if you can look at a client's perm record card so you can see what details are recorded for future use.

Contra-indications and their impact on services

It is of vital importance that you recognise contra-indications as they can affect the delivery of perming services.

The following contra-indications may prevent or affect perming, neutralising and chemically rearranging services:

- History of previous allergic reaction to perming products
- Other known allergies

- Skin disorders
- Previous chemical treatments
- Medical advice or instructions
- Incompatible products, such as those containing metallic salts
- Recent removal of hair extensions or plaits.

You must ask appropriate questions to check whether your client has ever had any of the problems described in the table below.

Contra-indication	How and why it affects the delivery of the service	Possible effect on the service
Previous allergic reaction to perming products	How – the client may have an allergic reaction. Why – the client is more likely to suffer an allergic reaction to the perm product or a chemical rearranger if they have previously had an allergic reaction to perm products.	If your client has had an allergic reaction to perming products before, carry out a skin test using your chosen perm lotion or chemical rearranger. If you are unsure, do not start the service, but recommend an alternative service. Ask the client to seek medical advice before opting for the service in the future.
Other known allergies	How – the client may have an allergic reaction. Why – the client is at an increased risk of suffering an allergic reaction to perming-type products if they have allergies to other products.	Ask your client what their allergies are. Check the ingredients in the chemical rearranger, perm lotion and neutraliser and carry out a skin test with the chosen product. If you are unsure, do not perm and recommend an alternative service.
Skin disorders	How – the service may not be able to go ahead due to client discomfort or infectious conditions. Why – the disorder may cause discomfort to your client if the skin is open or sore. It may also be contagious and infectious.	If your client has a skin disorder on their head, check if it is open, sore or weeping. If it is, do not carry out the service. If it is not and you can protect it, proceed with care. Check that the disorder is not infectious or an infestation. If it is, do not carry out the service.
Incompatible products	How – the service may not be compatible with previous products used on the hair. Why – incompatible products (those containing metallic salts) may react with the perm products or chemical rearrangers and cause a chemical reaction or damage to the hair, skin or scalp.	Check with your client which products have already been used on the hair. If you have concerns that these products are not compatible with the perm lotion, carry out an incompatibility test on the hair. If the result is positive, do not carry out the service.

Contra-indication	How and why it affects the delivery of the service	Possible effect on the service
Medical advice or instructions	How – the service may not be able to proceed if a GP advises against a service. Why – the hair may not be suitable for a chemical service if the client is on certain medications or is suffering ill health. You will not be insured if you proceed against a GP's advice.	Ask your client if they are on any medication. If you are unsure as to the likely reaction of the hair while on this medication or the client's health as a result of perming the hair, do not carry out the service and refer your client to their GP for further advice.
Previous chemical treatments	How – the service may not be compatible with previous products or services. Why – the hair may already have too many chemicals present on it. This could mean the condition may not be good enough to sustain another chemical service, or the chemicals on the hair may not be compatible – see 'incompatible products' above.	Check with your client which products have already been used on the hair. Carry out porosity and elasticity tests and if you have concerns, carry out an incompatibility test. If the result is positive, do not carry out the service. If a client with African-type hair has previously had a relaxing service to straighten the hair and hydroxides have been used, it is not possible to carry out a perm – thioglycollate and hydroxide are not compatible and if the two chemicals are overlapped the hair will break.
Recent removal of hair extensions or plaits	How – the service may not proceed if the scalp is tender or there is evident hair loss. Why – the scalp may be tender and the hair follicle inflamed after the removal of hair extensions or plaits. This could lead to hair loss if excessive tension is applied when perm winding or an infection of the follicles if perm lotion and/or chemical rearranger is then applied.	Check the scalp area for hair loss and inflamed follicles. Ask your client if they have any discomfort. Do not carry out the service if there is evidence of hair loss, inflamed follicles or if extensions or plaits have been removed within seven days. It is important that the client has a course of strengthening treatments prior to a perm and after the removal of extensions or braids.

HANDY HINT

For every question you ask your client about contra-indications, you must record the answer on the client's record card and ask them to sign it for confirmation. This will provide accurate information for future services and in the event of an adverse reaction. It also provides documented proof of your client's responses in case of litigation.

HANDY HINT

Skin tests are only needed if the manufacturer's instructions state this. Perm lotions and rearrangers are irritants so usually there is no way of carrying out a skin test. Never carry out a perming service if the client has had an allergic reaction to perming products in the past.

THE HAIR PROFESSIONAL AT WORK

Always seek guidance from your manager if you are unsure what to do about a contra-indication.

Active ingredients in perming and neutralising products

The main chemical ingredient of an alkaline perm is ammonia thioglycollate. Alkaline perms are available for all hair types – resistant, normal and tinted. The main ingredient in chemical rearrangers is also ammonia thioglycollate.

The main ingredient of acid perms is glycerol monothioglycollate. Although acid perms are kinder to the hair, more clients suffer from allergic reactions to acid perms than alkaline perms. Remember to carry out skin tests on all clients with sensitive skin or with a history of allergies.

The most common ingredient in neutraliser is hydrogen peroxide; others contain sodium bromate. The hydrogen peroxide can cause some coloured hair to fade after perming.

Effects on the hair structure

In Chapter 6, you saw that the hair is made up of amino acids and peptide bonds which originate in the hair follicle. The many amino acids and peptide bonds form the polypeptide chains (coils), which are held together by permanent and temporary bonds inside the cortex layer of the hair.

KEY TERM

Disulphide bonds – two sulphur atoms bonded together.

The diagram below shows a single hair from the cuticle layer to the cortex layer. The polypeptide chains (coils) are found inside the cortex.

When you are blow drying, setting or styling with heated equipment, the temporary bonds are softened by the water and heat, and temporarily set into their new shape. When hair is permed, the bonds are permanently changed with the use of chemicals. These bonds are called **disulphide bonds** (permanent bonds).

The temporary bonds hold the polypeptide chains in place along the length of the coils.

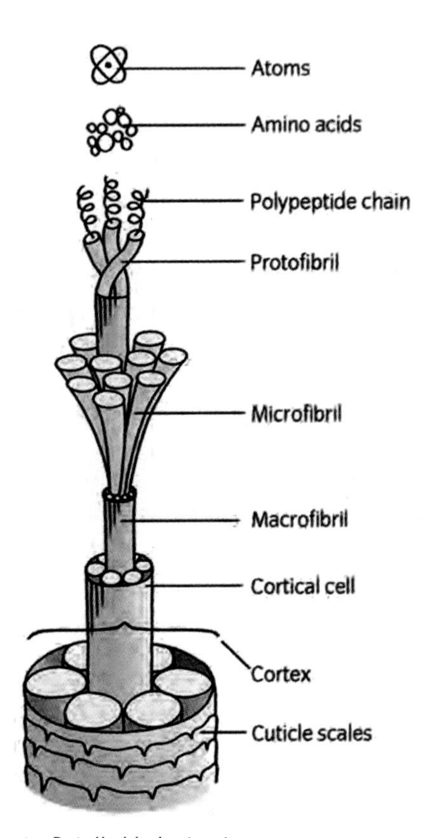

▲ Detailed hair structure

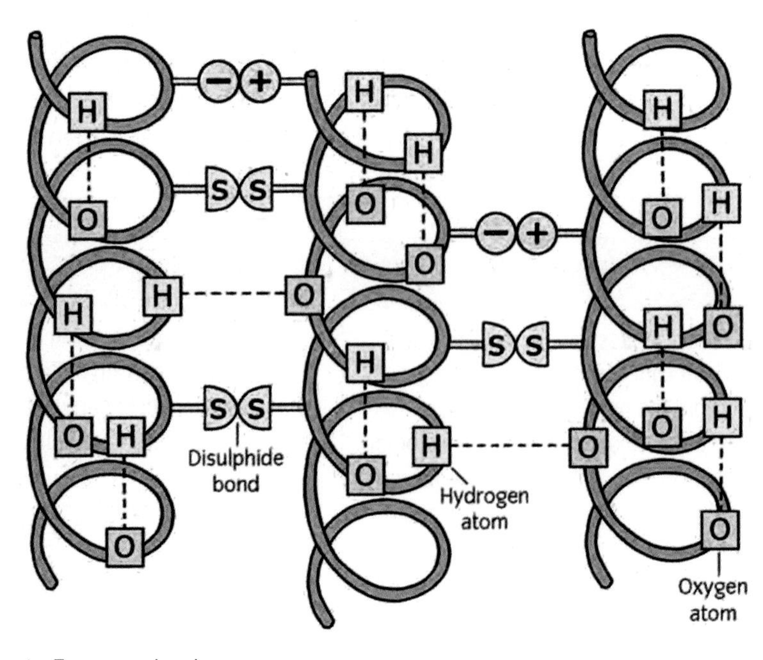

▲ Temporary bonds

The bonds that are changed during perming are the disulphide bonds that hold the polypeptide chains in position across the coils from left to right.

A disulphide bond is also known as a cystine molecule, and is shown in the diagram.

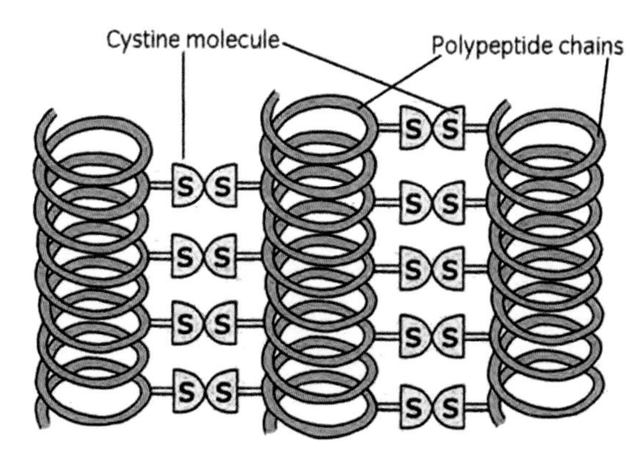

▲ Disulphide bonds before the perming process

The perm/chemical rearranger and neutralising process goes through three stages:

1 softening stage
2 moulding stage
3 fixing stage.

The perm lotion/chemical rearranger starts the softening stage, the development process is the moulding stage and the neutraliser fixes the hair in its new shape. Perm lotions and neutralisers are generally in a liquid form and chemical rearrangers are in a cream form.

Softening stage

When an acidic perm lotion is added to the hair, it generates heat to open the cuticle layer. With an alkaline lotion or a chemical rearranger it is the pH that causes the cuticle layer to open. As the cuticle layer opens, the perm lotion penetrates the cortex layer and begins to soften the disulphide bonds that hold the polypeptide chains together.

When the perm lotion/chemical rearranger is applied, it also adds hydrogen to the hair and the hydrogen breaks down some of the disulphide bonds, as shown in the diagram.

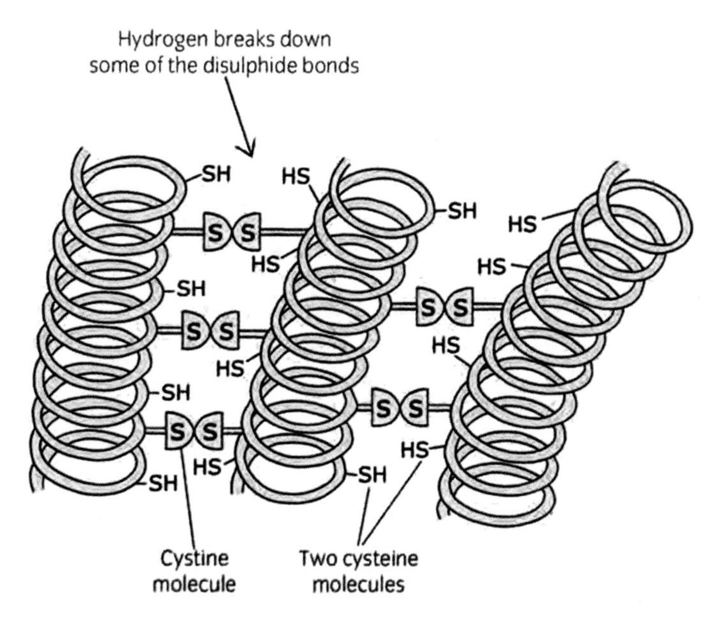

▲ Hair during the perming process

Moulding stage

As the disulphide bond is broken by the hydrogen, the cystine molecule is reduced into two cysteine molecules, as shown in the diagram above.

When perming, the softened hair then starts to take on the shape of the perm rod, and begins to mould into its new shape.

When chemically rearranging, the hair is softened by the cream and combed straight to mould into its new position. This is to ensure that the hair is smoothly wrapped around the perming tool and will adapt to its new shape in a smooth and even curl formation. The hair is then permed and re-moulded around a perm rod to create a soft curl before being fixed by neutraliser.

▲ Hair during the neutralising process

Fixing stage

The neutraliser stabilises the hair and permanently fixes it in its new shape.

The neutraliser is an oxidising agent and therefore contains oxygen. When the neutraliser is added, the oxygen combines with the hydrogen in the cysteine molecules, so there are now two hydrogen molecules and one oxygen molecule on the hair. This is also known as H_2O, the chemical formula for water, as shown in the diagram on the right.

The oxygen bonds with the hydrogen, which leaves the cysteine molecules. This allows the recreation of one cystine molecule. The hair is now in its newly formed permanently bonded shape, as shown in the diagram.

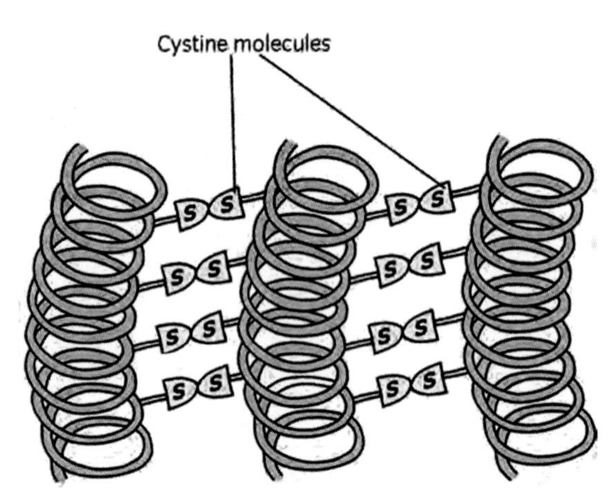

▲ Hair after the neutralising process

The diagram summarises the three stages of perming and neutralising.

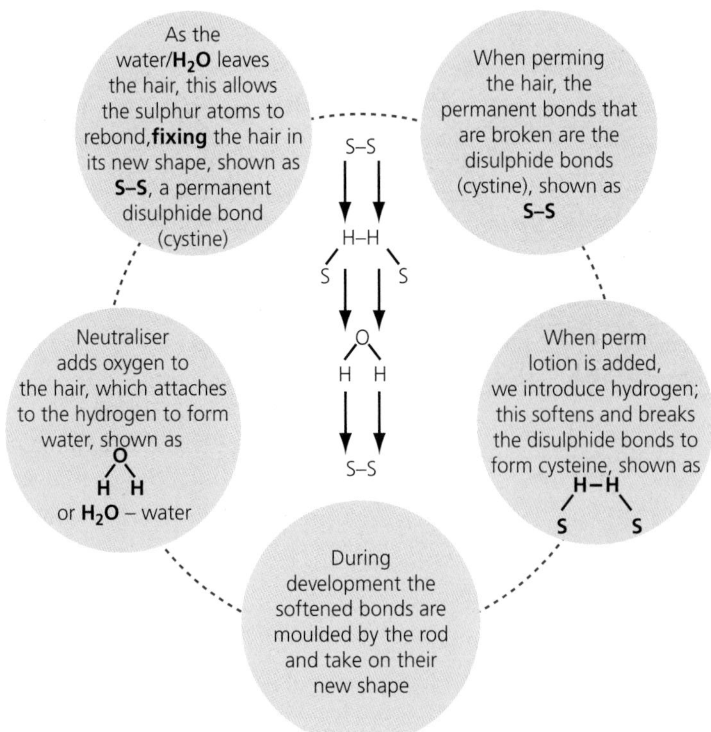

HANDY HINT

During the development process, about 25–30 per cent of the disulphide bonds should be broken. Any more than that and the hair could become frizzy and the hair structure will be permanently damaged. The development process can take 5–20 minutes, depending on the hair's condition.

Chemical rearranging

To partially relax naturally curly hair, a chemical rearranger is used on African-type hair before a perm. This cream product is applied onto the hair which is then combed and smoothed into a straighter form. The rearranger softens the hair, swelling the cuticle and allowing penetration into the cortex. After it is developed it is rinsed off and the hair is then permed with a perm lotion.

Effect of temperature on the perming process

Heat speeds up the processing time, while a cold environment will increase the development time. Acid perms need an activating ingredient which produces heat to enable the cuticle layer to open and the perm to penetrate into the cortex layer. (Alkaline perms and chemical rearrangers don't need this heat.)

Tools and equipment

Before your client arrives, ensure your trolley is prepared with the items in the table below.

Tools/equipment	Purpose
Apron and gloves	To protect your clothes and skin from the chemicals.
Pintail comb	To section the hair during the winding process. A metal pintail comb cannot be used when winding with lotion (pre-damp technique) as the metal may react with the chemicals in the perm lotion.
Section clips	To hold longer hair in sections in order to aid methodical working. Section clips are also used for sectioning a nine-section perm wind.

HANDY HINT

Perm lotion is also known as a reducing agent because it reduces the cystine molecules to cysteine molecules. Neutraliser is also known as a fixing agent because it fixes the hair into its new shape.

To help you remember the order for cystine and cysteine, use the number of 'e's from each word:

- There is *one* 'e' in cystine for *one* molecule
- There are *two* 'e's in cysteine for *two* molecules.

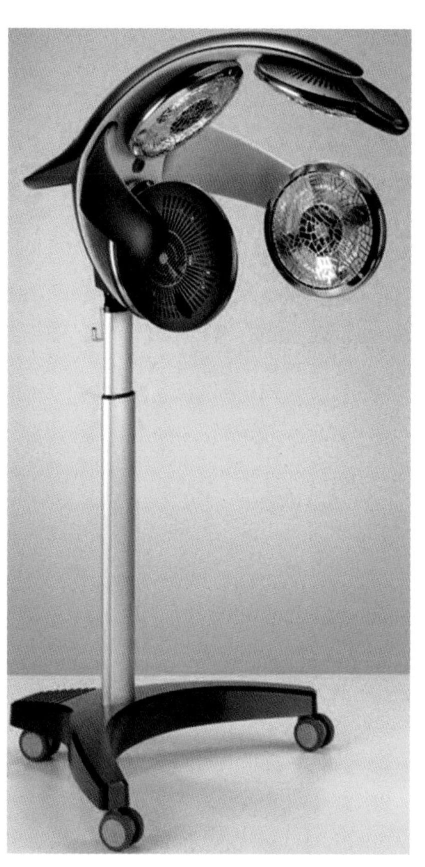

▲ A Climazone can be used to decrease the perm development time

KEY TERM

Fishhooks – buckled ends from poor winding technique.

Tools/equipment	Purpose
Detangling comb	To detangle the hair. This wide-toothed comb will prevent damage to the hair and minimise discomfort for the client.
End papers	To be used on the ends of the client's hair when winding the hair down the rod, enabling you to control the ends of the hair and wind without causing **fishhooks**.
Barrier cream	To be applied around the hairline before the damp cotton wool is applied. This prevents the perm lotion coming into contact with the scalp and skin, thereby avoiding discomfort or chemical burns.
Cotton wool	To be placed around the client's hairline when the perm lotion or neutraliser is being applied. Make sure the cotton wool is replaced if it becomes saturated or it might hold the chemicals against the client's skin.
Water spray	To be used during winding. Wound hair should be misted all over with the water spray to maintain an even moisture balance.
Plastic cap	To be placed over the wound hair once the perm lotion has been applied in order to keep in the natural heat from the head and aid development.
Timer	To time the development of the perm and the neutralising process.

Once you have completed your consultation, relevant hair tests and decided which rod sizes are required to achieve the desired result, you can add the following items to your prepared trolley.

Tools/equipment	Purpose
Small to medium perm rods	These are generally used when a client requests tighter curls but can also be used to achieve medium curls on dense hair. Longer hair may also require a slightly smaller rod, as the weight of the hair may pull the curls down, making them a little looser.
Medium to large perm rods	Provide a looser curl for softer-looking curls.
Bendy rods	Bendy rods come in different sizes and can be used to produce spiral curls, tight curls and loose curls. The curl will depend on the hair length, density, chosen wind and size.
Accelerator	An accelerator can be used to speed up the development process of the perm (always check the MFIs).

When the perm has been completed and the neutralising process needs to take place, you will need two more items at the basin area.

Tools/equipment	Purpose
Bowl	Required to contain the neutralising product (if you are applying it with the bowl-and-sponge technique).
Sponge	To froth/foam the neutralising product in the bowl before applying it.

ACTIVITY

Re-read the lists above and then prepare your trolley for a perm service. Write down anything you missed and discuss this with your tutor/manager.

Types and uses of products

Perming products

KEY TERM

Exothermic – producing heat through a chemical reaction.

Perming products are available in various forms, such as acidic, alkaline and **exothermic**, and come in varied strengths to suit all hair types. When perming African-type hair, use the perm lotion that comes from the same system as the rearranger, because the pH and supporting ingredients will work effectively together. These are usually alkaline perms.

Perm lotion types may be written as:

- 0 or R – for resistant hair types, or hair that is difficult to perm (such as coarse hair)
- 1 or N – for normal hair types
- 2 or T – for tinted or coloured hair that is porous.

When deciding whether to use an acidic or an alkaline perm lotion, you should consider:

- what curl movement the client would like
- the condition of the hair and what products are already on the hair
- the hair texture, density and length
- whether the client wants a soft, looser curl result or a longer-lasting, tighter curl result.

▲ Varying strength perm lotions for difficult-to-perm natural hair

▲ pH neutral perm lotions

Acid perms

Acid perms are pH 6–7 and are therefore less damaging to the hair than alkaline perms. Acidic perms require a heat activator to help open the cuticle layer of the hair. This activator either comes in a separate bottle or can be 'hidden' in the screw cap of the perm lotion bottle. When the cap is twisted, it pierces the seal and the activator mixes with the perm lotion, effectively activating it. Whether you add a separate activator or activate the product from the cap, when the two products mix, mild heat is generated. This heat helps to open the cuticle layer to allow the perm lotion into the cortex layer. You must activate the product when the hair is wound and ready to be damped. If you activate it too early, the product strength will weaken. Therefore, acid perms can be used only for post-damp applications.

Acid perms are most suitable for sensitive hair, fine hair and softer curl requirements, but they are available in varying strengths for resistant, normal and tinted hair.

▲ Acid perm

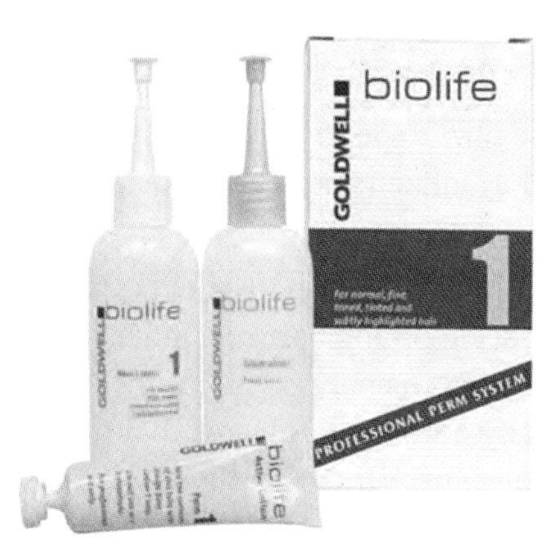

▲ Alkaline perm lotion

Alkaline perms

Most alkaline perms are pH 8.5–9.5 but some can be much lower, around pH 7.1. The lower the pH, the milder the lotion and therefore the less damaging it is to the hair. Alkaline perms give firmer curls and are most suited to resistant, strong hair, oily hair and white hair.

HANDY HINT

The main chemical ingredient of an alkaline perm is ammonia thioglycollate and these perms are available for all hair types – resistant, normal and tinted. The main ingredient in chemical rearrangers is also ammonia thioglycollate.

ACTIVITY

Take two test cuttings of white hair and see how well it perms with an acid perm lotion and an alkaline perm lotion.

Exothermic perms

Exothermic perms may be acid or alkaline, as the pH value of the products varies. Exothermic perms produce their own heat when two separate chemicals are mixed together and the neutralising lotions also create heat when mixed together. These provide similar benefits to the acid perm lotions and are available for all hair types.

Chemical rearranger

A chemical rearranger is generally used on type 4 and African-type hair to partially relax natural curls before a perm. Due to the natural shape of excessively curly hair, with its many twists and turns along the strand of hair, the surface is uneven. The product is often a cream emulsion, rather than a lotion, and it is applied to the hair in a four-section sequence to reduce the natural curl pattern. Once the hair is straighter, the rearranger is removed by rinsing thoroughly. Chemical rearrangement will facilitate easy winding as the hair will be more easily adaptable. After development, it is rinsed off and the hair is then permed with a perm lotion. Chemical rearrangers are alkaline and have a pH above 9.

▲ Chemical rearranger

Neutralisers

You should always use the neutraliser that comes with your chosen perm lotion, as the manufacturer will have designed the two products to work together. Neutralisers are pH 3–5 and can be applied in different ways; refer to the MFIs.

▲ Neutraliser

PERM AND NEUTRALISE HAIR

To understand how to perm and neutralise hair, you must understand the factors that may influence the service and the techniques that can be used.

Factors that may influence the service

To help you decide on the best rod/roller size and lotion choice and strength, you need to analyse your client's hair. By analysing the hair, you can identify any potential problems that may occur. You should feel the hair and visually check it to identify these factors:

- hair classification
- hair characteristic

- temperature
- direction and degree of movement required
- hair length
- length of regrowth
- colour-treated hair.

Effect of hair classifications on the service

The table below shows how hair classification factors affect the service.

Hair classification	Description	Impact on service and resolution
Type 1 – Straight hair Alkaline perm lotion	Fine/thin – hair tends to be very soft, shiny and oily and it can be difficult to hold a curl.	This type of hair can be difficult to perm as it has tightly packed cuticles and is often shiny and oily. A slightly stronger perm lotion may be required to help lift the cuticle scales, or a smaller perm rod for a firmer curl.
	Medium – hair has lots of volume and body.	This hair type is likely to take well to perming and a lotion should be chosen to suit the hair condition and desired curl.
	Coarse – hair is normally extremely straight and difficult to curl.	A stronger perm product is likely to be required. It will need to be developed for the full development time and smaller rods may be needed for the curl to be achieved.
Type 2 – Wavy hair Acid perm lotion	Fine/thin – hair has a definite 'S' pattern. Normally can accomplish various styles.	This hair type is likely to take well to perming and a lotion should be chosen to suit the hair condition and desired curl.
	Medium – hair tends to be frizzy and a little resistant to styling.	This hair type is likely to take well to perming and a lotion should be chosen to suit the hair condition and desired curl. Care is needed to ensure the hair does not become frizzier. A pre-perm treatment may be required to help even out porosity.
	Coarse – normally very frizzy; tends to have thicker waves.	This hair type is likely to take well to perming and a lotion should be chosen to suit the hair condition and desired curl. However, additional care is needed to ensure the hair does not become frizzier and you need to use a pre-perm treatment to even out porosity. Choose the size of rod carefully as the hair may curl very easily. A post-perm conditioner should be applied at the end of the service to prevent the hair from drying out further.

Hair classification	Description	Impact on service and resolution
Type 3 – Curly hair Chemical rearranger	Loose curls – can be thick and full with lots of body, with a definite 'S' pattern; also tends to be frizzy.	To create smaller or tighter curls, you would need to consider the rod size, the use of pre- and post-perm treatments and the lotion strength and choice, because the hair is likely to curl quickly and tightly. Otherwise the result could be frizzier hair. A larger perm rod could be used on this hair type to soften the curls.
	Tight curls – with a medium amount of curl.	Tight curly hair may need to be chemically rearranged to pre-soften the curls prior to winding a perm on larger rods to achieve the desired result.
Type 4 – Very curly hair Curl boost perm (after-rearranger perm lotion)	Soft – tightly coiled and has a more defined curly pattern.	Very curly hair will need to be chemically rearranged to pre-soften the curls prior to winding a perm on larger rods to achieve the desired result.
	Wiry – tightly coiled, but with a less defined curly pattern; has more of a 'Z' pattern shape. This hair texture tends to be the most porous of all hair types.	

▲ Diversity

THE HAIR PROFESSIONAL AT WORK

You will work on many different hair types to cover the range required. Some of the hair types you perm or chemically rearrange could be European hair, Asian hair or African-type hair. Clients will come from different ethnic groups, cultures and religions. Make sure you respect other people's culture and religion, even if it differs from your own personal views. See the Behaviours section in Chapter 1 for more information on personal ethics.

THE HAIR PROFESSIONAL AT WORK

Refer to the section 'Key work skills – professionalism, values, behaviour and communication' in Chapter 1 for more information on personal and professional ethics, selecting the most appropriate ways to communicate with clients and adapting your behaviour to respond effectively to different client behaviour.

Effect of hair characteristics on the service

The table below shows how hair characteristics affect the service.

Hair characteristic	Impact on service and resolution
Hair density Choose the right size curlers	When checking the density of the hair, you are identifying whether the hair is sparse, medium or abundant. For sparse hair, a brick wind is the most suitable technique to use, as this prevents too many roller marks or partings that would expose the scalp. Avoid too much tension, avoid winds that create roller section marks, use less lotion than normal and use a product that is milder on the hair. For abundant hair, you'll need more rods, more lotion and smaller sections when winding, so allow yourself sufficient time to wind the hair. Use larger rods on thick, abundant hair, as smaller rods may result in frizzy curls.
Hair texture Choose the right perm lotion	When checking the hair's texture, you are identifying whether the hair is fine, average or coarse. Perms on fine soft hair may develop quicker than on coarse hair, and will require a softer perm lotion. However, if the hair is fine and resistant then it will take longer to develop and you are likely to need a stronger lotion. Coarse hair will take longer to develop, depending on its condition, and larger rods may be required. More lotion is likely to be required for coarse hair.
Elasticity	An elasticity test must be carried out to test the strength of the cortex layer. If the hair is weak, alternative services must be recommended instead of a perm, or you can suggest a series of conditioning or penetrating treatments for a few weeks before retesting the hair's strength. If the hair is normal or strong, then consider the lotion strength required.
Porosity Pre-perm treatment	You must always carry out a porosity test to identify if the cuticle layers are open or closed and if the hair is porous, non-porous or even resistant. Porous hair will absorb the chemicals quickly so the ingredients will be active immediately. This hair will therefore need protecting from the chemicals and you may need to use a **pre-perm conditioner**, which is designed to even out the porosity of the hair. Resistant hair is likely to require more lotion, longer development time and smaller rods, and sometimes you may benefit from pre-damping the hair with lotion prior to winding. Different hair types vary immensely in porosity – see the table above on classifications and their varying characteristics.

Hair characteristic	Impact on service and resolution
Condition	The hair's condition will affect the porosity and elasticity of the hair – see above. Longer hair may have areas of weaker condition and pre-perm lotions may be required to even out the porosity and condition of the hair. A strand test is required during a service using a chemical rearranger to establish the effect the product has on the hair's condition.
Hair growth patterns Consider hair growth patterns like cowlicks	You should consider the growth patterns of the hair and wind accordingly. Consider a direction wind to work with strong double crowns or troublesome cowlicks.

Other factors that may affect the service

Factor	Impact on service and resolution
Temperature	When you process the perm, you need to ensure that the salon environment is warm enough. Carrying out the service in a cold salon will increase the development time, as cool air slows down the process. A warm salon or additional heat, such as an electronic accelerator, Rollerball, Climazone or hood dryer, will decrease the development time. It is not recommended to use an accelerator on a chemical rearranger; instead use a plastic cap to regulate temperature, as this will retain heat generated from the head. Always check if the MFIs allow additional heat to be applied.
Movement	You should consider the client's requirements for the direction of movement and how much movement and curl are required. The more curl and movement that is required, the smaller the perm rod will need to be. For a softer and looser curl, a larger perm rod will be needed.
Hair length	For longer hair, you will need more time for the wind, more lotion to coat the hair and you may also need to consider your winding technique. If the hair is long and in good condition you may decide to wind with lotion – a technique called **pre-damping.** This ensures that all the hair is covered with lotion through to the ends, as the lotion may not penetrate to the ends if it is applied after winding.

KEY TERM

Pre-damping – winding with lotion already applied to the hair.

Factor	Impact on service and resolution
	Longer hair will go around a rod more times than shorter hair and therefore create more movement. Although you may decide to use larger rods because of this, you must remember that the weight of long hair can pull the curls looser, so you must consider the density of the hair before making your final decision on rod size. When working with African-type hair, remember that the natural compact curl pattern disguises the length of the hair and it will be elongated after chemical rearrangement.
Length of regrowth	If the hair has a previous perm, you need to check how long ago the service took place. You will need to find out if the hair needs to be cut before it is permed, whether it needs a pre-perm conditioner on the mid-lengths and ends and whether it is in good enough condition to take another chemical service.
Colour-treated hair	Hair that has been highlighted and tinted can often be permed with a perm lotion designed especially for highlighted hair. However, a course of penetrating treatments may be required before perming. Hair that has been bleached must not be permed. Before deciding on your perm choice, you will need to answer these questions: • Is there colour on the hair? • Is it even and over the whole head or are there highlights, which may give an uneven porosity? • Is there bleach on the hair? You should carry out an incompatibility test or a pre-perm test curl, if you are unsure what is on the client's hair.

TECHNIQUES, TOOLS, EQUIPMENT AND PRODUCTS AND THE EFFECTS THEY ACHIEVE

To decide which technique to use, you need to:

- consult with your client and confirm the curl result required
- analyse your client's hair
- identify any contra-indications and factors that could affect the desired result
- carry out the relevant hair tests.

Sectioning techniques

When perming, the most common sectioning patterns are:

- basic winds
- directional winds
- brick winds.

Basic wind

The basic sectioning technique uses six or nine sections.

Winding a nine-section perm helps you to control longer hair lengths and work in a methodical manner.

- Sections 1 and 2 go from the crown to the back of the nape, about the width of a rod.
- Sections 3 and 4, and 5 and 6, are on either side of sections 1 and 2, going from the top of the head to the back of the ear and down to the nape, and splitting these areas in two – from the ear to the occipital bone.
- Sections 7 and 8 are the two front sections on either side.
- Section 9 is the top front section.

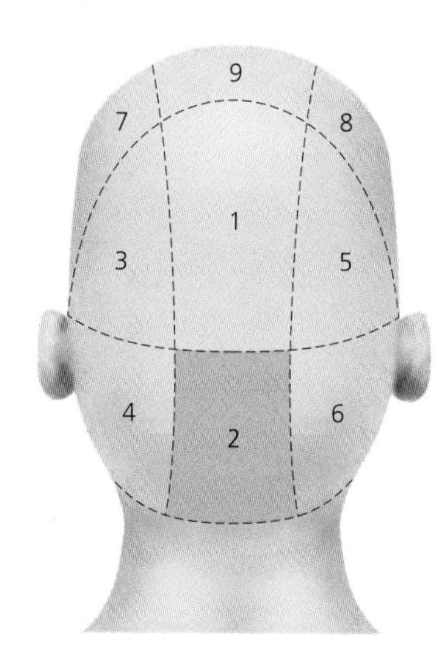

▲ 9-section wind sections

The benefits of a nine-section perm wind are:

- it results in methodical winding
- it is easier to control the hair length.

For a six-section perm wind, section the hair as follows:

- Sections 1 and 2 combined – crown to nape
- Sections 3 and 4 combined – left back section to nape
- Sections 5 and 6 combined – right back section to nape
- Section 7 – front left section
- Section 8 – front right section
- Section 9 – top section.

Directional wind

A directional wind is similar to a directional set; you wind the hair in a directed manner to suit the style requirements. The benefits of a directional wind are:

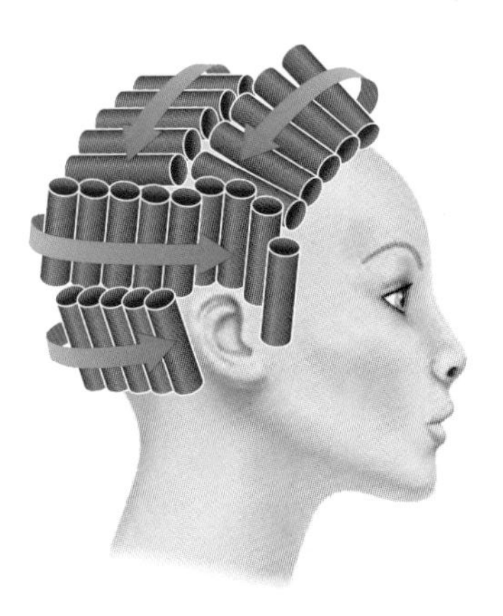

▲ Directional wind

- the roots are wound in the direction that the style will be worn
- the hair is wound to suit the partings worn
- it is suitable for any hair length.

Brick wind

A brick wind perm has the same winding pattern as a brick wind setting technique. Wind the first row straight across, and on the second row, off-set the rollers/rods, so that each roller/rod sits across the gap from the previous row above.

The benefits of a brick wind perm are:

- it avoids partings
- there are no rod/roller marks.

When you are winding the hair, your rods should ideally be wound to sit on their own base. But, as with setting, you can wind on-base to achieve maximum root lift or off-base to prevent root lift (see photos).

▲ Brick wind

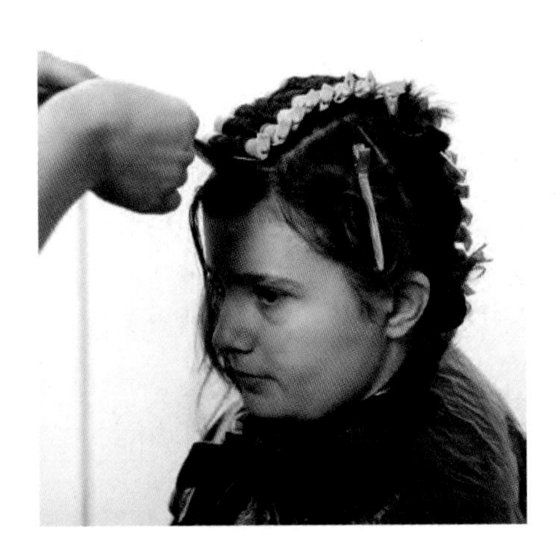

▲ Wind on-base

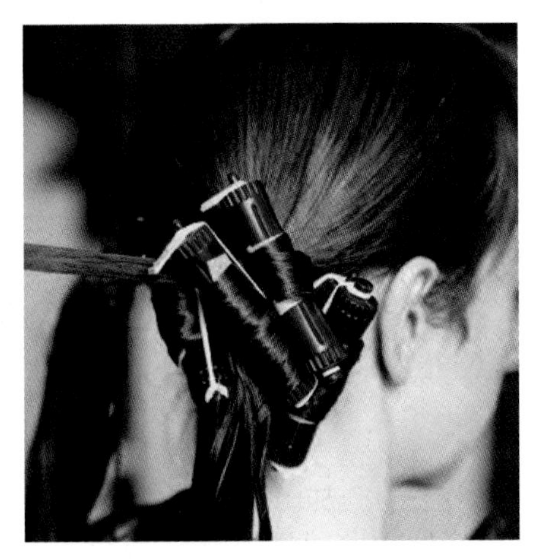

▲ Off-base perm winding

HANDY HINT

Use a pre-perm lotion on coloured hair to even out porosity.

Pre-perm treatments

Along with perm lotions, chemical rearrangers and neutralisers, you will also use a range of pre-perm shampoos, conditioners and treatments.

▲ Pre-perm shampoo

Pre-perm treatments generally refer to conditioners rather than shampoo. However, using a pre-perm shampoo is advisable.

Pre-perm shampoo

A pre-perm shampoo has a neutral pH (pH 7). It therefore slightly opens the cuticle layer to allow the perm lotion to penetrate the cortex layer, where the changes during the perming process take place. A pre-perm shampoo helps to remove any dirt, products and oil residue that may coat the cuticle layer and create a barrier to the perm lotion.

Pre-perm conditioner

A pre-perm conditioner should be used on the mid-lengths and ends of the hair if you have identified that the hair has an uneven porosity. A pre-perm conditioner can be sprayed (or sprinkled directly from a **phial**) on the hair before sectioning or winding the hair with the rods. It is important that you avoid spraying on hair that has good porosity; instead, aim it directly onto the porous and uneven areas of the hair. These conditioners even out the porosity and allow the perm lotion to penetrate evenly into the cortex layer.

KEY TERM

Phial – small bottle.

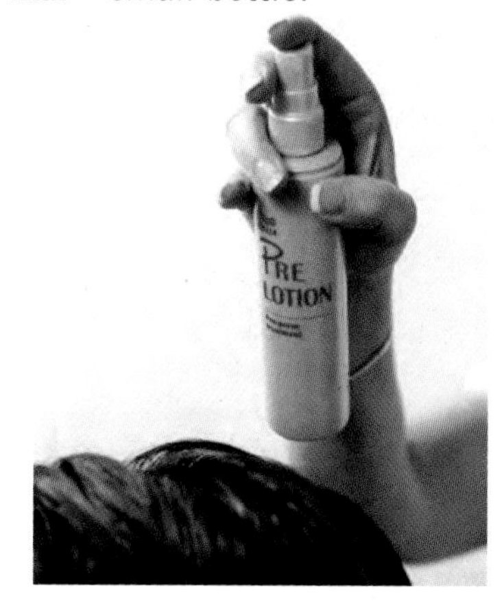

▲ Pre-perm conditioner

HANDY HINT

Never use a normal surface conditioner before a perm or a chemical rearranger, as this will coat the cuticle layer, creating a barrier and preventing the perm lotion from entering the cortex layer evenly.

Methods of applying perm lotions and neutralisers

Perm lotions and neutralisers may be applied **post-damp** or **pre-damp**. Post-damping is winding the hair around the rods and then applying the perm lotion to each rod, one after the other. Pre-damping is applying a weak perm lotion to the hair prior to winding. For pre-damping, you will need to wind the hair quickly to avoid over-processing the hair. Remember to wear PPE to avoid allergic reactions or contact dermatitis from the chemicals used.

KEY TERMS

Post-damp – applying the lotion after the wind.

Pre-damp – winding the hair with the lotion already applied. Not all perm manufacturers allow pre-damping, so always read the MFIs.

Pre-damping is not recommended on hair that has already been treated with a rearranger.

When deciding whether to use post-damping or pre-damping, you need to consider:

- the sequence of the winding technique – particularly for pre-damping
- MFIs – post-damping is the only option for some perms
- the hair length – you might decide that pre-damping is the best option to ensure that you thoroughly cover long hair
- the hair texture and condition – never pre-damp fine or porous hair types, but do consider the benefits to coarse, resistant hair or hair that is difficult to wind.

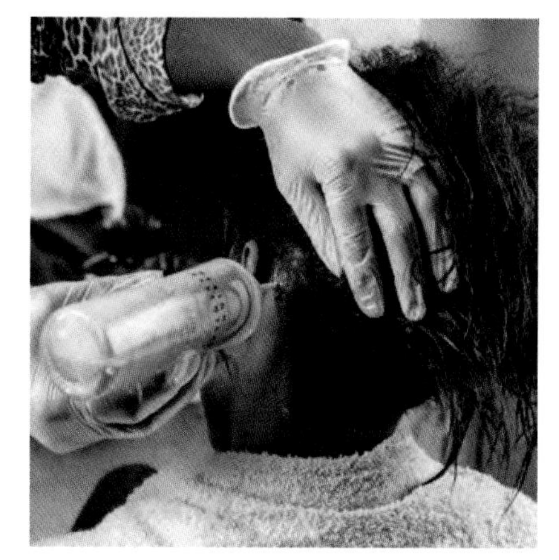

▲ Scalp protector being applied before a chemical rearranger

Scalp protectors

Scalp protectors are applied around the nape and hairline area prior to the application of rearranger solution.

Neutralisers

Neutralisers are pH 3–5 and can be applied in different ways (always refer to the MFIs). Some products must be applied directly from the bottle onto the rinsed rods; others may be diluted in a large applicator bottle

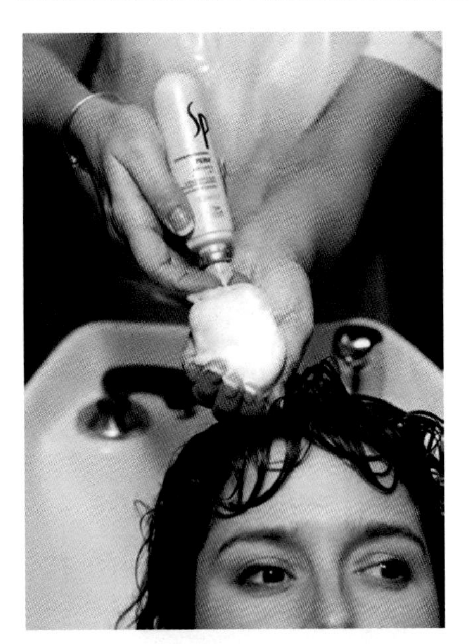

▲ Post-perm treatment

and sprinkled over the rinsed rods. Another way to apply neutraliser is to pour the contents into a bowl and 'foam' it with a sponge. The neutraliser is then applied to the rods with the sponge and left to develop.

Applicators used for chemical rearrangers

Chemical rearrangers are applied differently to perming products.

As with a relaxing service, chemical rearrangement is carried out on dry hair, using thioglycollate and applied with a tint brush or spatula before being left to develop.

Perm conditioners

After every perm service, a pH balancing conditioner should be used. These are referred to as post-perm treatments or conditioners. They have special properties and will return the hair to its natural pH.

HANDY HINT

It is important to restore the hair's pH balance after the perming and neutralising process to ensure that the cuticles are closed, the hair is returned to a pH of 4.5 to 5.5 and the moisture is locked into the hair, preventing it from drying out and becoming brittle.

Factors that may influence the services

In order to achieve your client's desired result, you must consider all factors that may affect the hair, the curl size and the final result.

When choosing your perm rod size, you must consider:

- the desired curl result – the smaller the rod size, the tighter the curl
- the length of the hair – longer hair wrapped around a rod will naturally be looser towards the root area if wound from point to root
- the condition of the hair – if it is slightly porous or of weaker elasticity, the curl will develop quicker and therefore a larger rod size may be required, to prevent the curls being too tight.

HANDY HINT

Chemical rearranging is necessary to partially relax naturally curly hair before a perm. The rearranger softens the hair, swelling the cuticle and allowing penetration into the cortex. After it is developed it is rinsed off and the hair is then permed with a perm lotion to create a softer, looser curl result.

Application methods of chemical rearrangers

The method of applying the chemical rearranger will vary depending on the length of the hair and whether or not it is a regrowth or virgin head application.

For virgin application on longer hair lengths, the cream-based rearranger should be applied to the mid-lengths and ends first, followed by the root area. This is because of the heat produced from the head and also because the new growth of hair is **freshly keratinised** and is more sensitive to chemicals.

For short hair lengths, the product can be applied from root to tips, while for hair that has been previously permed, only the new growth towards the roots should be treated with the chemical rearranger.

KEY TERM

Freshly keratinised – new cells produced in new hair growth.

HANDY HINT

A pre-perm treatment should be applied before a chemical rearranger or perm lotion if the hair is of uneven porosity.

Importance of testing the hair and scalp prior to and during services

The hair and scalp should be checked and analysed before any perming chemicals are applied to the hair. The hair should be tested for strength and elasticity and porosity. For details about these tests please refer back to page 532.

HANDY HINT

Use all products economically to avoid waste and to ensure you are working cost effectively. Waste is costly for your salon and has negative effects on the environment too. Follow the MFIs regarding the correct amounts to use and consider the client's hair length and density.

Importance of following salon and manufacturers' instructions during services

Manufacturers' instructions (MFIs) can vary immensely, so it is of paramount importance that these instructions are read before the service commences.

Development and rinsing times must be strictly followed to ensure the results are achieved, the hair is not over or under developed and the hair's condition is not compromised.

Problems that may occur during services

As with all services, problems can occur. Problems with perming can often be overcome, once you know what has caused them.

When carrying out the chemical rearranger service, it is very important that the chemicals are not overlapped. Overlapping products on previously chemically-treated hair will lead to deterioration of the hair's condition and could lead to breakage. The client's unhappiness with the service could also result in legal proceedings.

The tables show the problems that can occur during the perming or neutralising service, their likely causes and how they can be remedied.

HANDY HINT

In some cases, the salon's insurance company may need to be notified if the client is dissatisfied or if there is damage or breakage to their hair or skin.

Problems during the service

Problem	Likely cause	Remedy
Scalp irritation	• Lotion on the scalp • Allergic reaction to the lotion • Tension or rods too tight	• Rinse the hair and scalp with cool water. • Refer to GP if required
Rods fall out when rinsing the hair	• Water pressure too high • Hair too short • Rods wound too loosely	• Lower the water pressure • Use a hair net to secure in place • Rewind the rods
The perm process is slow	• Salon is too cold • Insufficient lotion used • Lotion too weak	• Add heat and use an accelerator (check MFIs) • Add more lotion • Add stronger lotion

Problems noticed immediately after the perm process

Problem	Likely cause	Remedy
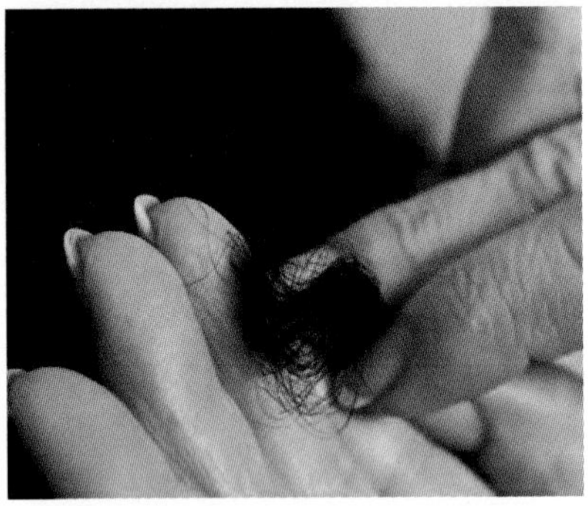 **Fish hooks**	• Poor wind – the hair has been buckled or bent during the wind	• Trim the ends of the hair
 **Some straight pieces**	• Sections too large • Rods too large • Poor wind – too loose • Uneven application of lotion • Rods loosened during rinsing	• Re-perm the straight pieces if the hair condition allows
 **Frizzy hair**	• Rods too small • Wind too tight • Lotion too strong • Overdeveloped • Overlapped products	• Apply conditioning treatments • Regular trims in order to remove the damaged hair gradually

Problem	Likely cause	Remedy
 Hair breakage	• Poor wind – bands are twisted or positioned too close to the root • Rods are too tightly wound • Incompatible products • Lotion too strong • Overdeveloped • Overlapped products	• There is no remedy other than cutting to reduce the visible effects of breakage. • Conditioning treatments, restructurants and regular trims may help prevent further breakage.
 Discolouration of hair	• Incompatible products • Neutraliser has faded recent colour service	• Use a semi-permanent or temporary colour to tone the hair colour
 The curl is too tight	• Rods too small • Sections too small • Overdeveloped	• Apply deep conditioning treatments • If condition allows, you could re-perm on larger rods or relax the hair
 The hair is straight	• Barrier on the hair • Resistant hair • Incorrect perm choice – too weak • Underdeveloped • Faulty lotion	• Re-perm the hair if the condition allows

Problem	Likely cause	Remedy
The curl is uneven	• Sections too large • Poor wind – uneven • Incorrect rod size • Uneven product application • Rods loosened during rinsing stage	• Re-perm if condition allows

Problems noticed days after the perm process

Sometimes clients experience problems a few days after the service, causing them to return to the salon.

Problem	Likely cause	Remedy
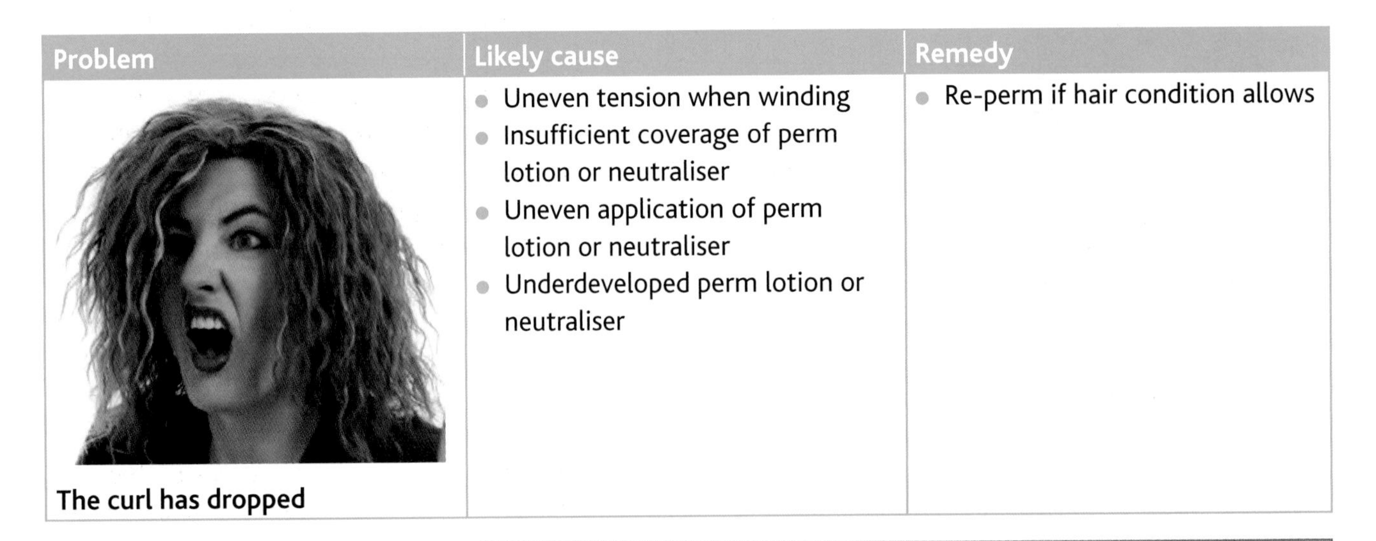 The curl has dropped	• Uneven tension when winding • Insufficient coverage of perm lotion or neutraliser • Uneven application of perm lotion or neutraliser • Underdeveloped perm lotion or neutraliser	• Re-perm if hair condition allows

THE HAIR PROFESSIONAL AT WORK

Find out from your salon manager which of these problems you can deal with yourself and which ones you should seek support.

HANDY HINT

If you encounter a problem, refer to the values and behaviours described in Chapter 1 for more information on:

- explaining clearly to clients why their needs or expectations cannot be met
- keeping the client informed and reassured
- adapting your behaviour to respond effectively to different client behaviour.

Perming and neutralising tests

Test	Purpose of test and when to carry it out	How to carry out the test and expected results	Influence of results on perming service
Curl reduction test	Carry out a curl reduction test to confirm the degree of straightness has been achieved during the chemical rearranger process.	Wipe off excess rearranger from the hair and check the degree of reduced movement in the hair.	If the degree of straightness is not yet achieved, allow further development but monitor every few minutes. If the degree of curl reduction is achieved, thoroughly rinse out the chemical rearranger from the hair with tepid water.
Development test	To check if the perm development time has been sufficient. This test is carried out during the perm development process.	Partially unwind a perm roller and push the hair back towards the root. Do this in three to four areas around the head. A positive result shows an adequate S-bend in a similar size to the roller.	If the curl result is not achieved, re-wind the perm rod and develop for a longer period of time, following the MFIs. Later retest the same rod and an additional area.
		A negative result can be either: • underdeveloped – a weak S-bend, meaning the development time is insufficient • over-developed – too many bonds have been broken within the hair and the S-bend will be much tighter than required.	If the curl result has been achieved, then the hair is ready to be rinsed and neutralised.

Action to take in the event of an adverse reaction

If the perm is overdeveloped then damage to and/or disintegration of the client's hair or skin may occur. The hair will need to be treated with a penetrating conditioner.

The desired outcome may not be achieved if the perm is underdeveloped.

Legal action may be taken by the client if their hair or skin is damaged, in which case your manager should inform their insurance company.

Importance of water temperature

When you shampoo the hair in preparation for the perm, you should use warm water to help cleanse the hair to remove products, oil and dirt. Warm water will also aid the opening of the cuticle layer, ready for the lotion to be applied.

When you rinse the perm lotion from the hair, again use warm water to keep the cuticle layers open, ready for the neutraliser to fix the hair in its new shape. Remember that the scalp may be sensitive from the chemicals, so consider your client's comfort and ensure the water is not too hot.

HANDY HINT

If the water is too hot, your client may suffer discomfort or scalp irritation and the perm may process more quickly than expected. Alternatively, if the water is not warm enough, the cuticle layer will not be sufficiently opened to allow the chemicals to penetrate the cortex layer, which could slow down the development process.

Effects on the hair structure

After a service involving a chemical rearrange, perming and neutralising, it is very important to restore the hair's pH balance by using a post-perm treatment or a pH-balancing conditioner.

As well as returning the hair back to its natural pH of 4.5 to 5.5, a post-perm treatment also:

- stops chemical processing from continuing
- stops **creeping oxidation**
- closes the cuticle layer and stops the hair from losing moisture and becoming brittle.

KEY TERM

Creeping oxidation – when chemicals are left in the hair and they carry on working and cause damage.

▲ Post-perm treatment

Provide advice and recommendations

It is important that you provide your client with aftercare advice following a perm because of the strength of the chemicals used. Your client needs to know how to maintain the curl and their hair condition.

Always give clear, accurate and constructive advice, and consider your client's time constraints in relation to maintaining their hairstyle. If your client has an active lifestyle and/or enjoys swimming, make sure that you consider this and recommend suitable products.

Explain to your clients that they should not wash their hair for 24–48 hours after a perm and should avoid excessive tension on the hair, as this can cause the curls to loosen.

Recommend products

Advise your clients which shampoos and conditioners they should use to maintain moisture levels and the condition of their hair. Suggest regular deep-penetrating conditioning treatments which can either be used at home or carried out in the salon.

You should make recommendations to your clients about the use of styling and finishing products. Advise them which styling products to use when the hair is wet, to avoid the hair looking frizzy, and which finishing products to use to hold the curls in place. Show your clients how much of the product to use, depending on their hair length, and how to use it with their styling tools.

HANDY HINT

When making your recommendations, use your communication skills, maintain eye contact and use positive, open body language to promote trust and a good client–stylist relationship.

Recommend tools and equipment

Always clearly explain to your client which brushes and combs they should use, and which to avoid. Inform your clients that they should always use a wide-toothed comb on wet hair. Promote the use of a diffuser when drying hair to maintain the curls without disturbing or separating them or causing the hair to look fluffy or frizzy. Explain that excessive use of heated styling equipment will increase porosity and reduce elasticity, causing damage to the hair.

▲ Recommend products suitable for permed hair

Recommend further services

Future colouring services may need to be suggested or avoided, depending on the condition of the client's hair. If a colour has faded slightly during the perming process, you may need to recommend a semi-permanent or a temporary colour to brighten the faded colour. The perm service carried out may, however, restrict your client to certain colour services in the future, and you must make your client aware of this.

Recommend to your clients when to return to the salon for a trim, and make them aware of the signs that indicate that their hair needs to be cut and styled.

Make suggestions for future colouring services and conditioning treatments, and tell your clients how long the perm should be expected to last.

▲ Dry permed hair with a diffuser

WHAT YOU MUST DO

For your practical assessments you must:

- Apply safe working practices when perming hair
- Prepare for perming and neutralising
- Perm and neutralise hair.

Apply safe working practices when perming hair

Throughout the service you must ensure you maintain your responsibilities for health and safety.

You must prepare your client to meet salon requirements and protect their clothing. Ensure your own personal hygiene, protection and appearance meets accepted industry and organisational requirements.

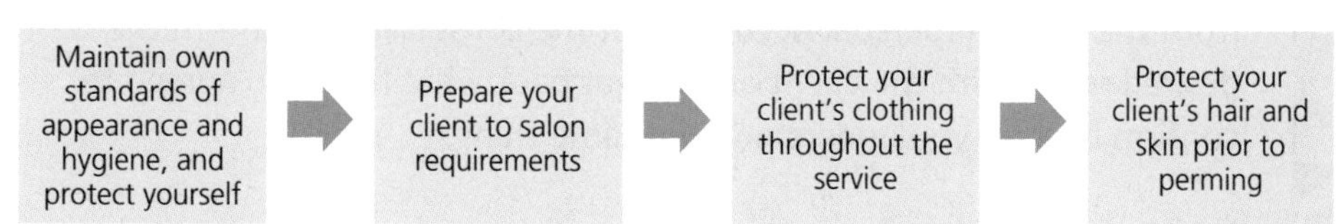

▲ Prepare for services

HANDY HINT

Encourage your clients to book their next appointment while they are still in the salon and your advice is clear in their mind.

During the service, make sure you use working methods that minimise wastage of products and the risk of cross-infection and make effective use of your working time. You will need to complete the service within a commercially viable time, using the correct sectioning techniques so that the hair is sectioned cleanly and evenly to achieve the desired look.

To work safely and hygienically:

- wear PPE when using perming and neutralising chemicals
- position your client to meet the needs of the service without causing them discomfort
- ensure your own posture and position while working minimises fatigue and the risk of injury
- keep your work area clean and tidy throughout the service
- minimise the risk of cross-infection
- use clean resources
- follow workplace and suppliers' or manufacturers' instructions for the safe use of equipment, materials and products
- dispose of waste materials
- follow manufacturers' instructions
- apply perming lotion and neutralisers evenly to all wound hair
- monitor and time the development of the perming and neutralising processes
- apply suitable pre- and post-conditioners, where necessary, to protect the hair from damage.

Prepare for perming and neutralising

To prepare for the service, you must:

- consult with your client about the services and outcomes of tests
- select suitable products, tools and equipment.

Consult with clients

You must use the consultation process to make sure you are clear about your client's desired effect. Discuss their needs and wishes for the service and explain if and why this cannot be achieved for their hair type. Suggest alternative services if the desired result is not achievable. Before the service, ask your client relevant questions to identify if they have any contra-indications to perming services and record their responses to questioning on a record card. Conduct the necessary tests on their hair following manufacturers' instructions and recognised industry procedures. You should record the outcomes of these tests on the client's record card too. If contra-indications and/or reactions to tests cause doubts as to the suitability of the service for your client, seek assistance from the relevant person. At the end of the consultation, confirm the desired result with the client and repeat back what has been agreed to confirm both of you understand the same thing.

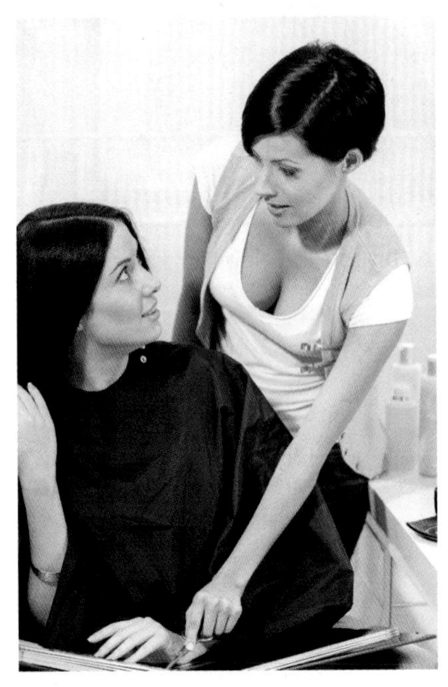

▲ Client consultation

Select suitable products, tools and equipment

Before you start the service, choose the most suitable products, tools and equipment based on the results of tests, the consultation with your client and any factors influencing the service.

Prepare the most suitable products following manufacturers' instructions and protect your client's hair and skin prior to perming.

Identify the most suitable sectioning techniques to use in order to achieve the desired result for:

- basic wind
- directional wind
- brick wind.

Perm and neutralise hair

Having completed the consultation, identified any contra-indications and completed the relevant hair tests, you are now able to confirm the perming product most suitable for giving the desired result to your client's hair and whether straightening, if required, has been achieved by the rearranging process.

You must use the products correctly and choose the correct techniques, ensuring you have taken into account any factors that may influence the service.

Sectioning, winding and securing the hair

Once you have decided which winding technique and rod size to use, you can begin to wind.

Each section of hair must relate to the size of your rods. If you are using varied sizes, then your section sizes must vary too. If the section size is too large for the rod, the curls may be uneven or too loose. If the section size is too small, you may struggle to get all the rods on the head and your resulting curls may be too tight.

As you carry out the winding process, maintain an even tension throughout. Make sure all wound perm rods sit on their own base.

To secure the hair in place as you wind, you must use an end paper. These are used on the ends of the hair to keep all the hairs in place and prevent buckled ends or fish hooks.

Once you have wound the hair around the rod, secure it with a perm band. This band must go straight across the hair, without any twists. Bands that are twisted or secured too closely to the root area can break the hair.

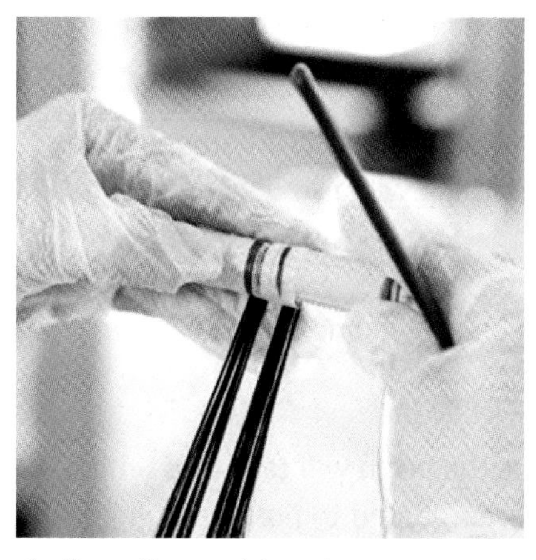

▲ Correctly wound-in end paper

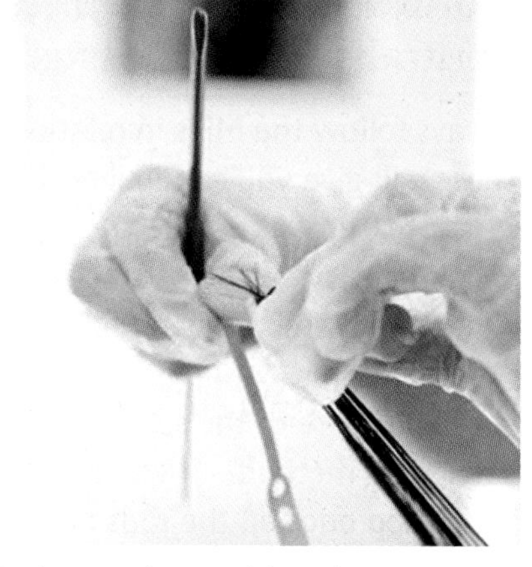

▲ Incorrectly wound-in end paper

Use appropriate products and techniques

The factors that can affect your choice of perming and neutralising products include:

- how straight or curly a client's hair is and their desired result
- the length, condition, density and texture of the hair
- the previous service on the hair
- any contra-indications.

Make sure you check all of the above and take these points into consideration when reading the MFIs.

Chemical rearrangement

If you are chemically rearranging the hair prior to perming, you must confirm that this has achieved the desired degree of straightening. Once it has, rinse the rearranger from the hair thoroughly. Ensure you leave the hair and scalp clean and free from chemicals and excess moisture prior to the winding process.

HANDY HINT

Remember, do not flood the scalp when you apply the perm lotion – you are perming the hair not the scalp!

Perming process

Once you have wound a full head of rods, prepare the client for the perm lotion application:

1. Ensure they are protected with a gown, towel and waterproof cape.
2. Apply barrier cream around the hairline.
3. Attach misted/damp cotton wool around the hairline.
4. Mist the hair with water to ensure even porosity.
5. Activate and prepare the perm lotion of your choice.
6. Apply a few drops to each rod, starting from the back and working towards the front (from the resistant areas to the weaker areas).
7. After the initial application, thoroughly coat each rod a second time, without flooding the scalp with lotion.
8. Change the cotton wool if the lotion drips.
9. Place a disposable cap on the client's head.
10. Use heat if suitable.
11. Offer your client refreshments and explain the development process and roughly how long it will take.

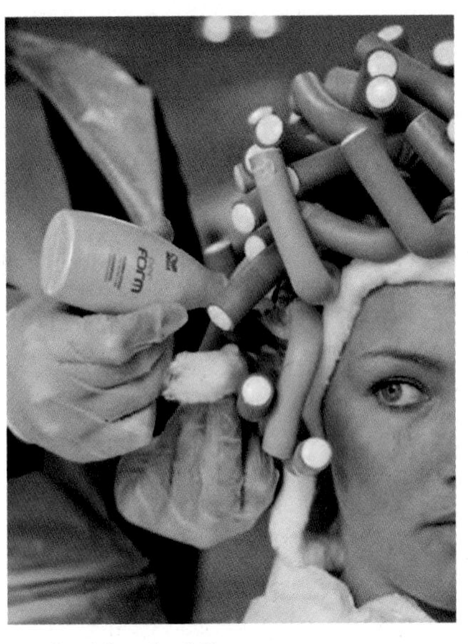

▲ Applying the lotion

Monitor the development of the perming and neutralising processes

Always follow the MFIs in relation to the suggested development times. These will give you a guideline, but the timing will also depend on:

- hair texture
- hair density
- hair type – remember white hair can be misleading
- hair length
- temperature of the salon
- winding method – if you pre-damped, the perm will take less time to develop once all the rods are in place, compared to post-damping.

HANDY HINT

Instructions for perming and neutralising products vary immensely, so always read them carefully before applying the products to your client's hair to ensure you achieve the best result and do not cause damage to their hair, skin or scalp.

If the perm lotion is underdeveloped, an insufficient number of bonds will break and the hair won't take on the new shape. If the neutraliser is underdeveloped, the curl will not be fixed in its new position. Either way, the curl is likely to drop and produce an unsatisfactory result.

If the perm lotion is overdeveloped, too many (over 20 per cent) of the disulphide bonds will be broken and the hair may become frizzy. If either the perm lotion or the neutraliser is overdeveloped, the hair condition can deteriorate and the hair's structure may be weakened.

1. Leave the perm to develop without disturbing the hair for at least 5–10 minutes, depending on the MFIs.
2. Complete a development test, checking that a test curl produces an S-bend that resembles the size of the rod.
3. If the hair requires further development, leave it for another 5 minutes and then check every 2–3 minutes.
4. When the development test is positive, escort your client to the basin area.

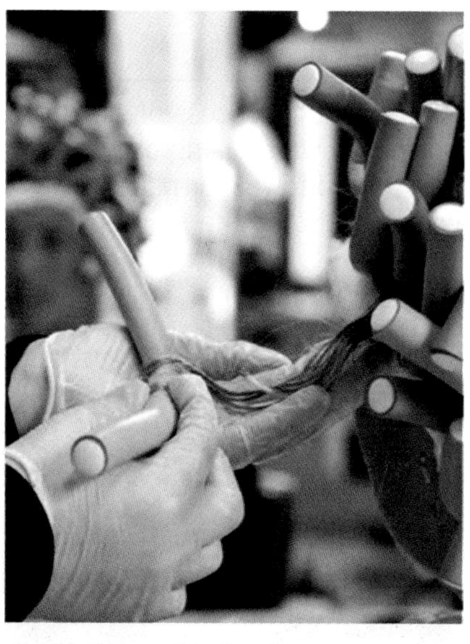

▲ Development test curl

Rinsing the hair

When the development test indicates that about 20 per cent of the disulphide bonds are broken, the hair must be thoroughly rinsed to remove all traces of perm lotion. Make sure the water temperature is comfortable for your client.

Perm lotion and neutraliser react together and can cause chemical burns to the hair and scalp, so you must rinse the hair, not only to stop the perm lotion from continuing to work, but to prevent chemical burns when the neutraliser is applied.

When developed, the neutraliser must also be thoroughly rinsed from the hair to prevent overdevelopment, as this will damage the hair's structure.

▲ Developing the perm

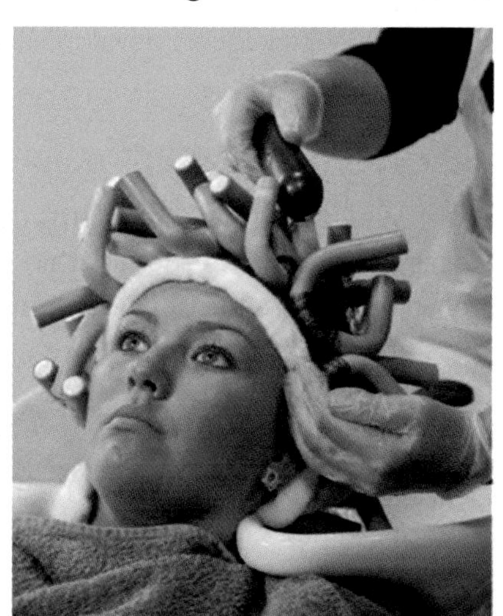

▲ Rinsing the hair

HANDY HINT

You must accurately time a perm's development to prevent over-processing the perm and damaging the hair. Make sure you calculate this time correctly by considering the lotion strength used, hair length, temperature of salon or added heat, result required and the hair's condition.

How would the following two scenarios differ?

- Patsy has chemically treated above-shoulder-length hair and you are using an acid perm to create a soft result.
- Stephanie has long, dark, strong European virgin hair and you are using an alkaline perm for a firmer curl result.

KEY TERM

Blot dry – the process of soaking up excess water using cotton wool, hand towels or paper towels, without rubbing the hair.

▲ Applying post-perm treatment

Rinsing and neutralising the hair

1. Ensure your client is adequately protected.
2. Rinse the hair for at least five minutes, depending on the MFIs and the hair length, taking care with the water temperature, flow direction and pressure.
3. Carefully blot the rods dry with hand towels, paper towels or cotton wool, so as not to disturb them. This is essential because excess water will dilute the neutraliser. Reapply cotton wool to the hairline.
4. Apply the neutraliser from the applicator bottle or foam it in a bowl and apply with a sponge.
5. Leave the hair to develop for about five minutes, depending on MFIs, and then either remove the rods and gently reapply the neutraliser to the unwound hair, or leave the rods in place and reapply the neutraliser.
6. Leave the hair for a further five minutes, depending on MFIs, and then remove the rods if you have not already done so.
7. Remove all the cotton wool from the hairline.
8. Thoroughly rinse the hair and apply a pH-balancing or post-perm conditioner.
9. Leave the conditioner on for three to five minutes, depending on the MFIs, and thoroughly rinse the hair.
10. Towel dry the hair and comb through with a wide-toothed comb.
11. Escort your client back to the workstation for any further service.
12. The client's desired look should have been achieved. Check that your client is happy with the result.

ACTIVITY

If you have several different perm products in your salon or at college, compare the manufacturers' instructions and note any variations in application techniques, development times and rinsing of products.

HANDY HINT

Remember to turn off taps in between rinses to save water.

Resolve problems

You should identify any problems during the perming and neutralising processes and resolve them within the limits of your own authority. Any problems that are outside your limits of authority must be referred to the relevant person for action.

HANDY HINT

Always rinse the perm lotion and neutraliser thoroughly from the hair to ensure the products are removed and to prevent the hair from over-processing.

ACTIVITY

What would happen if you did not rinse the perm lotion from the hair prior to adding the neutraliser? For the purpose of research, and under the supervision of your manager or tutor, mix a small amount of perm lotion with an equal amount of neutraliser in a measuring jug. Feel the container and note how hot the two products become when mixed together. Remember to wear PPE!

Now think how your client would feel if this was put on her head!

Advice and recommendations

Throughout the service and at the end, you will need to provide aftercare advice and make recommendations on:

- how to maintain the perm
- time interval between services
- additional products
- additional services.

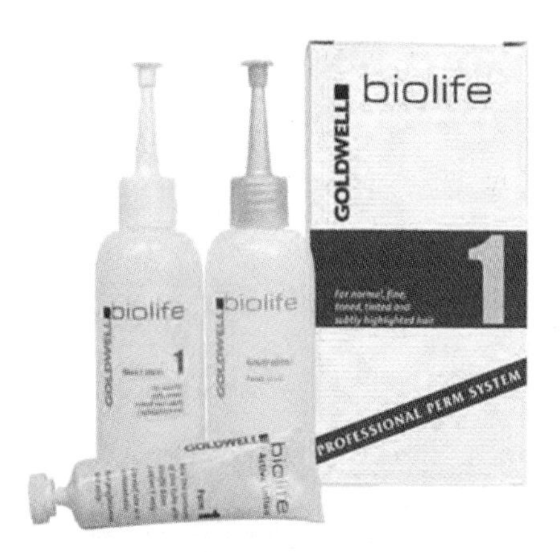

▲ Perming products for colour-treated hair

STEP BY STEP

In this part of the chapter you will look at how to carry out the perming and neutralising service, including:

- chemical rearrangers
- basic winding techniques
- directional winding techniques
- brick winding techniques.

Applying chemical rearranger

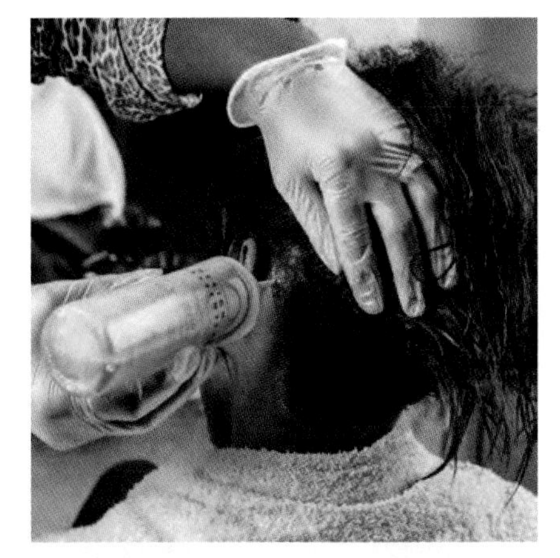

STEP 1 – Apply the scalp protector to the hairline and nape of the neck. Detangle the hair first using your hands, then using a wide-toothed/afro comb. Check for any cuts or abrasions.

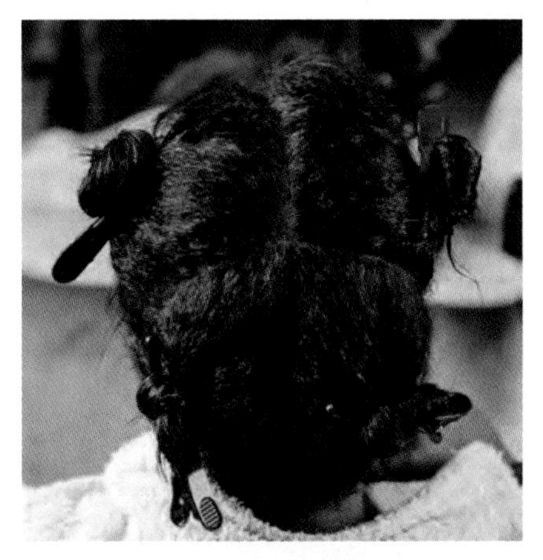

STEP 2 – Divide the hair into four neat sections from hairline to nape and ear to ear. Use plastic clips to secure the hair. Wear gloves.

STEP 3 – Take ½ cm (¼ in) sections and using a spatula or tint brush, apply the rearranger solution, starting on the ends and then the mid-lengths of the hair. Once the ends and mid-lengths are covered, begin applying the rearranger solution to any new growth area, being careful to avoid contact with the skin as the rearranger solution can cause damage to the scalp and skin.

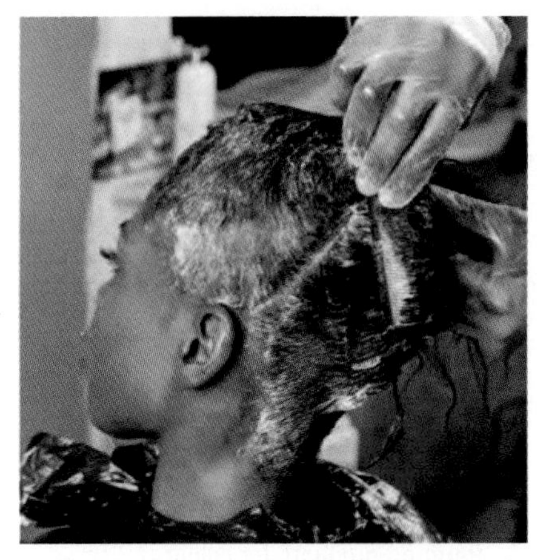

STEP 4 – Repeat application of the rearranger until the entire head of hair is covered. Once the application is complete, smooth the rearranger into place with gloved hands or the back of the comb. Set the timer according to the MFIs.

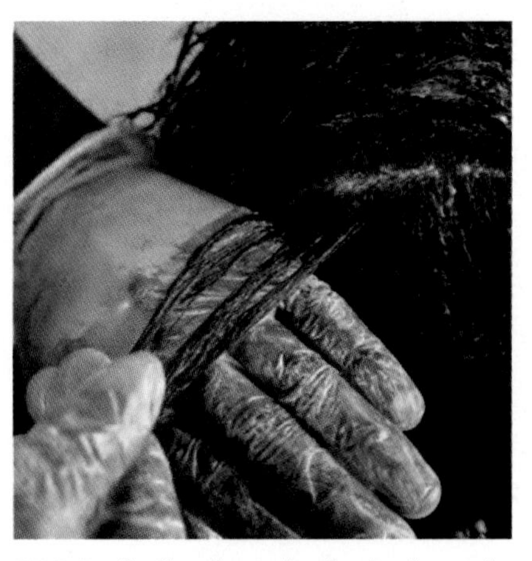

STEP 5 – Continually monitor the development of the rearranger, carrying out curl reduction tests to evaluate curl reduction after 10 minutes. Do not over-straighten the hair as this will cause the hair to become weak and increases the potential for breakage. Check client comfort throughout the process. Always follow the MFIs for maximum development time. Check for curl reduction every five minutes.

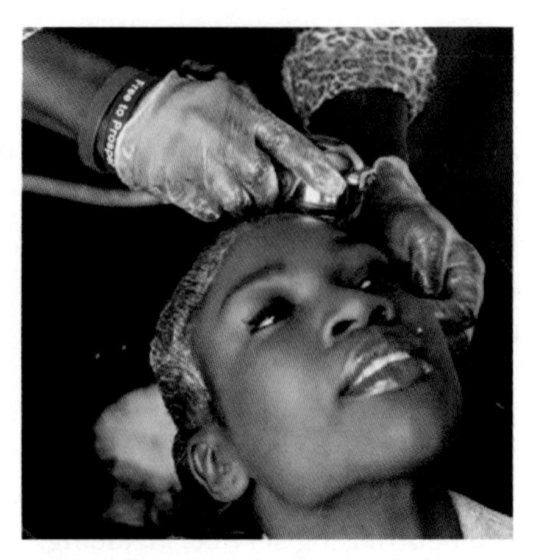

STEP 6 – Thoroughly rinse out the chemical rearranger from the hair with **tepid** water, avoiding excess water pressure or rough handling of the hair. Proceed to the winding phase.

KEY TERM

Tepid – lukewarm

Directional perm wind

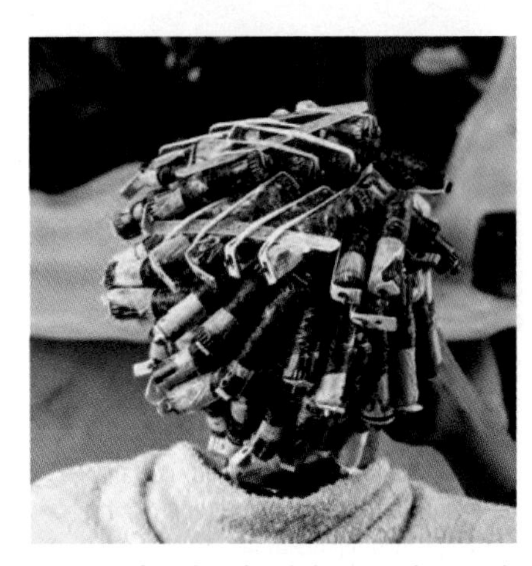

STEP 1 – Complete the whole area to be wound. Apply perm lotion to the hair, following the MFIs.

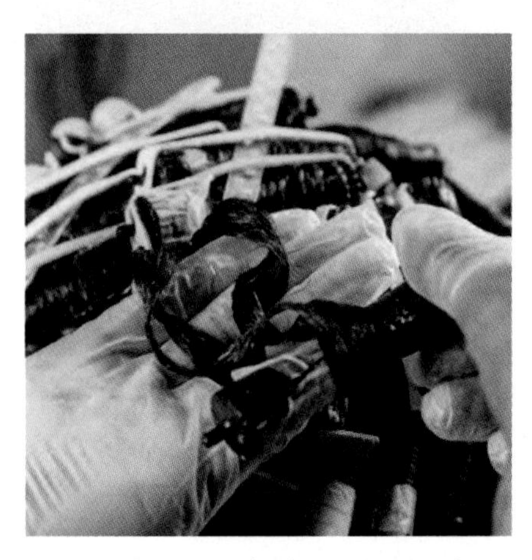

STEP 2 – Carry out a development test curl.

STEP 3 – Once the correct level of curl has been achieved, rinse the hair thoroughly at the basin to remove all traces of perm lotion.

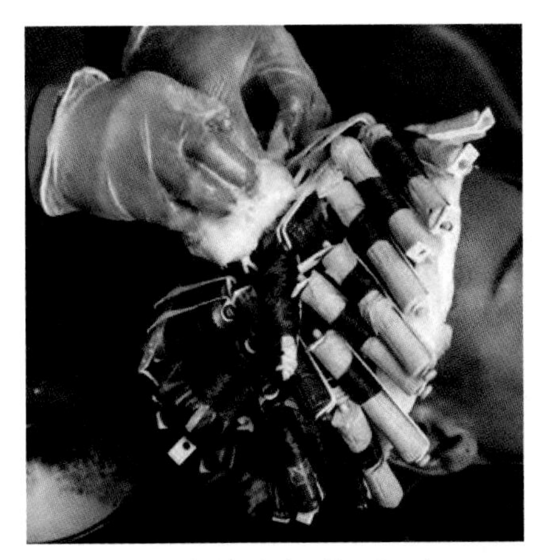

STEP 4 – Blot dry the hair with a towel, so that you do not dilute the neutraliser. Apply neutraliser following MFIs.

STEP 5 – Develop for five minutes (or according to MFIs) and then rinse on the rods.

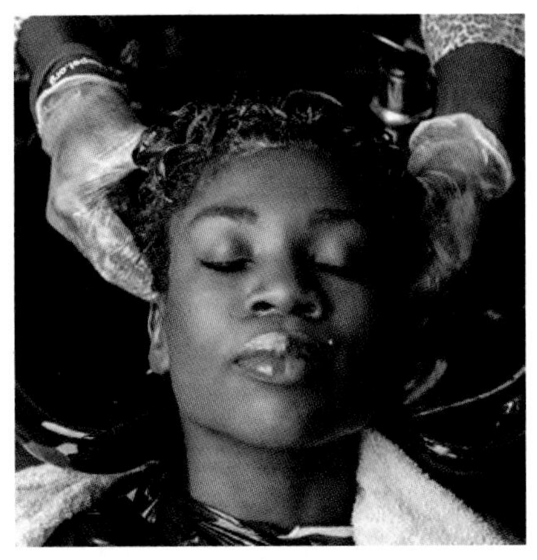

STEP 6 – Gently remove the rods and rinse the hair thoroughly. Apply post-perm conditioner treatments.

STEP 7 – Style and dress the hair to complete the look.

STEP 7 – The completed look.

Basic perm wind (nine sections)

STEP 1 – Divide the hair into nine sections. Start to wind from the top front section, or the crown, towards the back.

STEP 2 – Continue the winding process down towards the nape section.

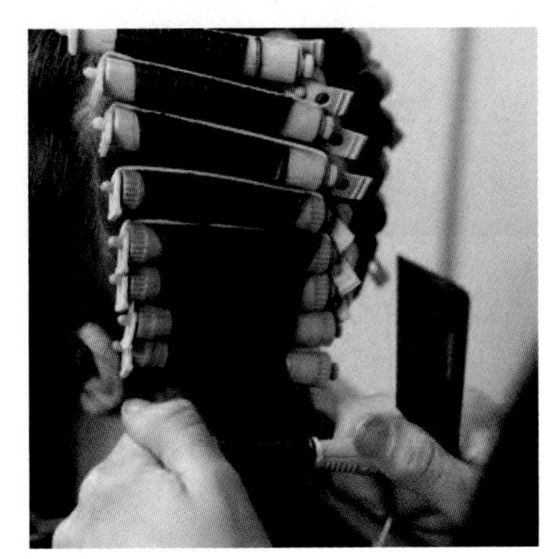

STEP 3 – Complete the nape section and start on the side sections.

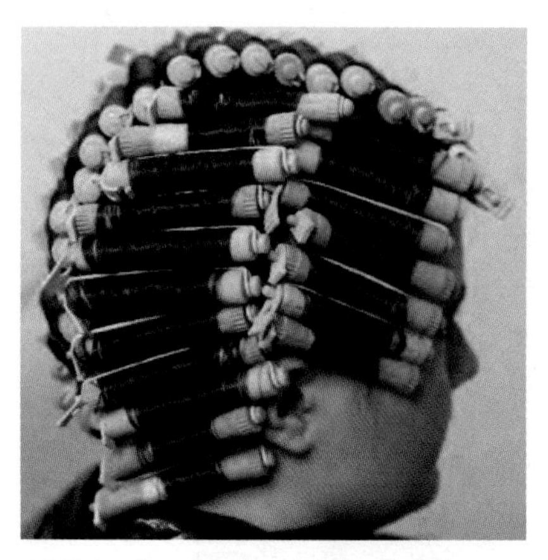

STEP 4 – Complete the whole head wind, maintaining tension throughout.

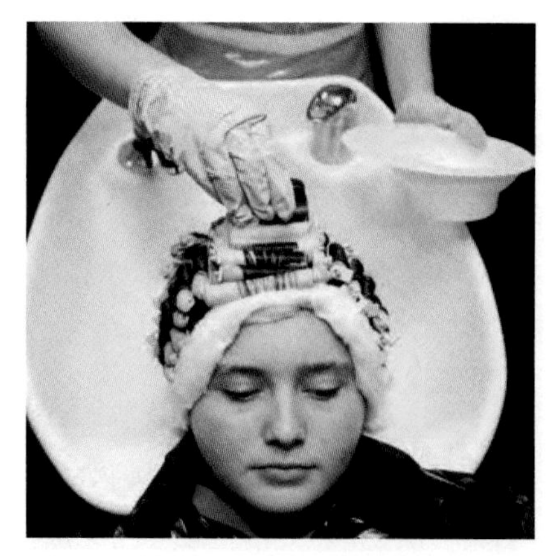

STEP 5 – Develop the perm then rinse the hair. Neutralise using a bowl-and-sponge technique. Apply post-perm conditioners at the end of the neutralising process.

STEP 6 – The completed perm and desired result.

HANDY HINTS

You must ensure that you maintain the tension from root to point when winding the hair, or the end result may be uneven.

Keeping the hair misted with water while winding makes it easier to control.

Ensure that the completed wind is not too tight, as this can cause scalp irritation and damage the hair.

Partial head brick wind perming

STEP 1 – Start at the top of the head using a brick winding technique.

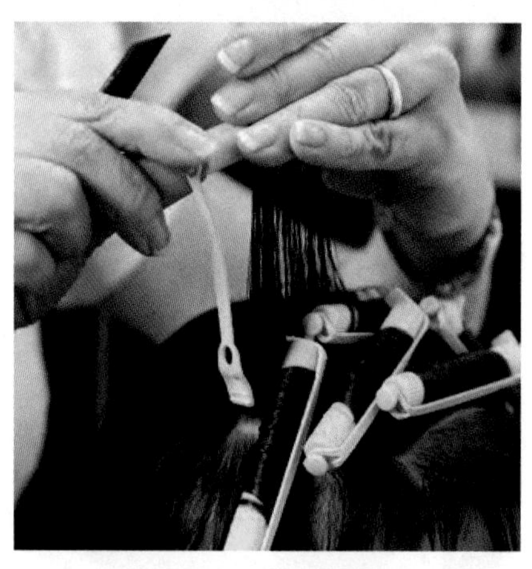

STEP 2 – Wind the crown area, maintaining even tension throughout.

STEP 3 – Complete the rest of the crown in a brick wind.

STEP 4 – Work down towards the nape area.

STEP 5 – Ensure your bands are not twisted or too tight.

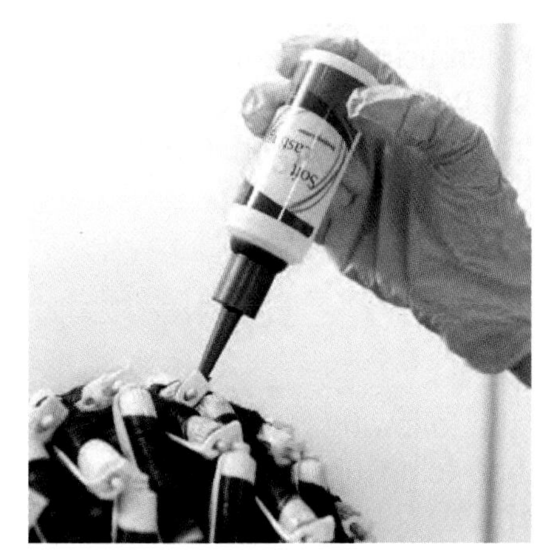

STEP 6 – Apply perm lotion, being careful not to flood the scalp, and develop the perm.

STEP 7 – Once developed, neutralise the hair and at the end apply a post-perm treatment.

HANDY HINT

Always decide whether you are winding on-base or off-base before you begin. If your aim is to wind on-base and you create root drag as you wind, the resulting curl will be similar to that of off-base winding, and no root lift will be achieved.

Test your knowledge

Question 1

Which type of perm lotion is best for sensitive hair?

Question 2

Describe the aftercare advice you would provide a client after a chemical rearranger and perm service.

Question 3

Describe the characteristics of a post-perm conditioner.

Question 4

Explain when a pre-damping technique may be used.

Question 5

Explain when you are mostly likely to use acid perm 0 strength.

Question 6

A client has very abundant, coarse hair. Describe the best perm solution for her hair.

Multiple choice questions

7 Are the following statements true or false?
Statement 1: COSHH controls the use, storage and disposal of substances that can be inhaled, absorbed or ingested.
Statement 2: Chemical burns are a risk involved with perming hair.

a True, true
b True, false
c False, true
d False, false

8 Which one of the following is the most difficult hair to curl?

a Type 1 coarse hair
b Type 2 fine hair
c Type 3 medium hair
d Type 4 soft hair

9 Are the following statements true or false?
Statement 1: Porous hair will absorb perm lotion quickly; a pre-perm conditioner will protect the hair by slowing the process.
Statement 2: When using a chemical rearranger, a strand test is used to establish the effect on the hair's condition.

a True, true
b True, false
c False, true
d False, false

10 Which one of the following is a technique used on long hair to ensure the lotion has even coverage?

a Pre-damping
b Post damping
c Pre-conditioning
d Post-conditioning

Glossary

Absorption – the passage of a substance through the skin.

Abundant – great in amount or number.

Accelerator – appliance used to apply heat to the hair and speed up a service, for example steamers, rollerballs and climazones.

Acetone – soluble material or chemical solvent

Act – a government law.

Adipose tissue – cells that store energy as fat.

Adverse – unfavourable, poor, difficult or not suitable.

Adverse reaction – an unfavourable response to a product.

Ailment – condition/disease/illness.

Aligned – brought into line and in this instance 'levelled'.

Ammonia – an alkaline gas.

Anti-oxidant – a substance that stops the oxidation process.

Arrector pili muscle – muscle attached to the hair follicle at one end and dermal tissue on the other.

Ascertain – find out something for certain.

Asymmetric – unbalanced, not equal, uneven, not symmetrical.

Basale layer – the deepest layer of the skin.

Body tissues – for example, the skin and muscles.

Blot dry – the process of soaking up excess water using cotton wool, hand towels or paper towels, without rubbing the hair.

Callous skin – hard skin.

Cantankerous – argumentative, difficult or unreasonable.

Caucasian – description of people of Northern European origin with lighter skin tone.

Characteristics – qualities or features.

Chevron – v-shaped stripe.

Chignon – roll of hair, worn at the back of the head.

Chipping – a texturising technique used to remove bulk from the tips of the hair.

Commercially viable – to make a profit and remain competitive within the industry.

Commercial pace – industry recommended time frame for a service; in the case of shaving it is about 20–30 minutes.

Complex – intricate.

Consistency – density or thickness.

Consumer – shopper/customer/client.

Contour – Outline or curve or shape of the face or head.

Contra-indication – a reason that prevents a service or treatment from being carried out.

Cortex – layer of the hair under the cuticle.

Covering letter – a letter sent with your CV explaining the contents of the CV and why you would like to work for the company.

Creeping oxidation – when chemicals are left in the hair and they carry on working and cause damage.

Cross-checking – checking the haircut for balance and evenness throughout.

Cross-contamination – spreading of infections or infestations. Cross-infection or cross-infestation.

Cross-infection – spread of germs and bacteria.

Cross-infestation – transfer of mites and lice from one person to another.

Cuticle – outer layer of the hair.

CV – Curriculum Vitae, a brief description of your education and previous employment history.

Depilatory – causing hair removal.

Derivative – off shoot or by product of.

Dermis – middle layer of the skin.

Diminishes – fades or reduces.

Disulphide bonds – two sulphur atoms bonded together.

Dual heritage – having parents from two different ethnic or cultural backgrounds.

Elastosis – the process by which skin loses strength and elasticity.

Elliptical – oval shaped.

Emulsify – the mixing of a small amount of water with the colouring product to ensure thorough removal from the hair and scalp.

Epidermis – outermost layer of the skin.

EU directive – a legal Act which countries who are members of the EU must follow.

Evident – easily seen.

Exhibits – shows.

Exothermic – producing heat through a chemical reaction.

Fairtrade – Fairtrade companies guarantee that their products have been made with fairer trading conditions and opportunities for producers in developing countries.

Fishhooks – buckled ends from poor winding technique.

Freshly keratinised – new cells produced in new hair growth.

Grade – an attachment placed on to the clipper blades to cut hair at varied fixed lengths.

Highlights – sections/woven pieces of hair that are coloured a lighter shade.

Hispanic – of Spanish descent.

Hub – the centre point of an environment; often the busiest point.

Humidity – moisture/dampness (in the air).

Hydrogen peroxide – the solution that activates the colouring product to allow the colouring process to take place.

Hygroscopic – absorbs moisture

Hyperextension – over extension/ over stretched.

Implication – a likely effect or consequence.

Incompatible – unsuitable.

Inhaling – breathing in.

Keratinocytes – these produce keratin, an insoluble protein which makes the cell more resilient.

Lacklustre – drab.

Legal tender – money that is legal in a given country.

Linear – straight, direct lines.

Litigation – legal action.

Local by-laws – local government rules.

Longevity – long-lasting effects, durable.

Lowlights – sections/woven pieces of hair that are coloured a darker shade.

Mandible – jawbone.

Manipulate – control.

Manipulated – handled and controlled.

Meche – size of section.

Medulla – central layer of the hair.

Melanin – pigments that give colour to the hair and skin.

Melanocytes – melanin-producing cells.

Metabolism – chemical transformations within living cells.

Metallic salts – these can be found in some home hairdressing products and contain lead/metallic compounds or a variety of other metals, depending on the shade of colour required, which react with professional colouring chemical ingredients.

Microbial pathogen – a pathogen is a type of microbe, such as a bacteria or virus, which has the potential to cause harm.

Micro-organic – relating to a tiny living cell (for example, an infection) which can only be seen under a microscope.

Mitosis – cell division.

Neutralise – to make neutral or balance each other out.

Occipital bone – the bone between the crown and the nape area that normally sticks out a little bit.

Off base – brush or roller is dragged below the section/meche of hair.

Olaplex restructurant – restructures the hair internally by linking broken disulphide bonds in the cortex of the hair.

Ombré – shaded.

On-base – brush or roller sits directly on top of the section/ meche of hair.

Organic – produced without the use of artificial chemicals.

Oxidation – a chemical process that combines a substance with oxygen.

Oxy-melanin – a colourless molecule.

Palm – hold your scissors in the palm of your hand with the blades closed.

Penetrate – enter into.

Perimeter – length or baseline of the cut.

Periodically – at regular intervals.

Personal protective equipment (PPE) – your personal protective equipment, not your client's!

Phial – small bottle.

Philtrum – the area between your nose and your mouth which is formed by two ridges/lines and a valley.

Pigment – the substance that colours our tissue (hair and skin).

Pollution – contamination of the environment.

Pollutants – toxins or impurities.

Porosity levellers – products which coat the cuticle layer of the hair to aid the levelling of porosity.

Porous – absorbent.

Post-damp – applying the lotion after the wind.

Pre-damp – winding the hair with the lotion already applied. Not all perm manufacturers allow pre-damping, so always read the MFIs.

Pre-lightened – method used to lighten darker hair with a lightener prior to applying desired colour and tone.

Pre-perm conditioner – a spray-in conditioner that evens out the porosity of the hair.

Pre-pigmenting – a technique to replace the pigments that have been removed during the lightening stages of hair colouring.

Prepubescent – before puberty.

Pre-soften – a technique where 6% liquid peroxide is applied to the hair before the tint application to open the cuticle.

Prominent and **protruding** – sticking out.

Proximity – closeness to, in terms of space.

Psoriasis – a non-contagious skin disease, which causes patches of red, itchy, flaky and scaly skin.

Rake cut – cutting with the lever on the clipper at 90°.

Rapport – a personal link or understanding between people.

Regulations – the rules of the Act.

Respiratory problems – breathing problems.

Revenue – income or money received from clients for services provided by the salon.

Salon policy – your salon's rules.

Sanitised – clean and germ free.

Sarcopenia – reduction of muscle mass and strength associated with the ageing process.

Scissor cut – marks made in the hair when cutting with scissors.

Scissor over comb – cutting the facial hair by moving the comb through the facial hair and removing the hair length above the comb.

Sebaceous glands – glands in the skin that secrete oil.

Serrated – blades with around 30 'teeth' on one or both blades.

SMART – targets that are Specific, Measurable, Achievable, Realistic and Timely.

Socioeconomic factors – factors related to an individual's income, health status, environment, education level, social class, etc.

Sparse – thin or scarce.

Sterilised – free of live bacteria.

Stratum – layer.

Styptic stick – a medicated stick that restricts blood flow and stops bleeding.

Subcutaneous layer – fatty tissue layer.

Subdermal – under the skin.

Surface tension – the skin-like surface layer of a liquid.

Tepid – lukewarm

Terminal (androgenic) hair – the hair on our heads, underarms and genital areas of the body. Thick, long, darker hair found on the body after puberty.

Toxic – poisonous

Trans – short for transgender, which means a person's identity and gender does not correspond with their birth sex.

Treatment – a process to improve condition; it could refer to a penetrating conditioner that improves the condition of the cortex, or a scalp treatment that remedies a scalp disorder.

Turnover – trade.

Vellus hair – fine, light-coloured, downy hair that appears all over our bodies except the palms of the hands and soles of the feet. Present on the body during childhood.

VOCs – Volatile Organic Compounds

Index